MADRID'S ROYAL PALACE

Text by Fernando Fernández-Miranda

Diagramming and reproduction by the technical staff of
EDITORIAL ESCUDO DE ORO, S.A. with the collaboration
of the Patrimonio Nacional.

Co-edition of EDITORIAL ESCUDO DE ORO, S.A. and the
PATRIMONIO NACIONAL.

8th Edition, April 1994

I.S.B.N. 84-378-1214-3

Dep. Legal B. 4043-1994

Editorial Escudo de Oro, S.A.

MADRID'S ROYAL PALACE

According to the writings of the Marquis of Lozoya, mediaeval Madrid comprised a castle with one or two houses and churches, all within a narrow walled enclosure. The castle once occupied the same site as the present-day Royal Palace, and references to it may be found in the oldest extant documents concerning Madrid. The Arabs used it as a key piece in the defence of Toledo against the incursions of Castilians and Leonese. Likewise during the Reconquest, the Christians gave great importance to the fortress, which supported the advance towards the Tagus valley. Ramiro II, in the 10th century, was the first to conquer the Arab *Magerit;* it was lost again a very short time afterwards, and finally recovered by Alfonso VI in the 11th century on his march towards Toledo.

The Madrid of the Arabs and of the Reconquest was no doubt of only middling importance. This notwithstanding, its "famous castle", though not built on inaccessible rocks or at a great height, did have a

Corner of the north and east fronts of the Palace.

North front giving onto the Sabatini gardens.

commanding position on the Manzanares valley on the edge of the semi-plain of Castile, where it provided a haven for the Arabs, Jews and Christians living east and south within its walls.

Madrid gradually grew towards the end of the Middle Ages, and the Kings of the House of Trastamara took a liking to residence in the city because of their penchant both for the game which abounded in the surrounding forests and the nearby El Pardo hunting grounds. What was more, the climate was a healthy one, and water was both good and abundant. It became necessary to rebuild and enlarge the Alcázar (fortress) during the times of Henry II. John II was a frequent resident in Madrid. Henry IV, though a great admirer of Segovia, died in Madrid. Madrid was also a

frequent venue of the Spanish Parliament during the 14th and 15th centuries.

It was here that Charles I found a cure for his malaria, and so took a great liking to the place; so much so that he determined to modify and once again enlarge the Alcázar in 1537. This work was entrusted initially to the architects Luis de Vega and Alonso Covarrubias, and was continued by Juan de Toledo, Juan de Herrera and Francisco Moral during the reign of Philip II, then Juan Gómez de Mora during the reign of Philip III.

Philip II was the first Spanish monarch to make Madrid the permanent venue for his Court, an event accomplished in 1561, when the King established his residence in the Alcázar. It would appear that the

Main Courtyard.

building of the Monastery of San Lorenzo in El Escorial was a determining factor in the choice of Madrid as Royal capital. Using a long-range telescope, the King was able to follow construction of the great Monastery, as well as pay frequent inspection visits there in view of its proximity.

Thus it was that the Alcázar was chosen as the Royal Residence of the House of Austria for the better part of the year. It ceased to hold this title only in spring, when the Court went to Aranjuez, and in autumn and other short periods, when the Escorial was used. For a few short years during the reign of Philip II, the Royal Court was temporarily transferred to Valladolid. The artistic wealth of the Alcázar of the House of Austria is confirmed by the palace inventories and the list of travellers and historians of the times. Of especial importance are the collections of paintings of old masters which fill all the apartments, as well as the magnificent gold-embroidered tapestries which have been preserved for posterity and which constitute the world's largest and richest collections of its kind.

With the demise of the House of Austria on the death of Charles II, the Spanish Crown passed to the Bourbon dynasty. When, during the War of Spanish Succession, Madrid took up the cause of Philip V, the loyalty of the city gained it the status of capital of the kingdom.

Philip V took up residence in the old Alcázar of the House of Austria, a severe abode for a prince used to the more accommodating art of Versailles. As a result, the King determined to raise a new residence more in keeping with his tastes and habits, and so work was begin on the Palace of San Ildefonso in the Valsaín pine forest.

One the night of 24th December 1734 a violent blaze totally destroyed the Madrid Alcázar, and the King was thus obliged to plan another to replace it. Philip V turned to Italy in search of an artist to design his new fortress, and eventually appointed the Messina Father Filippo Juvarra. Juvarra was architect of the Turin Court, had directed the building of the Stupinigi hunting lodge and the Palazzo Madama as well as that of the Royal Palace in Lisbon, and conceived a large-scale palace to be built on the so-called "Heights of San Bernardino", near the present day Paseo de Rosales. However, plans did not come to fruition since the King was determined to have the building raised on the same site as the old Alcázar, overlooking the river Manzanares, Juvarra died in 1736 and a pupil of his, Giovanni Battista Sacchetti, was directed to build on the site of the burned-down Alcázar. Given this condition, Sachetti had to introduce changes in his master's original plans, giving vertical mass to what had been envisaged horizontally, because of the restricted space; thus Juvarra's original three stories became six by the addition of mezzanines, such a frequent feature in Italian palaces.

The first stone was laid on 6th April 1738. It was plac-

Terrace of the large central courtyard and dome of the Royal Chapel.

West front from the Campo del Moro gardens.

ed in the central axis of the main door of the Palace at a depth of eleven metres and consisted of a hollow granite ashlar containing a lead casket with samples of each of the coins then accepted as legal tender. The outside surface of the ashlar block bore the following inscription in Latin: "Aedes Maurorum / Quas Henricus III Composuit / Carolus V amplificavit / et / Philippus III ornavit / Ignis Consumpsit Octavo Kal. Janvari / MDCCXXXIII / Tandem / Philippus V Spectandas restitutit / Aeternitati / Anno MDCCXXXVIII".

Sachetti's ground-plan follows the traditional Spanish rectangular, almost square, central court with thrusting salient corners, reminiscent of the towers of the old Alcázar. The parade ground is an open esplanade in front of the main, south-facing, front and is similar to the one affording access to the destroyed palace of the Austrias.

The fact that the building stands on a site with steep slopes on the river side meant that large-scale buttressing was necessary on two of the fronts. This was accomplished by a series of stepped platforms with inner vaulting on the west which almost reaches the river. Seen in elevation, the building's lower part consists of a bossage base with windows supporting the ensemble. The base supports an upper body adorned with Ionic corner columns and Doric pillars on the intermediate walls. Between these open out the large balconies on the main floor which let light into the main halls of the Palace. Then comes a new mezzanine with bays (for the most part blind) topped by the more modest windows of the upper floor. A very

*Main
Staircase.*

salient corniche crowns the building, and above stands the attic with its white stone balustrade. The enormous statues originally standing atop this attic (representing Spanish Kings from Atawulf to Ferdinand VI) were removed during the reign of Charles III, with the change in decorating tastes introduced by the new king; they were later re-sited (in the 18th and 19th centuries) around the Palace, in the gardens of the Buen Retiro and various other places in Spain. Also removed were the statues on the imposts of the fronts (not re-placed on the south and west fronts till the present day); in addition statues of the kings of Navarre, Aragon, Portugal, Mexico and Peru, as well as of the patron saints of Spain, mounted on circular pedestals, were placed on the corners formed by the ledges and the impost of the main floor. A large shield bearing the coat-of-arms of Spain and the Bourbons, held on the west by lions and on the east by griffons, was placed on the corniche at the intersection of the east and west fronts. The south front is decorated with a representation of Spain Triumphant, the conception of the Benedictine father Martín Sarmiento, an 18th-century erudite and designer of the whole of the Palace's outside decoration. The original plans were reduced in the making, and the end result is very similar to the annex to the Alcázar of the House of Austria during the reign of Philip V. It is decorated with a large clock flanked with reliefs depicting the sun travelling through the zodiac. Above the main balcony is a representation of Spain holding the Constantinian *labarum;* at her feet lies a bearded old man representing the river Tagus; on the flanking balconies are reliefs of fruit and animals, representing the natural produce of *Hispania.*

On the north front is a representation of the Church Triumphant on medallion, expressed in the form of the mystic Lamb on the Book of the Seven Seals, in the midst of brilliance and above a pagan temple. To the sides, Sts. Andrew and Gideon, alluding to the Golden Fleece, the work of the sculptors Pablo Martínez and Antoine Dumandré. On both north and south fronts there are large shields, bearing the royal coat-of-arms atop the corniche, above these representations.

Finials consisting of cartouches were placed on the tower corners, and were topped by busts of Spain's mythological heroes.

All work was done in stone for fear of further fires; the only wood used was in the doors and windows. Thus all the rooms and apartments are vaulted, resulting in massive walls (four metres thick on the bottom floor) in order to bear the weight. The thrust of the high vaults of the main staircase, the Halberdiers' Room, and the Columns Hall is countered by a system of flying butresses over the terraces of the central courtyard.

The fronts are a combination of Guadarrama granite (undecorated facing) and Colmenar limestone (columns, pilasters, sills, balustrades), providing contrasting tones of light on dark.

Construction was greatly accelerated during the reign of Ferdinand VI, when the whole of the outside was completed. Work on the inside took much longer to finish, and Charles III could not take up residence in the palace until the year 1764 — and even then decoration on some of the rooms had yet to be completed.

The building was therefore twenty-six years in the making. Work on it continued into successive reigns until it was finally completed during the Regency of Queen María Cristina of Habsburg-Lorraine.

The chief architect was Sacchetti. Under him worked other master builders, the most outstanding amongst them being Ventura Rodríguez (initially deputy architect, then chief architect during the times of Ferdinand VI. His role was particularly important since he provided the necessary continuity as the building was entrusted to different builders with the passing of time). While still fairly young, Sachetti worked alongside Juvarra as his draughtsman; on the death of this master, Sacchetti introduced changes into the original drawings, and entrusted their draughting to

Guardroom (Halbardiers' Room).

Ventura Rodríguez; the latter's close collaboration with his master can be seen in the drawings done by him. Ventura Rodríguez's style was forged in the school of the Italian masters who came to Spain and fused with traditional Spanish Baroque; it is both graceful and intensely Spanish, and it is indeed a pity that he could not fit in with the fashions of the reign of Charles III. His work fell into disfavour, and designs which had been created by him for the outside decoration (enclosing the Royal Armoury, garden designs and others) between 1757 and 1759 were shelved. With the coming of Charles III to the throne, Ventura Rodríguez was eclipsed by Sabatini and his ideas forgotten.

Once the Palace was finished in the reign of Charles III, it turned cut to be too small to house the Secretaries of State, the Archives and various other deparments. The Chapel itself was inadequate for the holding of large religious ceremonies, and so a large-scale extension was embarked upon, the design being entrusted to Sabatini. His idea was to close off the Plaza de Armas or de la Armería (Armoury Square) with a series of buildings designed to house the different departments, and add an immense building at the north end, thus repeating the Palace structure. Work was begun but soon interrupted, the only remaining evidence being the vaults of the enlargement of the lower part of the Chapel; the foundations were buried under the esplanade built later. On this esplanade gardens were to be built, but plans for

Columns Hall.

them did not reach fruition either. Instead Royal Stables were constructed, again by Sabatini. When the stables were demolished in 1932 the gardens which had for so long been envisaged by different architects over two centuries were finally built.

Due to the fact that the Palace was situated on a rise visible from afar, with broad esplanades to the north and east, and a steep slope to the south, plans for gardens and outbuildings had to be in keeping with the magnificence of the main building. Sacchetti planned a series of parterres with fountains, statues, platforms and communicating stairways between the different levels of the Campo del Moro gardens, plus staggered rockeries forming cascades (as had been done in San Ildefonso), copses and bowers. These gardens were planned years later by Ventura Rodríguez with much more Spanish Baroque features. Later plans laid by Sabatini were not to see the light of day either. Large amounts of money had already been spent on the Palace outbuildings, and further embellishment of the surroundings was postponed in view of the need for major hydraulic engineering to supply the large amounts of water required. Re-landscaping of the Campo del Moro gardens did not commence until the reign of Isabella II when a large number of trees were planted, pathways laid out, and an irrigation system introduced. A hothouse was also built for the acclimatisation of fruit and exotic plants. Unfortunately however, this work was partially lost due to neglect in the wake of

Vicente López: "Creation of the Order of Charles III".
Vault of this room (1828).

the 1868 revolution. The park was once more an object of attention in 1890, and it was given the shape it still has today. It was laid out following the precepts of 19th-century English garden landscaping, with an imitation of nature, thick tree copses and meandering paths; the traditional plans made for it in the 18th century were completely forgotten.

The gardens cover some twenty hectares and are bounded by the Cuesta (slope) de la Vega, the promenade of the Virgen del Puerto and the Cuesta de San Vicente; since the times of the Queen Regent María Cristina of Habsburg-Lorraine, the Palace's east front has been surrounded by one-and-a-half-kilometres of wrought-iron railings surmounting a stone-and-brick wall which encloses the other three sides. These gardens have been linked to the royal palace since the 16th century and are known by the name of Campo del Moro; the name derives from the fact that here in the Middle Ages, the hosts of an Arab leader set up camp in an attempt to win Madrid and its Alcázar from Christian hands. The exact identity of the Arab leader is still a matter of debate amongst the experts, although it is generally agreed that he lived in the 12th century. All attacks on the Alcázar during this century came to nothing — though the city was sacked and the surrounding land pillaged. But whoever it was who camped here, what is certain is that it was an Arab, and though the assailants struck camp and departed, the name remained.

Charles III
Room.

The park's fountains are its main decoration: the Triton fountain (de los Tritones), transferred from the Aranjuez gardens in 1845, now stands opposite the Camelias hothouse; the Shell fountain (de las Conchas) is the work of Francisco Gutiérrez and Manuel Alvarez based on drawings by Ventura Rodríguez. It was originally designed for the Boadilla palace but presented to María Cristina of Bourbon for her Vista Alegre gardens; thence it was later brought to the Campo del Moro.

The arches and apartments bordering the Plaza de la Armería on the Calle de Bailén side date from the times of Isabella II. The buildings opposite the Campo del Moro, with the stairway descending to the park, were begun in 1883 and completed in 1891 during the regency of María Cristina of Habsburg.

The Palace's main COURTYARD is 39 metres square and has nine arches on each side on the lower and main floors. These arches form porticoes and are barrel-vaulted with splayed arches and truncated

Yellow Room.

Ordinary dining room.

vaults on the corners supporting the main gallery (glassed in in 1765); the window-frames are the work of the ironsmiths Alfonso de Ortega and Francisco Montalvo.

This GALLERY was carpeted and hung from end to end with tapestries from the Royal collection on holidays when the ''Public Chapel'' was celebrated. Bas-reliefs of the military, political and mythological history of Spain decorated the overdoors leading to the various rooms and apartments. They are the work of various hands and follow the plan created by Father Sarmiento. The series was meant to have forty-four reliefs, but only twenty-eight were actually made, and none of them ever occupied its intended place. Twenty-two may be seen in the Prado Museum and six in the Academy of San Fernando.

Occupying pedestals under the narrower arches of the square (numbers four and six on the north and south sides) stand the statues of Spanish-born Roman emperors. Those of Arcadius and Trajan are the work of Felipe de Castro, and those of Theodosius and Honorius the work of Domenico Olivieri. These statues originally stood by the three main doorways of the main front. Immediately by the main court there are another two smaller ones (on the north-east and north-west corners) which communicate with it. The main court has broad access points from the exterior: the Puerta del Príncipe

(Prince's Gate), or the Plaza de Oriente (East Square). Another two are the side entrances of the Plaza de la Armería (the porticoed forecourt) which allowed carriages to pass through, an event which may still be seen. Yet another access point is the large hall of the main front, which has now been closed off with French doors.

The MAIN STAIRWAY as it stands today is a modification by Sabatini of Sachetti's original 1745 design in which an additional flight had been included, starting from the place now occupied by the statue of Charles III as a Roman emperor. The change was introduced at the behest of the king, since the entrance to the royal apartments seemed to him inadequate; with a double-flight stairway only a dark passageway communicated it with the Saleta Oficial (reception room leading to the royal antechamber) and the Throne Room. The modification also enabled the space created by the omission of the second flight to be used for a grand ballroom, today known as the Columns Hall (Salón de Columnas).

The present stairway provides a gentle slope built of

Queen Maria Cristina's "Saleta".

Tapestries Room.

seventy-two steps each cut from a single five-metre-long slab of San Pablo (Toledo) marble. It has a single flight from the base to the first landing, and thence divides into two parallel flights with balustrades, adorned with two marble lions, the one on the left the work of Felipe de Castro, and that on the right of Robert Michel.

The stairwell is the work of Sacchetti. It has large window recesses with abutting arches and columns, plus pilasters of capitals with volutes, a collar of the Golden Fleece, lions and castles.

The vault has lunettes, large oculi at its base and is decorated with gilt and white stuccowork, moulding the painting recesses and decorating them with garlands, fleurons, coffers, trophies and similar adornment, attributed by some to Giovanni Battista Andreoli and by others to Robert Michel. The paintings are by the hand of Corrado Giaquinto, who came to Spain at the request of Ferdinand VI in order to decorate the Palace. The centre is occupied by a composition entitled *Triumph of the Church and Religion,* personified by two enthroned matrons to whom homage is rendered by Spain with her sheaf of ears of corn and accompanied by her traditional virtues of Prudence, Justice, Constance and religious zeal (an old man with lashes); offerings are also made in the form of fruit, trophies and victories which are represented (bottom) by the three figures of Africa,

Asia and Europe. In the corners there are *chiaroscuro* medallions with the four elements (Earth, Air, Water and Fire); between them there are child figures with characteristics of the House of Bourbon. The corniche holds allegories of Freedom, Happiness, Magnanimity and Peace; above the door of the Halberdiers' Room, the triumph of Spain over the invaders, and inside the arch, Victory; on the tympanum part, Hercules uprooting the Pillars before Neptune in his chariot (accompanied by nereids and tritons), an allegory of Spanish sea ventures and discoveries. A Cosmography takes up the medallion of the minor vault.

On the MAIN FLOOR there are various groups of apartments and Rooms whose names reflect the purpose they serve. First of all comes a group constituting the entrance or vestibule, comprising the Guards' or Halberdiers' Room (the real entrance to the whole of the main floor) and the Columns Hall (Salón de Columnas) where banquets and balls were held up until 1879, the year of the death of Queen María de las Mercedes, the first wife of Alfonso XII;

Arms Room.

Official Antechamber.

her lying-in-state was in this very Hall, and so it was decided to build a new ballroom which today is known by the name of the Ceremonial Dining Room (Comedor de Gala). The Columns Hall is also the venue for the "Washing and Feeding of the Poor" on Maundy Thursday, when by tradition the King and Queen washed the feet of and fed twenty-five poor people of both sexes, in the presence of the Grandees of Spain, Ministers of the Crown, the diplomatic corps and ecclesiastical authorities, accommodated on platforms specially provided for that purpose along the sides of the Hall.

Architecture here is a carbon copy of the main stairway, since this hall was the stairwell designed by Sacchetti. Some of the other apartments and Room groups are the royal rooms, the private apartments of King Alfonso XIII and Queen Victoria Eugenia, the Royal Chapel, plus the apartments of Charles IV and María Luisa, of Queen María Cristina, and the different Museums (Paintings and Decorative Arts, Tapestry, and Modern Painting).

The official rooms take up the south bay, and main front, as well as half of the east and west fronts, which form the two junctions with the south front. The private apartments are located on the extension of the Palace built by Sabatini on the Plaza de la Armería and Calle de Bailén. The Royal Chapel takes up the centre of the north wing; the Museum of Paintings and Decorative Arts is to be found at the junction of the north and west fronts; the Tapestry Museum and the apartments of Charles IV and María Luisa occupy the rooms on the east inside bay over the gallery, the

Modern Painting Museum and the apartments of Queen María Cristina are on the same bay but occupy the outer rooms in the north-east tower and north façade (overlooking the Sabatini gardens) as far as the Chapel group on the Sacristy side.

This general description of the Palace brooks no detailed description of each of these large groups, so we shall do no more than pick out the most noteworthy features in the collections they contain and provide a thumbnail sketch of the apartments and Rooms whose wealth of decoration or outstanding architecture make them most worthy of attention in this remarkable place, i.e. the Gasparini Room, Porcelain Room, Ceremonial Dining Room, Mirror Room, Throne Room and Royal Chapel. However, this does not mean that the remaining rooms in the Palace go unmentioned — photographs of all of them may be found in this guide. Thus, in the south bay (Plaza de la Armería), the Throne Room stands in the centre and is flanked by the Gasparini "Saleta" (reception

Official "Saleta".

Queen Maria Cristina's Chamber.

room leading to the royal antechamber) antechamber and chamber, rooms which in the times of Charles III were known collectively as "the King's Room". At the back of the Gasparini chamber, at the beginning of the west front of the tower, are the small rooms of Francis of Assisi, consort to Isabella II; these rooms were once the "Indies Wood Chambers" of the King's Room just mentioned. Then come the Charles III Room and the adjacent Porcelain and Yellow Rooms, the latter affording access to the Ceremonial Dining Room in the centre of this same front. Then come the Museums of Paintings and Decorative Arts. On the bays and east front the Arms, Tapestry and Mirror Rooms and the so-called "Tranvía de la Cámara", link in with the south-east tower and Official Chamber; after this comes the everyday dining room (front centre) and then the Saleta, Antechamber and Chamber of Queen María Cristina, mother of Alfonso XIII. Parallel to these rooms lies the Tapestry Museum and the apartments of Charles IV and María Luisa.

On the south front, to the left of the Official Chamber, lie the rooms known as the Antechamber, Official Saleta and Grandees Room, leading to the Throne Room.

In the north wing various rooms house the Museum of Modern Painting, the Royal Chapel (next to the antesacristy and sacristy in the east wing), and the antereliquary, reliquary and "Strongroom" in the west. The Museum of Paintings and Decorative Arts link up with the north-west tower.

THE GASPARINI ROOM

The Gasparini Room, one of the Palace's most beautiful, is the only one of the so-called "King's Room" that has still preserved its period decoration. It was here that the King, following the dictates of the time, dressed in the presence of his Court.

Its highly original Rococo *chinoiserie* decoration is due to Mattia Gasparini, who was called from Naples by the King in 1760. This decorator/designer provided not only the adornment for this room but also that of other "King's Room" where it has now been lost since they were refurbished in the times of Charles IV, Ferdinand VII and Isabella II (i.e. King Francis' Rooms, Charles III Room — the monarch's bedroom and deathbed — the Gasparini Antechamber and Saleta). The coloured silk and silver embroidery patterns on the walls and furniture (made by José Campos) match the other decoration. The embroidery patterns were also designed by Gasparini, as was the wood inlay work on the seating and mirrors (done in rosewood, mahogany, ebony and bronze), the marble

Gasparini's Room.

Wall decoration and sofa in the Gasparini Room.

Large candelabra from
the Four Parts of the
World series (Europe).

"The Shepherd", Rococo
clock by Jacquet Droz.

Chandelier in the
Gasparini Room.

Gasparini Room: chinoiserie plasterwork on the vault.

Bronze pedestal table and mosaic by Gherardo Bolponi and Guglielmo Chidel, under the supervision of Filippo Agricola (1848).

floor mosaic and the very delicate relief stuccowork decoration on the vault: large gilt rocaille-work stands out on white and green, framing or mingling with brilliantly coloured groups of flowers, fruit, birds, exotic trees and Chinese couples (in the corners).

This 150-square-metre room is one of the Palace's largest. Other items of decorative interest are the Rococo clock over the fireplace; it is the work of Pierre Jacquet Droz and has automata dressed in 18th-century costume which dance when the hour is struck by a seated shepherd playing a flute; the enormous 54-candle gilt bronze and fine crystal chandelier, a piece of French craftsmanship from the reign of Ferdinand VII and his third wife María Amalia of Saxony (1819-1829), whose intertwining initials decorate it.

Gasparini "Saleta".

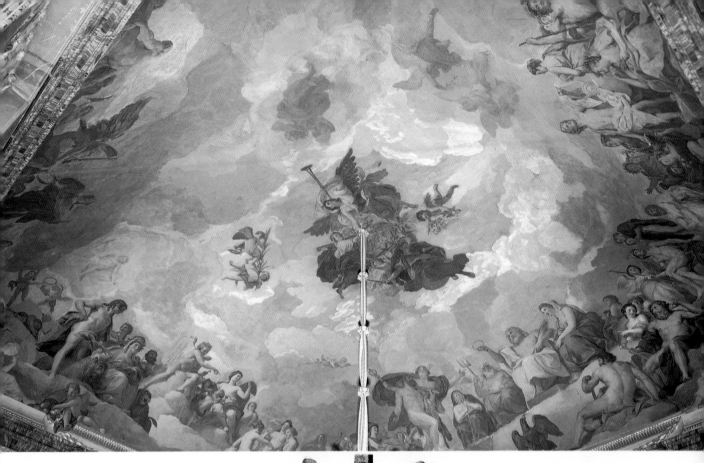

Vault and chandelier of the Gasparini Antechamber.

Vault of the Gasparin "Saleta".

Goya: Charles IV in the uniform of a colonel of the Bodyguard.

Goya: Queen Maria Luisa of Parma in court dress.

Gasparini Ante-chamber.

The Porcelain Room.

Detail of the Porcelain Room.

THE PORCELAIN ROOM

The walls and ceiling of the Porcelain Room are covered entirely in the material that gives it its name, fixed on a wooden framework which is so joined as to make the carpentry invisible under the porcelain cloth and stalks. This work was done during the early period of the Buen Retiro works when it was at the height of its splendour. The work was carried out between 1765 and 1770, and is by the hand of Giuseppe Gricci and the painters Gennaro Boltri and Juan Bautista de la Torre, the same artists who worked on the Porcelain Room in Aranjuez Palace, though the style in the Madrid Palace is completely different. Here in the use of stems and Baroque mouldings to hide the joints of the pieces of porcelain the Rococo *chinoiserie* gives way to a more sobre colour scheme and more serene composition, nearer to Neoclassicism.

Gasparini was also responsible for the design of the marble mosaic floor. A valuable 19th-century planetary clock (the work of Breguet) stands in the centre of the room.

THE CEREMONIAL DINING ROOM

This 400-square metre room comprises three of the apartments making up the "Queen's Room", (i.e. the Antechamber, Chamber, Dining Room and Reception Room) of María Amalia of Saxony, wife to Charles III, who never used them since she died before the King took up residence in the Palace.

King Alfonso XII gave the order to refurbish it into a new dining room and ballroom, and it was inaugurated in 1879 on the occasion of his marriage to his second wife María Cristina of Habsburg-Lorraine. The walls of this great room are decorated with 16th-century Brussels tapestries from the *Story of Vertumnus and Pomona* series, and are woven in gold, silver, silk and wool by Wilhelm Pannemaker; in addition there are twelve large 18th-century China porcelain pots, and on the balcony recesses stand six bronze vases bearing Sèvres pottery plaques, from the times of Charles X (1826-1830).

On the 145-place dining table stand large silver centre-pieces and candelabras.

The Ceremonial Dining room.

THE MIRROR ROOM

This room was used by Queen María Luisa of Parma as her boudouir; in recent times it was used as a music room and lounge by the Spanish Royal Family. For lovers of late-18th-century Neoclassic decoration, this room is one of the most beautiful in the Palace. The striking effect is achieved by the pink marble dados and delicate, predominantly white-and-blue stuccowork on the walls. The large upright mirrors that give the room its name are decorated in blue and gold, and are framed by stuccoes in the shape of plant motifs, butterflies, birds and cages, the work of the Italian stuccoists Domenico and Giuseppe Brilli. There are beautifully ornamented white stucco relief overdoors and lids as well as non-allegorical groups. In the corners there are four huge porcelain vases from the Buen Retiro factory with mythological motifs done in relief, plus garlands of multi-coloured porcelain flowers, dating from the reign of Charles IV.

Mirror Room.

*Mirror Room: Sèvres porcelain
Wedgwood-type cover of the
pedestal table.*

*Mirror Room: Sèvres porcelain
Wedgwood imitation jar.*

Also worthy of note is the central mahogany and gilt bronze table (built by Thomire and the cabinetmaker Kaspar Schneider in 1788) with its Wedgwood-style Sèvres porcelain top depicting Apollo and the Muses. Also of interest is the alabaster figure of the Infanta Cristina as a child, by Mariano Benlliure.

The vault fresco is the work of Francisco Bayeu and depicts Hercules on Mount Olympus. This conquering hero is seen after his twelve travails in the company of several gods and muses, receiving a garland of flowers from Minerva in recognition of his triumph; at the same time Apollo is offering him various prizes. On the corner medallions there are allegorical representations of Music, Poetry, Philosophy and Painting.

Mirror Room: details of plasterwork on the overdoors.

Mirror Room: monumental Buen Retiro porcelain clock.
Clockwork by Manuel Rivas (Madrid).

Mirror Room: Buen Retiro porcelain jar.

Throne Room.

THE THRONE ROOM

Known in the 18th century as the "Ambassadors' Room" or "Kingdom Room", the Throne Room still preserves the character of the reign of Charles III, when it was decorated. The wall hangings and canopy of the throne are covered in red velvet with Rococo silver gilt fringes (brought from Naples especially for this room) which time has blackened but not dimmed. Beneath the canopy there are two gilt carved chairs, again upholstered in red velvet with the same fringes (with figures of Their Majesties King Juan Carlos I and Queen Sofia of Greece) — exact reproductions of the original Charles III throne. On either side of the daises, and again covered in red velvet, stand four gilt bronze lions by the Italian Matteo Bonicelli, made in 1651 for the then King of Spain; together with another eight lions now standing in the Prado Museum, these lions were formerly used as decorative elements in the Kingdom Room of the old Alcázar.

Twelve carved gilt Rococo console tables also stand in the room, each with its mirror from the San Ildefonso factory, and each of them a variation on a theme. They were probably designed by Ventura Rodríguez and custom-built for the place they now occupy; together with the mirrors, they depict the four seasons, the four elements and the four continents.

Throne Room: rock crystal chandelier (Royal Factory in La Granja).

Throne Room: statue of Justice in blued bronze.

The sculptures in the room are important decorative elements; there are twelve patinated bronze pieces from different periods. That representing Germanicus (1650) is a bronze reproduction of the Roman marble sculpture in the Louvre Museum and stands to one side of the entrance door; that of the Satyr (1651) is a reproduction of the statue in the Vatican, and stands beside the exit door. Both were made in Rome by Pietro del Duca and César Sebastián respectively, artists who collaborated with Bernini on his great Roman works. They were brought to Spain by Velázquez as part of the lot of works of art he acquired for Philip IV to decorate the Alcázar. The statues of Mercury, Jupiter, Saturn and Mars, together with the Earth, Neptune and Venus in the Columns Hall, make up the group of the Seven Planets, and are the work of Jonghellinck. They come from Flanders and were the gift of Cardinal Infante to Philip IV. There are statues of the four Virtues (Prudence, Justice, Fortitude and Temperence), the work of Foggini, against the throne wall.

The Room is lit by two splendid chandeliers of cut rock crystal pieces threaded on silver wire matching the candlesticks; these same chandeliers illuminated the Room in the reign of Charles III.

The allegory of the Grandeur of the Spanish Monarchy was painted by Tiepolo in 1764. In it, clouds surround figures symbolising Christian virtues in praise of King Charles III; hence Magnanimity, represented by a majestic standing matron leaning on a lion holding the symbols of power, accompanied by cupids. To the right Advice seen as a respectable elderly man with a laurel crown, and to the left another group with the delightful figure of Faith.

Abundance offers her fruits to the Monarchy, and with her other figures and cupids, one of them carrying the collar of the Toison d'Or through the air. To the right a flying Mercury, the messenger of the Gods; Time, seen as a winged old man with additional attributes; and Neptune in his chariot of white horses. The rainbow traverses the vault from one side to the other, as a symbol of peace and happiness, leading to the god Aeolus accompanied by zephyrs and breezes, represented by young people with large butterfly wings. To one side a recumbent Jupiter in conversation with Minerva; and finally the Ocean with tritons and nereids and an erect Thetis holding a large pearl-laden shell.

The entire perimeter of the vault's springing-line is taken up by a gilt dado with a series of figures in the foreground representing the provinces and states of the Crown of Spain, together with the flora and fauna which characterise each of them. These are accompanied by heroes and Spanish conquistadors, Estremadura or Castile labourers in their typical attire as well as other groups of figures of coloured races which represent the West and East Indies, places where Spain had some of her dominions. There are gilt medallions in the corners, each supported by stuccowork high relief male figures; here are represented the four elements with the four seasons of the year, and the whole is the work of Robert Michel. Above the doors there are two large ovals supported by two stuccowork spirits with grisaille paintings — Virtue and Merit over the entrance door, and Abundance over the exit door. Both were painted by Tiepolo.

Throne Room: white marble and blued bronze clock, by J.L. Godon.

Part of the Royal Chapel.

THE ROYAL CHAPEL

On the main floor, in the centre of the north side, stands the entrance door to the Chapel, one of the most interesting architectural ensembles in the Palace. The architects were the Italian Giovanni Battista Sacchetti (who drew up the original design), and the Spaniard Ventura Rodríguez, Sacchetti's close collaborator in both the basic design and ornamentation; the final approval was given in 1749 by the king, after three different plans had been presented, each introducing modifications into the original one by Sacchetti. Work began in that same year, and was finished eight years later in 1757. The walls of the Chapel are decorated by sixteen black Mañaria marble columns, each cut from a single slab except for those in the atrium and the pilasters imitating it; further decoration comes in the shape of gilded stuccowork capitals and bases imitating the bronze in which they were never cast. The dome rests on a drum with four oculi in turn resting on spandrels. At the bottom end of the chapel there are several low galleries for royalty, with the choir above them; other smaller galleries open at the capitals. Opposite the entrance there is a small altar with an unfinished painting of the Annunciation (dated 1779, the year in which the artist, Mengs, died). Under the altar in an urn stands a wax figure containing the relics of St. Félix.

The exquisite marble high altar and dais stand at the top end of the Chapel; on the altar stands a painting of the Archangel St. Michael, a Ramón Bayeu copy of the original painting by Giordano (now lost). Halfway along the arch over the altar is stuccowork by the hand of Olivieri, representing angels adoring the Eucharist.

The canopy and chairs from the pontifical ensemble of the reign of Ferdinand VI have been on permanent display for a good few years now; decoration is in silver and silk, and is the creation of the court embroiderer Antonio Gómez de los Ríos. The frescoes on the dome, the squinches, the choirstalls and the atrium's elliptical vault are by Corrado Giaquinto.

The dome fresco displays the Crowning of the Virgin, with the Virgin Mary and St. John the Evangelist before the Holy Trinity, surrounded by angels, choirs of saints and Old Testament figures, with Fathers of the Church around the vault. The spandrels display St. Isidore the Farm-Servant, St. Mary of La Cabeza, and Sts. Leander and Hermenegild (sketches in the Escorial). The choir vault shows an allegory of Religion. The atrium shows St. James the Apostle in the Battle of Clavijo succouring the Christian army.

The exceptionally well-preserved Chapel organ is an example of great perfection and technical advancement for its time; it was built by the Majorca organ-maker Jorge Bosch-Bernat Verí in 1778. From the Chapel a visit may be made to the Antereliquary, the Reliquary and the "Strongroom" (Cámara Fuerte) which is accessed via the left door of the atrium.

The Antereliquary is decorated with interesting paintings from the Italian and Spanish schools; these comprise a *St. Joseph with the Child* (Antonio de Pereda, 1654), a *Christ and the Woman of Samaria* (Italian school, 17th century), a *Conversation with Mary Magdalen* (Bologna school, 16th century), as well as a series of silver-framed paintings done on copper representing the Virgin with Child, dating from the first half of the 18th century and attributed to Giacomo Amiconi.

This chapel contains an outstanding piece: the bronze and semi-precious stone tabernacle which sometimes occupied a place on the high altar. It is signed and dated thus: D.º G.ª / DOMENICO MONTINI. SINESE. ARGENTIERE. a FATTO. IN. MESI. NOVE a 1619. NON OSTANTE.

This Sienna artist took nine months (as he himself says) to fashion this masterpiece. Earlier work by him includes a lamp (1616) and another tabernacle (1618) for the church of the Annunziata in Naples.

The tabernacle takes the shape of a small hexagonal temple with six agate columns and three doors. In the centre there is a semi-precious stones floor forming a large vase with a bunch of flowers. Between the columns there are the bronze statues of St. Clare and St. Francis of Assisi. The entablature is crowned by the four Evangelists, St. Thomas Aquinus, St. Peter, St. Benedict and St. Januarius (Gennaro), bishop of Naples (the latter mentioned giving rise to the belief that the Madrid tabernacle took its inspiration from its Annunziata counterpart in Naples). Over the side doors hang Philip III's coats of arms. A finely worked figure of the Saviour occupies the centre of the dome.

The Chapel leads on to the Reliquary, which remains much as it did in the times of Ferdinand VII. According to extant documents in the Palace archives, decoration on this room was begun in the reign of Charles IV. The stuccowork ceiling is the work of José Ginés. An entablature with voussoired arched spaces, open in the centre, highlights the Triangle, the symbol of the Trinity, surrounded by rays. The Reliquary has a straight apse faced in different marbles and bronzes in a clear-cut Charles IV style. The altarpiece of the high altar comprises a bronze and agate frame resting on two lions; in the centre there is a silver bas-relief (by Alessandro Algardi) depicting the moment at which Pope Leo stops Attila at the very gates of Rome. In 1650 this same Italian baroque sculptor had executed a relief of Attila stopped by Pope Leo for the chapel of the Virgin of the Colonna in St. Peter's in Rome; the sketch for this work was placed above the door of the mother house of the Congregation of the Oratory. Pope Innocent X commissioned the artist with a silver casting of the original drawing, which he then sent to King Philip IV and Mariana of Austria as a wedding present.

There is a floor-to-stuccoed-ceiling glass case along the walls, dividing the room and leaving a narrow corridor in the foreground. The carpentry is in mahogany with gilt carving appliques, probably the work of Maeso, Fernando VII's cabinet-maker.

There are four floors. Small chests with red velvet have been placed on the upper two, and contain a great many historical pieces. From left to right there is a succession of different items from the 16th to the 20th centuries; most of them are altar pieces such as chalices, ciboria, cruets, candlesticks, crosses, monstrances and the like. Noteworthy is the baptismal jar (by García de Sahagún) dating from the beginning of the 17th century; there are also various examples of alms chalices from the reigns of Philip V and Isabella II, a set of cross and candlesticks by the silversmith Antonio Martínez. Of interest among the foreign work is the mid-19th-century set of chalice, ciborium and cruet by Pierre Paraud. Noteworthy among the reliquaries is a small Neogothic silver group of a calvary, which, according to the inscription at the foot of it, is the work of the sculptor Pedro Berruguete; in 1548 he presented this piece to the Archbishop Bartolomé Carranza. Of great spiritual interest is the 16th-century crucifix with a metal crab at its foot. Tradition has it that this crucifix was thrown by St. Francis Xavier into the sea in order to calm a storm when nearing the shores of Cipango; on beaching, he saw it coming towards him, borne on the back of a crab.

In the ''Strongroom'' (Cámara Fuerte), the third of these rooms, there are exhibits of great material value. The oldest are the remains of the Visigoth treasure of Guarrazar; the votive crown of Abbot Theodosius, the Cross of Lucencius and a cut emerald with the scene of the Annunciation.

There is a collection of chests and boxes dating from

Reliquary: Chest of Isabel Clara Eugenia, ivory cross, 16th-century rock crystal and silver cross, crucifix of St. Francis Xavier.

different epochs, ranging from the 16th to the 20th centuries. One fine example is the gold and enamel box crowned by a statue of St. George as a welcome gift from the city of London when King Alfonso XIII made his first visit there, but the most outstanding piece is the chest belonging to the Infanta Isabella Clara Eugenia. This magnificent chest is done in gilt silver sgraffitoed on a lapis lazuli background, and inlaid with a plethora of pearls, emeralds and rubies. The lower part is set with cameos, lapis lazuli, agate and jasper; cut rock crystal ovals decorate the sides and top. The piece is attributed to the silversmith G.B. Croce and the sculptor A. Fontana, who cut the crystal. Another 17th-century Florentine tortoiseshell chest inlaid with silver and semi-precious stone mosaic, is also of great interest.

Crosses on exhibition are also of rock crystal and semi-precious stones. The oldest of them is a processional cross and is made up of cut rock crystal threaded on silver-gilt wire. The second is an altar cross, completely done in rock crystal with a bronze stand; it was made in Bohemia in the 17th century.

Also 17th-century is a silver-gilt reliquary, made in Seville and which contains a relic of the Saint King Ferdinand, taken when his tomb was opened in 1729 and sent to Isabella II as a gift from Seville Cathedral in 1866.

Dating from the same epoch, but differing greatly in style, is an Italian silver-gilt reliquary in the shape of a retable, containing a copy of the Holy Face in the Vatican.

Other items of interest are: the 19th-century French

Reliquary of fine woods with gilt applique (18-19th centuries). On the altar, a bas-relief by Alessandro Algardi.

Chest of the Infanta Isabel Clara Eugenia (16th century).

romantic rock crystal and agate cups, inspired by the jewels of the Italian Renaissance; a silver-gilt christening set of princes and Infantas (by Marschal and Ildefonso Urquiza) from the times of Ferdinand VII; silver-gilt oratory sets of Charles IV (by Urquiza) and the Queen's silver oratory set from the times of Ferdinand VII.

We shall bring this look around the "Strongroom" to a close with the mention of the royal crown and sceptres, used for the proclamation of His Majesty Juan Carlos I as King of Spain in the Spanish Parliament on 22nd November 1975.

The 16th-century sceptre is of cut rock crystal, silver and enamel; the 18th-century crown is gilt silver. Next to them stands the 19th-century cross used in the ceremony; it belongs to the Aranjuez Oratory and was made in the Martínez factory. Another piece of great material value is a 19th-century group comprising the crown of the Virgin of Atocha, that of the Christ Child and a head-dress of the latter statue; it has a great many diamonds and large topazes, and was the gift of Isabella II to the Virgin of Atocha in thanksgiving for her rapid recovery from the assassination attempt she suffered in February 1852.

Relief by Alessandro Algardi, in the Reliquary.

Small room known as the "tranvia" because of its shape, leading to the Official Chamber.

THE PRIVATE APARTMENTS

The Private Apartments are the residential quarters of the monarchs Isabella II, Alfonso XII and Alfonso XIII, and take up the Palace extension designed by Sabatini stretching towards the Plaza de la Armería and Calle de Bailén. In view of the reduced space here, group visits are not considered feasible and so there are restrictions on public access to the apartment.

The apartments bear the names they had during the reign of Alfonso XIII, and comprise a group lying parallel to the Official Chamber known as the Nunciate's Room, the Antebureau and Official Bureau of the King (also used today by His Majesty King Juan Carlos I during palace audiences). Strictly speaking the 'private apartments' comprise a second group of rooms, i.e. the Queen's Reception Room, the ''Corbeille'', the Tea Room, the Queen's Library, the Music Room, the Queen's Office, the Royal Bedroom, the Queen's Dressing Room, the King's Bedroom and the King's Breakfast Room. The final group is perhaps the least private of the three, and comprises the King's Office, the Library and the Cabinet Room.

Music room of Queen Victoria-Eugenia.

Watteau: "Shy young man in love".

Velázquez: The Count-Duke of Olivares, miniature on panel.

COLLECTIONS

Painting

The painting collection will serve as introduction to the several collections contained in the Palace. First of all we shall describe the works found in the Palace's various rooms, and then those on display in the painting Museums. The Arms Room (Salón de Armas) contains fifteen tablets mounted in the shape of a triptych, the remaining ones of an originally 47-tablet triptych belonging to Isabella I; they are by the hand of her court painter John of Flanders and were executed between 1496 and 1504. A sharp contrast of times is provided in the Gasparini Antechamber by the four splendid Goyas: portraits of Charles IV (in hunting costume and uniform of colonel of the Guard Corps), and his queen María Luisa (in court dress and in black with mantilla). In the Gasparini Saleta there are another four pictures by the Baroque painter Luca Giordano (known in Spain as Lucas Jordán): *Solomon introducing his daughters, Solomon adoring the idols, Sacrifice of Quintus Curcius* and *Death of Seneca.* Equally worthy of mention are: (Ordinary Dining Room) the portraits of Philip V and Isabella Farnese, as well as those of Ferdinand VI and Isabella of Bragança, all by Van Loo; the portrait of Isabella II with the Infanta Isabella as a child, by Winterhalter; (Official Antechamber) the portraits of María Carolina, sister to Marie Antoinette of France, and her husband Ferdinand IV of the Two Sicilies, by Giuseppe Bonito; the half-length portrait of Charles III, by Mengs; (Charles III Room) a portrait of the monarch in the suit, cloak and ensembles of the Order founded by himself and so bearing his name, by Mariano Maella; ("Tranvía de la Cámara") a delightful portrait of the Infanta Isabella, daughter of Isabella II, by Vicente Palmaroli; the two

Juan Carreño de Miranda: "Head of a lady". ▷

R. Van der Weyden: "Philip the Good, Duke of Burgundy".

Velázquez: "Head of a lady".

Watteaus, *Shy Young Man in Love* and *Singing Lesson;* and the portrait of Alfonso XII as Captain General, by José Casado del Alisal, and the king's second wife the Queen Regent María Cristina of Habsburg-Lorraine, by José Moreno Carbonero.

Of note in the private apartments are the portrait of the Infante Felipe Pedro, son of Philip V, by Michel Ange Houasse; portraits of the Prince of Asturias and the Infantes Don Juan, Don Gonzalo and Doña Beatriz, the offspring of Alfonso XIII and Victoria Eugenia, by Laszlo; the portraits of Louis XIV, Louis XV and Philip V by the French painter Rigaud; the portraits of Ferdinand VI as Prince, by Ranc; and finally the portraits of Ferdinand IV of Naples and his

wife María Carolina, from the brush of Anton Raffael Mengs.

Noteworthy pictures among the oldest paintings of the royal collection in the Museum of Paintings are: the portrait of Isabella of Castile, attributed to Bartolomé Bermejo; the portrait of Philip the Good, Duke of Burgundy, by Van der Weyden; the great panel of the Flemish Mannerist Michel Coxcie, entitled *Road to Calvary,* which Charles I apparently had in Yuste; of the 16th and 17th Italian schools the most outstanding example is Merisi da Caravaggio's *Salomé,* one of the few paintings in Spain of this master; another important item is the anonymous *Abraham repudiating Agar and Ishmael,* attributed by some to

Portrait of Isabella the Catholic, attributed to Bartolomé Bermejo. ▷

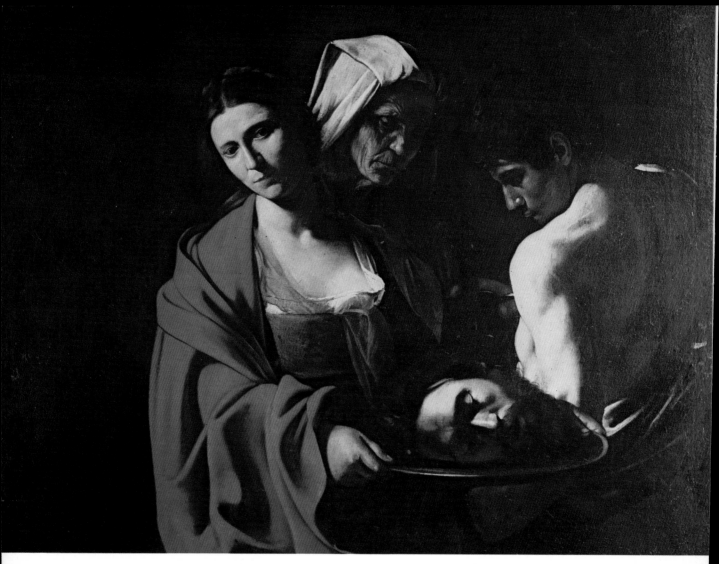

Caravaggio: "Salomé".

Guercino and by others to Mattia Preti; yet other believe it Napolitan with a strong Bologna school influence, perhaps from Stanzione. One of Goya's first cartoons for the Royal Tapestry Factory, *The Boar Hunt,* hangs in this Museum; his too is one of the three grisailles commissioned in 1816 for the boudoir of Queen Isabella of Bragança, the second wife of Ferdinand VII and representing St. Elisabeth of Hungary helping the poor — the other two (the Baptism and Imprisonment of St. Hermenegild) are by Vicente López.

Velázquez's *White Horse,* a woman's head and another woman's bust with high stiff collar, an *Ecclesiastic's hand* (holding a paper with the artist's signature), a miniature portrait of the Count-Duke of Olivares, and the *Stag's antler* are also on display in the Museum.

Other important pictures in this Museum are the equestrian portrait of John of Austria, by Ribera, a *Woman's Head* by Carreño, *View of the Royal Site of the Buen Retiro* by Del Mazo, and *Christ attended by Angels after Fasting in the Wilderness* or the *Miraculous Refreshment* attributed to De Roelas.

Nineteenth and twentieth-century works in the Museum of Paintings collections include: the portraits of Ferdinand VII, General Narváez, Francis I, King of the Two Sicilies, and that of Queen María Cristina of Bourbon, all by Vicente López; *Ferdinand VII's illness,* the full-length portrait of the Dukes of Montpensier and the busts on oval canvasses of the Queen

Velázquez: "White horse". ▷

Regent and her husband the Duke of Riansares, by Madrazo.

The former dining room of the Queen Regent María Cristina contains: several portraits of Alfonso XIII, *The Hobby-horse* (portrait of Alfonso XIII as a child riding a hobby-horse), by Loppay; three portraits of the Prince of Asturias in his cradle, and a colourist full-length portrait of King Alfonso XIII in the uniform of the Hussars, both by Sorolla.

Sculpture

The Palace's collection of sculptures cedes pride of place of the painting collection, but nonetheless the 17th-century series from the Alcázar of the House of Austria (mentioned in the description of the Throne Room) is magnificent.

In the Columns Hall, in addition to the sculpture of the planets already mentioned, there is a group entitled *Charles I dominating fury* (1878) an excellent reproduction by Barbedienne of the 16th-century group by Leoni in the Prado Museum.

The 1st-century stone bust of the Romans Gaius and Lucius, and various 17th-century porphyry and jasper busts and heads of Roman emperors are also noteworthy. Other interesting items are the so-called bust of Seneca (attributed to Bernini), the large 18th-century group of Kings and Princes of Spain and America (intended as Palace ornamental finish and including works by Luis Salvador Carmona, Domingo Martínez, José Bustos, Antonio Valerio Moyano, Andrés de Elgueros, Juan de Villanueva, Juan de León, Felipe del Corral, Robert and Pierre de Michel, Giovanni Domenico Olivieri and Felipe Castro; the latter two mentioned are also responsible for the statues of the Spanish-born Roman emperors Trajan, Arcadius, Theodosius and Honorius standing in the main courtyard), as well as the larger-than-life sculpture of King Charles III in the uniform of a Roman general, facing the main stairway, the work of Pierre de Michel.

There are several busts of kings and queens: Philip V and Isabella Farnese (white marble on grey marble pedestals, with the Bourbon and Farnese coats-of-arms in gilt bronze, by the Frenchman René Fremin); Charles IV and his spouse María Luisa of Parma (white marble, 1797, by Juan Adán); Isabella II and her husband Francis of Assisi (1847/8, by Francisco Pérez; the Queen Regent María Cristina of Habsburg-Lorraine (1890, by Agustín Querol); Queen Victoria Eugenia of Battenberg (by Mariano Benlliure); a

THEODOSIO

René Fremin: bust of Philip V.

"Charles I dominating fury", a copy of the Leoni group.

Discus thrower, 17th-century bronze.

delightful alabaster sculpture of the Infanta Cristina as a child with her clothes billowing in the wind and holding a dove in each hand (also by Benlliure); Alfonso XIII (marble, by Vicente Navarro) and finally Alfonso XII as a child (bronze, by Oliva). There are also a great many decorative statuettes, the most noteworthy being an artistically valuable Hercules and Theseus (1643 and 1645 respectively, by Lorenzo Bernini). The remainder are copies: a Perseus with the head of the Gorgon from the Lanzi loggia in Florence (by Cellini); a Mercury and Fame, a small-scale version of the ones in the Place de la Concorde in Paris (by Coysevox); a small-scale reproduction of the groups entitled *Angelica and Medorus, Apollo and Daphne,* and the so-called *San Ildefonso* group (the original Italian marble one being kept in the Prado Museum); *The Nest Child* and *The Bird Child* (marble reproductions of originals by Pigalle); a seated Venus (1790, from the original by Falconet, by Broch de Belfort). Other sculptures of interest are: Isabella II (silver, full-length statuette, in Court dress); an equestrian Philip V, a Charles III (blued bronze) and a Charles IV (the king and harness in gilt bronze, his horse in black bronze, on a bronze and marble stand); and finally Alfonso XII as a child (1864, by Venancio Vallmitjana).

Chair of Queen Maria Luisa.

Empire-style writing-desk, by the cabinet-maker Weisweiler, the painter Sauvage and the ceramists Dhil and Guerhard (between 1805 and 1807).

Furniture

The fact that almost all the furniture in the Palace is period means that the value is incalculable; the modern reproduction is a rare item indeed. In fact the furniture reflects the history of the Palace itself, and styles range from the early days of construction, through the successive reigns — an uninterrupted series of choice pieces in splendid series of Rococo, Neoclassic, Empire and Isabelline styles. Though some of the items have already been mentioned (Gasparini, Throne and Mirror Rooms) there are other pieces which are deserving of mention. One of these is the Empire-style Sphinxes Table (early 19th century) in the Columns Hall, designed by Percier and cast by the bronzesmith Thomire. The semi-precious stone mosaic top rests on six gilt bronze sphinxes, and on it was signed the treaty of accession of Spain to the European Communities (12 June 1985); another is the pedestal table (bronze and Sèvres porcelain) in the Antechamber, decorated with allegories of the rivers of Spain, the races which settled here and scenes of the reign of Ferdinand VII, to whom the table was presented as a gift on the occasion of the help he gave to Gibraltar during an epidemic there (the scene can be seen in the central medallion), signed by H. Renaud and Lachassaigne and dated 1825; another is the hexagonal table in the Official Saleta, decorated in rich woods, gilt bronze with porcelain top, from the factory of the Duke of Angoulême in Paris, by the ceramists Dhil and Guerhard, and decorated with scenes from the fable of Cupid and Psyche (Le Roy, 1804) and medallions by Sauvage. Around the bronze hoop can be seen the royal coat of arms of Spain alternating with the initials of Charles IV and María Luisa; another is the one in the Charles III Room (bronze and Sèvres porcelain), with biscuit-ware figures of standing women, representing the six regions of France. On the top there are miniatures with scenes of the history of King Charles X of France, and it is signed ''C. Devally,

◁ *Charles III as a Roman general, by Pierre de Michel.*

63

Detail of the official Office.

rounded by the nine Muses standing on a grey marble top, the malachite-plaque drum resting on six blued-bronze griffins (Guillaume Déniere, early 19th century). In addition there is: the great Isabelline divan in the Gasparini Saleta; this is of French manufacture (by Thomire and Co.) and is upholstered by Aubusson; the late Neoclassic round settee in the Gasparini Antechamber; the table in the Tapestry Room with its semi-precious stone top set in lapis lazuli (Florence, 17th century) forming a mosaic with sea motifs, and made for Queen Marie Antoinette (to whom it once belonged) by the cabinetmaker Riesner.

Also worth describing are the console tables in the

1826''; another is the *jardinière* pedestal table in the Gasparini Room, with bronze leg and mosaic top, representing (centre) the temple of Venus, and signed by Gerardo Valponi and Guglielmo Chidel, under the supervision of Filippo Agricola, 1848; another is the one in the Antechamber of Queen María Cristina, the upper part in gilt engraved bronze, a small temple with malachite columns with the figure of Apollo sur-

Chair of the Charles III Room (19th-century).

The sphinxes table (Empire-style, 19th century).

various rooms, made in the Royal Workshops in the 18th century and decorated with bronzes by Ferroni. They comprise: Louis XIV, Louis XV and Louis XVI-style carved gilt tables; Neoclassic tables (Halberdiers' Room and Tranvía de la Cámara) with marble inset top from the collection of Philip IV. Also of interest is the so-called "Indies Wood Bureau" (Apartments of Charles IV and María Luisa) where everything from the dados, friezes, and furniture (writing-desk, commodes and chair) is the work of the cabinetmaker Canops and the bronzesmith Ferroni, executed in the Royal Workshops (after designs by Gasparini) during the reign of Charles III.

Equally interesting are the Empire-style furnishings of the Charles III Room; the six mahogany and rose-wood chairs with peineta (Spanish comb) backs in the Yellow Room, with wood latticing and marquetry showing scenes of children playing, the motifs being repeated by pairs; and the writing-desk and commode in this same soom (c. 1790 by Forestier, after designs by Dugourc) with gilt bronze engravings by Gouthière.

In Queen María Cristina's Chamber there are three noteworthy pieces of furniture: a small *Bonheur du jour*-type mahogany rosewood writing-desk with Sèvres porcelain plaques; an Empire-style mahogany commode with glass plaques decorated in gold; and a Louis XVI bronze-and-wood jewelry box decorated with Paris paintings and porcelains bearing the signature of Guerhard, Dhil and Sauvage.

Part of the Queen's bedroom.

The Gasparini Antechamber.

Carpets

The Palace has an extraordinarily rich collection of carpets, and practically all of them are to be found in the rooms for which they were originally intended. Some of them are very characteristic of the artistic modes of the times in which they were made; others are magnificent in size, such as the 305 m² carpet in the Throne Room.

The Santa Bárbara Royal Tapestry Factory in Madrid once started to manufacture carpets, though on a smaller scale than tapestries. In the early days manufacture was by means of the delicate techniques of tapestry, which soon developed into knotting.

The end of the 18th century, with its Pompey style, was one of brilliance as far as carpet making is concerned. In 1800 the head of manufacturing asked the king to allow his nephew Juan Bautista Stuyk to paint originals to weave carpets; to him we owe some of the most delightful examples from the times of Ferdinand VII, known as *cortina* ("curtain"). From that time onwards hardly any tapestry-work was done, and the Factory gave itself over wholesale to the weaving of highly appreciated Turkish-knot carpets. The reigns of Ferdinand VII and his daughter Isabella II were also times of splendour for carpet manufacture. Almost all the carpets have the stamp of the Factory and date of manufacture woven into the edge, either on the obverse or reverse side (depending on the time of manufacture).

Other noteworthy examples of knotted carpets come from the factory in the street of Cruz del Espíritu Santo (reign of Charles III), some of which may still be seen.

Clocks

The Spanish National Heritage Collection of clocks is no doubt the country's largest, and one of the principal collections in the world.

Many of the key pieces are kept in this Palace, such

French clock in the form of birds in a cage (18th century).

Table-top clock, made in Madrid by Hatton (18th century).

as the *Calvary* in the Arms Room, a piece from the early 17th century made in Nuremberg; together with the *Lamp* (built by Hans de Evalo in 1583), it is one of the oldest pieces in the collection.

The major part of the collection is constituted by 18th-century clocks. In the Throne Room stand the monumental marble and gilt bronze clocks of Godon and Furet with their stands. At each side of the throne there is a free-standing clock; one is Louis XVI and the masterpiece of the many made by the Swiss clockmaker Berthoud. It is a wall pendulum clock with an ebony sound box and gilt bronzes in the purest Louis XVI style, bearing the stamp of Lieutaud, one of the most famous Paris cabinetmakers of his day. The splendid mechanical part comprises a com-

pensated pendulum with barometer; on two spheres of different sizes it marks the phases of the moon, plus sunrise and sunset; it tells the year, month and day of the week, day and night, as well, of course, as striking the hour. The other clock is an exceptional mid-18th-century piece by the English clockmaker John Ellicott; it has an ebony sound box with bronzes in the purest English Rococo.

Another entirely different clock is to be found on the mantelpiece in the Gasparini Room (see description of Room). It is known as the *Shepherd* and is the masterpiece of Jacquet Droz (1721-1790) from Chaux de Fonds, the inventor and maker of famous androids and clocks with automata. In addition to the delightful figure of the shepherd (hence the clock's

Table-top clock. Ebony and gilt bronze case. Clockwork by J. Ellicott (18th century).

Louis XVI table-top clock, by Houdin the younger.

name) in 18th-century dress and playing the flute to mark the hours, it has a barking dog and bleating sheep, a lady who seems to be singing solfa and a cupid with twittering bird, as well as a pair of cupids on a swing. It was acquired by Ferdinand VI in 1758 and caused a sensation in his Court.

Of all the clocks produced by Godon, one of the most noteworthy for its technical expertise and artistry is the monumental clock in the Gasparini Antechamber. It is a unique and priceless piece with the figure of Time bearing on its shoulders the celestial globe where the star-studded sphere rests.

De Belle deserves mention apart. He was clockmaker to Louis XVI of France and when the French Revolution broke out was living in Rue Arbre Sec in Paris. For Napoleon De Belle made an automaton (now in a private collection in New York), which the Emperor then presented to Josephine. This piece brings together the two separate automata — *Vulcan's Forge* and *Charon's Boat* — preserved in Madrid's Royal Palace (Charles III Room), placed respectively on the bellies of bronze jars which each had a small sliding door showing the automata when opened.

Both Charles III and his son and heir Charles IV were particularly enthusiastic about clockmaking in their Courts, and the founding of the Royal School of Clockmaking (1770) is a result of that enthusiasm; nonetheless there are very few Madrid-made clocks in the collection, and this in spite of the noteworthiness of some of them, such as: the small gilt bronze table clock built by the brothers Charots, French clockmakers and engineers who in 1765 presented King Charles III with this masterpiece as it were to make themselves deserving of the directorship of the Royal School of Clockmaking bestowed on them; the clock by A. Mathey of Neuchâtel (Charles IV's court clockmaker), with the curiosity of having the sphere on the pendulum disc; the clock by Salvador López (1797) for the Royal Pharmacy Office, where it still is; and an all steel long-case clock with open-work sphere and visible moving parts, by Manuel Gutiérrez.

French writing-desk with Sèvres porcelain plaque.

Swiss clock by Berthoud. Louis XVI case signed by Lieutaud.

The most important of all these Madrid clocks is the one by Manuel de Rivas, during the reign of Charles IV. De Rivas was an established clockmaker who was master at the Royal School of Clockmaking for eight years; in 1804 he was commissioned by the Spanish prime minister Manuel Godoy (given the title Prince of the Peace in recognition of his negotiation of the Peace of Basel in 1795) to make the clock today standing in the Mirror Room for King Charles and Queen María Luisa. The clock's extraordinary interest resides in its merging machinery and art: to its excellent movement must be added its Buen Retiro Neoclassic porcelain case and flute music composed by A. García Jurado, Queen María Luisa's court musician.

There are numerous gilt bronze French Empire-style table clocks, all belonging to the end of the 19th century, the last days of clockmaking as a mastercraft; since they may be seen in a good many other collections, we shall not go into a detailed inventory here. However, one of them should be mentioned — the clock made in Marseille by Varcollier for Charles IV. This clock has a gilt bronze case with a male and a female figure sitting at a table playing draughts; though its clockwork movement is nothing out of the ordinary, nevertheless it is demonstrative of Charles IV's great penchant for clocks in general.

This look at the best and most beautiful clocks in the Palace collection will be completed by the description of a small astronomical table clock, a gift from the President of Peru to Alfonso XIII in 1906. The materials used in its making (gold, silver and ivory) and its movement (placed within a crystal ball supported by a figure representing Urania) make it a jewel of a piece. It was exhibited in the Paris Universal Exhibition in 1878 and its creators the clockmaker H. Lioret, the ivory sculptor Froger and the goldsmith Felize were awarded first prize.

Apartments of Queen María Cristina: chandelier in the form of a ship done in gilt bronze and cut crystal (19th century).

Chandeliers and candelabra

During the second half of the 18th century, when the Palace was built, interior lighting was by means of "suspended candelabra" i.e. what are today known as chandeliers. These had come to replace the free-standing (and often cumbersome) robustly-built candelabrum which had to support the weight of the great candles then in use. During the reigns of Charles III and Charles IV, the chandeliers hanging from the ceilings of the great rooms intended for official ceremonies of the Court were made of crystal or glass mounted on metal with a small number of candelabra and their corresponding candles. Other rooms in the Palace were illuminated by means of wall-lamps or on single- or double-tier supports. This is the way they are described in palace inventories, with their provenance also recorded: thus we have "a crystal chandelier from Germany, ...from Venice, ...from La Granja" and so on and on forth. The most elaborate were the one-, two- and three-tiered German chandeliers. In the Royal Factory in La Granja

(founded by Philip V), chandeliers were generally made of blown glass with brilliant sockets, modelled pendants and had from six to sixteen candles.

The Throne Room has two such chandeliers of this period, both of them originally designed for it, and they are probably the most beautiful of the collection: Rococo in style, they are made of cut rock crystal beads on silver thread and are listed in the Palace inventory made on the death of Charles III.

These magnificent chandeliers with their splendid bronze mountings embellished with cut rock crystal plaques, today hanging from the Palace ceilings and an important part of the decoration, date from the reign of Ferdinand VII, the king who was in more sense than one the "Enlightener" of the Royal Palaces.

Following a tradition which harked back to the reign of Philip V (as well as matters of personal taste), Ferdinand sent his orders to France, and so most of the chandeliers in the Palace today (as well as other items such as furniture, silks, clocks, porcelain and bronzes) are of French origin.

Chandelier in the Official "Saleta".

So it was that the most renowned names in French decorative arts received commissions thick and fast from the Spanish Court. Paris chandelier makers such as Pierre Philippe Thomire, Chaumont, Ravrio and Viennais were the royal suppliers; documents show that between 1827 and 1830 they shipped no fewer than fifty-six monumental chandeliers, original both in size and design, some of which were baptised with the name of the shape in which they were fashioned. An example is the all-bronze pure Empire-style *Palm-Tree* chandelier in the Queen's Yellow Room; another is the twenty-four candle chandelier in the Sovereign's Library, its great cap decorated with the heads of seraphims and flower garlands in relief; yet another a chandelier in the shape of a fleur-de-lys, with thirty-six bunches of white lilies surrounding as many fleurs-de-lys, with gilt bronze stamen and leaves surmounted by a gilt bronze royal crown (Charles III Room).

Of the bronze and crystal chandeliers, there is a remarkable one originally made for the King's Chamber and which today hangs in the Gasparini Room. It bears the initials of Ferdinand VII and his third wife María Amalia of Saxony (see description of Gasparini Room). A *chinoiserie* chandelier (Mirror Room) is known as *The Spool,* and has three platforms of triangular sections covered with mirrors, the three bodies being linked by crystal chains; it has thirty twin-candle candelabra with attached small hanging bells. *Abundance* (Ordinary Dining Room) is the name given to another chandelier comprising a central palm-tree shaped body with a gilt engraved bronze hoop holding twelve three-candle candelabra and twelve horns of plenty filled with cut crystal plaques.

A curious touch is provided by a clockwork-driven gilt bronze chandelier in the shape of a fountain (Queen Victoria Eugenia's Chamber); its central part holds lions' heads from whose jaws shoot forth cut crystal fountains in imitation of the water supposedly poured forth by other crystal shells held by dolphin figures. The clockwork mechanism, placed inside the central body, moves the fountains, and the chandelier is signed *Moinet Ainé à Paris, fecit, 1829.*

And finally a word about the chandelier known as *The Cathedral* (Official Chamber). It is a large Neogothic gilt bronze piece with stained-glass clerestory motifs; it was one of those included in the final shipment, when the no longer fashionable Empire style was getting rather long in the tooth and ceding pride of place to the increasingly popular Gothic (c. 1830).

Lighting inside the Palace is completed by means of candelabra placed on consoles and bronze or marble high pedestals in room corners. There are some exceptionally fine 18th-century examples: a pair of blued bronze Faun and Bacchanals (Arms Room), each holding a gilt bronze horn of plenty whence spring three single-candle candelabra (c. 1770, by the French sculptor Clodion); a Louis XVI pair in the shape of a tripod holding a small black marble jug with five branches of candles (c. 1775, attributed to Gouthiere); a third pair (1790-91, signed by Thomiere) is of bronze and Sèvres porcelain and imitates the red-figure Greek vases. Other interesting pieces (though of a later period) are the candelabra with musical boxes, to be found in the corners of the Gasparini Room. These comprise groups of gilt bronze free-standing figures, together representing the four corners of the earth.

Empire-style candelabrum.

Silver and porcelain

The silver and porcelain exhibits are to be found in specially prepared glass cases in two adjacent rooms at the end of the Painting and Decorative Arts Museum.

The silver and silver-gilt exhibits are numerous, and come from the reigns of Ferdinand VII, Isabella II, Alfonso XII and Alfonso XIII, and are almost all items of everyday use. The exhibition has been organised chronologically so as to give an idea of the development of this art through the 19th and early 20th centuries. Deserving of special mention are the dressing-table items presented by Madrid City Hall to María Isabella of Bragança, second wife of Ferdinand VII. They are silver-gilt and were made in 1816 in the Martínez Royal Silver Factory; the set comprises a large number of items, of which the most noteworthy from a design and finish point of view are the perfume atomizer, the soap holder, the different boxes for powders, creams and cloths, the writing case, and the two large goblets used as jewel caskets. The different trays for hairpins, combs and brushes were also used by Queen Isabella II, and therefore bear her

Room with chinaware and crystalware sets.

Chinaware of Charles III and Maria Amalia of Saxony. Meissen porcelain (18th century).

"Ribbon" chinaware. Meissen porcelain from the times of Marcolini (18th century).

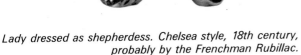

Lady dressed as shepherdess. Chelsea style, 18th century, probably by the Frenchman Rubillac.

anagram. There is also a magnificent silver and silver-gilt water jug set with precious stones and enamels, the work of the Paris-based Froment-Meurice establishment; it was a gift to the Dukes of Montpensier from Queen Isabella II on the occasion of the baptism of her daughter, later Queen Mercedes.

Also on display are various pieces by the silversmiths Francisco Marzo and Luis Perinat, a pupil of Mariano Benlliure, the latter a contemporary of Alfonso XIII.

In the adjoining room there is a wide selection of chinaware from different factories, ranging from Philip V through to Alfonso XIII. Philip V is represented by his coffee and chocolate service made by the Indies Company in its Kiang-Si factory.

Eighteenth-century craftsmanship is represented by Meissen "Scales" (decorated with flowers and fruit) and "Ribbon" (coloured, with gilt borders on white background) chinaware; Berlin "Medicinal Plants" chinaware, where each piece is decorated with a different plant and its name; and finally come a variety of Saxony pieces.

Charles III and María Amalia of Saxony are represented by a single piece: a small tray decorated in green and gold with a romantic scene and the joined coats of arms of Saxony and Two Sicilies (Meissen, 1745), a wedding present to the royal couple. The remaining surviving pieces have been scattered among the Metropolitan Museum of New

York, the National Archaeological Museum and various private collections. Charles IV and María Luisa of Parma are represented by several original Sèvres pieces dated 1789, plus a later copy made in the Buen Retiro factory.

Ferdinand VII and Isabella II are represented by the so-called Landscape chinaware. The name derives from the various landscape views of Spain, France, Switzerland and Italy which decorate the pieces, and the set was manufactured in Paris in 1828. In 1856 several pieces were replaced, the replacements being made in the same place but by different people, and so the marks vary somewhat. The first shipment was ordered by Ferdinand VII and the second by Isabella II. With its over six hundred pieces, this is one of the most complete chinaware sets still preserved.

Also on display is a mid-19th century Copenhague coffee set belonging to the Queen Regent María Cristina.

Other chinaware sets belonging to Isabella II are those made in Paris in the Saint Honoré factory (Boulevard Poissonier), one of them decorated with the coat of arms of the Queen's family, and another with her in-itials. Also on display is the so-called Louis Philippe chinaware, manufactured in Sèvres in the first half of the 19th century, and decorated with gold lions and castles on a cobalt blue background.

The reign of Alfonso XIII and Victoria Eugenia is represented by five chinaware sets. Three of them are for everyday use and are known respectively as the Anagram set (the King's and Queen's initials in gold intertwined with a narrow gold border), the Blue set (again with the monarchs' initials but with blue bordering) and the Red set (initials and red bordering) and made by Coalport at the beginning of the century; and two of them are ceremonial sets, one a gift from the British Parliament to the royal couple on the occasion of their marriage (made in Copeland and decorated in red, blue, silvered and gilt tones with *chinoiserie* motifs) and the other (also a wedding gift) made in Sèvres in 1905.

Free-standing glass cases contain plates decorated with figures and landscapes which once formed part of diverse chinaware sets; they come from the early work of Paris factories and bear the names of Dhil, Guerhard and Thiroux amongst others.

Paris porcelain plate (end of 18th century).

"Scales" chinaware. Meissen porcelain (18th century).

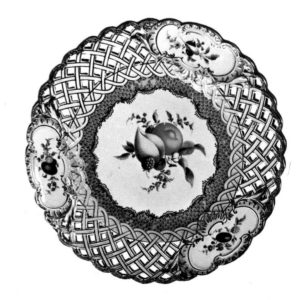

Tapestries

The Spanish National Heritage tapestry collection is the former collection of the Spanish Crown, and is probably the largest and most important in the world. It was begun in the times of the Catholic Monarchs Ferdinand and Isabella and grew with each successive reign, above all in the 16th century with the acquisitions of Charles I and Philip II. With the arrival of the first monarch of the Bourbon dynasty, King Philip V, commissions to Flanders ceased and the Royal Tapestry Factory was founded on the initiative of the king. Two names are intimately linked with this factory — that of Goya, the most brilliant of all its cartoonists, and that of the Vendergoten family from Antwerp, who came to Spain to look after the technical management of the factory.

Several rooms in the Palace have their walls hung with tapestries. The Ceremonial Dining Room was hung with some of the pieces from the series entitled *Vertumnus and Pomona* on the occasion of the marriage of Alfonso XII and María Cristina of Habsburg. This series, one of the Palace's richest and most beautiful, was women in Brussels in the 16th century,

Tapestry Museum. Room of the "Golden Tapestries" "Nativity of Jesus" and "Coronation of the Virgin", 15th-century Flemish tapestries.

Tapestries Room: the "Story of David and Bethsheba"
(Brussels, 16th century).

and incorporates a wealth of gold and silver thread into the weft; the original cartoons have now been unquestionably attributed to Jan Cornelisz Vermeyen, the painter who accompanied Charles I on his campaing to Tunis, the same artist who did the sketches for the famous *Conquest of Tunis* series.

Two French-made series form part of the collection: *The Story of Diana* and the so-called *Heroes of the Trojan War,* made in Paris (17th century) and Beauvais (18th century) respectively; today they hang in Room 9 and Queen Cristina's Antechamber. In another of the rooms named after the same Queen hang the tapestries from the series entitled *Grotesques with Apes,* made in Flanders *circa* 1560-1565; they are characteristic of the Flemish grotesque cultivated with such singular mastery by Cornelis Floris, Cornelis de Vos and Hans Vredeman de Vries. The latter is known to have worked a great deal in the pay of Charles I and Philip II, having a special predilection for the representation of apes in his grotesques — so we have attributed the cartoons of the last mentioned series (one of the most decorative and beautiful) to this artist.

The Palace also boasts some of the most important series to come out of the Madrid Royal Factory: various pieces from the *Story of Don Quixote,* woven in 1744 after cartoons by the painters Procaccini and Domenico Maria Sani; and the complete series of *The Four Seasons* after cartoons by Giacomo Amiconi, *circa* 1760.

Apartments of Charles IV and Maria Luisa.

"Descent", woven in gold, silk and wool by Pieter Van Aelst (Brussels, 16th century).

The walls of the Yellow Room (a small study between the Porcelain and Ceremonial Dining Rooms) are hung with tapestries with some of the pieces woven between 1770 and 1775 for the bedroom of Charles III; this series is unique in Spain in that gold thread is incorporated into the weave. The cartoons were done by the painter Guillaume Anglois (with the help of José del Castillo) who followed the Louis XV style in composition. Their technical perfection and richness of materials make the tapestries in the Charles III Bedroom without any doubt the most important items to have come out of the Royal Tapestry Factory.

The Palace also possesses some examples of tapestries in the manner of Teniers (i.e. genre scenes of Low Countries peasant life), the style that probably made the Royal Factory most popular: *The Alchemist, Skittles, Drinkers, Dancers, Smokers, Drawing Water from the Well, Loading Fruit,* and *Grape Harvest* (some of these examples were woven over and again). Of tapestries woven after Goya's cartoons there is the *Blind Man's Buff* made in 1791 for the Infantes' bedroom in the Pardo Palace; *The Swing* woven in 1779 for the antebedroom of Prince and Princess of Asturias, Charles and María Luisa; *Madrid Fairs,* again for the bedroom of the Prince and Princess; and finally *Hunter loading his Shotgun,* designed for the Dining Room of the Palace itself.

The *Tapestry Room* is so called because of the tapestries which once hung there and which were specially woven for the room in the Royal Factory by José de Castillo at the time of the Palace's construction. The cartoons are by Corrado Giaquinto and José del Castillo, copies of the originals by Luca Giordano and Solimena. Some of these cartoons may be seen in Toledo Cathedral's sacristy.

Another room with tapestry-decorated walls is the *Arms Room;* its dark tones and decoration (wooden dados, Baroque carved walnut furniture) belong to the late 19th century. The wall tapestries are from the series entitled *Galleries, Gardens, Temples and*

Flower Vases (woven in Brussels in the 17th century), and the *Story of Scipio* (Brussels, second half of the 16th century), woven in gold, silk and wool after cartoons by Julio Romano. They are all fragments of the following tapestries: *Carthage sends an Embassy to Scipio, Scipio awards a Crown to Lelius, Meeting between Scipio and Hannibal,* and *Scipio's Conflict.*

The Columns Hall is decorated with five tapestries from the series *Acts of the Apostles* (Brussels, first half of the 17th century); the Cartoons are by Raphael, and the scenes are: *The Punishment of Elymas* (on two complementary tapestries), *St. Peter and St. Barnabus in Lystra* (again two tapestries) and *The Miracle of the Paralysed Man.* Opposite the entrance hangs an early 18th-century silk-and-wool tapestry from the *Coats of Arms* series, with the coat of arms of Spain (Castile and Leon) from the times of Philip V, woven at the Royal Tapestry Factory.

In 1968 the Palace saw the inauguration of what has now become a permanent exhibition — a magnificent collection of 15th-, 16th- and 17th-century tapestries, the great era of this art in Brabant. Some of the series on show, such as the so-called *Triumph of the Mother of God* (also known as *The Golden Tapestries),* have no equal anywhere in the world; this tapestry, woven in Brussels in the late 15th century, has such an amount of golden thread woven into it that, since the name of the cartoonist remained a mystery, he was dubbed the *Master of the Golden Tapestries.* Documentary evidence shows that it was brought to Spain by Doña Juana, daughter of the Catholic Monarchs.

Another 15th-century tapestry, *The Nativity of Jesus,* is woven in the form of an altarpiece and is characterised by its marked primitivism both in composition and drawing. In addition there are two tapestries from the series *Episodes from the Life of the Virgin* (Brussels, early 16th century) after cartoons by Jan van Room (painter to Margaret of Austria, regent of the Netherlands), documented in 1509 and entitled *Fulfillment of the Prophecies of the Birth of the Son of God* and *Presentation of Jesus in the Temple.*

There are also three tapestries from the High Renaissance period in Brabant, from the series *Story of David and Bethsheba.* The magnificent technical expertise in their weaving is complemented by an abundance of gold and silver thread, introducing tones and highlights into the splendid colour scheme in the silk and wool. The *Story of St. John the Baptist* comprises four tapestries and was woven after cartoons attributed to Bernaert van Orley, the founder and head of the Netherlands Romanist school; each of them displays masterly thematic composition and highly effective decoration.

The four tapestries of *The Passion of Christ (Prayer in the Garden, Fall on the Road to Calvary, Crucifixion,* and *Descent from the Cross)* are from the same period and are also based on cartoons attributed to Van Orley. These tapestries were sent from Flanders by Charles I to his wife the Empress Isabella in 1526, together with another depicting the Last Supper, made by Brussels' most distinguished weaver Pannemaker, again after cartoons by Van Orley.

Because of their importance in the history of tapestries, the following pieces must be mentioned: *St. Jerôme at Prayer,* woven in gold, silver, silk and wool at the beginning of the 16th century, beautiful in design and composition and still Gothic through and through; *Pentecost,* one of the finest tapestries of the royal collection, with a wealth of gold and silver thread, a delicate colour scheme, and a splendid bordure comprising very naturalistic flowers, leaves and fruit; finally *The Adoration of the Magi* (bordure comprising groups of fruit, flowers and birds, with scenes from the life of Jesus as a child in the corner roundels) from the collection of Charles I, who took it with him to his retreat in Yuste (the unknown cartoonist is no doubt a pupil of Van Orley, since the influence of the great master of the Renaissance is clear).

Tapestry from the Royal Factory of Santa Barbara. Cartoon by Goya: "The maja and the cloak-wearers".

THE ROYAL LIBRARY

The Royal Library takes up the northeast corner of the Palace. It has two floors; the lower (the object of our visit) comprises sixteen rooms entirely filled with splendid mahogany bookcases; another eight comprise the Reading, Index, Press and Periodicals Rooms. The severe sumptuosity of its rooms, the richness of its furniture and furnishings, the preservation of its many volumes (many of them with artistic bindings) makes the Palace Library one of the world's finest.

The Library has a distinct scientific bent, so consultation is restricted to research workers. The following sections are included: Printed books, Manuscripts, Fine Arts (Engravings, Drawings, Music and Photography), Maps and Plans, Reviews and Journals, commemorative medals and coins (the last two together form a Museum of the genre).

The collection of 18th- and 19th-century bindings is the largest in Spain. The oldest go back to the 15th century (represented by *mudéjar* pieces), 16th and 17th centuries. The section of foreign bindings is large, with a very important group from Spanish

Great Hall of the Library.

"Alfonso XI's Hunting Book" (out on the hunt). 14th-15th century manuscript. Castilian art.

a garganta de sta maria q es entre la hoz de escarabaiosa
y el monte dela vaqriza y el pie de sancho belasco y roble
de feteros y dos fornyllos y nuño aro es todo vn mon
te y es bueno de osso y de puerco enla otoñada y enel Juuerno y so
las lozerias la vna por cima dela caueça de sta maria fasta el collado
dela samoca y dende abestueco malo y la otra deste bestueco malo fas
ta el ceruunal y dende el ceruunalejo por dos fornyllos y por el pi
ar dela maia fasta pie de labox y es el armada en pie de otra.

a pinosa delas torres y los gauylanes y la centenera y el
enzinar de belasco chico es todo vn monte y es bueno de osso
en Juuerno y en verano y es la lozeria desde el forno dela
figueruela por cima delas gramonosas y por cima de ynxanta

America. Also noteworthy are the collections of 15th-century Books of the Hours (such as the one with the coat of arms of Aragon and Enríquez), the incunabulae, the Cervantine and Romantic Book collection.

The collection amount to some 300,000 printed documents, 4,000 manuscripts, 3,000 music scores, 3,500 maps, 200 engravings and drawings, and somewhere in the region of 2,000 coins and medals. The Medals Museum begins in a small hall with two tall built-in glass cases containing diverse commemorative plaques and similar metal objects, souvenirs of homages and visits of monarchs and royalty. Also on display are finely-worked chests, gifts to royal personages, containing diverse parchments of homage or commemoration — two of them are in embossed silver and the third in bronze-gilt with malachite plaques.

The first room exhibits Spanish and foreign 16th- to 20th-century medals. Most of them are bronze and

One of the rooms of the Royal Library.

bear effigies of royalty, famous people and outstanding events. The first two cases contain Spanish medals from the Houses of Austria and Bourbon, from the reigns of Charles I to that of Alfonso XII. Especially noteworthy are the extraordinary pieces of Charles I, the work of Leone Leoni and Hans Reinhart, as well as the bronze piece of Isabella Farnese, made by Párraga with detailed high relief and three-quarters position. Noteworthy pieces from the reign of Isabella II are the commemorative medals of her marriage to Francis of Assisi, as well as the bronze medal commemorating the birth of the Infanta Isabella, the work of the Frenchman Charles Douvet. Noteworthy among the foreign medals is the oldest one, that of Louis XII of France, who reigned towards the end of the 15th century.

The Main Room with its twelve cases and central table contains mainly gold medals, a selection of silver ones, and the old bronze ones. The first three cases display a series of gold medals with the effigies of Spanish monarchs from Philip V through to Alfonso XIII. There is a fine one with the bust of Philip V, a unique piece made in Madrid in 1707 by Isidro Párraga.

On the central table lies a copy of the Spanish Constitution of 1812, presented to Ferdinand VII in a case imitating a medal of this same monarchs, and various 19th- and 20th-century Spanish medal dies, together with medals struck from them.

The Royal Library also houses the Music Museum, in a spacious room with large glass cases (from the workshops of the Spanish National Heritage) proudly exhibiting the Museum's wealth of string instruments: the quintet made by Stradivarius between 1694 and 1696, which he always wished to reserve for the Spanish Court which acquired it, not during the reign of Philip V, the sovereign for whom it was intended, but later in 1775 on behalf of the Prince of Asturias Don Carlos, later Charles IV. Its musical value can only be compared with its intrinsic value —

in other words, priceless. On display is also a magnificent violoncello (also by Stradivarius), various violins attributed to Amati, as well as an 18th-century double bass. Also of interest are two guitars, one with mother-of-pearl and coloured stone inlay, by the Seville guitarmaker José de Frías (1796), played with a plectrum because of its size; and another, made by Riudavets, presented to Ferdinand VII in 1818, bearing a portrait of the monarch made with differently-coloured fine wood inlays.

The collections are completed by Neoclassic harps and a really outstanding set of pianos: an Empire-style piano from the times of Ferdinand VII with fine wood inlay and fired-gilt decorated crystal inlay; another is Neoclassic and from the times of Charles IV, depicting a library; there is also a four-pedal grand piano, again from the reign of Ferdinand VII, and finally two small toy pianos, one 19th-century and the other 20th-century, gifts to the Infantes.

Medals Museum: Philip V by Isidoro Párraga (gold, 1707).

ROYAL PHARMACY MUSEUM

The Royal Pharmacy Museum is one of the very few of its kind in existence in the world. Its collection of flasks, pots and jars, instruments and the outstanding section of quinines underline its importance as a museum.

In the rebuilt Distillation Room, standing on stoves and burners which are exact replicas of those used in the 18th century, is a display of glass and copper flasks and retorts used in the sublimation and distillation of compound medicines to obtain "spirits, oils and salts" regarded in those days as active ingredients in the remedying of ills; also on view are portable iron stoves and copper alembics used to distill the essence out of aromatic plants and flowers; likewise there are rootcutters and presses for the extraction of plant juices, as well as marble and bronze mortars for the crushing of medicines to a fine powder, and so on. The bronze mortars are of particular interest; there is an undecorated one from the Pharmacy of Ferdinand VI, stamped with the date

One of the rooms of the Museum of the Royal Pharmacy.

Room of the Charles IV Pharmacy, with the glass bottles and pot collection from La Granja and porcelain from Buen Retiro.

Oven in the the Distilling Room of the Pharmacy Back-room, with alambics, mortars and retorts (18th-century).

1747, another with two thick handles and the inscription *Of Charles III, May God Him Preserve, 1777;* another large one with a hanging pestle, decorated with eight small banister-type columns, bears the inscription *I am from the Madrid Royal Pharmacy, Year 1790;* another bears the inscription *Aranjuez Pharmacy. Year 1801;* and yet another two (of different sized and with no date) are noteworthy for their beauty of line, being decorated in relief with two large coats of arms and royal escutcheons.

The next two rooms are the Pharmacy proper, and are today as they were when they rendered service to Alfonso XII and Alfonso XIII. In these rooms are to be found surviving porcelain jars from the Buen Retiro and the Moncloa factories as well as glasswork (from the Royal Factory at La Granja) which Charles IV had made in 1794 and Ferdinand VII in 1816. These two rooms are the finest in the whole Museum, together forming a most splendid and harmonious single entity, and one is at a loss to decide whether to admire more the quality of their marvellous porcelain and glass containers or the splendidly conceived lines, whether the drawings or the colours and gilding on the wide variety of these magnificent specimens. In the adjacent room (the Inner or Back Room of the Pharmacy) where stocks of medicines were kept, there are shelves with assorted 18th-century Talavera glazed earthenware pots in a variety of shapes and sizes with coats of arms and inscriptions corresponding to their original destiny. Thus there are twelve *albarelos* (tall containers with concave sides) bearing the inscription of the Royal Hospital of Almadén, and which once belonged to the pharmacy of that hospital, built on the orders of Charles IV to succour the mine-workers who fell ill.

There are two large beautiful Talavera earthenware jars with double crowned coats of arms. In addition the Pharmacy possesses curious recipe books from the 17th and 18th centuries, in which all the details of medicines dispensed to the Royal Family were record-

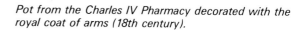

Pot from the Charles IV Pharmacy decorated with the royal coat of arms (18th century).

ed: the preparation, day and time of administration, whether or not carried by the Head Pharmacist or assistants, if not by whom and so on. These books are a veritable mine of information concerning medical practice in each period as well as the development of medicine through time. These recipe-books contain a wealth of soothing remedies for Charles IV and María Luisa, such as goat's whey, a refreshing broth, the "remedy" or plaster for the Queen, the *therica magna;* post-natal treatment for Queens; medication given to wet nurses so that it might be transmitted through their milk to sick infants and so on.

The Museum also possesses an original leather bag and calf-leather box of Peru quinine bark, the remains of a shipment sent to Charles IV in 1807. The powdered bark of the quinine plant was one of the greatest revolutions in the history of medicine. It reached its high-water mark in the 17th century, and widespread use has continued down to the present day. Volumes have been written about its discovery by the Spanish in Peru and the rôle played by the Countess of Chinchón (wife to the Victory of Peru and one of the first persons to benefit from the drug's curative properties when relieved of malignant fevers in 1638) in making it better known. She brought great quantities of the drug back with her on her return to Spain in the company of her doctor Vega, and since then use of quinine spread not only throughout Spain but also the entire Old World. The books containing detailed records of receipt and dispatch of quinine shipments are placed in glass cases.

The last rooms of the Museum contain examples of the jar and pot collection conserved in the San Carlos Hospital; these items were given by the County Council to the Spanish National Heritage Collection for safe-keeping.

Earthenware Talavera jar (18th century).

THE ROYAL ARMOURY

As far as the historical and artistic importance of its collections is concerned (practically entirely made up from the Arms Rooms of the Kings of Spain), the Madrid Royal Armoury is second to none. Some of the mediaeval pieces are of incalculable historical value and come from the treasure which the Catholic Monarchs kept in the Alcázar in Segovia. There are interesting pieces of Spanish armour from the end of the 15th century, brought from the Hall of Lineages in Soria. There is a piece of Flemish armour belonging to Philip the Fair, other noteworthy Valencia pieces, plus some others he inherited from his father the Emperor Maximilian I, kept by Charles I in his personal armoury. The magnificent war and ceremonial armour belonging to the Emperor Charles were all made to be used by the great warrior and jouster that he was. In his dominions he had the two most important centres of their day, Milan and Habsburg, rivalling each other in the art of working and decorating iron. The highly renowned makers of these universally acclaimed pieces of art in armour were the Negroli in Milan and the Colman Helmschmeid in Habsburg.

Royal Armoury. Jousting and war harness room.

Philip II also had his personal armoury, and in his youth was a skillful jouster. Continuing with his enlightened attitude and love of art which he had already shown in previous foundations, he gave the Armoury the status of historical museum, and stocked it with his own armour and that of his predecessors, adding all the trophies won in Lepanto; near the Alcázar he ordered a building to house the Armoury and Stables to be built. His successors maintained it in the same state, and placed their own defensive and offensive weapons in the Armoury, together with items won from famous captains, as well as trophies taken from the enemy.

During the War of Independence (Peninsular War), the Armoury fell into disorder and many pieces of cold steel and firearms disappeared from it. During the reign of Isabella II it was re-stocked, and the first Catalogue published in 1849. The most exhaustive study and praiseworthy organisation of the Armoury

Dress armour, possibly belonging to King Sebastian of Portugal, the work of Anton Peffenhauser (15th century).

however did not come until later during the reign of Alfonso XII and the Regency, and was carried out by the Widower Count of Valencia de Don Juan. However, disaster struck just before the opening of the Armoury to the public in 1884, when a raging blaze caused widespread damage, including the destruction of sixty-two banners won from the enemy. This however proved to be no obstacle to the continued zeal in the reorganisation of the Royal Armoury, and it was housed in the new building (finished in 1893) in the left wing of the Royal Palace's parade ground. New acquisitions were added to it: the famous armoury of the Dukes of Osuna (in Madrid) and the eleven 15th-century cuirasses (in Aragon), the largest single collection of these very scarce and highly appreciated pieces of armour. Some of the more important pieces taken from the Armoury in previous years were rescued from abroad, and another collection of shafted weapons was also added.

The Count of Valencia de Don Juan was responsible for the classification and identification of the objects belonging to Charles I, basing it on the splendidly illustrated inventory of water colours describing the pieces of armour, and on the manuscript known as *List of Valladolid,* two extant testimonies of great authority that served to hand on the Armoury in the Last Will and Testament of the Emperor. And so the Count poured all his vast knowledge of ancient arms into his outstanding *Historical and Descriptive Catalogue of the Royal Armoury in Madrid,* published in 1898.

The Armoury was damaged in the Spanish Civil War. Exhibits were transported and stocked within Madrid itself, but the actual losses suffered pale in comparison to the potential risk. Once more recovered and put in order, the Armoury has since been added to and notably improved.

The room on the main floor houses armour from the late 15th and early 16th centuries, as well as that of Charles I of Spain. The room's glass cases show the marvellous collection of arms, diverse pieces of armoury and trophies, ranging from a Visigothic horse's bit to early 19th-century firearms.

CARRIAGE MUSEUM

Both the old Alcázar of the House of Austria and the New Palace of the Bourbons possessed stables housing the carriages and horses intended for use by royalty on their public or private outings, trips to other royal residences, journeys and so on.

The Alcázar's stables were located on the site today occupied by the church of Our Lady of the Almudena, in a building constructed by Gaspar de Vega in the times of Philip II and demolished in the 19th century. The architect Sabatini was responsible for the design of the present Palace stables, built on the esplanade adjacent to the north front of the Palace. Demolished in 1932, the site was converted into gardens, today known as the Sabatini gardens in memory of the famous architect.

The carriages, coaches and similar equipment in the present stables hark back to the times of Charles IV (except for the Black Carriage, see below), and it was María Luisa Teresa of Bourbon who was given the task of acquiring in Paris the coaches which are today the best conserved. The fame of the French coachmakers in the times of Napoleon was such that

Gild berline, from Ecija from the house of the Marquises of Alcántara (first half of 18th century).

it was imitated by Spanish makers such as Julián Rodríguez, Fernando Durán, Francisco Rodríguez, Garrones and others, who nevertheless produced carriages which could more than hold their own against the best produced by the workshops of Gautier or Berkmann.

The present Museum has five hexagonal floors and is located in the Campo del Moro, is tailor-made to its purpose, and offers the added advantage of allowing future extensions.

Of the carriages, the most noteworthy is the so-called *Black Carriage* (made of beech and ash stained black) built in the second half of the 17th century. The 18th century is represented by a berlin from the House of the Marquises of Alcántara, as well as the *Amaranth, Golden Panels,* and *Shell* berlins. The most noteworthy of the 19th-century coaches is the *Royal Crown* berlin, built in 1832. The 19th century is also represented by a large collection of coaches of the most varied kinds.

For those interested in further details concerning the Carriage Museum, we would strongly recommend a guide written by Isabel Turmo.

Corner of the first module in the carriage Museum.

GENERAL ARCHIVES

On his return from Valençay in 1814 Ferdinand VII quickly organised his Royal Household so as to become familiar with revenue due to the Royal Heritage and to determine the running costs of the Royal Family, since until then they had been included in the Public Treasury and were not the beneficiaries of any taxation, being simply the recipients of a lump sum. In this way the monarch took the first steps towards getting endowments for the Archives of the Royal Household and its Heritage, today the general Archives of the Spanish National Heritage.

The forerunners of this system may be found in the older posts of *Côntrolleur* and *Greffier;* such was the nature of their duties that they may be considered as being posts proper of the King's Household.

By the Regulations of 1761 Charles III ordered that all Decrees, Consultations, Warrants or Ordinances signed by the "Royal Hand or its Ministers" should be sent to the office of the Greffier, which thus became, *de facto,* the General Archives, acting as a clearing house for: all papers ancient and modern of the Royal Houses of Castile, Burgundy and France; of the Stables, the Old Pages and Guards House; of the dowager Queens of Philip IV, Charles II and Philip V; of the servants of the Princes and Infantes, consultations and decisions, orders of the Master of the Household, Lord Chamberlain, Lord Steward, and Vice-Chamberlain; decisions of the ancient Royal Court of Justice, reports, certificates, books and accounts of ordinary and extraordinary working days; of all the official notes of the "Royal Mouth, Chamber and Hand"; reports and proof of nobility of the Royal Bodyguards, titles of other Court officials; etiquette and regulations for the Royal Servants; books of news concerning public acts and royal functions; Testaments and Commissions of Credit, Lawsuits and Police Instruments as well as a long list of other documents too numerous to be mentioned here. All told they make up a weighty bundle of dossiers and the like, the forerunners of which hark back to the reign of Charles I.

As late the the reign of Charles IV there was still no such thing as the Palace or Royal "Archives" as such, in the sense of a place for safeguarding and classifying documents according to their nature, until the political situation in 1808. The Royal Decree of 23rd September 1808 specified the functions of a Civil Officer in the royal household (given the name of Superintendant General), one of whose duties was to oversee the Crown Archives.

This Decree, therefore, was the first to mention the documents kept in the offices of the Côntrolleur, Greffier and Private Secretaries as belonging to the "Crown Archives". From 1814 to 1931 they came to be known as the "General Archives of the the Royal Household and its Heritage"; the name was changed to "Archives of the National Palace" during the Spanish Second Republic, and was finally established as "General Archives of the National Heritage".

Today the Archives occupy three spacious floors and comprise forty-nine rooms with nigh on four kilometres of shelf space holding 20,000 dossiers, 7,000 boxes of dossiers and 6,500 registers, in addition to an auxiliary library which possesses more than 2,000 titles concerning the History of Spain.

contents

MADRID'S ROYAL PALACE   2
THE GASPARINI ROOM   24
THE PORCELAIN ROOM   32
THE CEREMONIAL DINING ROOM   33
THE MIRROR ROOM   34
THE THRONE ROOM   38
THE ROYAL CHAPEL   42
THE PRIVATE APARTMENTS   51
COLLECTIONS - Painting   52
Sculpture   59
Furniture   63
Carpets   66
Clocks   66
Chandeliers and candelabra   71
Silver and porcelain   74
Tapestries   77
THE ROYAL LIBRARY   82
ROYAL PHARMACY MUSEUM   86
THE ROYAL ARMOURY   89
CARRIAGE MUSEUM   91
GENERAL ARCHIVES   93

Collection ALL EUROPE

#		Spanish	French	English	German	Italian	Catalan	Dutch	Swedish	Portuguese	Japanese	Finnish
1	ANDORRA	•	•	•	•	•						
2	LISBON	•	•	•	•	•				•		
3	LONDON	•	•	•	•	•					•	
4	BRUGES	•	•	•	•	•		•				
5	PARIS	•	•	•	•	•				•		
6	MONACO	•	•	•	•	•						
7	VIENNA	•	•	•	•	•						
11	VERDUN	•	•	•	•		•					
12	THE TOWER OF LONDON	•	•	•	•							
13	ANTWERP	•	•	•	•	•						
14	WESTMINSTER ABBEY	•	•	•	•	•						
15	THE SPANISH RIDING SCHOOL IN VIENNA	•	•	•	•	•						
16	FATIMA	•	•	•	•	•				•		
17	WINDSOR CASTLE	•	•	•	•	•					•	
19	COTE D'AZUR	•	•	•	•	•						
22	BRUSSELS	•	•	•	•	•		•				
23	SCHÖNBRUNN PALACE	•	•	•	•	•						
24	ROUTE OF PORT WINE	•	•	•	•	•				•		
26	HOFBURG PALACE	•	•	•	•	•						
27	ALSACE	•	•	•	•	•	•					
31	MALTA			•	•	•						
32	PERPIGNAN		•									
33	STRASBOURG	•	•	•	•							
35	CERDAGNE - CAPCIR		•				•					
36	BERLIN	•	•	•	•	•	•					

Collection ART IN SPAIN

#		Spanish	French	English	German	Italian	Catalan	Dutch	Swedish	Portuguese	Japanese	Finnish
1	PALAU DE LA MUSICA CATALANA	•		•			•					
2	GAUDI	•	•	•	•	•					•	
3	PRADO MUSEUM I (Spanish Painting)	•	•	•	•	•					•	
4	PRADO MUSEUM II (Foreign Painting)	•	•									
5	MONASTERY OF GUADALUPE	•					•					
6	THE CASTLE OF XAVIER	•	•	•			•					
7	THE FINE ARTS MUSEUM OF SEVILLE	•	•	•	•	•						
8	SPANISH CASTLES	•	•	•								
9	THE CATHEDRALS OF SPAIN	•	•	•								
10	THE CATHEDRAL OF GERONA	•										
14	PICASSO	•	•	•	•	•					•	
15	REALES ALCAZARES (ROYAL PALACE OF SEVILLE)	•	•	•	•	•						
16	MADRID'S ROYAL PALACE	•	•	•	•	•						
17	ROYAL MONASTERY OF EL ESCORIAL	•	•	•	•	•						
18	THE WINES OF CATALONIA	•										
19	THE ALHAMBRA AND THE GENERALIFE	•	•	•	•							
20	GRANADA AND THE ALHAMBRA	•										
21	ROYAL ESTATE OF ARANJUEZ	•	•	•	•	•						
22	ROYAL ESTATE OF EL PARDO	•	•	•	•	•						
23	ROYAL HOUSES	•	•	•	•							
24	ROYAL PALACE OF SAN ILDEFONSO	•	•	•	•	•						
25	HOLY CROSS OF THE VALLE DE LOS CAIDOS	•	•	•	•							
26	OUR LADY OF THE PILLAR OF SARAGOSSA	•	•	•		•						
27	TEMPLE DE LA SAGRADA FAMILIA	•	•	•	•	•	•					
28	POBLET ABTEI	•	•	•			•					

Collection ALL SPAIN

#		Spanish	French	English	German	Italian	Catalan	Dutch	Swedish	Portuguese	Japanese	Finnish
1	ALL MADRID	•	•	•	•	•					•	
2	ALL BARCELONA	•	•	•	•	•	•					
3	ALL SEVILLE	•	•	•	•	•					•	
4	ALL MAJORCA	•	•	•	•	•						
5	ALL THE COSTA BRAVA	•	•	•	•	•						
6	ALL MALAGA and the Costa del Sol	•	•	•	•	•			•			
7	ALL THE CANARY ISLANDS (Gran Canaria)	•	•	•	•	•			•	•		
8	ALL CORDOBA	•	•	•	•	•					•	
9	ALL GRANADA	•	•	•	•	•						
10	ALL VALENCIA	•	•	•	•	•						
11	ALL TOLEDO	•	•	•	•	•						
12	ALL SANTIAGO	•	•	•	•	•						
13	ALL IBIZA and Formentera	•	•	•	•	•						
14	ALL CADIZ and the Costa de la Luz	•	•	•	•	•						
15	ALL MONTSERRAT	•	•	•	•	•	•					
16	ALL SANTANDER and Cantabria	•										
17	ALL THE CANARY ISLANDS II, (Tenerife)	•	•	•	•	•			•	•	•	•
20	ALL BURGOS	•	•	•	•	•						
21	ALL ALICANTE and the Costa Blanca	•	•	•	•	•						
22	ALL NAVARRA	•	•	•								
23	ALL LERIDA	•	•	•			•					
24	ALL SEGOVIA	•	•	•	•							
25	ALL SARAGOSSA	•	•	•	•							
26	ALL SALAMANCA	•	•	•	•	•				•		
27	ALL AVILA	•	•	•	•							
28	ALL MINORCA	•	•	•	•							
29	ALL SAN SEBASTIAN and Guipúzcoa	•	•	•								
30	ALL ASTURIAS	•										
31	ALL LA CORUNNA and the Rías Altas	•	•	•								
32	ALL TARRAGONA	•	•	•	•							
33	ALL MURCIA	•	•	•								
34	ALL VALLADOLID	•	•	•								
35	ALL GIRONA	•	•	•	•							
36	ALL HUESCA	•	•									
37	ALL JAEN	•	•	•	•							
38	ALL ALMERIA	•	•	•	•							
40	ALL CUENCA	•	•	•								
41	ALL LEON	•	•	•								
42	ALL PONTEVEDRA, VIGO and the Rías Bajas	•	•	•								
43	ALL RONDA	•	•	•	•	•						
44	ALL SORIA	•										
46	ALL EXTREMADURA	•	•	•								
47	ALL ANDALUSIA	•	•	•	•	•						
52	ALL MORELLA	•	•	•			•					

Collection ALL AMERICA

#		Spanish	French	English	German	Italian	Catalan	Dutch	Swedish	Portuguese	Japanese	Finnish
1	PUERTO RICO	•		•								
2	SANTO DOMINGO	•		•								
3	QUEBEC		•	•								
4	COSTA RICA	•		•								
5	CARACAS	•										

Collection ALL AFRICA

#		Spanish	French	English	German	Italian	Catalan	Dutch	Swedish	Portuguese	Japanese	Finnish
1	MOROCCO	•	•	•	•	•						
2	THE SOUTH OF MOROCCO	•	•	•	•	•						
3	TUNISIA		•	•	•							
4	RWANDA		•									

The printing of this book was completed
in the workshops of
FISA - ESCUDO DE ORO, S.A.
Palaudarias, 26 - Barcelona (Spain)

Pregnant females: First trimester, ≤ 500,000 IU/24 hours; second trimester, 10,000 to 25,000 IU/24 hours; third trimester, 5,000 to 15,000 IU/24 hours

Clot retraction
50%

Coccidioidomycosis antibody, serum
Normal titer < 1:2

Cold agglutinins, serum
Normal titer < 1:16

Complement, serum
Total: 41 to 90 hemolytic units
C1 esterase inhibitor: 16 to 33 mg/dl
C3: Males, 88 to 252 mg/dl; females, 88 to 206 mg/dl
C4: Males, 12 to 72 mg/dl; females, 13 to 75 mg/dl

Complement, synovial fluid
10 mg protein/dl: 3.7 to 33.7 units/ml
20 mg protein/dl: 7.7 to 37.7 units/ml

Copper, urine
15 to 60 mcg/24 hours

Copper reduction test, urine
Negative

Coproporphyrin, urine
Men: 0 to 96 mcg/24 hours
Women: 1 to 57 mcg/24 hours

Cortisol, plasma
Morning: 7 to 28 mcg/dl
Afternoon: 2 to 18 mcg/dl

Cortisol, free, urine
24 to 108 mcg/24 hours

Creatine phosphokinase
Total: Men, 23 to 99 units/liter; women, 15 to 57 units/liter
CPK-BB: None
CPK-MB: 0 to 7 IU/liter
CPK-MM: 5 to 70 IU/liter

Creatine, serum
Males: 0.2 to 0.6 mg/dl
Females: 0.6 to 1 mg/dl

Creatinine, amniotic fluid
> 2 mg/100 ml in mature fetus

Creatinine clearance
Men (age 20): 90 ml/minute/1.73 m²
Women (age 20): 84 ml/minute/1.73 m²
For older patients, concentrations normally decrease by 6 ml/minute/decade.

Creatinine, serum
Males: 0.8 to 1.2 mg/dl
Females: 0.6 to 0.9 mg/dl

Creatinine, urine
Men: 1 to 1.9 g/24 hours
Women: 0.8 to 1.7 g/24 hours

Cryoglobulins, serum
Negative

Cryptococcosis antigen, serum
Negative

Cyclic adenosine monophosphate, urine
Parathyroid hormone infusion: 3.6 to 4 μmoles increase

D

Delta-aminolevulinic acid, urine
1.5 to 7.5 mg/dl/24 hours

D-xylose absorption
Blood: Children, 730 mg/dl in 1 hour; adults, 25 to 40 mg/dl in 2 hours
Urine: Children, 16% to 33% excreted in 5 hours; adults, > 3.5 g excreted in 5 hours

E

Erythrocyte sedimentation rate
Males: 0 to 10 mm/hour
Females: 0 to 20 mm/hour

Esophageal acidity
pH > 5.0

Estriol, amniotic fluid
16 to 20 weeks: 25.7 ng/ml
Term: < 1,000 ng/ml

Estrogens, serum
Menstruating females: day 1 to 10, 24 to 68 pg/ml; day 11 to 20, 50 to 186 pg/ml; day 21 to 30, 73 to 149 pg/ml
Males: 12 to 34 pg/ml

Estrogens, total urine
Menstruating females: follicular phase, 5 to 25 mcg/24 hours; ovulatory phase, 24 to 100 mcg/24 hours; luteal phase, 12 to 80 mcg/24 hours
Postmenopausal females: < 10 mcg/24 hours
Males: 4 to 25 mcg/24 hours

Euglobulin lysis time
≥ 2 hours

F

Factor II assay
225 to 290 units/ml

Factor V assay
50% to 150% of control

Factor VII assay
65% to 135% of control

Factor VIII assay
55% to 145% of control

Factor IX assay
60% to 140% of control

Factor X assay
45% to 155% of control

Factor XI assay
65% to 135% of control

Factor XII assay
50% to 150% of control

Ferritin, serum
Men: 20 to 300 ng/ml
Women: 20 to 120 ng/ml

Fibrin split products
Screening assay: < 10 mcg/ml
Quantitative assay: < 3 mcg/ml

Fibrinogen, peritoneal fluid
0.3% to 4.5% of total protein

Fibrinogen, plasma
195 to 365 mg/dl

Fibrinogen, pleural fluid
Transudate: Absent
Exudate: Present

Fibrinogen, synovial fluid
None

Fluorescent treponemal absorption, serum
Negative

Folic acid, serum
2 to 14 ng/ml

Follicle-stimulating hormone, serum
Menstruating females: Follicular phase, 5 to 20 mIU/ml; ovulatory phase, 15 to 30 mIU/ml; luteal phase, 5 to 15 mIU/ml
Menopause females: 5 to 100 mIU/ml
Males: 5 to 20 mIU/ml

Free fatty acids, plasma
0.3 to 1.0 mEq/liter

Free thyroxine, serum
0.8 to 3.3 ng/dl

Free triiodothyronine
0.2 to 0.6 ng/dl

G

Gamma glutamyl transferase
Males: 6 to 37 units/liter
Females: < age 45, 5 to 27 units/liter; > age 45, 6 to 37 units/liter

Gastric acid stimulation
Males: 18 to 28 mEq/hour
Females: 11 to 21 mEq/hour

Gastric secretion, basal
Males: 1 to 5 mEq/hour
Females: 0.2 to 3.8 mEq/hour

Gastrin, serum
< 300 pg/ml

Globulin, peritoneal fluid
30% to 45% of total protein

Globulin, serum
Alpha₁: 0.1 to 0.4 g/dl
Alpha₂: 0.5 to 1 g/dl
Beta: 0.7 to 1.2 g/dl
Gamma: 0.5 to 1.6 g/dl

Glucose, amniotic fluid
< 45 mg/100 ml

Glucose, cerebrospinal fluid
50 to 80 mg/100 ml

Glucose, fasting, plasma
70 to 100 mg/dl

Glucose, plasma, oral tolerance
Peak at 160 to 180 mg/dl, 30 to 60 minutes after challenge dose

Glucose, plasma, 2-hour postprandial
< 145 mg/dl

Glucose, urine
Negative

Growth hormone, serum
Men: 0 to 5 ng/ml
Women: 0 to 10 ng/ml

Growth hormone stimulation
Men: Increases to ≥ 10 ng/ml
Women: Increases to ≥ 15 ng/ml

Growth hormone suppression
0 to 3 ng/ml after 30 minutes to 2 hours

H

Haptoglobin, serum
38 to 270 mg/dl

Heinz bodies
Negative

(continued inside back cover)

HEALTH ASSESSMENT HANDBOOK

Springhouse Corporation
Springhouse, Pennsylvania

Developmental Editor   Regina Daley Ford
Designer   Lynn Foulk
Copy Supervisor   David Moreau

Nursing85 Books™

The clinical procedures described and recommended in this publication are based on research and consultation with medical and nursing authorities. To the best of our knowledge, these procedures reflect currently accepted clinical practice; nevertheless, they can't be considered absolute and universal recommendations. For individual application, treatment recommendations must be considered in light of the patient's clinical condition and, before administration of new or infrequently used drugs, in light of latest package-insert information. The authors and the publisher disclaim responsibility for any adverse effects resulting directly or indirectly from the suggested procedures, from any undetected errors, or from the reader's misunderstanding of the text.

Adapted from *Assessment* (Nurse's Reference Library®), Copyright 1983, 1982 by Springhouse Corporation. Editorial Director—Diana Odell Potter, Clinical Director—Minnie Bowen Rose, RN, BSN, MEd.

NEW NURSING SKILLBOOK™ SERIES
Giving Emergency Care Competently
Monitoring Fluid and Electrolytes Precisely
Assessing Vital Functions Accurately
Coping with Neurologic Problems Proficiently
Reading EKGs Correctly
Combatting Cardiovascular Diseases Skillfully
Nursing Critically Ill Patients Confidently
Dealing with Death and Dying

NURSING PHOTOBOOK™ SERIES
Providing Respiratory Care
Managing I.V. Therapy
Dealing with Emergencies
Giving Medications
Assessing Your Patients
Using Monitors
Providing Early Mobility
Giving Cardiac Care
Performing GI Procedures
Implementing Urologic Procedures
Controlling Infection
Ensuring Intensive Care
Coping with Neurologic Disorders
Caring for Surgical Patients
Working with Orthopedic Patients
Nursing Pediatric Patients
Helping Geriatric Patients
Attending Ob/Gyn Patients
Aiding Ambulatory Patients
Carrying Out Special Procedures

NURSING NOW™ SERIES
Shock
Hypertension
Drug Interactions
Cardiac Crises
Respiratory Emergencies
Pain

NURSE'S CLINICAL LIBRARY™
Cardiovascular Disorders
Respiratory Disorders
Endocrine Disorders
Neurologic Disorders
Renal and Urologic Disorders
Gastrointestinal Disorders

NURSE'S REFERENCE LIBRARY®
Diseases
Diagnostics
Drugs
Assessment
Procedures
Definitions
Practices
Emergencies

Nursing85 DRUG HANDBOOK™

Library of Congress
Cataloging in Publication Data
Main entry under title:

Health assessment handbook.
"Adapted from Assessment"—T.p. verso.
Bibliography: p.
Includes index.
1. Nursing. 2. Medical history taking.
3. Physical diagnosis. [DNLM: 1. Nursing Process—handbooks. WY 39 H434]
RT48.H445 1985 616.07'54'024613 84-23732
ISBN 0-916730-88-3

Table of Contents

Advisory Board and Contributors iv

Consultants v

Assessment Abbreviations vi

Foreword viii

Chapter 1   Approach to Assessment 1

Chapter 2   The Health History 4

Chapter 3   The Physical Examination 28

Chapter 4   Psychological Assessment 62

Chapter 5   Nutritional Assessment 78

Chapter 6   Skin, Hair, and Nails 96

Chapter 7   Eyes and Vision 114

Chapter 8   Ears and Hearing 136

Chapter 9   Respiratory System 156

Chapter 10   Cardiovascular System 184

Chapter 11   Gastrointestinal System 220

Chapter 12   Urinary System 246

Chapter 13   Male Reproductive System 262

Chapter 14   Female Reproductive System 278

Chapter 15   Nervous System 302

Chapter 16   Musculoskeletal System 338

Chapter 17   Blood-Forming and Immune Systems 364

Chapter 18   Endocrine System 384

Chapter 19   The Pregnant Patient 406

Chapter 20   The Neonate 424

Selected References 444

Index 445

Advisory Board, Contributors, and Clinical Consultants

At the time of publication, the advisors, clinical consultants, and contributors held the following positions:

Advisory Board

Contributors

Common Assessment Abbreviations

A

A₂ - aortic component second heart sound
AAL - anterior axillary line
ACG - apexcardiography
ADA - average daily allowance
ADL - activities of daily living
AGE - angle of greatest extension
AGF - angle of greatest flexion
A-P diam - anterior-posterior diameter
ARDS - adult respiratory distress syndrome
ausc - auscultation
A-V - arteriovenous
A&W - alive and well

B

BE - barium enema
BP - blood pressure

C

c̄ - with
C1...C7 - first cervical vertebra... seventh cervical vertebra
CAD - coronary artery disease
CC - chief complaint
CHF - congestive heart failure
cm - centimeter
CN - cranial nerve
CNS - central nervous system
c/o - complains of
COLD - chronic obstructive lung disease

COPD - chronic obstructive pulmonary disease
CV - cardiovascular
CVA - costovertebral angle (or cerebrovascular accident)

D

dB - decibel
DOE - dyspnea on exertion
DM - diabetes mellitus
DPT - diphtheria, pertussis, tetanus
Dx - diagnosis

E

ED - emergency department
EEG - electroencephalogram
EENT - eyes, ears, nose, and throat
EKG - electrocardiogram
EMG - electromyogram
ENG - electronystagmogram
EOM - extraocular movements

F

FH - family history

G

Gen - general
GEO - geographic
GI - gastrointestinal
G, g - gram
GU - genitourinary
GYN - gynecology

H

HEENT - head, eyes, ears, nose, and throat
H&P - history and physical

HPI - history of present illness
ht - height
Hx - history
Hz - hertz

I

ICS - intercostal space
ID - identifying information
insp - inspection
IVP - intravenous pyelogram

K

kg - kilogram

L

L1...L5 - first lumbar vertebra... fifth lumbar vertebra
LAAL - left anterior axillary line
LBCD - left border cardiac dullness
LICS - left intercostal space
LLQ - left lower quadrant
LLSB - lower left sternal border
LMP - last menstrual period
LOC - level of consciousness
LRSB - lower right sternal border
LSB - left sternal border
LUQ - left upper quadrant
L&W - living and well

M

MAL - midaxillary line
MCL - midclavicular line
mg - milligram
MIL - midinguinal line
mm - millimeter

m₁ - mitral component first heart sound
MMR - measles, mumps, rubella
MS - musculoskeletal
MSL - midsternal line, midscapular line

N _____
nl, NL - normal
N&V - nausea and vomiting
NSR - normal sinus rhythm

O _____
OB - obstetric
OD - right eye
OS - left eye
OU - both eyes

P _____
P₂ - pulmonic component second heart sound
PAL - posterior axillary line
palp - palpation
Pap - Pap test
PCO₂ - carbon dioxide pressure
perc - percussion
PERRLA - pupils equal, round, reactive to light
PH - past history
PMI - point of maximal impulse
PO₂ - oxygen pressure
PO(M)R - problem-oriented (medical) record
prn - as circumstances require
P/SH - personal and social history
Psych - psychiatric
pt - patient
PTA - prior to admission

Q _____
q - each

R _____
RAAL - right anterior axillary line
RICS - right intercostal space
RLQ - right lower quadrant
R/O - rule out
ROM - range of motion
ROS - review of systems
RSB - right sternal border
RUQ - right upper quadrant
Rx - treatment

S _____
s̄ - without
S₁ - first heart sound
S₂ - second heart sound
S₃ - ventricular gallop
S₄ - atrial gallop
SH - social history
SOB - shortness of breath
stat - at once

T _____
T₁ - tricuspid component first heart sound

T1...T12 - first thoracic vertebra... twelfth thoracic vertebra
TB - tuberculosis
TM - tympanic membrane
TOPV - trivalent oral polio vaccine
TPR - temperature, pulse, respiration

U _____
ULSB - upper left sternal border
URI - upper respiratory tract infection
URSB - upper right sternal border
UTI - urinary tract infection

V _____
VS - vital signs

W _____
WNL - within normal limits
wt - weight

Symbols

μ	Micron (common term for micrometer).
$+$	Plus; excess; acid reaction; positive.
$-$	Minus; deficiency; alkaline reaction; negative.
$\pm$	Plus or minus; either positive or negative; indefinite.
$\#$	Number; following a number; pounds.
$=$	Equals.
$\simeq$	Approximately equals.
$>$	Greater than; from which is derived.
$<$	Less than; derived from.
$\not<$	Not less than.
$\not>$	Not greater than.
$\leq$	Equal to or less than.
$\geq$	Equal to or greater than.
$\neq$	Not equal to.
$\therefore$	Therefore.
$\square$, $\male$	Male.
$\bigcirc$, $\female$	Female.

Foreword

The past 20 years have seen an explosion in biomedical information and technology. In response, your responsibilities as a health-care professional have grown as well, particularly in the area of patient assessment. To meet this new challenge of decision-making in patient care and to develop individualized intervention strategies, you need a comprehensive data base. But where can you turn for the accurate and comprehensive information you need to guide you through this essential phase?

The answer is the HEALTH ASSESSMENT HANDBOOK. This new volume fills the void between theory and practice, telling you what you need to know to perform patient assessments with confidence.

HEALTH ASSESSMENT HANDBOOK is divided into four parts, covering:
- foundations of assessment (Chapters 1 to 3)
- psychological and nutritional assessment (Chapters 4 and 5)
- assessment of body systems (Chapters 6 to 18)
- assessment of the pregnant patient and the neonate (Chapters 19 and 20).

Chapters 1 to 3 cover the fundamentals of assessment—the critical technique of history taking, and methods for conducting the physical examination. I think you'll find these chapters so valuable you'll return to them again and again.

Chapters 4 to 20 begin with brief introductions. Then, they discuss the important points of collecting appropriate history data and conducting the physical examination. Helpful illustrations, diagrams, tables, charts, and supplementary pieces of text augment these chapter sections. Pediatric and geriatric sections—unique to this book—round out Chapters 4 through 18. Here you'll learn about significant variations in assessment techniques and findings in children and the elderly.

The organization and scope of HEALTH ASSESSMENT HANDBOOK make it a suitable text for any health-care professional, whether student or seasoned practitioner. You may read it in sequence or in selected segments. And because of its easy-to-use format, it can serve both as a source of new knowledge and as a means to reinforce what you've already learned.

HEALTH ASSESSMENT HANDBOOK is an indispensable text. I recommend it highly. Don't let it gather dust on your library shelf; instead use it frequently to help you fulfill your role as a contemporary health professional.

KATHLEEN GAINOR ANDREOLI, RN, DSN, FAAN
Vice-President of Educational Services
Interprofessional Education and International Programs
Professor of Nursing
The University of Texas Health Science Center
Houston, Texas

1
Approach to Assessment

Accurate patient assessment—history, physical examination, and laboratory data—is vital to your patient's health and well-being. Consequently, assessment skills are essential for *all* health-care professionals, not just doctors. Indeed, planning patient care on the basis of accurate assessment is the foundation of current practice.

As a practicing health-care professional, you must learn to gather assessment information, analyze it, and learn to make patient-care decisions based on your findings. You also must learn that patient-care planning, intervention, and evaluation depend on the quality of the assessment data for their effectiveness. Today, many are skilled in assessment and in diagnosis. And those that still feel uncertain about using assessment are gradually accepting it.

The defined data base
The information you collect in taking your patient's history, performing his physical examination, and identifying necessary laboratory tests is your assessment data base. Make your patient history as comprehensive as you can while choosing your data carefully. You can't collect or use *all* the information that exists about your patient. Your goal is to gather information that will be most helpful to you in assessing your patient. To define, or limit, your data base appropriately, ask yourself these questions: What data do I want to collect? How should I collect the information? How should I organize it to make decisions, before I intervene?

Your answers will help you to be selective in collecting meaningful data during patient assessment.

The well-defined data base for a patient may begin with his admission signs and symptoms, chief complaint, or medical diagnosis. It also may center on the type of patient care given in a specific hospital unit, such as the intensive care unit or the emergency department (ED). For example, you wouldn't ask a trauma victim in the ED if she has a family history of breast cancer, and you wouldn't perform a routine breast examination on her either. You would, however, do these types of assessment during a comprehensive health checkup in an ambulatory-care setting.

If you work in a setting where patients with similar diagnoses are treated, choose your data base from information pertinent to this specific patient population. Ask yourself these questions:

● *What is my defined patient population?* Begin by describing the typical patient you care for in your practice. What common problems do your patients experience or risk experiencing? For example, if many of your patients are immobilized and risk hypostatic pneumonia, your defined assessment data base should include a careful physical examination of the respiratory system. Perhaps many of them are insulin-dependent diabetics. Then the defined data base should include information about the knowledge and skill of the person giving the injections, as well as examination of the patient's skin at the injection sites *and* at pressure points on his arms and legs.

● *What are the standards for care of the people in my defined patient population?* Consider both the standards set by experts in the field and those set by your hospital. For example, cardiology specialists tell us that a proper assessment of a patient with heart disease includes checking his heart rate and rhythm. You palpate his radial artery for 1 minute, then auscultate his apical pulse for 1 minute, then compare the two findings. Therefore, these techniques should be included in your data base for a cardiac population. Another example: Most hospitals require that you monitor a patient's vital signs when he's admitted, so assessment of vital signs must be included in your data base.

● *How can I provide good care to the specified patient population?* Typically, a patient enters your sphere of influence in one condition and leaves it in a different (you hope improved) condition. The information you collect according to your defined data base should be sufficient to plan, implement, and complete all the care needed between these two points in time. For example, in an ED, where patients enter with life-threatening problems and are transferred to other units when stabilized, your data base must include assessing respiratory, cardiac, and central neurologic function. Long-term care considerations and discharge planning need not be included. Or, suppose a patient enters a screening clinic to find out if he has hypertension. Taking his blood pressure is appropriately included in your defined data base, but a rectal examination would be inappropriate and not included.

● *What are my available resources?* Your physical assessment can only be as complete as your knowledge and skill, and the time and equipment available, allow it to be. If the staff on your unit can't perform the palpation component of an abdominal examination, the defined data base shouldn't include it—until the staff members develop the necessary skills. Similarly, if an otoscope is unavailable, tympanic membrane inspection has no significance in the defined data base.

A practical defined data base results when you ask and answer these questions before doing a patient assessment. This data base, when used to guide data collection in assessment, produces the essential information for planning and delivering appropriate patient care.

Subjective and objective data

The three types of data you'll collect and analyze in the assessment decision-making process—history, physical examination, and laboratory data—fall into two important cat-egories, subjective and objective. Here's how they differ:

Your patient's *history* consists of the subjective data you collect from him, using interviewing skills that help him describe his biologic, social, and psychological responses to the particular anatomic, physiologic, and chemical processes involved in his illness or injury. In addition, he may recall events in his own or relatives' lives that place him at increased risk for certain pathologic processes to occur. The subjective data collected in your history include his chief complaint or concern, history of present illness (current health status), past history, family history, psychosocial history, activities of daily living, and review of systems.

The patient's history, embodying his *personal perspective* of his problems, is your most important source of assessment data. In fact, some clinicians claim that approximately 80% of the information on which they base their diagnoses and patient management decisions comes from the history. It remains the most subjective source of patient information, however, and must be carefully interpreted.

In the *physical examination* of a patient—involving inspection, palpation, percussion, and auscultation—you collect objective data about your patient's health status, or about the pathologic processes that may be related to his illness or injury. Besides adding to your patient data base, this information helps you interpret the patient's history more accurately by providing another source of information for comparison. Use it to validate and amplify the historical data. However, don't allow the physical examination of your patient to assume undue importance—even though it's an exciting new aspect of your practice.

Laboratory test results are the most objective form of assessment data. They provide another source of patient data for validation and amplification of your history and physical examination findings. The advanced technology involved in laboratory tests lets you measure anatomic, physiologic, and chemical processes that your senses and your patient's senses aren't capable of measuring. For example, if your patient complains of feeling tired (history) and you observe conjunctival pallor (physical examination), check his hemoglobin and hematocrit (laboratory data).

You need both subjective and objective data for comprehensive patient assessment. They're complementary, too, in that they validate each other and together provide more data than either could provide alone. For example, *subjective data* for a patient with an apparent respiratory disorder might include his description of having difficulty breathing, while the *objective data* would include finding rales by auscultation, tibial edema by palpation, and cardiomegaly on the X-ray film. Similarly, a patient's report of abdominal pain might be the *subjective* finding that correlates with a palpable enlarged liver or hyperresonant bowel sounds found *objectively* on physical examination.

Respect the value of both subjective and objective data when assessing a patient. And consider all three types of assessment information—history, physical examination, and laboratory data—in their appropriate relationship to one another. Performing an accurate physical examination requires technical skill that in itself is valuable. It becomes even more valuable, however, when you place the examination findings in perspective. Use them to validate historical and laboratory data, and recognize that the physical examination is only one aspect of total patient assessment. This and other considerations are part of the discipline you need for learning and using assessment skills.

Here's something else to remember: During the data collection phase of assessment, don't *interpret* your findings. Describe what you see, hear, and find when you take your patient's history and examine him, but guard against any tendency to write what you think statements, sounds, or lumps may mean. A lump may be a malignant tumor but, of course, it may not be. Are your patient's tears caused by depression? Maybe—or perhaps he has hay fever. Because each assessment observation can represent any of a number of possible causes, *suspend* decision-making related to your patient's problem(s) until you've collected *all* the subjective and the objective data and have created your assessment data base.

2

The Health History

A thorough health history provides about 80% of the information you use in assessing a patient. It is *the patient's story*. It provides the *subjective* data base for your assessment, to be supplemented by the objective data gathered during your physical examination of him. Your own observations and opinions shouldn't intrude in this assessment phase. Ideally, a health history tells the reader a great deal about your patient and nothing about you—except that you've mastered the skills necessary to be a good interviewer.

If your attitude during the interview promises help and support, your patient will cooperate with your history-taking efforts. Approach him considerately; then listen carefully and phrase your questions thoughtfully.

Interviewing skills

The therapeutic relationship
You need empathy, compassion, self-awareness, and objectivity to promote a trusting relationship with your patient. Your behavior should demonstrate dependability and reliability, as well as respect for the confidential nature of the interview. Remember, the best way to establish a therapeutic relationship is to communicate to the patient that his thoughts and behavior are important to you.

Trust, the basis of all health-care relationships, takes time to develop—but the health history interview usually signals the *start* of your relationship with your patient. How can you gain his trust quickly, so the interview can proceed? First, be on time for the interview. To begin your conversation, ask the patient what name he prefers you to use in addressing him; use this name consistently throughout

the interview. As the interview progresses, be sensitive to areas of information your patient seems reluctant to share, and respect his privacy concerning them.

The influence of attitudes
Your personal values and biases influence the course of your relationships with your patient—and sometimes create communication barriers. During the health history interview, you need to recognize the ways in which your values and your reactions to the patient are influencing the interviewing process. For example, if the interviewer can't understand or accept her patient's decision to have an abortion, she may become impatient, rude, and abrupt with the patient. She then impedes the interviewing process and blocks appropriate care.

However, you needn't give up your personal attitudes and beliefs to understand a patient's point of view. Instead, your recognition of his different perceptions as the interview progresses helps you explore every significant area of his experience objectively.

The uses of silence
Talking with another person involves silence as well as speech. Learn how and when to be silent during the health history interview. Listen carefully to what the patient says in response to your questions. Don't rush him or attempt to figure out what he's going to say before he says it. Sometimes accepting a few moments of silence until you or the patient feels like talking again can be therapeutic. Interpreting silences thoughtfully can greatly increase the effectiveness of your health history interviews.

To use silence effectively when interviewing

a patient, imagine yourself in the patient's situation, keeping in mind the circumstances for his seeking health care. Of course, some people are normally less talkative than others. Or, the patient's lapse into silence may indicate that he's thinking carefully about how to answer your question. Give him time. But when your patient is unresponsive to your questions—whether throughout the discussion or just at a single point—you need to understand what's happening so the interview can continue.

In considering how you'll handle such situations, examine your own responses to silence—how *you* react when a patient doesn't reply to your questions. You probably feel anxious about how the interview is progressing. To relieve your anxiety, analyze the situation in terms of how the *patient* may be feeling, and respond to his need for reassurance. Perhaps you need to restate the question in a less threatening way. Keep your anxiety under control, and don't think of your patient's silence as a vacuum you must rush to fill. In addition, avoid labeling the patient as uncooperative, or otherwise interpreting his silence negatively.

Other reasons for a patient's silence do exist, of course. Maybe he's angry, fearful, or suspicious about the need for the interview, or about the kinds of questions you're asking. Help him relax by speaking calmly and reassuringly, and be sure you explain fully why the interview questions are important.

The verbose patient

Like the silent patient, the individual who is extremely talkative during the interview may be trying to avoid confronting anxiety by keeping you and your questions at a distance. As long as he's talking, he remains in control of the interview. When dealing with a talkative patient, strive to decrease his anxiety. Provide him gentle feedback about his talkativeness. Say something like: "I feel concerned that you haven't heard me, because you seem to be thinking about what to say next. It's important to me that we understand each other." In addition to reminding him that you need to have his answers to your questions, this direct statement of the problem shows you're really interested in him and his responses.

Sometimes a patient who talks on and on

can irritate you and frustrate your efforts to take a comprehensive health history. Be direct with him (without being offensive), and keep the discussion going so you can obtain the history information you need.

The basics of interviewing

A sound knowledge of therapeutic interviewing skills can help you get a clear picture of your patient that can lead, in turn, to a complete and accurate physical assessment. During the health history interview you'll gather information about your patient's past and present health status. Straightforward questioning usually succeeds in eliciting most of this information. At times, however, you'll have to explore your patient's concerns about his condition, which can call for more sophisticated interviewing skills. In either situation, asking the right questions during the interview, listening attentively, and interpreting your patient's responses objectively and accurately are important.

Taking a health history involves both intellectual and motor skills. Intellectually, you plan and conduct the interview and interpret the results. Your motor activities consist of recording the data, as well as speaking, listening, and gesturing (to emphasize what you say). Coordinating these skills during an interview is difficult, but with experience you'll gain confidence in your interviewing technique.

Timing the interview

Your sense of timing is crucial to a successful interview, especially if your patient is hospitalized. A time convenient for you may not be convenient for your patient. Show him you're willing to let him have some control over his schedule. To enlist his cooperation, for example, say, "I'd like to spend some time talking with you about your health history. Is this a good time for you?" If the patient says no, find another time that's convenient for both of you.

Think about your patient's probable frame of mind, too, before approaching him for a health history interview. For example, if he just received distressing news from his doctor, postpone the interview until he has had time to absorb what he has learned. Keep your schedule flexible. If necessary, plan more than one interview session with your patient, especially if his history is detailed or if he's critically ill or debilitated.

The interview environment

Both you and the patient must be comfortable to communicate with each other effectively. If he's in pain, try to alleviate as much of his discomfort as possible before attempting to interview him. Make sure you and the patient agree on the temperature and lighting in the room. If the room is too warm or too cool, have the temperature adjusted (if possible), after asking the patient's permission; or, provide the patient with extra blankets or ventilation as necessary. If the room is too dark, you may have trouble maintaining eye contact with your patient and observing his gestures and facial expressions. Before you change the lighting, ask the patient's permission to do so. He may want the room dark because he has a headache or irritated eyes, or because he feels depressed. Explain why you want to change the lighting, too. For example, you might say something like: "I'd like to adjust the shades because sunlight is causing glare in your room. Is that all right with you?"

Make an effort to create a private environment for your talk with the patient. Try to avoid interruptions during the time you've set aside for the interview. If the patient is in a semiprivate room but ambulatory, you can take him to a quiet area outside the room. If the patient isn't ambulatory but his roommate is, you might ask the roommate to leave you alone with the patient for the length of time you need for the interview. If you can't achieve privacy with your patient in or outside his room, draw the curtains around the bed and speak in a low tone to convey respect for his privacy.

The interview setting should be quiet as well as private. If a television or radio is on in the room, ask the patient if you may turn it off or lower the volume. If the corridor or neighboring rooms are noisy and you can't move the patient to a quieter area, ask the noisy persons if they would mind keeping their voices down. Then close the patient's door.

By creating a comfortable, private, and quiet environment for the health history interview, you let your patient know you're interested in what he tells you, and that you respect the confidentiality of the information he shares with you.

Hospitalization anxiety

During a stay in the hospital, a patient passes through stages of adjustment—from denial to anger, to depression, to helplessness. To obtain the necessary history information from a patient whose attitude is blocking communication, accept and work with his particular emotional and behavioral responses. Try to determine the meaning of his behavior by looking at the interview through his eyes. Then decide what verbal and nonverbal responses would be therapeutic.

In addition to the emotional responses a hospitalized patient has to his medical problems, he may feel dehumanized by the health-care system's rapid pace and advanced technology. Hospitalization can shut off his usual means of maintaining self-esteem. Furthermore, he may be frightened by loss of control over his body and his environment, because of illness. Forfeiting his normal daily routine and adapting to the hospital's schedule also may cause him anxiety.

If you sincerely communicate that you care about your patient and his well-being, and respect his individual needs, you can reduce the dehumanizing effects of his hospital stay.

Strategies you can employ in helping your patient cope with hospitalization anxiety include obtaining his permission to perform certain procedures at particular times, discussing his food preferences with him, adjusting his sleeping schedule—and periods of rest and privacy—to reflect his wishes, and asking him how he wants to schedule visitors. Don't be afraid to discuss the patient's anxiety with him to help him understand its cause. The direct approach often works best. You might say something like: "Many times hospitalization and illness produce a lot of anxiety. These situations are often difficult, but I'll be glad to assist you in any way I can that will make this time easier for you."

Conversational interviewing techniques

After introducing yourself to the patient, begin the interview by explaining the history's purpose so the patient understands why you'll be asking him personal questions. Remember, your attitude about history-taking is important. Be calm, relaxed, and unhurried. The patient who sees these qualities in you and also understands the purpose and importance of the history will be more apt to provide the information you need.

Communication is a continuous process by which we relate to our environment and other persons in it. All kinds of behavior that you use to interact with patients—verbal and nonverbal, consciously and unconsciously motivated—are forms of communication. In the health history interview, the way you direct the conversation can enhance the communication process—or hinder it. For example, the patient shouldn't have to defend himself. Use nonjudgmental and nonthreatening language. Say, "Tell me about..." or "What happened after..." "What was the experience like for you?" Don't say, "Why did you do that?" or "Explain your behavior."

Another conversational technique you can use is *reflecting*—repeating the patient's words back to him in an inquiring way. By using his words, you avoid adding your personal viewpoint to what he's said. And he's encouraged to continue his story.

Try *restating* or *summarizing* what the patient has just told you. If he confirms that you've understood him correctly, you can confidently move on to the next history question.

Mannerisms such as nodding to acknowledge what your patient's just said, saying "Yes" or "I see" when the patient pauses briefly, and maintaining eye contact with the patient are called *facilitation*. They let the patient know you're listening to him and want him to continue.

When you have to ask your patient for additional clarification about some point, don't make him feel he hasn't presented his story clearly. Preface your request for more information with "I'm not quite sure about..." or a similar approach. In this way you assume responsibility for not fully understanding what the patient said; you don't arouse defensive feelings.

In all these conversational techniques, the key element is *listening;* the more conscientiously you listen, the more skillfully you will interpret what your patient tells you and respond appropriately. Listening attentively also allows you to identify recurring themes in your patient's history and to clarify any statements or issues you don't understand. Above all, you must let the patient know you care about him and want to know his problems.

Communicating without words

The verbal and nonverbal exchanges that occur between you and your patient during the first few minutes set the tone for the entire interview, and usually affect how much he'll cooperate with you. During the health history interview, you and the patient communicate on many levels simultaneously. Along with your careful choice of words, you communicate with your eyes, gestures, and facial expressions. Even the distance between you and the patient affects your ability to communicate.

Maintaining *eye contact* with your patient during the interview—without staring—can help close the physical and the psychological distance between you. Intermittent eye contact suffices to show your interest in the patient and your respect for his privacy. Suppose your patient refuses to make eye contact. He may feel embarrassed or hesitant about talking with you, or he may simply want to avoid the interview. When your patient won't look you in the eye, use conversational interviewing techniques, such as reflecting and restating, to involve him in the discussion. Examine your own willingness to make eye contact, too. You may need to practice this technique with patients. As your confidence increases, so will the effectiveness of your interviewing technique.

Gestures often speak louder than words. When your patient says he'll put his belongings in "that closet" and points to the closet, the meaning of his gesture is clear. But sometimes a patient's gestures express feelings he's unaware of—or doesn't want to reveal. If he taps his fingers continuously on the table while you're questioning him, crosses and uncrosses his legs, sighs deeply, or coughs repeatedly, he's probably tense, anxious, or bored. Your interpretation of such gestures can help you assess your patient's mood and structure the interview accordingly. Be sure you've interpreted his gestures correctly before you respond. If you're not sure what his gesture means (or whether it has any particular significance), make the patient aware of it and explore the matter further, if necessary.

Your patient's *facial expressions* can also tell you a lot about him. Like gestures, facial expressions can have direct or indirect meaning. They're probably the most common form of nonverbal communication. A smile, for instance, may be a happy greeting, or it may be a mask for sadness or pain. Some people need to present themselves as strong and always in control; they may use a smile to cover up their pain or anxiety.

Listen closely. Sometimes a patient's words don't match his facial expression; this is called *incongruency*. If he says, "I'm fine, no problems" but looks sad and tearful, he needs your encouragement to talk about his feelings. To help, say something like: "I'm concerned about you. You say you're fine, but you look unhappy. How can I help?"

Be aware of *your* facial expression, too. A patient usually notices it before he notices anything else about you. Keep this in mind when you approach a patient to interview him.

Posture and *body appearance* are additional ways in which you communicate with patients. Your positive self-image gives the patient confidence and also shows your concern for what he may think of you. In turn, observation of your patient's appearance can give you important clues about his body image, self-esteem, and hygienic practices.

The *space* or *distance* you put between yourself and others affects your ability to communicate. On the one hand, if you attempt to interview your patient while standing or sitting too near to him, he'll probably feel uncomfortable and react accordingly. On the other hand, if you talk with a patient who's in bed while you're standing in the doorway of his room, he'll be reluctant to communicate; he can't be sure you really want to make contact. Many people feel more comfortable sitting at an angle with respect to another person, perhaps with a small table or stand between them, which gives each person a sense of his own space.

Of course, the most comfortable distance between you and your patient during the history interview varies with individual patients and interviewing situations. Let your awareness of your own comfort and sensitivity to your patient's wishes guide you.

Family interviews

A family usually consists of a husband, wife, and children; this unit is known as the *nuclear* family. *Extended-family* members (also called *significant others*) include grandparents and other relatives. A person's family gives him his strongest sense of community and generally lends stability and security to his life.

Your patient's hospitalization has great impact on the well-being and functioning of his family. By sharing information about his condition with his family, you can decrease their anxiety and increase their cooperation.

Of course, you interview the patient himself to record his health history, if possible. If he is too ill, or if you suspect his history information isn't completely reliable, talk with a family member or friend—after obtaining the patient's permission to do so. Reassure the patient and his family that you'll keep this information confidential.

Family members often help you validate, clarify, and elaborate on the patient's history, especially his daily activities. For example, you may learn that the patient frequently overindulges in alcoholic beverages, or that he hasn't told you of recent stressful events. In addition, observing the interaction between the patient and family members may give you clues to his role and responsibilities in the family, and to the strength and character of his relationships with family members.

Of course, the basic principles of interviewing patients apply when you interview your patient's relatives and friends. Never give a family member information without your patient's permission or you risk undermining his trust in you. For example, a husband and wife in the process of getting a divorce may not want to share personal information with each other. You wouldn't disclose information to either one without the other's consent.

When you interview someone close to the patient who isn't part of his family, be sure to note the nature of the relationship and the length of time the individual has known the patient. For instance, in your documentation, write something like this: *Information received from John Jones, a friend, who has lived with the patient for 3 years.*

The health history record

Effective history-taking methods

Health history data must be recorded in an organized fashion, so the information will be meaningful to everyone involved in a patient's care. Some hospitals provide patient questionnaires or computerized checklists for gathering history data. These forms make history-taking easier, but they're not always available. Therefore, you must know how to take a comprehensive health history without them. This is easy to do if you develop an orderly and systematic method of interviewing. Ask the history questions in the same order every time. With experience, you'll know which types of questions to ask in specific patient situations.

No matter which format you use, be sure to record negative findings as well as positive ones. Note the absence of symptoms that other history data indicate could be present. For example, if a patient reports pain and burning in his abdomen, ask him if he has experienced nausea and vomiting, or noticed blood in his stool. Record the presence *or* absence of these symptoms.

The importance of accuracy

While recording history data, remember that the information will be used by others caring for the patient. It may even be used as a legal document in a liability case, malpractice suit, or insurance disability claim. With these considerations in mind, record history data precisely. Continue your questioning until you're satisfied you've recorded sufficient detail. Don't be satisfied with inadequate answers, such as *a lot* or *a little*. These words mean different things to different people and must be explained to be meaningful. If the patient seems anxious about your note-taking at any point during the interview, explain the importance of it so he'll feel more at ease. To facilitate accurate recording of your patient's answers, familiarize yourself with standard history data abbreviations (see APPENDIX).

The parts of a complete health history

A complete health history provides the following information about a patient:
- biographical data
- chief complaint (or concern)
- history of present illness (or current health status)
- past history
- family history
- psychosocial history
- activities of daily living
- review of systems.

Follow this orderly format in taking your patient's history, but allow for modifications on the basis of your patient's chief complaint or concern. For example, the health history of a patient with a localized allergic reaction will be much shorter than that of a patient who complains vaguely of mental confusion and severe headaches.

A patient may not even have a chief complaint; he may be feeling fine and simply seeking a complete physical checkup. Such a patient's health history would be comprehensive, with detailed information about his lifestyle, self-image, family and other interpersonal relationships, and degree of satisfaction with his current health.

The health history of a patient who has a chief complaint must provide information to help you decide if your patient's problems are from physical pathology or psychophysiologic maladaptation, as well as how your interventions can help him. The depth of such a history depends on the patient's cooperation and your skill in asking insightful questions.

Biographical data

Begin the health history interview by collecting biographical data about your patient. This includes the following information: full name, address, telephone number, sex, age, date of birth, race, marital status, nationality, religion (optional), occupation, and source of referral. If any of this information is available in the patient's medical record, hospital admission form, or some other document in his file, don't ask him for it again. Just ask him if the information you have is correct.

Aside from the obvious purpose of identifying the patient, this part of the health history helps you assess the patient's reliability as an informant, since his chart usually already contains correct biographical data. If you can't obtain this information from the patient, or if you're not certain about the patient's reliability as an informant, try to interview a friend or relative. Be sure to identify the informant in the health history.

Chief complaint (or concern)

For this part of the health history, ask the patient to briefly describe his reason for seeking health care. The best way to prompt a patient to identify his chief complaint or concern is to ask him an open-ended question. Record his response, in his own words, using quotation marks.

Don't elaborate on the chief complaint or concern in this section of the history. If the patient has more than one complaint, record each one separately; if he doesn't have a chief complaint, record his reason for requesting a physical examination.

History of present illness

This is probably the most challenging part of the health history and requires adept questioning and an adequate knowledge base. Begin by asking your patient to describe the progression of his chief complaint or concern, from the time it started to the present. Skillful questioning will clarify the clinical ramifications of the chief complaint and provide the framework for arriving at a diagnosis. Ask general questions about the chief complaint at first, to give the patient direction in describing it chronologically. To do this effectively, ask only open-ended questions. You might say, "Tell me about your problem, from when it first began until now." Don't suggest answers or interrupt the patient while he's talking.

When the patient finishes recalling the history of his illness and associated symptoms, you may need to ask questions that will elicit further essential information. Question him directly about each symptom, using the PQRST mnemonic device (see *History of Present Illness,* page 11). Record negative findings if they help to clarify the significance of symptom clusters. Such findings are often critical in completing an accurate clinical picture.

Past history

A comprehensive survey of a patient's past history provides you with information about his previous major health problems, his experiences with the health-care system, and his at-

titude toward it. This part of the health history usually yields important clues about the patient's present condition. It also helps determine the treatment plan and may suggest the patient's prognosis.

Ask your patient about the following elements of his past history:

● *Childhood and infectious diseases.* Concentrate your questioning on diseases with sequelae. For example, if a patient reports he had rheumatic fever, determine if the disease was diagnosed by a doctor, how old the patient was when he contracted it, and whether he is taking antistreptococcal drugs prophylactically.

● *Immunizations.* Vaccinations for poliomyelitis and rubella are especially important, since these diseases can affect unvaccinated adults and pose serious risks for women of childbearing age. Don't forget to ask about vaccinations your patient may have received in the armed forces or before a recent trip to a foreign country.

● *Accidents.* Consider your patient's history of accidents apart from his history of illnesses. Does he appear to be accident-prone? If injuries suffered in an accident have potential legal implications, record as many details about the accident as your patient can provide. Don't forget to ask specifically about fractures, since patients frequently forget to mention broken bones from childhood accidents. A good way to elicit this information is to ask the patient if he was ever treated in an emergency department.

● *Surgical procedures and hospitalizations.* For this part of the past history, ask the patient if he's had any major illnesses that required hospitalization or surgery. His chief complaint may be associated with a previous illness. When asking your patient about such previous surgery, include mention of common procedures like tonsillectomy and appendectomy. Record information in this section chronologically, listing events by date or by the patient's age at the time of hospitalization or surgery.

● *Allergies.* To determine the cause of an allergic reaction, ask the patient for precise details of the precipitating circumstances. Inquire about allergies to foods, medications, substances (such as soap), and textiles. Asking about medications is especially important, since patients often confuse drug side effects

History of Present Illness

When discussing the history of present illness with your patient, make sure he describes his problems fully. To do this, ask him the following questions about each complaint:

- *Time of onset.* When was the first date (the problem) happened? What time did it begin?
- *Type of onset.* How did (the problem) start: suddenly? gradually?
- *Original source.* What were you doing when you first experienced or noticed (the problem)? What seems to trigger it: stress? position? certain activities? arguments? If describing a discharge: thick? runny? clear? colored? If describing a psychological problem: Do the voices drown out other sounds? Whose voice does it sound like?
- *Severity.* How bad is (the problem) when it's at its worst? Does it interfere with your normal activities? Does it force you to lie down, sit down, slow down?
- *Radiation.* In the case of pain, does it travel down your back or arms, up your neck, or down your legs?
- *Time relationship.* How often do you experience (the problem): hourly? daily? weekly? monthly? When do you usually experience it: daytime? at night? in the early morning? Are you ever awakened by it? Does it ever occur before, during, or after meals? Does it occur seasonally?
- *Duration.* How long does an episode of (the problem) last?
- *Course.* Does (the problem) seem to be getting better, to be getting worse, or does it remain the same?
- *Associations.* Does (the problem) lead to anything else? Is it accompanied by other signs and symptoms?
- *Source of relief.* What relieves (the problem): changing diet? changing position? taking medications? being active?
- *Source of aggravation.* What makes (the problem) worse?
  You can remember *all* these questions using the letters PQRST:

P   *Provocative/Palliative*
       What causes it? What makes it better? What makes it worse?

Q   *Quality/Quantity*
       How does it feel, look, or sound, and how much of it is there?

R   *Region/Radiation*
       Where is it? Does it spread?

S   *Severity scale*
       Does it interfere with activities?
       How does it rate on a severity scale of 1 to 10?

T   *Timing*
       When did it begin? How often does it occur? Is it sudden or gradual?

From E.L. DeGowin and R.L. DeGowin, *Bedside Diagnostic Examination* (3rd ed.; New York: Macmillan Publishing Co., 1976). Used with permission of the publisher.

with true allergic reactions.

- *Current medications.* Knowing the medications a patient is taking provides helpful information about a chronic illness. It can also help explain a medical condition that may have occurred secondary to drug toxicity or overdose. Be sure to ask your patient about over-the-counter *and* prescription drugs. Use brand names and nonmedical terms so he understands your questions. And be alert for clues that suggest he needs patient teaching. For example, if you suspect that your patient's condition stems from a drug interaction, discuss it with him so he'll be aware of this danger in the future. Also, notify the doctor. Knowing all you can about your patient's current medications can prevent drug interactions and also help identify drugs that may affect laboratory tests.

Family history

A brief description of the medical history of the patient's family helps to identify familial patterns common to some illnesses. For example, diabetes mellitus, migraine headaches, heart disease, and hypercholesterolemia all have hereditary tendencies. Ask your patient if anyone in his family had allergies, asthma, tuberculosis, hypertension, heart disease, or a stroke. Inquire about anemia, hemophilia, arthritis, migraine headaches, diabetes, cancer, and emotional problems. As in the portion of the history dealing with present illness, record negative findings as well as positive ones.

You can use a written statement and a diagram to record and depict your patient's family history. A family tree diagram showing the age and general health of each living family member, and the cause of death of each deceased family member, can help you trace hereditary disease patterns (see *Family History Chart,* page 13).

Knowing something about the general physical and emotional health of the patient's family may help you to better understand his illness. A patient's family, for example, can be a source of stress, which may underlie the chief complaint. When appropriate, explore your patient's family relationships. With whom does he live? What are his family relationships like? Inquire about previous and current marriages, and find out if your patient has any children. If remarried, how does he compare his present family with his original family? Ask, too, how far away extended-family members live, and how important they are to your patient as sources of physical, emotional, and economic support. Can he describe the family members with whom he has the closest relationships?

Determine if the patient's illness has affected the way the family lives. Does the patient have concerns about his family? Ask if there have been other major family changes recently besides his illness. Is the family financially able to cope with crises?

Have there been family conflicts over money,

sex, childbearing, religion? Which topics are openly discussed among family members? Which are never discussed? Don't forget to ask about positive factors in the patient's family, the sources of harmony as well as discord.

Unless your questions uncover strong indications of a possible hereditary cause of your patient's problems, ask only about the immediate family's health. Where possibilities of hereditary factors do exist, follow up with further questioning in these areas.

Psychosocial history

To formulate an effective nursing diagnosis, you often have to know a lot more than just the status of the patient's physical health; you have to consider certain aspects of his personal life as well. The psychosocial history serves this purpose. Here you're seeking to define the patient in terms of his place in society, relationships with others, and satisfaction with self.

The patient's reason for seeking health care determines the kinds of questions you ask in this part of the health history interview. For example, if the patient's illness requires him to change activities of daily living significantly, then asking about his *place of residence* is appropriate. Ask where he lives, and in what kind of house or apartment. How are the rooms and furniture arranged? How many flights of stairs does he have to climb? Does the layout of the house pose any health hazards?

Inquire whether there are shops near your patient's house. Does he have a way of getting to them? Does the community provide adequate recreational opportunities? If so, does he take advantage of them? Explain to your patient that all this information will be used to help him adjust to his illness after returning home from the hospital.

If your patient expresses concern about being able to cope with financial pressures, ask about his *economic situation.* Before asking these questions, explain that this type of information helps you to identify patients who need referral for financial assistance.

Is his annual income adequate for his needs and the standard of living he prefers? What kind of insurance (if any) does he have? If he seems to be preoccupied with financial matters, help him determine how much income

Family History Chart

An easy way to keep track of your patient's family history is by using a genogram. The three-tiered genogram shown here displays three generations.

First, draw a family tree. Enter the age and major medical problems of each family member who is living. Then, enter the age at death and cause of death of each deceased relative. This system readily displays illnesses common to several family members.

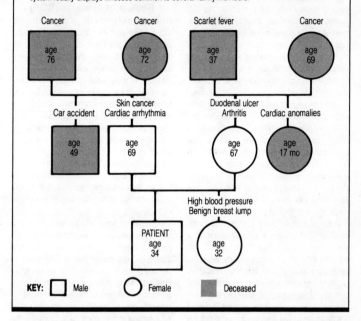

KEY: □ Male   ○ Female   ■ Deceased

goes toward maintaining his standard of living and how much toward paying medical bills.

If a patient's chief complaint seems related to his work, record further *occupational information.* Appropriate queries include the following: How long have you held your present job? How would you describe the responsibilities of your position? Does the job entail any health hazards, such as exposure to chemicals, heavy metals, or excessive dust or noise levels?

Explore the patient's feelings about his job. Is it satisfying, or a source of constant frustration? Does his present condition interfere with the performance of his usual duties? Your patient's past occupational history and military service record may be helpful here, too.

Questions relating to the patient's social life may also be pertinent. Does the patient have friends whom he sees regularly? If so, how often does he see them? Do they provide emotional support in times of trouble? Does he have one friend who is closer to him than anyone else?

The patient's methods of coping with past *medical* or *emotional* crises may be revealing. Ask what worked best for him during these difficult times. What proved least effective or did more harm than good?

One of the most difficult parts of taking a psychosocial history may be asking your patient questions about his *sex life.* Effective communication about this delicate subject depends on how comfortably you can discuss the subject and how well you choose appropriate words and phrases. Questions about a patient's sex life are necessary whenever the patient's illness appears related to sexual function. Before you proceed, bear in mind that the patient may never have discussed his sex life with a health-care professional before. Try to put him at ease by using words you think he'll be comfortable with. Phrase your questions in such a way that you encourage the patient to discuss this part of his life without putting undue pressure on him. You might begin by saying, "Are you having any problems with your sexual functioning that you'd care to discuss?" Point out the importance of this information in your assessment of his illness.

As you proceed with this line of questioning, observe the patient's nonverbal behavior carefully. He may become uneasy or uncommunicative. Remind him several times during the discussion that if any question makes him uncomfortable, he doesn't have to answer it. If he doesn't want to discuss his sex life at all, don't persist. Say you'll be available to discuss the topic at another time, if he wishes. Just note his discomfort and that he chooses not to discuss his sex life.

If the patient's chief complaint seems directly related to his sex life, ask him if he is currently sexually active. If so, tactfully ask whether he's satisfied with his sex life. Does he use any form of contraception? How does he protect against contracting a sexually transmitted disease? Other possible lines of questioning include asking the patient if there's anything he would like to change about his sex life.

Activities of daily living (ADL)

This part of the health history describes your patient's activities during the course of a normal day. Your questions help determine how his personal habits affect his health. Ease your way into this series of questions by asking the patient to describe a normal day. What does he usually do? Where does he go? Whom does he see? Then ask specific questions (see *Adult Activities of Daily Living,* page 15) about each of these four categories:

• diet and elimination
• exercise and sleep
• recreation
• tobacco, alcohol, and drug use.

The answers to these questions will help you better understand the patient's problems and plan appropriate nursing interventions. They may also indicate a need for patient teaching. For example, if your patient says he can't sleep without first having an alcoholic drink, explore this point and discuss other means of ensuring a good night's sleep.

Review of systems (ROS)

For this part of the health history, review the major body systems (and certain body regions) to find out if your patient is having (or has had) cardinal signs and symptoms of systemic disorders. You may use a prepared checklist or a standard form for this part of the health history, to facilitate recording and to serve as a memory aid (see *General Review of Systems,* page 16). Although medical terminology is used on these checklists or forms, substitute or add simpler terms, when necessary, to help the patient understand exactly what you're asking. Remember that the information you record, like the rest of the health history, must be subjective data. The patient *tells* you whether he's had any of these signs or symptoms.

If the patient reports a sign or symptom that seems to be related to his present illness, explore it further with questions like those asked during the *history of present illness* part of the health history. (Don't forget to record all pertinent negative signs and symptoms.) Your notes from this part of the history should adequately review the body system affected by your patient's chief complaint. Don't ask the patient to repeat this information during the review of body systems unless something remains unclear or you feel you need more specific information. When your discussion gets to the affected system, refer in your notes to the earlier information.

A health history perspective

Once you complete your patient's health history, it becomes part of his permanent written record. It will serve as a subjective data base with which you and other health-care professionals can monitor the patient's progress. Remember that history data must be specific and precise. Avoid vague generalities. Instead, provide pertinent, concise, detailed information that will help determine the direction and se-

Adult Activities of Daily Living

Recording daily activities can provide you with a comprehensive view of your patient's history. To learn as much as possible, ask the patient all these questions:

Diet/Elimination
• How would you describe your appetite?
• What do you normally eat in a 24-hour period?
• What do you like and dislike to eat? Is your diet restricted in any way?
• How much fluid do you drink during an average day?
• Are you allergic to any foods?
• When do you usually go to the bathroom? Has this pattern changed in any way recently?
• Do you take any foods, fluids, or drugs to help you maintain your normal bowel and urination pattern?

Exercise/Sleep
• Do you have any special exercise program? What kind? How long have you been following it? How do you feel after exercising?
• How many hours do you sleep each day? When? Do you feel rested afterward?
• Do you fall asleep easily?
• Do you take any drugs or do anything special to help you fall asleep?
• What do you do when you can't sleep?
• Do you awake during the night?
• Do you have sleepy spells during the day? When?
• Do you take naps routinely?

Recreation
• What do you do when you're working?

• What kind of nonpaid work do you do for enjoyment?
• How much leisure time do you have?
• Are you satisfied with what you can do in your leisure time?
• Do you and your family share leisure time?
• How do your weekends differ from your weekdays?

Tobacco/Alcohol/Drugs
• Do you use tobacco? What kind do you use? How much do you use each day? Each week? For how long have you used it? Have you ever tried to stop?
• Do you drink any alcoholic beverages?
• How much alcohol do you drink each day? Each week? What time of day do you drink, usually?
• What kind (beer, wine, whiskey) do you drink?
• Do you usually drink alone or with others?
• Do you drink more when you're under stress?
• Has drinking ever hampered your job performance?
• Do you or your family worry about your drinking?
• Do you feel dependent on alcohol, coffee, tea, or soft drinks? How much of these other beverages do you drink in an average day?
• Do you take any drugs not prescribed by a doctor (marijuana, sleeping pills, tranquilizers)?

---

quence of the physical examination—the next phase in your patient assessment.

Communication problems

Cultural patterns and beliefs
Most of your patients' backgrounds and health beliefs vary somewhat from yours. In the health history interview, explore your patient's background, life-style, values, norms, and experiences with the health-care system. Try to identify major influences that might affect his adaptation to hospital care. For example, suppose your patient is a 70-year-old woman who is an Orthodox Jew and lives alone. She enters the hospital, for the first time in her life, for exploratory surgery to rule out colorectal cancer.

Several factors may influence this woman's adjustment to hospitalization. Her age, first of all, is an obvious factor, since elderly people experience a great deal of stress on entering a hospital. Second, her religious beliefs, especially as they relate to dietary restrictions, will have to be taken into consideration. The fact that this is her first hospitalization—for an unknown and possibly fatal illness—will significantly affect her ability to adapt to hospital-

General Review of Systems

Use this review of systems as a guide. Ask the patient, in your own words, if he has experienced or noticed any of the following:

General: Overall state of health, ability to carry out ADL, weight changes, fatigue, exercise tolerance, fever, night sweats, repeated infections

Skin: Changes in color, pigmentation, temperature, moisture, or hair distribution; eruptions; pruritus; scaling; bruising; bleeding; dryness; excess oiliness; growths; moles; scars; rashes; scalp lesions; brittle, soft, or abnormally formed nails; cyanotic nail beds

Head: Trauma, lumps, alopecia, headaches

Eyes: Near-sightedness, far-sightedness, glaucoma, cataracts, blurring of vision, double vision, problem with tearing, burning, itching, photophobia, pain, inflammation, swelling, color blindness, injuries. Also ask about use of glasses and date of last checkup.

Ears: Deafness, tinnitus, vertigo, discharge, pain, tenderness behind the ears, mastoiditis, otitis or other ear infections, earaches, ear surgery.

Nose: Sinusitis, discharge, colds, coryza more than four times a year; rhinitis, trauma, sneezing, loss of sense of smell, obstruction, breathing problems, epistaxis

Mouth/throat: Sores on tongue, dental caries, loss of teeth, toothaches, bleeding gums, lesions, loss of taste, hoarseness, sore throats (streptococcal), tonsillitis, voice changes, dysphagia. Also ask about date of last checkup, use of dentures or bridges.

Neck: Pain, stiffness, swelling, limited movement

Breasts: Change in development or lactation pattern, trauma, lumps, pain, discharge from nipples, gynecomastia, changes in contour or in nipples, mastectomy

Cardiovascular: Palpitations, tachycardia, or other irregularities; pain in chest; dyspnea on exertion; paroxysmal nocturnal dyspnea; orthopnea; cough; cyanosis; edema, ascites; intermittent claudication; cold extremities; phlebitis; postural hypotension; hypertension; rheumatic fever. Also ask if EKG has been performed recently.

Respiratory: Dyspnea, shortness of breath, pain, wheezing, paroxysmal nocturnal dyspnea, orthopnea (number of pillows used), cough, sputum, hemoptysis, night sweats, emphysema, pleurisy, bronchitis, tuberculosis (contacts), pneumonia, asthma, other upper respiratory tract infections. Also ask about results of chest X-ray and tuberculin skin test.

Gastrointestinal: Changes in appetite or weight, dysphagia, nausea, vomiting, heartburn, eructation, flatulence, abdominal pain, colic, hematemesis, jaundice (pain, fever, intensity, duration, color of urine), stools (color, frequency, consistency, odor, frequent use of laxatives), hemorrhoids, rectal bleeding, changes in bowel habits

Renal-genitourinary: Color of urine, polyuria, oliguria, nocturia (number of times per night), dysuria, frequency, urgency, problem with stream, dribbling, pyuria, retention, passage of stones or gravel, venereal disease (discharge), infections, perineal rashes and irritations. Also ask if protein or sugar is present in urine.

Reproductive: male—Lesions, impotency, prostate problems. Also ask about use of contraceptives; **female**—Irregular bleeding, discharge, pruritus, pain on intercourse (dyspareunia), protrusions, dysmenorrhea, vaginal infections. Also ask about number of pregnancies; dates of deliveries; complications; abortions; about onset, regularity, and amount of flow during menarch; last normal period; use of contraceptives; date of menopause; last Pap test.

Nervous: Headaches, convulsions, fits, seizures, fainting spells, dizziness, tremors, twitches, aphasia, loss of sensation, weakness, paralysis, balance problems

Psychiatric: Changes in mood, anxiety, depression, inability to concentrate

Musculoskeletal: Muscle pain, swelling, redness, pain in joints, back problems, injuries (i.e., broken bones, pulled tendons), numbness, tingling, balance problems, gait problems, weakness, paralysis, deformities, limited motion

Hematopoietic: Anemia (type, degree, treatment, response), bleeding, fatigue, bruising. Also ask patient if he's receiving anticoagulant therapy.

Endocrine, metabolism: Polyuria, polydipsia, polyphagia, thyroid problem, heat-cold intolerance, excessive sweating, changes in hair distribution and amount, nervousness, swelling neck (goiter), sugar in urine.

ization. Lastly, the fact that this woman, who is used to being independent, may now become dependent on others will have considerable bearing on her hospital stay.

Consider, too, that certain types of questions and behaviors considered inappropriate in one culture may be sanctioned in another. For example, in some cultures, loud and prolonged weeping and wailing when someone dies is part of the grieving experience. In our culture, we usually mourn quietly and try to control our emotions.

Everyone has a right to his own social, political, religious, and economic beliefs. Try to assess every patient's cultural values and health beliefs accurately. Be careful about interpreting his behavior until you've explored his cultural background and determined its influence on his behavior.

Make every effort to find a translator for a patient who speaks a language that's foreign to you. If the translator is clearly instructed to translate and not to interpret or summarize, he can add the dimension of objectivity. Friends and relatives may also be helpful in such cases, but they may distort the patient's meaning by adding their own interpretation of what has been said, based on their knowledge of the patient.

The terminally ill patient

If you have to interview a dying patient for a health history, try to determine how he feels about his impending death. His attitude will have been shaped partly by his own health and personal history and partly by his reactions to the deaths of family members and friends. Listen carefully for any references to death the patient may make, directly or indirectly. Integrate the topic into the conversation when you think he's ready to talk about it.

The attitudes of your patient's friends and family members toward death will affect how much help they can give him. Talk with them, and describe in your notes their potential for helping the patient accept his condition.

The dying patient experiences various emotional responses, all related to the grieving process: shock and disbelief, denial, anger, bargaining, depression, and finally acceptance. Knowing this helps you understand the adaptation maneuvers and emotional reactions he's experiencing, so you can control the interview. *Bargaining* is essentially a private state that doesn't affect your patient's behavior during the interview. And *acceptance* represents a tranquillity that your questions won't disrupt. But shock and disbelief, anger, depression, and denial can impede the interview's progress.

If your patient's in the initial stage of *shock and disbelief,* postpone the interview until he's calmer. Guidelines to use in responding to your patient's *anger* or *depression* are discussed on page 19. Interviewing a patient who's *denying* his terminal condition presents a paradoxical situation: You need to discuss the reality of his present condition, but he's not acknowledging this condition. Important: Remember that his denial, by suppressing awareness of his impending death, is helping him maintain his emotional equilibrium. Don't try to force him to admit his condition, but don't hold out false hope for his recovery either. Instead, gently ask your questions at a pace your patient can tolerate. Use your awareness of verbal and nonverbal forms of communication to guide you.

Remember that most patients don't progress in an orderly manner from one phase of this grieving process to the next. For example, a dying patient experiencing anger about his impending death may displace it onto someone or something else, while denying being terminally ill.

The patient with multiple symptoms

You usually have to modify the history-taking process when interviewing patients with multiple symptoms. Cover each symptom in detail; then correlate your findings in one system with your findings in another. This requires a sound knowledge of compensatory mechanisms and of the relationships between body systems. If your patient has numerous symptoms, involving many body systems, but you can't find any obvious organic reason for them, investigate the possibility that he has serious emotional problems by taking a detailed psychosocial history (see page 12).

The mentally impaired patient

If your patient's intellectual capacity is limited, you'll certainly have to use different history-taking methods. Your first consideration is whether he's capable of understanding your questions. Then, does he have the language skills to answer them?

You can estimate the limits of a patient's intelligence by the vocabulary he uses, the amount of detail with which he describes his illness, and how well he recalls past events. In addition, assess his understanding and compliance with past medical-care instructions. Note the extent of his schooling, such as highest grade completed and courses of study taken, and what type of job he has. Use validation procedures to determine if the patient understands what you're saying. The patient's responses to questions involving general knowledge may give additional data.

A retarded patient may not be able to give you a reliable history. You may have to refer him for formal psychological testing to determine the extent of the deficit, and rely on family members or friends for the history information. This procedure is also useful when you interview a patient you suspect has organic brain syndrome. Don't try to obtain a detailed history from him.

Your patient's apparently limited intellectual functioning may be caused by a diminished level of consciousness. Of course, a patient who is critically ill or has a language barrier may also be unable to supply the history information you need. Here again, family members and friends can help.

The sensory-impaired patient

When interviewing a patient with *impaired hearing*, try the following techniques: Face the patient, so he has a direct view of your eyes and mouth; use common words; make your questions simple, short, and direct. Don't shout. Also, check whether the patient is wearing a hearing aid. If so, is it turned on? With an elderly patient who is hard of hearing, speaking in a low tone of voice will help you communicate, because his ability to hear high-pitched tones has deteriorated first. For a patient whose impairment is severe, you may have to conduct the history totally in writing or through family or friends, asking only the most essential questions. (Obtain additional data in subsequent contacts and interviews with him.) If the patient knows sign language, try to find a sign language translator who can

also speak, hear, and therefore communicate with you.

A *visually impaired* patient may be slow to respond to your questioning or may have difficulty following directions. Be patient with him, and remember to respond to him by speaking rather than gesturing. He'll be less confused if the lighting in the interviewing area is strong but not glaring, and doesn't vary in intensity.

The tired or uncomfortable patient

Fatigued patients and those in pain may find it difficult or impossible to respond fully to your history questions. If interviewing a patient who's in pain proves difficult, obtain an order for an analgesic and allow time for it to take effect. When you're ready to resume history-taking, approach the patient calmly. During the interview, pause now and then to give him a rest. You may need to take his history over the course of several interviews. Start by taking essential information, and ask questions that minimize your patient's requirement to respond. Take noncritical parts of the history in subsequent interviews.

The anxious or fearful patient

A patient may feel uneasy or anxious about the information he discloses during the health history interview. Signs of anxiety or fear that you may observe include blushing or pallor, restlessness, hyperventilation, and lassitude. In addition, your patient may report muscle cramps or tenseness, headache, nausea, diarrhea, excessive perspiration, dry mouth, rapid heartbeat, or insomnia—also suggestive, among other possibilities, that he's feeling anxious or afraid. (Make sure the patient isn't in a physical crisis demanding prompt medical attention.) To help relieve these feelings, reassure your patient that no one will see his health history except those involved in his care. Your challenge during the interview is to determine whether these signs are related to fear and anxiety, to the symptoms of his illness, or to a physiologic problem that may be developing.

Anxiety is an extremely contagious emotion. Don't allow your patient's anxiety to disturb your composure during the interview. To manage an anxious or fearful patient most effectively, discuss the situation openly with him. Ask him if he's feeling anxious, and encourage him to describe his feelings. Usually he'll relax somewhat, and you'll proceed more comfortably with the interview. If the patient denies anxious feelings, make sure your own anxiety isn't interfering with the progress of the interview.

The angry or aggressive patient

The patient who directly or indirectly expresses anger or aggression during the health history interview needs special attention. Anger, like silence, can be healthy, but it can also be destructive. If your patient becomes angry during the interview, remain calm and show that you accept his emotional response as an expression of important feelings. Then try to help the patient find out why he's angry. Anxiety, frustration, and helplessness are the most common causes. You might say, "Obviously, you're upset. Would you like to talk about it?" Don't say, "You look angry. Why?" (Generally, this approach only increases the patient's defensiveness and anger.)

The depressed patient

Interviewing a depressed patient for a health history can be especially difficult. The patient may be sullen, and refuse to answer your questions. He may also be an unreliable historian, since his depression can cause him to exaggerate his symptoms' severity.

A depressed patient may look older than his stated age, with a sullen facial expression. Suspect depression, too, if he's lost or gained weight over a short period. He may complain of insomnia or difficulty in concentrating. Disinterest in personal hygiene and physical appearance is also common. His posture may be poor, his gait slow and dragging.

Basically, an individual's body functions slow down in response to depression. Some examples of this are slowed respirations, a constant feeling of fullness, belching, and constipation from decreased alimentary tract motility. Remember that illness other than depression may also manifest itself in this way. Don't be misled into "labeling" depression. Many depressed patients turn out to have serious physical illnesses, such as ulcers or cancer, as well. So always explore the reasons for a patient's depression, using such communi-

cation skills as direct questioning, clarification, feedback, and expressions of support. Describe this part of the health history interview in detail in your notes to ensure thoughtful planning for your patient's care.

When dealing with depressed patients, be sure to consider their suicide potential (see *Suicide Potential,* page 67). Not every depressed person is suicidal, but the possibility always exists. You can help by empathizing with his despair, then trying to get him to recognize his strengths as well as the alternative choices he can make to improve the situation.

If you suspect your patient has suicidal or self-destructive feelings, try to get him to acknowledge them. If you succeed, the power and anxiety your patient associates with these feelings will diminish. Never agree to keep suicidal feelings confidential. You have a responsibility to communicate these feelings to the patient's doctor immediately and to take proper precautions.

The pediatric health history

Basic considerations

A pediatric health history is a modified version of an adult health history, with special emphasis on such areas as childhood diseases and, if the patient is still an infant, the mother's health during pregnancy. Usually you'll obtain information about the child's present health from one of his parents (note this on the health history). If someone other than the child's mother or father —such as a relative or guardian—gives you the information, mention this in the history, and state how much everyday contact this person has with the child. Sometimes the child himself will give you history information.

Take advantage of the opportunity to observe parent-child interactions when a parent is present during a child's health history interview. (Usually the child's mother brings him in.) Your observations may prove as enlightening as their answers to your questions. Don't overlook the chance to observe the apparent level of the young child's motor abilities and coordination. When appropriate, take the time to teach good health habits as related points are discussed during the interview. Above all, let the child and the parents get to know you so they'll trust you and confide in you as a friend.

Some children, especially those age 10 and older, may not wish to have a parent present during the interview. If your patient's an adolescent, you'll probably want to ask questions about sexual development; in this situation, the presence of a parent may inhibit your patient's responses. Be particularly sensitive to an adolescent's request for confidentiality. If you must share an adolescent's history information with a parent, get the patient's permission first.

The way you approach a child and phrase your questions can determine the success of the interview. Avoid a condescending manner; a child can sense this easily. To lessen a child's anxiety, you may want to wear casual dress instead of your uniform (if this is possible where you work). A child's personality and age also influence the way you phrase your questions, as well as the information you can expect to obtain.

State your questions simply, in a friendly manner. Be patient; let the child take his time responding. You may want to ask a very young child to draw a picture showing how he feels.

Children's cognitive skills

Children younger than age 7 are limited in their ability to understand and answer questions. They can't always understand things from another person's point of view. They're egocentric—that is, interested chiefly in themselves— so don't expect to obtain history information that doesn't pertain to their own experience. In addition, a child under age 7 can usually focus on only one perception at a time. When recalling an illness, for example, he may relate only its most vivid characteristic, such as a rash, even though the illness had more serious manifestations.

A child in this age-group may not be able to discuss hypothetical situations. For example, he may not be able to answer if you ask what he'd do if he cut his hand and couldn't stop the bleeding. Instead, he may reply simply that he didn't cut his hand. Similarly, he may not be able to understand or talk about events from another time. If he can't comprehend that his parents were children at one time, he won't be able to tell you clearly about his past history. Concepts of time and its duration are vague to young children, although most have some understanding of past, present, and future. For example, if your young patient tells you he had a stomachache *yesterday*, you may find that *yesterday* was actually several months ago. A cold that lasted 2 days may seem no different to him than a cold that lingered for a month.

A young child's ability to reason logically isn't fully developed. He usually can't generalize from specific instances or understand a specific consequence of a general statement. Rather, the child usually reasons from instance to instance. For example, he will say Johnny couldn't go to school when he had measles, so Alice can't go to school when she has measles. But he may not be able to reason that no children with measles can go to school. And if you told him only this, he could possibly not realize that *he* couldn't go to school if he had measles.

The child under age 7 also has difficulty categorizing illnesses according to anything but obvious qualities. For example, he'll assume that diseases with similar characteristics, such as a rash, are the same disease. A young child may also have trouble understanding a complex cause-and-effect relationship. He may understand that germs cause illness but would have trouble understanding that germs are more likely to cause illness when a person's resistance is lowered.

Many cognitive skills—seeing things from another's point of view, being able to focus thought on more than one perception simultaneously, imagining hypothetical situations, understanding time concepts, and reasoning logically—develop gradually in children between ages 7 and 12. You'll be able to communicate more easily with children in this age-group and obtain more accurate information from them. Remember, though, that each child differs in his rate of development.

When a child reaches adolescence, beginning at about age 12, his cognitive development is nearly complete. He is likely to have a fully developed ability to see another person's viewpoint. But his accelerated development, as well as self-consciousness about his personal appearance, may cloud his reasoning ability. In the health history interview, he may ask you about health measures to enhance appearance—for example, personal hygiene measures that will improve his acne. These concerns can cause your adolescent patient a great deal of anxiety. When appropriate, reassure him that he's developing normally. And let him know that you accept him as he is.

The child's chief complaint

If the child can describe his chief complaint (or concern) well enough, quote his exact words in your notes. Otherwise, record what the parents tell you. Frequently, the parents simply want the child to have a checkup. If the child has a chief complaint that suggests he may have a communicable disease, ask whether the child or anyone in the family has been exposed to a contagious disease within the past 3 weeks.

Always listen carefully to what a parent tells you. Sometimes you may be able to discern an underlying reason for bringing a child to be examined. For example, if a mother is anxious about her child's social development, she may view this concern as less legitimate—in terms of seeking care for the child—than an illness. The subconscious goal of exploring this concern may be her reason for bringing the child for a checkup or treatment of a minor injury.

The child's past history

In addition to recording the same kinds of information for a child as you would for an adult, you'll also note details of the child's birth and development. Keep the birth history brief unless your patient is under age 2 or you suspect he has a developmental deficiency. For these exceptions, obtain information about prenatal, natal, and postnatal events (see *The Birth History*).

If your patient has any siblings, ask his mother how she would compare this child's development to theirs. Was this child quicker or slower to arrive at developmental milestones? How does the child interact with his siblings?

Record other aspects of the child's past history as you would for an adult patient. Be sure to ask about all childhood diseases, and whether the child has frequent colds (more than four a year) or ear infections. Be alert for speech problems that may reflect hearing

---

The Birth History

If your patient is under age 2, or if you suspect a developmental deficiency, obtain a detailed birth history as follows:

Prenatal
Ask the mother where and when she received medical care during her pregnancy. Find out if she had any vaginal bleeding, illnesses, infections, prolonged nausea or vomiting, fever, or rashes. Was she injured in any way or hospitalized while pregnant? Was she exposed to X-rays? If so, was a lead shield used to protect her? Was she taking medications at any time during this period? What diet did she follow, and how much weight did she gain?

Ask her if the infant was full-term, premature, or postmature. Has she had any other children, or any stillbirths, abortions, or miscarriages? What is her blood group and that of the child's father?

Natal
Find out in which city and hospital the mother gave birth. How long and difficult was her labor? What type of delivery did she have? Did she receive an anesthetic? What was the infant's weight and physical condition at birth?

Postnatal
Ask about the child's condition during the first 28 days after birth. Did he have any problems in the nursery, such as jaundice, cyanosis, rashes, feeding problems, or unusual weight gain or loss? Did he leave the hospital with his mother? With a high-risk infant, learn as many details as possible about his problem and duration of hospitalization.

Next, question the parent about the child's development. At what age did the child first hold his head up, roll over, sit up, stand, walk, and talk? When did he start speaking in complete sentences? At what age did he achieve control of his bladder and bowels, both during the day and at night?

---

loss, especially in children with frequent ear infections. Ask about accidents, including whether the child has ever ingested any toxic substances. When discussing immunizations, ask about booster inoculations the child has received.

Family and psychosocial histories

When taking a child's family history, pay special attention to hereditary tendencies toward blood dyscrasias, mental retardation, and other familial conditions that can surface during childhood.

When exploring the child's psychosocial history, remember that the physical and the emotional aspects of a child's home life can affect his health and well-being. Does he live in a house or an apartment? In an urban, suburban, or rural community? How large is the home? Is it near his school and a playground? Does he have his own room, his own bed? Does the home have stairs that might be hazardous to the child? Where are poisonous substances stored? Does the child have a yard in which to play?

Ask about the parents' marital situation. Are there marital problems that might affect the child? Do his parents live together, or does he live with one or the other—or with someone else? Is life at home happy and cooperative, or antagonistic and chaotic? Who usually cares for the child? If the parents work, who stays with the child when they're not home? Does he go to a day-care center? Explore the financial, occupational, and other psychosocial aspects of the parents' or guardians' lifestyle if you need this information to care for your patient.

Pediatric activities of daily living

In most cases, the topics to investigate in this portion of a child's history are similar to those for an adult patient (see *Pediatric Activities of Daily Living*). You'll need information on diet, elimination, exercise, sleep, and recreational activities. For an adolescent, ask about tobacco, alcohol, and drug use, too, but try to reserve such questions until you're alone with the patient; the presence of a parent may prevent your patient from answering freely.

Don't forget to inquire about the child's school activities. Does the child go to school? If so, ask what grade he is in and whether he likes school. Is his schoolwork good? Does he

---

Pediatric Activities of Daily Living

To learn about a child's activities of daily living (ADL), you'll probably want to interview his parents instead of the child himself. But even though you're talking to an adult, you'll want to ask some questions different from the adult ADL survey. Here are questions you should ask to compile an ADL survey for a child:

Diet/Elimination
- How is the child's appetite?
- Is he on a formula? What type?
- When are his usual mealtimes?
- Does he eat with family members?
- Does someone help him eat?
- Does he use utensils?
- Does he have any difficulty eating? What sort?
- What are his favorite foods and beverages?
- Does he snack? What does he usually snack on?
- Does he take daily vitamins?
- Is he toilet trained? At what age did he learn?
- What are his usual bowel habits?
- Does he wet the bed?

Exercise/Sleep
- Does his daily schedule include play?
- Does he participate in sports?
- Does he have any special exercises he performs regularly?
- What is his normal amount of sleep? From when to when?
- Does he take naps?
- Does he have a routine before going to sleep (drinking a bottle, playing, being read to)?
- Does he sleep with other siblings or alone?
- What is his favorite sleeping position?
- Does he have any sleeping problems? Nightmares?
- Is he tired during the day?

Recreation
- How much time does he get for recreation each day?
- Does he have a group of friends with whom he plays?
- What are his favorite play activities?

have friends at school? What does he enjoy most about school? Question the child about after-school activities, too.

At this point in the history, discuss with the parents any concerns they may have about their child's habits. This is also a good time to find out if temper tantrums, masturbation, thumb-sucking, nail-biting, and bed-wetting are part of your patient's history—and how his parents manage such incidents (see page 69).

Pediatric review of systems

Use your standard format for the review of systems when your patient is a child, but be sure to include questions appropriate for his age (see *Pediatric Review of Systems,* page 24). For example, you'd probably ask the parent of a 1-year-old child whether any teeth are erupting—and whether they're causing any problems.

For all children, ask about any recent significant weight loss or gain. Does the child have trouble gaining weight? Is he irritable or nervous? Are there any problems with the child's growth or personality? Have there been any changes or deformities in his posture or gait?

For adolescents, your review of systems should also include questions about sexual development. If your patient is female, ask if she has begun to menstruate. If she has, find out how often she menstruates and if she has any problems with menstruation.

The geriatric health history

Basic considerations

Approaching an elderly patient for a health history and conducting the interview needn't be difficult if you anticipate his special needs. If possible, plan to talk with an elderly patient early in the day, when he's likely to be most alert. (Many elderly people experience the so-called *sundown syndrome,* which means their capacity for clear thinking diminishes by late afternoon or early evening. Some of these patients may even become disoriented or confused late in the day.)

Have a comfortable chair available for your elderly patient (if he isn't on bed rest), especially if the interview might be lengthy. Arthri-

tis and other orthopedic disabilities may make sitting in one position for a long time uncomfortable. Encourage your patient to change his position in the bed or chair and to move around as much as he wants during the interview.

A geriatric patient may have some hearing and vision loss, so sit close to him and face him. Speak slowly in a low-pitched voice. Don't shout at a patient who has a hearing problem. Shouting raises the pitch of your voice and may make understanding you more difficult, not easier. (Hearing loss from aging affects perception of high-pitched tones first.)

Try to evaluate your patient's ability to communicate, and his reliability as an historian, early in the interview. If you have any doubts about these matters before the interview begins, ask him if a family member or a close friend can be present.

Don't be surprised if your elderly patient *requests* that someone accompany him—he too may have concerns about getting through the interview on his own. Having another person present during the interview gives you an opportunity to observe your patient's interaction with this person and provides more data for the history. However, this may prevent the patient from speaking freely, so plan to talk with him privately sometime during your assessment.

Attitudes toward aging

Communicating with an elderly patient may challenge you to confront your personal attitudes and prejudices about aging. Examine these feelings before taking the patient's history, and decide in advance how you'll handle them. Any prejudices you reveal will probably interfere with your efforts to communicate, since elderly patients are especially sensitive to others' reactions and can easily detect negative attitudes and impatience.

Then consider your *patient's* attitude toward his body and health. An elderly patient may have a distorted perception of his health problems; he may dwell on them needlessly or dismiss them as normal signs of aging. A patient may ignore a serious problem because he doesn't want his fears confirmed. If your elderly patient is seriously ill, the subjects of dying (see page 17) and death may come up during the health history interview. Listen

Pediatric Review of Systems

Ask the parent of a child you're interviewing if the child has complained (or the parents have been aware) of any of the following problems:

Eyes: Vision difficulties, problem with tearing, crossed eyes
Ears: Hearing difficulties, earaches
Nose: Nosebleeds, sinus infections
Throat: Sore throats (streptococcal), pneumonia, colds (more than four a year)
Cardiovascular: Coloring (bluish), fatigue
Respiratory: Breathing difficulties, shortness of breath, frequent exhaustion
Gastrointestinal: Changes in bowel habits, diarrhea, constipation, bleeding, pain, vomiting
Renal: Frequency of urination, pain, bleeding on urination; males—straight urinary flow
Reproductive: Female—menstrual cycle onset
Nervous: Headaches, convulsions, fainting spells, tremors, twitches, blackouts, dizziness
Musculoskeletal: Painful joints, redness around joints, swelling, sprains, broken bones, coordination difficulties

carefully to any remarks your patient makes about dying. Be sure to ask about his religious affiliation and spiritual needs; many elderly patients find comfort in their religious beliefs and practices. You should also inquire tactfully about the matter of a living will.

The need for patience

Patience is the key to communicating with an elderly patient. He may respond slowly to your questions. Don't confuse patience with patronizing behavior. Your patient will easily perceive such behavior and may interpret it as lack of genuine concern for him. Keep your questions concise, rephrase those he doesn't understand, and use nonverbal techniques in a meaningful way.

To further foster your elderly patient's cooperation, take a little extra time to help him see the relevance of your questions. You may need to repeat this explanation several times as the interview progresses. But don't repeat questions unnecessarily. Ask only for information that is relevant to his condition. For example, you wouldn't obtain a detailed obstetric history from a 75-year-old woman who doesn't have a gynecologic problem.

Once you have obtained an elderly patient's cooperation, you may have some trouble getting him to keep his story brief. He has a lot of history to relate and may reminisce during the interview. Try to find time for this. Let the patient talk. You may obtain valuable clues about his current physical, mental, and spiritual health. If you must keep the history brief, let him know before the interview how much time you've set aside for it. Offer to come back another time to chat with him informally.

The elderly patient's past history

A geriatric patient's past medical history is likely to be extensive. His detailed recall of all major illnesses, surgical procedures, and injuries is necessary for you to complete the history. Fractures the patient may have experienced early in life, for example, may figure significantly now in osteoporosis. As you record his past history, try to get an idea of the amount of stress he has had recently and the way he has handled previous health problems. Don't be concerned if he can't relate this medical history chronologically; just be sure to record his age at the time each medical condition occurred.

Pay special attention to your elderly patient's medication history, since he probably takes medication routinely. Find out what medications—over-the-counter and prescription—he's now taking and has taken in the past, and the dosage for each. Ask him to show you samples, if possible, of all the medications he currently takes.

The elderly patient's psychosocial history

Make it a point to talk with your elderly patient about his family and friends. With whom does he live? How does he spend his time? Find out what significant relationships he has. If your patient is hospitalized and seriously ill, or must transfer to another type of institution (such as a nursing home), he'll need the emotional support of family and friends. If he's returning home after an illness, he may need their assistance.

If your patient doesn't have a family or any friends on whom he can depend for support, record this in the psychosocial history for possible later referral of the patient to a social agency. Record the names of his next of kin. Without your intervention here, loneliness may discourage an elderly patient from getting well.

If your patient is employed, inquire about his job to find out if his health problems will interfere with his returning to work. Talk with him about his plans for retirement, if he has any, and his attitude toward this phase of his life.

If your patient expresses financial concerns, explore them further in a financial history. Remember to ask your elderly patient if he receives any pensions or Social Security payments.

When appropriate, inquire about the patient's sex life. Don't ignore it because of the patient's age. Approach this aspect of the psychosocial history with the same sensitivity and respect for privacy that you would show with younger patients. If the patient is reluctant to discuss his sex life, don't press him for the information.

Geriatric activities of daily living

Your geriatric patient's activities of daily living may affect his health, and his health problems may, in turn, threaten his independence. Ask him to describe a typical day at home, including activities, sleep patterns, and eating habits (see *Geriatric Activities of Daily Living*, page 26). Because his eating habits may suggest other significant lines of questioning, find out how much of an appetite he usually has, how he prepares his food (does he use a lot of salt?), and how much fluid he normally consumes. You can put this information into a chart, showing which foods the patient eats at which times during the day.

Ask about matters related to the patient's mobility. Is he able to move around at home easily and safely? Can he supply the basic needs—food, clothing, and shelter? Does he drive to the supermarket, or does a friend or relative drive him? Does he use public transportation? Ask if he expects to be able to continue with his routine after he is discharged from the hospital. If necessary, consult with a social worker to discuss what you've learned about the patient's activities of daily living.

Geriatric review of systems

The review of systems for an elderly patient involves keeping in mind the following physiologic changes, considered normal in the aging process, and the common pathologic disorders described in the chart on page 27.

● *Skin, hair, and nails.* Skin color and texture commonly change as a person ages. Your patient may report that his skin seems thinner and looser—less elastic—than before, and that he perspires less. Hair thins, grays, and coarsens. Distribution of hair on the scalp, face, and body may also change, and the patient may tell you his scalp feels dry. Fingernails may thicken and change color slightly. Ask if the patient can take care of his own nails.

● *Eyes and vision.* Your patient may report increased tearing, or he may have presbyopia (diminished near vision due to a normal decrease in lens elasticity). Ask if he's experienced changes in his vision, especially night vision. Does he need more light than usual when reading?

● *Ears and hearing.* Your elderly patient's hearing may be affected by gradual irreversible hearing loss of no specific pathologic origin (presbycusis)—common among elderly persons.

● *Respiratory system.* Remember, shortness of breath during physical activity is normal, even if this tendency has increased recently, but sudden trouble with breathing is not. If your patient has trouble breathing, explore the precipitating circumstances. Does he cough excessively? Does the cough produce a lot of sputum, perhaps blood? Aging can also affect the *nose.* Your patient may report sneezing, a runny nose, a decreased sense of smell, or bleeding from mucous-membrane atrophy.

Geriatric Activities of Daily Living

When questioning an elderly patient about his daily activities, use general questions that will inform you of his usual habits and whether he has any problems performing them. An elderly patient may also have personal concerns, such as financial worries or transportation problems, that keep him from going about his daily routine. Structure your questions as outlined here.

Diet/Elimination
- What do you eat on a typical day?
- Do you feel hungry between meals?
- Do you prepare your own meals?
- With whom do you eat?
- What types of food do you enjoy most?
- Do you have any specific problems eating?
- Have you noted any change in your sense of taste?
- Do you snack? When are your snack times? What do you have for a snack?
- What are your usual bowel habits? Have you noticed any changes in them?

Exercise/Sleep
- Do you take daily walks?
- Do you do your own housework?
- Do you have any difficulty moving about?
- Has your doctor restricted your exercise or suggested a special exercise program?
- What time do you go to bed at night?
- What time do you awake?
- Do you follow a routine that helps you sleep?
- Do you sleep soundly or awake often?
- Do you take a nap during the day? How often and for how long?

Recreation
- Do you belong to any social groups, such as senior citizen clubs or church groups?
- What do you enjoy doing in your leisure time?
- How many hours a day do you watch television?
- Do you share leisure time with your family?

Tobacco/Alcohol
- Do you use tobacco? If so, do you smoke cigarettes, cigars, or a pipe? How long have you smoked? How much do you smoke each day? If you quit smoking, when did you quit?
- Do you drink alcohol? How often do you drink? Do you drink with friends or alone? How much do you normally drink? Has your drinking increased recently?

Personal concerns
- Do you wear dentures? Are they a hindrance when eating or talking?
- Do you wear glasses? Do you have any problems with your vision when wearing your glasses?
- Do you hear those around you with no difficulty? Does poor hearing hinder any of your activities?
- What is your source of income?
- Do you shop for your own groceries? If not, who does this for you?

- *Cardiovascular system.* More than half of all elderly people suffer from some degree of congestive heart failure. Ask your patient whether he's gained weight recently and if his belts or rings feel tight. In addition, find out if he tires more easily now than previously, if he has trouble breathing, and if he becomes dizzy when he rises from a chair or bed.
- *Gastrointestinal system.* An elderly patient may complain about problems related to his mouth and his sense of taste. For example, he may experience a foul taste in his mouth because his saliva production has decreased and his mucous membranes have atrophied. If he wears dentures, find out how comfortable they are and how well they work. An elderly person's sense of taste decreases gradually. This may be why your patient reports that his appetite has decreased, or that he craves sweeter or spicier foods.

An elderly patient may also have nonspecific difficulty in swallowing. Carefully assess the possible causes of regurgitation or heartburn. Ask if he has the same degree of difficulty swallowing both solid foods and liquids, or if food lodges in his throat. Does he experience pain after eating, or while lying flat? Also question him about weight loss, rectal bleeding, and altered bowel habits.
- *Urinary system.* Investigate any pattern of incontinence the patient reports. When incontinence occurs, does he feel that he has

Geriatric Review of Systems

Certain disorders commonly affect the elderly. When reviewing your elderly patient's systems, note the following possibly pathologic signs:

Skin: Delayed wound healing, change in texture
Nails: Brittleness, clubbing, pitting
Head: Facial pain or numbness
Eyes: Diplopia, tunnel vision, halo effect, glaucoma, cataracts
Ears: Excessive wax formation, use of wax softeners
Nose: Epistaxis, allergic rhinitis
Mouth/throat: Sore tongue, problems with teeth or gums, gums bleeding at night, hoarseness
Neck: Pain, swelling, restricted range of motion
Respiratory: Tuberculosis, difficulty or painful breathing, excessive cough producing excessive or blood-streaked sputum
Breasts: Discharge, change in contour, change in nipples, gynecomastia, lumps
Cardiovascular: Chest pain on exertion, orthopnea, cyanosis, syncope, fatigue, murmur, leg cramps, varicosities, coldness or numbness of extremities, hypertension, heart attack
Gastrointestinal: Difficulty swallowing, epigastric pain, abdominal pain, intolerance to certain foods, increased thirst, dysphagia, change in bowel habits, rectal bleeding
Renal: Flank pain, dysuria, polyuria, nocturia, incontinence, enuresis, hematuria, renal or bladder infections or stones
Reproductive: Male—hernia, testicular pain, prostatic problems; female—postmenopausal problems (bleeding, hot flashes, painful intercourse)
Endocrine: Goiter, tremor
Musculoskeletal: Pain, joint swelling, crepitus, restricted joint movement, arthritis, gout, rheumatism, lumbago, amputations
Nervous: Memory loss, loss of consciousness, nervousness, nightmares, insomnia, changes in emotional state, tremors, muscle weakness, paralysis, aphasia, speech difficulty, pain or numbness

lost control, or does he not sense the urge to urinate? If he says he gets up to urinate in the middle of the night, find out if the urge awakens him.

• *Female reproductive system.* Include questions about menopause in your review of an elderly female patient. Ask her when menopause began and ended (if it has), what symptoms she experienced, and how she feels about it. Ask whether she is receiving estrogen replacement therapy now, or has received it in the past (for how long?). Be sure to question an elderly female patient about symptoms of breast disease. Find out if she regularly performs a breast self-examination (and if she is physically capable of doing so).

• *Nervous system.* Inquire about changes in coordination, strength, or sensory perception. Does the patient have headaches or seizures, or any temporary losses of consciousness? Has he had any difficulty controlling his bowels or his bladder?

• *Blood-forming and immune system.* Remember that anemia is common in older people and may cause fatigue or weakness.

3

The Physical Examination

After taking your patient's health history to obtain the subjective data on which to base clinical decisions, the next step in the assessment process is the *physical examination*. During this assessment phase you obtain objective data that usually confirm or rule out suspicions raised during the health history interview.

You use four basic techniques to perform a physical examination: *inspection, palpation, percussion,* and *auscultation* (IPPA). If you learn to use IPPA skills effectively, then—after much careful study and practice—the chance that you'll overlook something important during the physical examination will be reduced.

You need also to develop a system for assessing patients that identifies their problem areas in priority order. By performing physical assessments systematically and efficiently instead of in a random or indiscriminate manner, you save time and identify priority problems quickly.

Examination sequences. The most commonly used methods for completing a total systematic physical assessment are *head to toe* and *major body systems.*

Using the head-to-toe method, you systematically assess your patient—as the name suggests—beginning at the head and working toward the toes. Examine all parts of one body region before progressing to the next region, to save time and energy for yourself and your patient. Proceed from left to right within each region, so you can make symmetrical comparisons. Don't examine the patient's left side from head to toe, then his right side.

The major-body-systems method involves systematically assessing your patient by examining each body system in priority order or a predesignated sequence.

Both methods are systematic and provide a logical, organized framework to help you collect physical assessment data. They also provide the same information; therefore, neither is more correct than the other. So choose the method (or a variation of it) that works well for you and is appropriate for your patient population. Follow this routine whenever you assess a patient and try not to deviate from it.

Equipment needed. Before you conduct a physical examination, collect and organize all the equipment you'll need—or make sure it's already in the examining room or at the patient's bedside. (Interrupting an examination to obtain a forgotten piece of equipment increases your patient's anxiety and weakens his trust in your competence.) Certain pieces of equipment are essential to a complete physical examination and should always be available (see *Essential Equipment,* page 29). You may also need additional specialized equipment—such as a Doppler ultrasound or an EKG machine—depending on the extent of the examination. In any case, determine what equipment you'll need, and have it ready before you begin the examination. This includes making sure the room is warm, well ventilated, and well lighted.

Your patient's anxiety. When you approach your patient to perform a physical examination, one of your first priorities should be to relieve the anxiety he's probably experiencing. Almost every patient you examine will be anxious about his health problems. His worry may be severe; for example, he may suspect he has a fatal illness or that extensive surgery or treatment will strain his finances. To help your patient relax, tell him what procedures you plan to perform during the examination. Then explain the procedures as you do them.

Essential Equipment

Here's a list of equipment you'll need to perform a basic physical examination. To make the examination run more smoothly, gather all the equipment beforehand.

- Thermometer
- Scale for measuring height and weight
- Wristwatch (with sweep second-hand)
- Stethoscope (with diaphragm and bell)
- Sphygmomanometer and blood pressure cuff
- Ophthalmoscope
- Otoscope (with assorted specula)
- Nasoscope, nasal speculum, or nasal tip for otoscope
- Eye chart (Snellen) and newspaper clipping for close reading assessment
- Opaque card or eye cover
- Penlight or flashlight
- 2″ x 2″ and 4″ x 4″ sterile gauze pads and cotton swabs
- Tuning forks (512 to 1,024 cycles/second to test hearing acuity)
- Tongue depressors
- Laryngeal mirror
- Examination gloves and water-soluble lubricant
- Vaginal specula and slides
- Reflex or percussion hammer
- Safety pin
- Cloth tape measure (indicating centimeter measurements)
- Hemoculture test slides
- Urine specimen container

Use words he can understand.

Professional courtesy dictates that you be reassuring and gentle to help ease your patient's fears. Perhaps less obvious is your patient's need to feel that you know what you're doing. Demonstrate professionalism by approaching him in an unhurried manner. Never display negative reactions, such as surprise, alarm, distaste, or annoyance, in response to his physical appearance or anything he says.

Before you begin a physical examination, give your patient an opportunity to urinate. Tell him about the different positions you'll ask him to assume. The physical examination will probably require that he assume several positions. For example, he'll need to sit up while you examine his head, neck, chest, and back. Then he'll have to lie supine so you can examine his heart, abdomen, genitalia, extremities, and—in a female—the breasts. Certain phases of the neurologic examination necessitate that the patient stand and move in a variety of ways. By organizing the examination sequence carefully, you can minimize the number of position changes.

Your patient will have to undress for examination of most body systems. Provide a gown, and drape him appropriately for examination of the particular body area you'll assess (see *Guidelines to Positioning and Draping,* page 30). Explain to the patient why it is necessary for him to undress, since he may be confused or embarrassed. A female patient, for example, may not understand the importance of removing her bra. Many women, particularly teenagers and young adults, are embarrassed by this but are reluctant to ask for an explanation.

Be sure, too, that you've arranged for privacy. If you must perform the physical examination at your patient's bedside, close the door, draw the curtains around his bed, ask visitors to leave the room, and take any other necessary steps to safeguard your patient's privacy. These measures demonstrate your respect for the patient and minimize his embarrassment. They also enhance his cooperation during the examination. Remember: Your manner while conducting a physical examination can strengthen or undermine the

Guidelines to Positioning and Draping

Requirements for patient positioning and draping vary according to which body systems or regions you plan to examine. These illustrations show the primary positioning and draping arrangements you'll use during a routine assessment.

To examine the patient's head, neck, and anterior and posterior thorax and lungs, have him sit on the edge of the examining table.

To examine the cardiovascular system and the abdomen, place the patient in supine position. To ensure privacy for a female patient during abdominal assessment, place a towel over her breasts and upper thorax. Pull down the sheet only as far as, but not exposing, her pubic symphysis.

To begin examining the female patient's breasts, place her in a seated position. For the second part of the examination, ask her to lie down. When she does, place a small pillow or folded towel beneath her shoulder on the side being examined, to spread her breast more evenly over the chest.

To perform a pelvic examination on the female patient, place her in lithotomy position. Drape a sheet diagonally over her chest and knees and between her legs. Her buttocks should be close to the edge of the table and her feet in the stirrups.

To perform a rectal examination, position the male patient so he's leaning across the examining table. If he can't stand upright, perform the examination with the patient lying on his left side, with his right hip and knee slightly flexed and his buttocks close to the edge of the examining table.

To perform some parts of the neurologic and musculoskeletal examinations, have the patient stand, when feasible, or sit.

rapport you've developed with the patient, as well as the degree of relaxation you've helped him attain.

The general survey

Definition

The physical examination actually begins with the general observations you make during the first few minutes with the patient—perhaps while you're introducing yourself or assisting him into a hospital gown. Note, for example, such characteristics as his general state of health, any signs of distress, his appearance in relation to his chronological age, facial expressions, skin color, and body development. This information, supplemented by basic statistical information—such as height, weight, and the status of vital signs—constitutes the *general survey*.

Conduct the general survey no matter which examination method you plan to follow—head to toe or major body systems.

Vital signs variations

Your patient's age, activity level, and physical and emotional status can affect his vital signs. In fact, even changing the time of day when you routinely measure his *body temperature, pulse rate, respirations,* and *blood pressure* can result in variations from the previous to the current determinations. You should keep these considerations in mind when you assess your patient's vital signs.

Taking a patient's vital signs allows you to:
• determine the relative status of vital organs, including the heart, blood vessels, and lungs
• monitor response to treatment
• establish baseline measurements that can be compared with future readings
• determine the need for further diagnostic testing.

Body temperature

Body temperature is the difference between the amount of heat the body produces and the amount of heat it loses. Heat-producing processes within the body—for example, metabolism, disease, exercise, shivering, unconscious tensing of muscles, and increased thyroid activity—sometimes produce more heat than is necessary to maintain a normal

body temperature of 97.7° to 99.5° F. (36.5° to 37.5° C.). To offset excessive heat production and restore normal temperature, the body uses some or all of these four processes: *radiation, conduction, convection,* and *evaporation.*

A *negative feedback system* allows the body to maintain a fairly constant temperature. Receptor cells in the skin, sensitive to heat and cold, respond to changes in cutaneous temperature. The cells' response to such alterations triggers nerve impulses, which are transmitted through the cerebral cortex to the hypothalamus—the brain's thermoregulatory center. The hypothalamus integrates the responses of the receptor cells in the skin with its own responses to blood temperature and arrives at a new *sensed* temperature. The hypothalamus then compares the sensed temperature to the body's *set point,* or *reference temperature.*

If a variation exists, the hypothalamus signals the appropriate heat-regulating mechanism to raise or lower body temperature. For example, when heat reduction is necessary, the hypothalamus sends out impulses that dilate cutaneous blood vessels and stimulate sweat glands. Radiation from the large volume of blood brought to the skin's surface, together with evaporation of the resulting perspiration, eliminates heat from the body and restores normal body temperature. The hypothalamus can also send out impulses that increase heat production and reduce heat elimination when decreased body heat threatens to drop body temperature below normal. These impulses inhibit secretion of sweat, increase the basal metabolic rate, and constrict superficial blood vessels to meet the body's demands for internal temperature regulation.

You can take a patient's body temperature *orally* or *rectally,* or by using the *axillary* method. Before deciding which method to use for a particular patient, consider the patient's overall condition and age. The oral route is probably most convenient, and reflects arterial temperature more accurately than a rectal or axillary reading. If your patient is unconscious, confused, or disoriented, is unable to keep his mouth closed, or is receiving oxygen by face mask, take a rectal or axillary temperature. The rectal or axillary route should also be used to measure the body temperature of infants and young children. For adults who won't cooperate by having their temperatures taken rectally, use the axillary route when the oral route is contraindicated.

If you use a glass thermometer to take a patient's temperature orally, leave it in place for 3 to 5 minutes. If the patient recently smoked, ate, or drank, wait 15 minutes before taking an oral temperature reading. For an accurate axillary temperature reading, leave the thermometer in place for 9 to 11 minutes. For a rectal reading, lubricate the thermometer and insert it 1½" (4 cm) into the rectum. Then keep it in place for 2 to 4 minutes.

A normal temperature reading varies with the route selected for taking the temperature and the time of day. Rectal temperatures register 1° F. higher than oral temperatures. All temperature readings are 1° to 2° F. lower in the early morning than in the late afternoon. Variations from normal body temperature can indicate *hypothermia* or *hyperthermia*. Hypothermia is below-normal body temperature, which slows down metabolic processes. The hypothermic patient may be drowsy or even comatose because of impaired central nervous system (CNS) functioning. His circulation rate may be slow and his heart rate irregular. If body temperature drops to 94.6° F. (34.8° C.), functioning of the hypothalamus is impaired; at 84.9° F. (29.4° C.), the hypothalamus stops functioning.

In hyperthermia (fever), certain processes cause body temperature to rise. The hypothalamus resets the set point, or reference temperature, at a higher level than normal. Causes of the malfunctioning include CNS disease or injury and infectious states. Regardless of the cause, the hypothalamus, responding to a blood (surface) temperature that is lower than the abnormally high level of the reference temperature, activates autonomic responses to elevate body temperature. When body heat reaches the hypothalamus' new set point, frank signs of fever will be exhibited.

When the disease process stops, the hypothalamus receives stimuli that allow it to reset the reference temperature at a lower (normal) level. Then the body's heat-loss mechanisms initiate vasodilation, stimulation of sweat glands, and muscle relaxation—at which point the fever usually breaks.

The pulse

During systole, the heart ejects blood from the left ventricle into a full aorta. This produces a flaring of the aorta and a resultant wave or pulsation throughout the arterial system, palpable as your patient's *pulse*. Each pulse beat corresponds to a heartbeat and results from the impact of the ejected blood on arterial walls.

The heart of a normal adult at rest beats an average of 60 to 100 times per minute, pumping 5.3 qt (5 liters) of blood per minute through the body. To calculate *cardiac output,* multiply the *heart rate* per minute times the *stroke volume* (the volume of blood ejected with each beat).

A decrease in heart rate—such as *bradycardia* (a rate below 60 beats per minute)— without a compensatory increase in stroke volume causes diminished cardiac output. Bradycardia occurs with stimulation of the parasympathetic nervous system. This may result, for example, from injection of certain drugs.

Conversely, an increase in heart rate can occur when stroke volume lessens, keeping cardiac output constant. A heart rate of more than 100 beats per minute is called *tachycardia*. Pain, fear, anxiety, or anger can cause stimulation of the sympathetic nervous system, causing heart rate acceleration. Other conditions associated with tachycardia include thyroid problems, fever, anemia, hypoxia, and shock.

The most accessible and commonly used artery for measuring a patient's pulse rate is the *radial artery,* which you compress against the radius to take the *radial pulse.* You can palpate other pulse sites when your patient's radial artery is inaccessible, or when testing circulation at a specific site (see *Peripheral Pulse Sites,* page 33).

To palpate a *pulse,* lightly place the pads of your index and middle fingers over the pulse point. Then compress the pulse point until you detect maximum pulsation. (Never use your thumb to take a patient's pulse because the pulsations from the radial artery in your thumb can interfere with an accurate reading.)

Assess all peripheral pulses in a patient scheduled for surgery (especially cardiac or peripheral vascular surgery) or in a patient admitted for a diabetic or arterial occlusive condition. If you have difficulty palpating a peripheral pulse, mark its location on the patient's skin with a pen or marker for future reference. Document what you've done.

Although the normal *pulse rate* of a resting adult is 60 to 100 beats per minute, the rate is slightly faster in women than in men, and faster still in infants and children. If your patient's pulse rate seems abnormally fast or slow, or irregular, count the number of radial pulsations for 60 seconds, then auscultate the apical heartbeat for 60 seconds. The difference between the radial rate and the apical rate is called the *pulse deficit.* A pulse deficit means that some heartbeats aren't strong enough to produce a palpable peripheral pulsation. Thus, the radial pulse would be slower than the apical pulse (never the reverse).

Moderate exercise usually causes the pulse rate to increase by about 20 to 30 beats per minute. The rate should return to normal within 2 minutes after cessation of exercise.

When you take a patient's pulse, you must know how to assess the quality of the pulse as well as its rate. *Quality* refers to a pulse's amplitude, rhythm, and contour.

- *Amplitude* is the force of the pulse, which can be bounding or full, normal, weak, or thready.
- *Rhythm* refers to the relative equality of the intervals between beats. Bigeminal rhythm, for example, is a pattern of two beats—the first usually stronger than the second—followed by a pause.
- *Contour* describes the wavelike flow of a pulse as it rises, crests, and then collapses.

Note any change in the quality of a patient's pulse, whether in amplitude, rhythm, or contour, so that appropriate diagnostic tests can be ordered.

Respiration

When assessing respirations routinely with other vital signs, focus on the rate, depth, and pattern of respirations. Note the patient's general physical appearance, especially his color, as well as the ease and regularity of his breathing and chest wall movements.

Throughout the respiratory process, the lungs maintain homeostasis of arterial blood by supplying it with inhaled oxygen. They also maintain the blood's pH by retaining carbon dioxide or disposing of it. If the major respi-

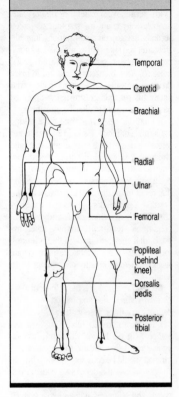

Peripheral Pulse Sites

- Temporal
- Carotid
- Brachial
- Radial
- Ulnar
- Femoral
- Popliteal (behind knee)
- Dorsalis pedis
- Posterior tibial

ratory muscles—the diaphragm and the external intercostal muscles—weaken and fail to provide sufficient ventilation to meet the body's oxygen demands, then accessory muscles, such as the scalene, sternocleidomastoid, trapezius, and latissimus dorsi, attempt to compensate. If your patient relies on accessory muscles for respiration but has no history of chronic pulmonary disease, include this information in your nursing notes.

The body's normal mechanisms for stimulating respiration may break down as a result of brain trauma, a chronic increase in Pco_2 in patients with chronic obstructive lung disease, or the use of drugs such as barbiturates and narcotics. Closely observe the respiratory status of patients with acute cardiac problems, evidence of increased intracranial pressure, or acute or chronic pulmonary disease, and of patients in shock.

To determine your patient's *respiratory rate,* unobtrusively count his respirations for 60 seconds. Try to count respirations immediately after you take a pulse, *without his knowledge,* while you continue to hold his radial pulse (or, with the stethoscope still in place on the chest wall). Remember, a patient who knows his respirations are being observed tends involuntarily to alter his breathing.

The normal respiratory rate for a resting adult (male or female) is 12 to 20 breaths per minute; a faster rate is normal in infants and children. A slower than normal respiratory rate (less than 12 breaths per minute) may occur with conditions such as CNS depression that result from use of certain drugs, administration of anesthetics, or carbon dioxide narcosis. Both psychological and physical conditions—fear, pain, anxiety, fever, hypoxia, diabetic coma, and midbrain lesions, for example—can accelerate respiratory rate to more than 20 breaths per minute in an adult.

Depth of respiration is the volume of air—or *tidal volume*—moving in and out of the patient's mouth or nose with each breath. A healthy adult normally inhales and exhales 500 cc of air per breath, which provides adequate ventilation. Ideally, the depth of respiration should be constant with each breath. To approximate the depth of a patient's respiration, observe his chest movement for adequate and symmetrical chest expansion. (If he's unconscious, place the back of your hand close to his mouth and nose to feel the air he exhales.) Depth of respiration is characterized as *normal, shallow,* or *deep.* Remember that respirations in men are usually abdominal, whereas respirations in women are chiefly thoracic.

The rate and depth of a patient's respirations influence the respiratory *pattern* or *rhythm.* Normal respirations follow one another evenly, with little variation from one breath to another. Generally, the respiratory process follows a four-step pattern: a fairly rapid inspiration, a slight pause, then a slightly longer expiration, followed by a longer pause.

Variations in respiratory pattern can be associated with specific disease processes. Metabolic acidosis and alkalosis, for example, can adversely affect the pattern or rhythm. Severe metabolic alkalosis causes a distinctive pattern of respirations, characterized by 5- to 30-second periods of apnea.

Arterial blood pressure

Blood pressure reading is an indirect measurement of the fluctuating pressures that blood exerts laterally on arterial walls as the heart contracts and relaxes. Arterial blood pressure reflects cardiac output, vascular resistance to circulating blood, blood viscosity and volume, and the ability of arterial walls to expand and constrict. Measuring arterial blood pressure aids the evaluation of a patient's circulatory status and fluid balance—two important indicators of overall physical status. A series of blood pressure readings, which may show the development of a trend, is nearly always more significant than a single reading.

The hemodynamics of blood pressure begins with contraction of the left ventricle, which sends blood flowing from the aorta to other arteries, and then to capillaries and veins. The pressure blood exerts against arterial walls as a result of contraction of the left ventricle (systole) is the *systolic pressure.* It indicates arterial pressure at the peak of pulsation. *Diastolic pressure* is arterial pressure at its ebb, during left ventricular relaxation (diastole), and is thus a measure of the minimum pressure being exerted on arterial walls. The difference between systolic and diastolic pressures is called *pulse pressure,* an important diagnostic indicator in such conditions as increased intracranial pressure, hypertension, and shock.

Many factors affect arterial blood pressure. The time of day, for example, can make a difference in blood pressure readings. A person's blood pressure is usually lowest in the early morning and rises when the person begins to move about. Body position also affects blood pressure; readings taken while a person is lying down will be lower than when he's sitting or standing. Another significant factor is the presence of fatty deposits lining the vessels. These deposits reduce the vessels' interior capacity and increase blood pressure, since greater force is required to propel blood through the narrowed passages.

How to measure arterial blood pressure

In most cases, you'll measure your patient's arterial blood pressure in millimeters of mercury (mm Hg), using three pieces of equipment: a sphygmomanometer, an inflatable cuff, and a stethoscope. Two types of sphygmomanometers are available to measure blood pressure: one has a calibrated column of mercury, the other a compact aneroid dial that gives direct readings.

Before taking your patient's blood pressure, make sure he's relaxed; for example, make sure he hasn't exercised or eaten within the past 30 minutes. When you take his blood pressure, he can be sitting, standing, or lying down. If this is the first time you've examined him, you may want to obtain baseline readings by taking his blood pressure twice in each arm—when he's lying down, then when he's sitting or standing. Remember, always wait 30 seconds before taking another reading, to allow the blood pressure to normalize.

Make sure the bladder of the inflatable cuff is about 20% wider than the diameter of the patient's arm or leg. Too narrow a cuff will produce a false high reading because of the greater pressure required to compress the artery. Conversely, a false low reading results from using a cuff that is too wide, since only minimal pressure is required for arterial compression.

To take a routine arterial blood pressure reading, keep the patient's arm level with his heart. Center the cuff over the brachial artery, and wrap it smoothly and evenly around the upper arm. The isometric contraction that occurs when a patient uses his own muscle strength to raise and straighten his arm can elevate systolic pressure about 10 mm Hg and distort the blood pressure reading. To prevent this, support his arm with your hand as you adjust the cuff. Then palpate the radial artery and rapidly inflate the cuff, until the radial pulse disappears. Continue inflating the cuff until the pressure has risen an additional 20 to 30 mm Hg.

Place the stethoscope's diaphragm over the brachial artery, about an inch below the cuff, and release the air in the cuff at the rate of 2 mm Hg per heartbeat. If you deflate the cuff too slowly, the blood vessels in the patient's arm may become congested and cause a false high reading. If you deflate the cuff too quickly, you won't have enough time to assess diastolic pressure accurately. As soon as you hear blood begin to pulse through the brachial artery again, note the height of the sphygmomanometer's mercury column—reading it at eye level—or aneroid dial. This is your patient's systolic blood pressure.

Continue to deflate the cuff until the pulsations diminish or become muffled. This reading on the sphygmomanometer indicates his diastolic blood pressure. Until recently, the point at which sound *disappeared* was recorded as the diastolic pressure. But current studies have shown that the muffling of sound is closer to the true intraarterial pressure. (The American Heart Association recommends recording blood pressures as systolic/muffling/disappearance—for example, 126/70/66.)

Normal and abnormal blood pressure readings

Normal arterial blood pressure varies greatly among individuals. Generally, systolic blood pressure in a healthy adult ranges from 100 to 135 mm Hg; diastolic pressure usually ranges from 60 to 80 mm Hg. If your patient has been relaxed for 5 to 10 minutes, and hasn't eaten or exercised for 30 minutes, expect to obtain blood pressure readings within these ranges. A rise or fall of 10 to 20 mm Hg, with no apparent reason for the fluctuation (such as a change in the patient's position or activity level), necessitates further investigation, especially if the patient has no history of such an irregularity. Naturally, all factors that can affect blood pressure, such as age, must be ruled out.

Consistently low blood pressure may be normal in some persons. Abnormally low blood pressure (below 95/60 mm Hg) indicates *hypotension*. This condition can result from acute myocardial infarction, which decreases cardiac output, or from any other condition that reduces the patient's total blood volume. (Examples are addisonian crisis; severe burns; dehydration from decreased oral intake in an elderly person, an infant, or a severely depressed person; diarrhea; vomiting; heat exhaustion; metabolic acidosis; and hypovolemic shock.) Signs of hypotension include increased pulse rate, diaphoresis, dizziness, confusion, weakness, lethargy, cool and clammy skin, and blurred vision.

Hypertension is persistently elevated blood pressure (above 140/90 mm Hg), which occurs when blood exerts excessive pressure against arterial walls. Hypertension usually reflects an underlying disorder, such as kidney disease, but you may encounter patients with *essential,* or *idiopathic,* hypertension, in whom no cause for elevated blood pressure can be found. Some disorders, such as aortic insufficiency, increase only systolic blood pressure—diastolic pressure remains normal. This is also classified as hypertension.

Four Basic Techniques: IPPA

Inspection: Informed observation

Of the four physical assessment skills, inspection is unquestionably paramount. It appears simple and so is often taken for granted. But this skill involves more than just looking at your patient. Inspection is *informed observation,* or looking with a purpose—keenly, intently, with an eye for relevant detail. This skill goes beyond what you see with your eyes, to encompass your senses of smell, touch, and hearing. For example, your nose may detect the odor of necrotic tissue. By touch, you assess your patient's temperature or the texture of his skin. Your ears can hear noisy respirations.

For some types of inspection, you may need to use equipment, such as an ophthalmoscope, an otoscope, or a speculum, to enhance your vision or gain access to an area.

Lighting is important when you're inspecting a patient. Take advantage of daylight, if possible. In most modern hospital rooms, a broad panel of lights extends over the patient's bed, and some even have fixtures that let you direct the light to where you want it. If this kind of arrangement isn't available, be prepared with a flashlight or portable lamp suitable for examining purposes.

Your personal data base of clinical nursing knowledge helps you to recognize the significance of inspection findings. This impression grows stronger or weaker after you analyze the information you've already gathered about your patient—particularly during the health history interview. What this means is that inspection requires you to look for physical findings similar to those you've found in the past, under similar clinical circumstances. At the same time you're looking for predictable physical findings, keep your eyes and mind open to the unexpected. Balance these two approaches to a patient and you'll be well on your way to mastering the difficult skill of inspection.

Be careful to maintain your objectivity. Don't distort your findings with preconceived ideas. (Sometimes knowledge of what *should be* distorts what *is.*) If what you expect to find isn't apparent, you shouldn't invent it.

Inspection draws on your most acute faculties. You need keen physical senses, adequate clinical knowledge, an agile mind that can quickly recall past clinical experiences, and the ability to draw accurate conclusions quickly. You can be sure of one thing: You'll never lack opportunities to practice inspection. By far the most frequently performed assessment skill, inspection comes into play every time you see a patient. As an astute observer, you'll notice changes in your patient that may signal deterioration or improvement in his condition, or the appearance of a new sign. Inspection is an ongoing process; it begins during the health history interview, continues through the physical examination, and shouldn't end until the day your patient's discharged.

General-to-specific inspection

After your general survey, move on to more specific inspections. Focus on problem areas that the patient or your general survey has identified. For each body area, use the general-to-specific approach. First, note the area's general appearance; then, observe and record distinctive details, such as the normal or abnormal size, shape, location, color, texture, and motion of structures. If appropriate, record the absence or presence of common landmarks, and compare the area you're inspecting with its counterpart on the other side of your patient's body.

To be sure you're inspecting each patient accurately and thoroughly, develop a systematic inspection method that you can follow routinely, but can also adjust for individual patients.

Base your initial inspection on what you already know about the patient—his age, general physical status, and reason for seeking health care. For example, suppose you notice a rash during your initial inspection. After completing your general observations, return to the rash, inspect it more closely, and describe all its observable characteristics. Your note might read: *Erythematous, flat, circumscribed lesions, less than 1 mm in diameter, scattered randomly over entire face, becoming very dense and merging in the periauricular regions.*

Palpation: The sense of touch

Generally, you'll perform palpation as the second step in assessing your patient, to rule out—or possibly confirm—suspicions raised during inspection. Sometimes you may inspect and palpate a patient simultaneously. For example, when your inspection of a patient reveals an enlarged scrotum, your palpation may detect a unilateral, nontender mass that feels like a bag of worms—a finding that suggests varicocele.

Palpation involves the trained and skillful use of your sense of touch to obtain clinical information about your patient. With your hands and fingers, you can determine the size, shape, and position of structures as well as their temperature, texture, moisture content, and movement. You can palpate all parts of your patient's body, including tissues, bones, muscles, glands, organs, hair, and skin. Palpation also helps you check for growths, swelling, muscle spasm or rigidity, pain and tenderness, and crepitus. You'll perform abdominal palpation often, to detect such problems as a distended bladder, a palpable spleen, an umbilical hernia, an enlarged liver, a prominent upper abdominal pulsation with lateral expansion—even the position of a fetus.

Like inspection, palpation relies on a sense that's important but often undervalued. Theoretically, anyone can touch or probe a human body with his hand to feel for a lump or some other abnormal sign. Only a knowledgeable and experienced health-care professional can perform such an examination thoroughly and

systematically, while causing the patient as little discomfort as possible.

Palpation techniques

Remember that touching a patient is apt to elicit fear, embarrassment, and other strong emotions. Be sure to explain what you're doing and why, as well as what he can expect—such as discomfort. Make sure your hands are warm. Try to get your patient to relax, because muscular tension or guarding can interfere with the performance and results of palpation. Instruct the patient to breathe deeply, through his mouth. If you've identified tender areas, palpate them last.

Part of the skill of palpation is in knowing which areas of your hands and fingers to use. Why is this important? Because your hands and fingers are not equally sensitive to all sensations—such as temperature. For example, you might suspect that your patient has an elevated surface temperature over a sprained ankle, or a lowered surface temperature in his hands from poor circulation. To investigate these and similar suspicions, use the *back of your hand or fingers,* because the skin there is thinner and more sensitive to temperature. You may find it helpful to palpate the suspect area with the back of one hand, while palpating an unaffected area with the back of the other hand. Then switch hands to confirm the differences you perceive between the two areas. For discriminating skin surface textures, first use your fingertips, to detect general differences, then use the backs of your hands and fingers for finer distinctions. Use the *pads of your fingertips* to determine the position, form, and consistency of structures—to palpate lymph nodes, for example. For determining muscle and tissue firmness, as well as joint positions, use your *thumb and index finger* to grasp the body part. To detect vibrations (such as thrills or fremitus), use the palmar surface of the metacarpophalangeal joints—the *ball of the hand.*

Light and deep palpation

To begin palpation (after making sure your hands are warm), apply slow, gentle pressure. Start with light palpation and progress to deep palpation (see *Light and Deep Palpation,* page 38). Be sure to palpate painful or hypersensitive areas last. You're palpating to identify

Light and Deep Palpation

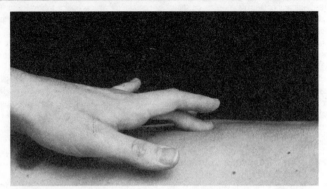

To perform light palpation, press gently on your patient's skin with the pads of your fingers, indenting about 1 to 2 cm. Move your hand in a circular motion.

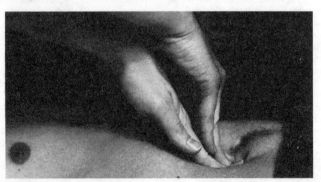

To perform deep palpation, increase your fingertip pressure, indenting about 4 cm. The examiner shown here is using both hands to perform *bimanual* deep palpation.

tender areas, the presence of masses, organ changes, and abnormal fluid collections.

Light palpation probes to a depth of 1 to 2 cm from the body surface. Used principally to detect slight tenderness and to assess muscle tone, this technique requires a gentle dipping and circular motion. With your hand parallel to the body surface being examined, extend your fingers, keeping them together; then, gently depress the body surface.

To use light palpation on a patient's abdomen, for example, place your palm on the abdomen, extend your fingers, and then press them into the area. (This is known as *scouting;* it allows you to detect any areas of tenderness.)

Deep palpation locates abdominal masses and organs. Using this technique, apply greater pressure than you'd use for light palpation, pressing down from the body surface to a depth of 4 to 5 cm. You can use one or both hands for deep palpation. To perform *single-handed* deep palpation, place the palm of your hand on the abdomen, extend your fingers, and press in with your fingertips at a slight angle. This causes the underlying tissues to slide back and forth against the pads of your fingertips. To perform palpation using both hands—*bimanual* palpation—place one hand on the abdomen in the usual manner. Then place your other hand—palm down—on top of it. The top hand exerts pressure on the bottom hand's relaxed distal phalangeal joints, and guides the bottom hand to detect and delineate underlying organs or masses. Use this method to apply the additional pressure needed to reach deep organs or masses, or to overcome resistance of excess body tissues, if your patient is obese.

During palpation, watch your patient's facial expressions continuously for any sign of pain, since both types of deep palpation may normally cause him some discomfort. Keeping your eyes on the patient's face while palpating also enhances your sense of touch and trains you to palpate accurately. If palpation causes the patient obvious pain, don't continue, since you could injure him. For example, palpation may cause an enlarged spleen to rupture.

Using deep palpation, you can check for rebound tenderness directly over the affected site (if your patient doesn't have too much pain) by slowly and firmly depressing the tender area with your fingers, and then rapidly removing the pressure. Be sure to note whether the patient experiences pain when you withdraw your fingers. To confirm true rebound tenderness, palpate a neighboring region—for example, palpate the lower right abdominal quadrant if you suspect rebound tenderness in the lower left quadrant. The sudden release of pressure in the unaffected area will cause a sharp pain in the suspect site if true rebound tenderness exists.

Ballottement

Ballottement (from the French for *tossing about*) is a palpation technique you use to determine if a freely movable mass is present beneath the abdominal wall. You'll be able to detect it with *light ballottement* because the light, rapid pressure causes solid tissue to bounce upward, toward your fingertips (see *Ballottement,* page 40). You should also be able to feel a lively bounce in the upper right quadrant of the abdomen, caused by resistance from dense liver tissue.

To begin abdominal light ballottement, start low on your patient's abdomen, bouncing your fingertips lightly and rapidly upward. Besides detecting evidence of a mass (if present), this technique also demonstrates any tendency toward guarding—a sign of possible underlying inflammation.

If fluid or ascites are present in your patient's abdomen, you'll need to use a more forceful motion to feel the enlarged liver—a special palpation technique in which you exert sudden deep pressure. (This is done mainly to detect the presence of true fluid in a body cavity, as in ascites, or the presence of masses underlying collections of fluid.) To perform *deep ballottement* on the abdomen, position your hand with your fingertips perpendicular to the patient's abdominal wall. Keeping your fingers together, push inward suddenly and deeply. Then, release this pressure but keep your fingertips in contact with the abdominal surface. This will allow you to feel any movement of an organ or mass provided the mass is freely movable.

Practice and palpation

Palpation is a sophisticated skill that you can perfect only through repeated practice. It requires more than manual dexterity; you must also be able to interpret your findings correctly. Organs and other body structures that can be palpated vary greatly in size and shape. Only through practice can you become familiar with normal findings and readily identify pathologic variations.

The skill you develop with practice will enable you to deal with difficult palpation situations. For example, if you localize a mass through palpation, next palpate it systematically to delineate its essential characteristics: size, shape, consistency, mobility, tenderness, and pulsation.

Obesity presents another challenge. Palpating the abdominal organs of an obese patient may be difficult because of the intervening excess adipose tissue. With such a patient, you may have to modify your technique, perhaps by using both hands to perform palpation adequately and applying greater pressure.

Percussion defined

Percussion involves tapping the body surface lightly—with a sharp, quick motion—to pro-

Ballottement

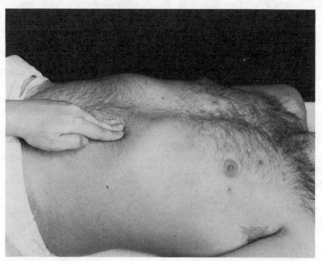

To perform light ballottement, apply light, rapid pressure, from quadrant to quadrant, on your patient's abdomen. Keep your hand on the skin surface throughout to feel tissue rebound.

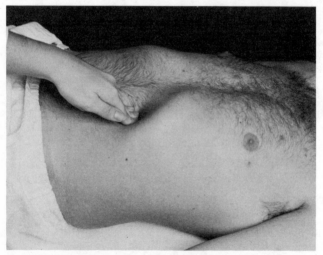

Exert abrupt, deep pressure when performing deep ballottement. Note that you should release pressure completely but maintain fingertip contact with the skin.

duce sounds that help determine the size, shape, position, and density of underlying organs and tissues. This technique seems to be the physical assessment skill with which nurses are least familiar. Here's how it works: Percussion drives sound into the body by causing the body surface to vibrate. The examiner then listens and feels for various characteristics of the returning sound, which will reflect the nature of the body cavity's contents.

This technique, used most commonly over the chest and abdomen, may validate or clarify data you've obtained by history-taking, inspection, or palpation. Percussion reveals density by signaling the presence of air or solid material—to a depth of 5 to 7 cm—in a body cavity or organ. It helps you determine the size, shape, and position of internal organs by outlining their borders and approximating their depth.

Mediate, immediate, and fist percussion

Depending on the body region you're examining, you may use any of three types of percussion: mediate, immediate, and fist (see *Percussion: Three Methods,* page 42).

In the most widely used percussion method—*mediate* percussion, most frequently used to percuss the thorax and abdomen—you strike the middle finger of one hand with the middle or index finger of the other hand. The finger that does the striking is called the *plexor;* the finger that is struck is called the *pleximeter.* To perform mediate percussion, place the distal phalanx of the pleximeter (not the entire finger) against the body surface. (Keep the palm and other fingers of this hand raised off the skin.) Then strike the base of the pleximeter's distal interphalangeal joint with the tip (not the fat pad) of the plexor (see illustration).

To perform *immediate* percussion—an older technique used mainly to percuss an infant's thorax or adult sinuses—simply strike the body surface with one or more fingers of one hand. (The other hand is not involved.)

To perform *fist* percussion, place one hand flat against your patient's body surface, then strike the back of this hand with your other hand, clenched in a fist. This form of percussion, used most commonly over the lower back, helps determine the presence of pain or tenderness from kidney, liver, or gallbladder inflammation or disease.

Mediate percussion technique

The key to eliciting clear percussion notes is a quick snap of the wrist. Your forearm shouldn't move at all; your wrist generates all the force. Don't drive the plexor into the pleximeter as though playing a piano, and don't use your elbow and shoulder as though hammering a nail—two common mistakes in mediate percussion. Keeping your hand relaxed and using only your wrist to supply power assure percussion strokes of equal force.

Place only the distal phalanx of the pleximeter *firmly* in contact with the patient's body. Maintain this contact after the tap by the plexor, but remove the plexor immediately. If the plexor remains there for even a second or two after striking the pleximeter, the resulting sound will be muffled.

A light tap generally produces the best percussion note. A too-forceful blow may obliterate the sound, besides making the pleximeter sore. (Keep the fingernail of your plexor trimmed to prevent damage to the pleximeter.) Percussion notes needn't be loud to be useful; equally important are the pitch, duration, and quality of a note, for which lighter percussion is often superior. (Excess adipose tissue may dampen a normal percussion note. You may have to be more forceful in examining patients who are obese or who have large muscle mass.)

You shouldn't have to percuss an area more than two or three times before moving to another area. If you have to percuss the same area repeatedly to produce a meaningful note, check your technique. Needless to say, keep external noise at a minimum so you can detect changes in percussion notes. Remove all of your jewelry, too—such as rings, bracelets, or a loosely fitting watch—that might make noise while you're percussing.

The correct percussion sequence

Organize the percussion sequence so you move from more resonant body regions to less resonant ones. (You can perceive a change from resonance to dullness more easily than a change from dullness to resonance.) For example, when percussing to identify the

Percussion: Three Methods

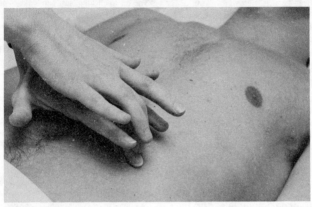

Mediate percussion
To perform mediate percussion, position your hands as the nurse is doing here. Note that her left hand is poised above, not touching, the skin. Remember, after tapping, to withdraw your right hand so you don't damp the vibrations.

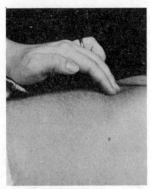

Immediate percussion
To perform immediate percussion, use only one hand, as shown here. Again, remember to keep the rest of your hand poised above, but not touching, the skin.

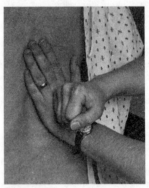

Fist percussion
To perform fist percussion, place the palm of one hand on the patient's back, as the nurse is doing here. Form a fist with the other hand and hit the back of the first hand with it.

lower border of liver dullness, start over the tympanic regions of the abdomen and then move up toward the dull area over the liver. To identify the liver's upper dullness border, begin over the lungs and percuss downward.

Characteristics of percussion sounds

Depending on the density of the organs and overlying tissues in the body region you're percussing, you'll hear percussion notes that have specific characteristics. The different qualities of the sounds are termed *resonance, hyperresonance, tympany, dullness,* and *flatness.* With practice, you'll be able to identify internal structures (such as the liver) and abnormalities (such as a gas-filled bowel from paralytic ileus) by the sounds they produce.

Sounds, of course, are difficult to describe in writing so as to be immediately identifiable when heard. The following guidelines may help you identify percussion sounds:

• *Intensity.* Is the sound loud or soft? You should hear loud tones when percussing over a normal lung and softer tones over the heart and liver.

• *Pitch.* Thinking in terms of a music scale, ask yourself if the note you hear is high or low. Dense structures emit a greater number of vibrations than less-dense structures, and so produce higher-pitched sounds. Normal bowel sounds are high pitched. A normal lung isn't dense, and so has a lower pitch than a consolidated lung.

• *Duration.* How long does the sound last?

Auscultation defined

One of the most difficult physical examination skills to master, auscultation involves listening (with the ear or a stethoscope) to sounds produced in the body—primarily by the lungs, heart, blood vessels, stomach, and intestines. This technique can detect turbulence in the flow of air or fluid, such as that produced by a bruit at the site of an aneurysm. It can also detect almost any other kind of sound that may occur in the body, such as the cracking of a joint.

Although you can perform auscultation directly over a body surface, using only your ear, the preferred method is *indirect* auscultation with an acoustic stethoscope. This instrument conducts sound to the ears (but does *not* amplify it) while blocking out environmental noise.

Proper auscultation technique

Before beginning auscultation, make sure your stethoscope is in working order. Air leaks from a damaged bell or diaphragm, or from cracked eartips or tubing, are common. Don't overlook these leaks. They can let external noise into the stethoscope, decreasing sound volume by as much as 10 to 15 decibels.

Remove all sources of potentially interfer-

ing sounds. Close the door, turn off the television or radio, and ask the patient not to talk. Warm your hands and the stethoscope heads before auscultating, so your patient doesn't shiver—which can produce ralelike sounds. *Make sure the stethoscope is open to the listening end (bell or diaphragm), which is against the patient's body.* Which end you use depends on whether you're assessing high- or low-frequency sounds. Hold the bell or diaphragm firmly, without moving; otherwise, sounds from the movement of intercostal muscles, joints, or skin may occur, possibly mimicking a friction rub.

Most significant body organ sounds are of low intensity. As in percussion, the sounds auscultation produces are classified by frequency, intensity, quality, and duration. Concentrate on one sound at a time, intently and exclusively. Focus on normal sounds first, to make subsequent detection of abnormal sounds easier. Keep such items as clothing, jewelry, and bedsheets from rubbing against the tubing and interfering with the transmission of sound. Sliding your fingers along the tubing or breathing on it may also cause confusing sounds. Be careful when you auscultate a body surface that is covered with hair; moving the bell or diaphragm over hair causes a sound that could be mistaken for rales.

Conduct of the Physical Examination

Examination methods

You need to consider several factors before deciding on the examination method—head to toe or major body systems—you'll use for a patient (see *Guidelines for a Head-to-Toe Physical Examination,* pages 44 to 55, and *Guidelines for a Physical Examination by Major Body Systems,* pages 56 to 58). (Remember, both methods of examination produce equally valid results.)

First, determine whether his condition is life-threatening. Identifying the *priority* problems of a patient suffering from life-threatening illness or injury—for example, severe trauma, heart attack, or gastrointestinal hemorrhage—is essential to preserve his life and function and to prevent compounded damage.

Guidelines for a Head-to-Toe Physical Examination

BODY REGION	HOW TO PROCEED	WHAT TO ASSESS	SAMPLE NORMAL DOCUMENTATION
Entire body	• Identify sex and race.		• White male
	• Observe general physical appearance.	• General state of health; signs of distress	• Follows instructions; is attentive and alert; displays no acute distress.
		• Appearance in relation to chronologic age	• Appears stated age.
		• Facial expression, mood, speech, and memory	• Alert, oriented, interested, and amiable; maintains eye contact; speech easily understood, with clear enunciation; responds appropriately; remote and recent memory intact.
		• Skin color	• Skin color uniform.
		• Body development and nutritional state	• Extremities symmetrical and well proportioned. Skin smooth and turgor normal. Arm span equals height; distance from head to pubis nearly equals distance from pubis to feet. Muscles moderate to well developed. • Hair evenly distributed over scalp, extremities, eyebrows, and eyelashes; hair growth normal for age.
		• Dress and personal hygiene	• Neat, clean, and appropriately dressed.
		• Stature, posture, motor activity, and gait	• Body aligned, with shoulders back and relaxed; arms at sides, feet on floor, body relaxed; movements coordinated, deliberate, and smooth. Can sit and stand with smooth, even motion. Can sit motionless for brief time. Gait is even, steady, and smooth; arms swing at sides. When patient turns, his body follows his face and head. Easily performs heel strike midstance, push off and swing phases.

(continued)

Guidelines for a Head-to-Toe Physical Examination (continued)

BODY REGION	HOW TO PROCEED	WHAT TO ASSESS	SAMPLE NORMAL DOCUMENTATION
Entire body (continued)	• Assess vital signs.	• Temperature (oral, rectal, or axillary)	• Oral temperature is 98.6° F. (37° C.).
		• Pulse rate	• Pulse 84/minute, strong and regular.
		• Respiratory rate	• Respiratory rate 18/minute
		• Blood pressure in both arms	• Blood pressure when standing: right—126/72/64, left—122/74/68; when lying down: right—116/68/62, left—114/64/60
	• Measure height and weight.		• Weight 126 lb (56.7 kg) unclothed; height 5′5″ (165 cm).
	• Identify equipment being used for hospitalized patient (for example, I.V. line, nasogastric tube, chest tube, oxygen, ventilator, and urinary drainage tubes).		• I.V. infusing well at 30 gtts/minute; nasogastric tube draining thick, brown liquid; O$_2$ via cannula at 2 liters/minute.
Upper extremities	• Identify presence of cast, contractures, or traction.		• No cast, contracture, or traction noted.
	• Inspect hands and arms.	• Muscle mass and skeletal configuration	• Muscle mass and development normal for age; no deformities noted. Arms and hands symmetrical.
		• Skin color and lesions (if any)	• Normal coloring; smooth skin, no lesions or swelling
		• Nail color and condition	• Nail beds pink and clean; nail bases firm on palpation; uniform thickness; nail edges smooth and rounded; normal dorsal curvature.
	• Palpate hands and arms.	• Skin temperature, texture, and turgor	• Warm to touch; smooth and even texture; skin moves easily and immediately returns to place on release.

(continued)

Guidelines for a Head-to-Toe Physical Examination (continued)

BODY REGION	HOW TO PROCEED	WHAT TO ASSESS	SAMPLE NORMAL DOCUMENTATION
Upper extremities (continued)		• Joint swelling, stiffness, boggyness, or bony enlargement	• No swelling or enlargements noted; smooth and even movement with no apparent discomfort.
		• Radial and brachial pulses, noting rate, quality, equality	• Radial and brachial pulses easily palpable; rate 80/minute, strong and regular.
	• Assess motor strength of small and large muscle groups.		• Muscle groups tested were strong and equal bilaterally.
	• Assess range of motion of patient's elbow, wrist, and metacarpal joints.		• Full range of motion in elbows, wrist, and metacarpals; smooth movement, equal bilaterally, with no pain or tenderness.
	• Assess neural reflexes.	• Decreased or hyperactive reflex	• Reflexes normal (2+)
	• Assess sensory response.		• Light touch, pain, and vibration to upper extremities normal and symmetrical.
Head	• Measure level of consciousness (using Glasgow coma scale or other appropriate test).	• Eye response	• Normal consciousness; scores 14 on Glasgow coma scale.
		• Verbal response	
		• Motor response	
	• Examine scalp and face.	• Symmetry, size, and contour of skull	• Rounded, symmetrical appearance; skull size falls within normal limits.
		• Facial skin color, lesions, periorbital	• Normal pigmentation; no periorbital edema, masses, abnormal movements, or abnormal hair growth noted.

(continued)

Guidelines for a Head-to-Toe Physical Examination (continued)

BODY REGION	HOW TO PROCEED	WHAT TO ASSESS	SAMPLE NORMAL DOCUMENTATION
Head (continued)		edema, masses, abnormal movements, or abnormal hair growth (in females)	
		• Hair color, quantity, distribution, and texture	• Hair is brown, thick, shiny, and smooth; evenly distributed over scalp.
		• Scaliness, lumps, lesions, or parasites on scalp	• Smooth scalp; no lumps, lesions, or parasites.
	• Assess facial sensory response.		• Light touch, pain, and vibration to face normal and symmetrical.
	• Examine eyes.	• Pupillary reaction	• Pupils equal, round, react to light and accommodation (PERRLA).
		• Conjugate gaze	
		• Redness or jaundice	• Sclera is white; bulbar conjunctiva clear, with some tiny, red vessels; palpebral conjunctiva pink, with no discharge, jaundice, or redness.
		• Visual acuity, visual field (blurring, diplopia, field cuts, photophobia, or decreased vision)—R/L glasses, R/L contact lenses	• Focuses on objects. Visual fields full. Can read newspaper smoothly and without hesitation at 18″. R/L vision measures 20/20 using Snellen chart.
	• Examine ears.	• Size, shape, and presence of any deformities, lumps, or skin lesions	• Symmetrical; size and shape normal; skin smooth; free of deformities, lumps, nodules, and lesions.
		• Drainage or pain on manipulation; objective tinnitus	• Cerumen present; no drainage or discomfort with manipulation.

(continued)

Guidelines for a Head-to-Toe Physical Examination *(continued)*

BODY REGION	HOW TO PROCEED	WHAT TO ASSESS	SAMPLE NORMAL DOCUMENTATION
Head *(continued)*		● Decreased hearing; R/L deafness; R/L hearing aid	● Hearing equal bilaterally. Hears whisper 1' to 2' from ear; hears watch ticking 1" to 2" from ear. Rinne and Weber tests normal, AC 2x > BC.
		● Balance and equilibrium	● Normal results for Romberg test—sways but can maintain position.
	● Examine nose.	● Deformity, symmetry, and inflammation	● Nostrils are symmetrical, dry, and patent.
		● Drainage or epistasis	● Normally red nasal mucosa, with no drainage.
		● Sneezing or obstruction	● No evidence of swelling or other obstruction. Air exchange through nostrils is free and noiseless.
	● Examine lips.	● Color and moisture	● Lips are pink, smooth, and moist.
		● Lumps, ulcers, and cracking	● Symmetrical at rest and when moving; slight vertical, linear markings; otherwise, no cracking, ulcers, or lumps noted.
	● Examine oral cavity.	● Movement, color, and smoothness of tongue and papillae	● Tongue pink, with papillae; moves strongly and symmetrically.
		● Color and pigmentation of buccal mucosa; presence of ulcers and nodules	● Pale pink-to-pink pigmentation; smooth surface; no ulcers or nodules; clear saliva covers the surface.
		● Inflamed, swollen, bleeding, retracted, or discolored gums	● Pink and slightly stippled, with defined, tight margins at teeth; no swelling or inflammation; no bleeding when slight pressure applied.
		● Position, shape, and sturdiness of teeth; presence of caries; missing teeth	● Teeth present: 32. Upper incisors override lower teeth. Top back teeth rest directly on lower teeth. Dental work evident. No caries noted. Little movement on manipulation.

(continued)

Guidelines for a Head-to-Toe Physical Examination (continued)

BODY REGION	HOW TO PROCEED	WHAT TO ASSESS	SAMPLE NORMAL DOCUMENTATION
Head (continued)		• Color and shape of hard and soft palates	• Hard palate pale and stationary; soft palate pink, movable, and smooth, with symmetrical elevation.
		• White areas, nodules, or ulcerations in U-shaped area under tongue	• U-shaped area under tongue is pink and smooth, with large veins. Frenulum and submaxillary duct opening are present.
	• Test reflexes.	• Gag reflex	• Gag occurs with stimulation of posterior of tongue and pharynx.
		• Swallowing reflex	• Water swallowed without difficulty.
		• Corneal reflex	• Blinks bilaterally when cornea is touched.
Neck	• Inspect neck.	• Asymmetry, abnormal pulsations, enlarged thyroid or lymph glands	• Head centered on neck. Trapezius and sternocleidomastoid muscles symmetrical. Thyroid gland not palpable. No palpable masses or nodes present.
		• Involuntary movements of head and neck	• Controlled, smooth movements; no involuntary movements noted.
	• Test range of motion.		• Full range of motion possible with no discomfort or limitations.
	• Palpate lymph nodes.		• Lymph nodes not palpable.
	• Gently palpate carotid arteries (one at a time).	• Rate, quality, and equality of pulses	• Carotid pulses symmetrical, 70 beats/minute, strong and regular.
		• Thrills	• No thrills noted.
	• Palpate trachea.	• Deviation	• Trachea midline.
	• Auscultate carotid arteries.	• Bruits	• No bruits noted.

(continued)

Guidelines for a Head-to-Toe Physical Examination *(continued)*

BODY REGION	HOW TO PROCEED	WHAT TO ASSESS	SAMPLE NORMAL DOCUMENTATION
Neck *(continued)*		• Referred cardiac murmurs	• No murmurs noted.
	• Auscultate thyroid gland.	• Bruits	• No bruits noted.
Posterior thorax	• Inspect and palpate musculoskeletal structure of back.	• Skin color and thoracic configuration	• Skin color normal; no lesions, masses, or tenderness; thorax symmetrical, without deformities. Anteroposterior diameter normal.
		• Tenderness of vertebral spine	
		• Tenderness of costovertebral areas	
	• Palpate, percuss, and auscultate posterior and lateral lung fields.	• Thoracic expansion, tactile fremitus, and crepitus	• Respiratory excursion symmetrical; tactile fremitus bilaterally equal; lung fields resonant throughout on percussion.
		• Diaphragmatic excursion	• Normal vesicular breath sounds in bilateral peripheral lung fields. No adventitious sounds.
		• Presence of normal and adventitious lung sounds	
Anterior thorax	• Inspect and palpate musculoskeletal structure of anterior chest.	• Skin color and thoracic configuration	• Skin color normal; thorax symmetrical, without deformities.
		• Tenderness of costovertebral areas	• No tenderness of costovertebral areas noted on palpation.
	• Inspect, palpate, percuss, and auscultate anterior lung fields.	• Rate, rhythm, depth of respirations, and breathing patterns	• Respiratory rate 16 to 20 beats/minute; regular rhythm and depth
		• Tactile fremi-	• Fremitus normal; felt most intensely at

(continued)

Guidelines for a Head-to-Toe Physical Examination (continued)

BODY REGION	HOW TO PROCEED	WHAT TO ASSESS	SAMPLE NORMAL DOCUMENTATION
Anterior thorax (continued)		tus, crepitus, and thoracic expansion	second intercostal space at sternal border, near area of bronchial bifurcation. No crepitus noted; thoracic expansion symmetrical. Lung fields resonant throughout; flat sounds heard over sternum; tympany over stomach. Normal vesicular breath sounds over anterior lung field. Normal bronchial breath sounds heard over large bronchioles.
	• Inspect and palpate breasts (in females).	• Size, shape, symmetry, and position	• Breasts within normal size limits. R breast slightly larger than L breast, otherwise, symmetrical. Both are firm.
		• Localized redness, inflammation, skin retraction, and dimpling	• Even skin coloring throughout; no redness, skin retractions, or dimpling noted.
		• In nipples, pigment change, erosion, crusting, scaling, discharge, edema, and inversion	• Areolar area is round; area bilaterally similar. Nipples erect and equal in size and shape; color even and skin smooth; no crusting, scaling, discharge, or edema.
		• Nipple secretion	• No nipple discharge on palpation.
		• In axillary and supraclavicular regions, retractions, bulging, discoloration, rashes, and edema	• Skin is smooth, with no bulging or retractions. Normal skin color; no sign of rash. On palpation, tissue is smooth, elastic, nontender, with no masses. Lymph nodes not palpable.
	• Inspect and palpate precordium.	• Precordial heave or lift and jugular vein distention	• Chest is symmetrical; respiratory movements even, with no lift or heaves. With patient elevated 45°, jugular veins are partially filled. Jugular venous pulsations are biphasic.
		• Apical impulse, sternal lift, and thrills	• Apical impulse located at fifth left intercostal space medial to midclavicular line. No abnormal pulsations palpated.
	• Auscultate precordium.	• Auscultatory areas—aortic,	• Rate strong and regular, 78 to 84/ minute. S_1 louder than S_2 at the apex.

(continued)

Guidelines for a Head-to-Toe Physical Examination *(continued)*

BODY REGION	HOW TO PROCEED	WHAT TO ASSESS	SAMPLE NORMAL DOCUMENTATION
Anterior thorax *(continued)*		pulmonic, tri-cuspid, and mitral. • Abnormal intensity or splitting of S_1 and S_2, presence of S_3 or S_4, presence of murmurs • Presence of physiologic splitting of S_2 at pulmonic area	S_2 louder than S_1 at the base. Normal physiologic splitting of S_2 on inspiration heard at pulmonic area. No S_3 or S_4 sounds heard. No murmurs heard.
Abdomen	• Inspect abdomen.	• Color, lesions, surgical scars, rashes, striae, hair distribution, and dilated vessels	• Abdominal skin is smooth and soft, with normal coloring. No surgical scars, rashes, or dilated vessels. Small amount of white hair distributed over abdomen.
		• Color of umbilicus, contour, herniation, and drainage	• Umbilicus is centrally located and sunken. Skin is smooth, with normal coloring. No herniation or drainage noted.
		• Abdominal contour: flat, scaphoid, rounded, distended, or protuberant; and symmetrical	• Contour is flat and symmetrical.
		• Abdominal movements caused by peristalsis or arterial pulsation	• Peristaltic movement and arterial pulsation *not* visible.
	• Auscultate abdomen.	• Bowel sounds in each abdominal quadrant	• High-pitched, irregular bowel sounds, occurring 5 to 10/minute.
		• Presence of vascular bruits or murmurs	• No bruits or murmurs heard.

(continued)

Guidelines for a Head-to-Toe Physical Examination (continued)

BODY REGION	HOW TO PROCEED	WHAT TO ASSESS	SAMPLE NORMAL DOCUMENTATION
Abdomen (continued)	• Percuss abdomen.	• Presence of solids, fluids, or gas	• Generalized tympany throughout abdomen.
	• Palpate abdominal quadrants.	• Softness, firmness, or tenderness; skin temperature; masses	• Abdomen feels smooth, soft, and warm. Muscle tension uniform throughout. No tenderness or masses. Liver and spleen not palpable. Kidneys palpable with deep palpation; contour smooth and firm, with no tenderness.
		• Assess skin turgor.	• Skin turgor normal.
Genitalia and area nodes	• Inspect and palpate male genitalia.	• Size of penis, urethral opening, and scrotum; lesions, edema, or swelling	• Urethral opening centrally located at distal tip of penis. No lesions, edema, or swelling.
		• Scrotal masses or tumors	• Scrotum hairless; rugae present; no tenderness, pitting, or masses.
		• Inguinal hernias and enlarged inguinal nodes	• No inguinal hernias. Inguinal lymph nodes not palpable.
	• Inspect and palpate female genitalia.	• Lesions, varicosities, hernias, tumor masses, edema, or swelling of urethral, vaginal, or rectal openings	• Inguinal and mons pubis skin is smooth, clear, and slightly darker than rest of body. Labia majora are closed and full. Labia minora appear normal in size and color. Clitoris is approximately 0.5 cm wide by 1.5 cm long. Urethral opening is in midline, with slitlike opening. Vaginal opening is thin and slitlike, with no discharge. Rectal opening is normal; skin darker and coarser than surrounding area. No abnormalities noted.
		• Enlarged inguinal nodes	• Inguinal nodes are small, mobile, and nontender. Inguinal areas soft, with no tenderness or discharge.
	• Perform vaginal speculum examination.		• Cervix is pink, approximately 1" (2.5 cm), and pointed in anterior direction. Thin, odorless, clear discharge from cervix. No lesions noted. Vagina appears pink, smooth, and moist, with transverse

(continued)

Guidelines for a Head-to-Toe Physical Examination *(continued)*

BODY REGION	HOW TO PROCEED	WHAT TO ASSESS	SAMPLE NORMAL DOCUMENTATION
Genitalia and area nodes *(continued)*			rugae. No tenderness, inflammation, or lesions.
	● Take smears and cultures.		● Pap test and gonorrheal culture specimens taken.
	● Examine urine.	● Color, concentration, odor, and quantity	● Urine is pale yellow. Specific gravity is 1.018, pH 5.0. Normal odor. Quantity sufficient.
Rectal area	● Inspect anal area.	● Presence of lesions, fissures, hemorrhoids, tenderness; sphincter tone	● Skin clean; no lesions, hemorrhoids, masses noted. Sphincter tone good.
	● Examine stool.	● Color, consistency, and presence of occult blood	● Stool is brown, soft, and well formed. Negative for occult blood.
Lower extremities	● Identify presence of cast, traction, or contractures.		
	● Inspect feet and legs.	● Mass and skeletal configuration	● Muscular development and mass normal for age. No swelling or deformities present. Legs, knees, and feet bilaterally symmetrical.
		● Skin color, lesions, edema, or varicosities	● Skin color is normal; smooth; no lesions, varicosities, or swelling.
		● Pattern of hair distribution	● Light-colored hair distributed over legs and feet in normal pattern.
		● Nail color and condition	● Toenails intact, of uniform thickness, with normal curvature. Nail beds firm on palpation.
	● Palpate legs and feet.	● Skin temperature, texture, and turgor	● Skin is warm and smooth. Turgor is normal. Skin moves easily and returns to place on release.
		● Muscle mass, tenderness, or lumps	● No swelling, masses, or tenderness.

(continued)

Guidelines for a Head-to-Toe Physical Examination *(continued)*

BODY REGION	HOW TO PROCEED	WHAT TO ASSESS	SAMPLE NORMAL DOCUMENTATION
Lower extremities *(continued)*		● Edema	
		● Joint swelling, stiffness, boggyness, tenderness, or bony enlargement	● Joints are normal, with full range of motion. No stiffness, tenderness, or enlargement noted.
		● Femoral, popliteal, posterior tibial, and dorsalis pedis pulse rates, qualities, and equalities	● Pulses palpable, strong, regular, and equal at 78 to 84 beats/minute.
	● Check for calf pain by dorsiflexing foot.		● Negative Homans' sign
	● Assess motor strength of small and large muscle groups.		● Small and large muscle groups strong and equal bilaterally.
	● Assess joint range of motion of ankle, and metatarsal joints.		● Hips, knees, ankles, and metatarsals have complete range of motion. Movement is smooth, strong, and equal bilaterally.
	● Assess neural reflexes.	● Decreased or hyperactive reflex	● Reflexes normal (2 +).
	● Assess sensory response.		● Light touch, pain, and vibration to lower extremities normal and symmetrical.

Guidelines for a Physical Examination by Major Body Systems

GENERAL INFORMATION
- Identify the patient's sex and race.
- Observe overall physical appearance.
Apparent state of health, mental status, and signs of distress
Appearance in relation to chronologic age
Facial expression, mood, and speech
Skin color
Body development and apparent nutritional state
Dress, and personal hygiene
Stature, posture, motor activity, and gait
- Monitor vital signs.
Temperature (oral, rectal, or axillary)
Pulse rate
Respiratory rate
Blood pressure
- Measure height and weight.
- Identify accessory equipment used for hospitalized patient (for example, I.V. line, nasogastric tube, chest tubes, oxygen, ventilator, or cardiac monitor).

SKIN
- Examine facial skin for abnormal color, lesions, periorbital edema, masses, or abnormal hair growth (in females).
- Assess quantity, distribution, texture, and color of hair.
- Inspect scalp for scaliness, lumps, lesions, or parasites.
- Inspect for overall color, texture, and turgor.

EYES
- Test pupillary reaction.
Pupil size
Reaction to light
Consensual movement
- Observe conjugate gaze.
- Inspect for redness, jaundice, or discharge.
- Test for blurring, diplopia, field cuts, photophobia, or decreased vision (R/L blindness, R/L glasses, R/L contact lens).

EARS
- Inspect for size, shape, and any deformities, lumps, or skin lesions.
- Check for drainage, pain on manipulation, and objective tinnitus.
- Test for decreased hearing (R/L deaf, R/L hearing aid).

RESPIRATORY
- Assess rate, rhythm, and depth of respirations, and identify abnormal breathing patterns.
- Look for signs of respiratory distress.
Lips and nail beds, noting color
Fingers, noting any clubbing
- Inspect nasal airway for deformity, asymmetry, or inflammation; drainage or nosebleed; sneezing or obstruction.
- Palpate neck, checking for asymmetry and enlargement.
Lymph nodes (preauricular, posterior auricular, occipital, tonsillar, submaxillary, submental, anterior cervical, supraclavicular, and infraclavicular)
Trachea
Thyroid gland
- Inspect posterior and anterior thorax for configuration and skin integrity.

(continued)

Guidelines for a Physical Examination by Major Body Systems *(continued)*

RESPIRATORY *(continued)*
• Palpate, percuss, and auscultate lung fields, noting tenderness, thoracic expansion, tactile fremitus, crepitus, and diaphragmatic excursion.

CARDIOVASCULAR
• Inspect, palpate, and auscultate thorax.
Precordium, noting any heave or lift
Jugular vein, noting distention
Apical impulse, noting any sternal lift or thrills
Heart sounds, noting rate, rhythm, and any abnormalities.
Auscultate at apical impulse and at mitral, tricuspid, aortic, and pulmonic areas.
• Examine peripheral vascular system.
Carotid vessels
Palpate each carotid artery, noting rate, quality, and equality of pulses, as well as presence of thrills.
Auscultate over carotid arteries for bruits or referred cardiac murmurs.
Arms and hands
Inspect skin color, noting any lesions or swelling.
Inspect nail color and condition, noting any clubbing.
Check skin temperature, texture, and turgor.
Take radial and brachial pulses, noting rate, quality, and equality.
Legs and feet
Inspect skin color, noting lesions, edema, or varicosities.
Note pattern of hair distribution.
Inspect nail color and condition.
Check skin temperature, texture, and turgor.
Check the femoral, popliteal, posterior tibial, and dorsalis pedis pulses, noting rate, quality, and equality.
Test for Homans' sign (possible indication of phlebitis).

GASTROINTESTINAL
• Examine lips for color and moisture, noting lumps, ulcers, and cracking.
• Examine oral cavity.
Tongue and papillae for color and smoothness
Buccal mucosa for color and pigmentation, noting any ulcers or nodules
Gums for condition and color, noting any retraction, bleeding, or inflammation
Teeth for position, shape, and sturdiness, noting any caries
Hard and soft palates for color and shape
U-shaped area under tongue for color and condition, noting any white areas, nodules, or ulcerations
Salivation, noting excessiveness
• Inspect, auscultate, percuss, and palpate abdomen.
Skin for color, color symmetry, hair distribution, and presence of lesions, surgical scars, rashes, striae, and dilated vessels
Umbilicus for color and contour, noting any herniation and drainage
Abdominal contour, noting whether it's flat, scaphoid, rounded, or distended (protuberant)
Abdominal movements caused by respiration, peristalsis, or arterial pulsation
Bowel sounds in each quadrant (beginning in lower left quadrant and working clockwise)
Presence of vascular bruits
Presence of solid, fluid, or gas
Auscultate from thorax down, following right and left midclavicular lines.
Abdomen, noting firmness or tenderness and the presence of any large masses
Stool for color and consistency
Test for occult blood.
Aspirate, if nasogastric tube is in place, for color, odor, consistency, and volume.

(continued)

Guidelines for a Physical Examination by Major Body Systems *(continued)*

URINARY
- Check for urinary drainage tubes (Foley, cystostomy, or urethral catheter).
- Examine urine color, concentration, odor, and quantity.

REPRODUCTIVE
- Inspect and palpate male genitalia.
Penis, urethral opening, and scrotum, noting size, as well as any lesions, edema, or swelling
Scrotal contents for any masses or tumors
External inguinal ring for any hernias or enlarged nodes
- Examine female genitalia.
Urethral, vaginal, and rectal openings, noting any lesions, varicosities, hernias, tumor masses, edema, or swelling
Examine with vaginal speculum. Note color, consistency, and odor of discharge.
Take smears and cultures.
Inguinal nodes, noting enlargement
- Inspect and palpate breasts.
Breasts for size, shape, symmetry, and position, noting any localized redness, inflammation, skin retraction, and dimpling
Nipples, noting any pigment change, erosions, crusting, scaling, discharge, edema, or inversion
Nipple secretion
Axillary and supraclavicular regions, noting retractions, bulging, discoloration, rashes, edema
Breasts and lymph nodes in axillary and supraclavicular regions
Palpate systematically, in clockwise fashion, from nipple to periphery.

NERVOUS
Assess level of consciousness (using Glasgow coma scale or other appropriate tests).
Eye response
Verbal response
Motor response
- Test reflexes.
Gag reflex
Swallowing reflex
Corneal reflex
Neural reflexes
Sensory reflexes

MUSCULOSKELETAL
- Examine head and neck.
Skull for symmetry, size, and contour
Head and neck for involuntary movements
Neck for range of motion
- Examine spine for contour, position, motion, and tenderness.
- Assess peripheral motor function and strength.
Upper extremities
Note contractures, cast, or traction.
Inspect arms and hands for muscle mass and skeletal configuration.
Palpate joints for any swelling, stiffness, tenderness, or bony enlargement.
Assess motor strength of both small and large muscle groups
Test joint range of motion by passively flexing and extending elbow, wrist, and metacarpal joints.
Lower extremities
Note contractures, cast, or traction.
Inspect legs and feet for muscle mass and skeletal configuration.
Palpate joints for any swelling, stiffness, bogginess, tenderness, or bony enlargement.
Assess motor strength of both small and large muscle groups.
Test joint range of motion by passively flexing and extending knee, ankle, and metatarsal joints.

Next, identify the *patient population* to which the patient belongs, and take the common characteristics of that population into account in choosing an examination method. For example, elderly or debilitated patients tire easily; for a patient in either category, you'd select a method that necessitates minimal position changes. Also, you'd probably defer parts of the examination, to avoid tiring your patient.

Try to view your patient as an integrated whole rather than as a collection of parts, regardless of the examination method you use. Remember, the integrity of a body *region* may reflect adequate functioning of many body *systems,* both inside and outside this particular region. For example, the integrity of the chest region may provide important clues about the functioning of the cardiovascular and respiratory systems. Similarly, the integrity of a body *system* may reflect adequate functioning of many body *regions* and of the various systems within these regions.

The chief complaint: Examination guide

You may want to plan your physical examination around your patient's chief complaint, or concern. To do this, begin by examining the body system or region that corresponds to the chief complaint. This allows you to identify priority problems promptly and reassures your patient that his primary reason for seeking health care is receiving proper attention.

Consider the following example. Your patient, Sarah Clemson, is a 65-year-old, well-developed, well-nourished woman who appears younger than her chronologic age. She complains of having difficulty breathing on exertion; she also has a dry, frequent, painful cough. Intermittent chills have persisted for 3 days. You'd record her vital signs: temperature, 103° F. (39.4° C.); pulse rate, 106/minute; respiratory rate, 29 to 30/minute; blood pressure, 128/82.

Because Mrs. Clemson's chief complaints are difficulty breathing, a cough, and chills, your physical examination would first focus on her *respiratory* system. You'd examine the patency of her airway, observe the color of her lips and extremities, and systematically palpate her lung fields for symmetry of expansion, crepitus, increased or decreased fremitus, and areas of tenderness. Then, after auscultating her lung fields for abnormal or adventitious sounds (such as rales, rhonchi, or wheezing), you'd percuss her lung fields for increased or decreased resonance.

Next, you'd examine Mrs. Clemson's *cardiovascular* system, looking for further clues to the cause of her signs and symptoms. You'd inspect her neck veins for distention and her extremities for edema, venous engorgement, and pigmented areas. Then, you'd palpate her chest to see if you could feel the heart's apical impulse at the fifth intercostal space, in the midclavicular line. You'd also palpate for a precordial heave and for valvular thrills. After determining her apical pulse rate, you'd auscultate for any abnormal heart sounds.

At this point in the examination, you would probably be aware of Mrs. Clemson's level of consciousness, motor ability, and ability to use her muscles and joints. You probably wouldn't need to perform a more thorough musculoskeletal and neurologic examination. You would, however, proceed with an examination of her gastrointestinal, genitourinary, and integumentary systems, modifying or shortening the examination sequences depending on your findings and Mrs. Clemson's tolerance. If her signs and symptoms worsened during the examination, you'd interrupt the procedure to report her condition to her doctor. You would then plan to come back and finish the examination after her condition is stabilized.

The examination record

Physical examination findings are crucial to arriving at a diagnosis and, ultimately, to developing a sound care plan. Record your examination results thoroughly, accurately, and clearly. Properly recorded information serves the following purposes:
- It identifies baseline parameters for future comparisons.
- It helps define patient problems through data analysis, synthesis of priority data, and problem identification.
- It communicates patient information to other members of the health-care team.
- It substantiates the adequacy of patient care for legal purposes or before audit committees.

While some examiners don't like to use a printed form to record physical assessment findings, preferring to work with a blank paper, others feel that standardized data collection forms can make recording physical examination results easier. These forms simplify comprehensive data collection and documentation by providing a concise format for outlining and recording pertinent information. They also remind you to include all essential assessment data.

When documenting, describe exactly what you've inspected, palpated, percussed, or auscultated. Don't use general terms, such as *normal, abnormal, good,* or *poor.* Instead, be specific. Include positive and negative findings. Try to document as soon as possible after completing your assessment. Remember that abbreviations aid conciseness.

The diagnostic impression
Throughout the physical examination, you must draw on your knowledge of basic anatomy and physiology, normal ranges for findings in each body region or system that you examine, and the pathophysiology of common disease processes. This knowledge base helps you to analyze the subjective and objective data that you collect, as well as to differentiate between normal and abnormal findings. You use the results of this data analysis to associate various signs and symptoms with particular body systems, and to recognize certain patterns of signs and symptoms as indicative of specific problems.

For example, to continue the case history of Mrs. Clemson, let's assume you identified the following priority data during your analysis of the examination findings:
• Temperature, 103° F. (39.4° C.); pulse rate, 106/minute and regular; respiratory rate, 29 to 30/minute.
• On palpation, left lower lung field reveals increased vocal fremitus; on percussion, dull sounds; and on auscultation, tubular breath sounds with increased intensity, and medium rales over the base.
• Apical impulse is palpable at the fifth intercostal space, midclavicular line.
• No neck vein distention, dependent edema, or abnormal heart sounds are present.

Analysis of these results, in connection with Mrs. Clemson's chief complaints—difficulty breathing on exertion; dry, frequent, painful cough; intermittent chills of 3 days' duration—would lead you to conclude that her ineffective

airway clearance possibly is due to a left lower lobe infiltrate. You'd verify your findings by consulting with Mrs. Clemson's doctor, reading her chart, and reviewing her chest X-ray and laboratory findings. Other than the slight increase in heart rate, which is probably related to her elevated temperature and increased anxiety level, Mrs. Clemson shows no signs or symptoms to indicate that her problem is related to altered cardiac function.

Physical examination practice

General guidelines
Mastering physical examination skills is a challenging task but also a rewarding one, in light of the benefits an accurate and thorough examination can bring a patient. As you build and refine your skills, keep the following guidelines in mind:
• *Choose one body system,* and focus on a specific skill essential to assessing this system until you master it. Select one step in the physical examination—such as auscultating heart sounds, palpating the abdomen, or percussing the lungs—and perfect your skill by practicing this procedure on each patient you assess. Concentrate on improving your technique each time you perform the procedure.
• *Learn to identify normal findings first.* Individual differences in physical examination findings vary greatly. Assess healthy persons repeatedly until you're familiar with the diversity of normal findings. Besides assessing your patients, practice your skills on family members and friends.
• *Once you're familiar with normal findings, move on to study abnormal conditions, using the same disciplined approach.* Perhaps you don't often see patients with disorders related to the assessment technique you're practicing. For example, suppose most patients you work with have normal chest findings, and you want to master auscultation of abnormal heart sounds. One solution: Try to arrange for study time in the hospital's coronary care unit.

Working with one or more colleagues skilled in performing physical examinations can facilitate your learning and make it more interesting. Consider the following suggestions:
• *Work with a preceptor.* Find a professional

associate willing to share her knowledge of physical examination skills. You may even be able to negotiate an exchange of skills so that each of you benefits from the other's expertise.

• *Learn physical examination skills with a friend or colleague.* Choose someone whose skill in performing physical examination is about equal to your own. Plan a regular time when you can perform examinations together. Criticize each other's technique and compare your findings. Then check them against the data recorded on the patient's chart.

• *Read about physical examination skills.* Research the subject of physical assessment in reference books and other texts. Study the material until you can label and interpret your findings accurately. Check your hospital or school library for tape recordings, videotapes, and slide series that may help you validate and interpret your findings.

• *Organize physical examination rounds.* This is particularly helpful if many people in your institution are attempting to master physical examination skills. Each week a different unit could present an assessment of the body system (or systems) of special concern to that unit.

• *Seek help from medical or nursing school faculty.* If you work in a teaching institution, don't hesitate to request instruction—perhaps on a regular basis. Seek out faculty members, in-service personnel, clinical specialists, and supervisors who are skilled in performing physical examinations and capable of validating your examination findings.

Scheduling practice time

Clearly, the physical examination is an integral part of professional practice, but you may feel that it takes too much time from your other responsibilities. Once you've mastered the physical examination skills, however, you'll be able to perform assessments quickly and efficiently. In addition, several procedures can help you find the time to use these skills:

• *Use a questionnaire to collect initial history data.* Take advantage of a patient's *down* time—the time between admission to the hospital and assignment to a nursing unit or service—by asking him to complete a history questionnaire while he's waiting. You can also mail a history form to a patient before admission. (Make sure he is functionally literate.) With the history form already complete, you can devote the time you'd normally spend interviewing the patient on admission to using your physical examination skills.

• *Combine some segments of the history, such as the review of systems, with the physical examination.* A word of caution here: If you use this approach, don't allow the physical examination to take precedence over the health history.

• *Schedule time in your patient's day for a physical examination.* Negotiate with your employer for assistance from support services to free you from nonclinical functions, so you'll have more time to conduct physical examinations. For example, other staff members could help your patients complete their lists of personal articles.

In an acute-care setting, determine the number of patients likely to be admitted during a given time, then negotiate for staggered admission scheduling. For example, one patient could be admitted at noon, another at 1 p.m., a third at 2 p.m.—based on your area's needs and resources. Of course, your request must also consider doctors' needs and those of support groups, including admissions, laboratory, and dietary services.

As you practice and become more comfortable with physical examination skills, you'll find yourself assessing patients in a more confident and composed manner. When you can concentrate on the results of your examination rather than on the skills, when you can clearly label and accurately differentiate normal and abnormal findings, then you'll have mastered the techniques of physical examination.

4

Psychological Assessment

The mental status examination, part of the general survey for physical assessment (see page 31), helps you screen for signs and symptoms of psychological problems, as well as for the patient's emotional needs. If the subjective or objective data from this examination indicate possible emotional difficulties, perform a comprehensive psychological assessment, as described in this chapter.

Psychological assessment consists of the patient's health history, mental status examination (including your observations about his appearance, hygiene habits, coping mechanisms, and ability to relate to others), laboratory data, intelligence tests, and projective personality tests (such as the Rorschach series).

History Data

Biographical data
Keep in mind the following considerations when recording a patient's biographical data:
● *Age.* Organic brain syndrome occurs most often in elderly patients, who also have a high incidence of such psychological disturbances as depression, paranoia, and substance abuse disorders.
● *Sex.* Depression is more common in women but more often leads to suicide in men.
● *Culture.* Cultural values are significant because they determine a patient's concepts of normal and abnormal behavior and influence family relationships.

History of present illness
One or more of the following psychiatric symptoms occur to some degree in nearly every patient with mental illness: anxiety, depression, anger or aggression, difficulties relating to others, thought disturbances (see *Guide to Psychological Disorders,* pages 72 to 77).

Here are some questions you may want to ask about these symptoms to explore fully the history of your patient's present illness:
● *Anxiety. How would you describe this feeling?* A patient usually describes anxiety as a general uneasiness, often associated with such physical symptoms as palpitations or tight neck muscles. He may also describe his anxiety as a feeling of impending doom. *What precipitates this feeling?* The patient may attribute his anxiety to one or more specific causes, or he may be unable to pinpoint the source *(free-floating anxiety).* If it results from an unresolved emotional conflict, it can cause maladaptive responses, such as phobias, obsessions, and conversion reactions (see *Common Defense Mechanisms,* page 63).
● *Depression. Can you describe how you feel?* Depression can range from general unhappiness to complete despair. *Do you often experience periods of depression?* Depression may occur in reaction to a specific event, such as the loss of a loved one *(exogenous or reactive depression),* or it may take the form of a pervasive sadness unrelated to any particular circumstance *(endogenous depression).* Depression also can result from anger turned inward. *Have you ever contemplated suicide?* Carefully assess the potential for suicide in depressed patients (see page 19).
● *Anger or aggression.* Anger that causes the patient to lose control can result from deep-seated anxiety and frustration, as well as from real or imagined threats. Often the angry patient has dependency needs that he

Common Defense Mechanisms

Denial—completely blocking out a painful reality
Displacement—transferring feelings, emotions, or drives to a substitute object or person
Projection—attributing one's own feelings to someone else
Rationalization—using an acceptable, logical reason to explain unacceptable feelings or behavior
Regression—returning (in the mind) to an earlier, safer mode of adapting (developmental stage) in response to severe anxiety
Compensation—covering up inadequate aspects of character by overemphasizing other aspects to maintain self-respect and gain recognition
Conversion—redirecting emotional reactions or anxiety to symbolic somatic complaints
Identification—imitating a person who has the attributes the patient considers admirable
Introjection—internalizing the feelings, values, and attitudes of another person, or using the hostility felt toward others against oneself
Isolation—effectively separating emotions from a painful memory, thought, or experience
Reaction formation—substituting an attitude with its opposite
Sublimation—redirecting unacceptable impulses or energy into socially acceptable, constructive activities
Fantasy—daydreaming as a temporary escape from a painful situation.

refuses to acknowledge. *How do you express your anger?* Showing aggressive behavior (such as shouting at family members or hitting walls or people) may result from the patient's inability to relieve his anger and frustration through acceptable outlets (see page 19).

• **Difficulties relating to others.** *Can you talk about what you're feeling?* Shy, suspicious, and withdrawn patients usually fear (and avoid) close personal relationships. Difficulties relating to others may be the result of unsatisfactory emotional experiences early in life. When you ask such personal questions, remember that a patient with this type of problem may become anxious and refuse to answer.

• **Thought disturbances.** *Do you have trouble thinking? Recently, has it been more difficult to concentrate?* Inability to think logically and to learn abstract concepts may occur in the anxious, depressed, or aggressive patient, as well as in those with physiologic problems.

Past history

Ask your patient if he's ever had serious emotional problems. Also, you'll want to know if he's ever attempted suicide or been hospitalized (or undergone treatment) for psychological disturbances. Dysfunction in any body system can change mental status, so note any of the following:

• **Serious illness.** Life-threatening illnesses, such as heart disease or cancer, may cause severe depression or anxiety and increase suicide potential.

• **Circulatory disorders.** Arteriosclerosis, transient ischemic attack, or cerebral hemorrhage may interfere with the brain's nutrient supply and cause thought disturbances.

• **Tumors and trauma.** These conditions may alter brain tissue structure, causing cognitive dysfunction.

• **Metabolic disorders.** Such conditions as chronic renal disease, hypoglycemia, or vitamin deficiency can cause affective and thought disorders.

• **Medications.** Psychological disturbances may develop after taking certain medications.

• **Food reactions.** Food additives or sugar may produce hyperactivity or even violent behavior.

• **Toxic or infectious agents.** Thought disturbances may result from infection or toxicity. High fever caused by infection, for example, can make a patient delusional or cause him to hallucinate. Digitalis toxicity can cause a patient to become confused.

Family history

Focus your questions concerning family history on the following areas:

• **Psychiatric problems.** *Has anyone in your*

family ever had a psychiatric problem or a stress-related disorder, such as coronary artery disease or peptic ulcers? You're looking for information about the kind of household the person grew up in, its emotional tone, and his parents' coping ability and possibly the way they related to their children. Some mental illnesses are familial; incidence is higher in an individual with a positive family history for the illness or disorder.

● *Personal relationships. Do your family and friends provide you with emotional support?* An unstable family can cause a patient to be withdrawn, depressed, dependent, suspicious, or manipulative.

● *Recent personal loss. Have you recently been separated from someone you love?* Grieving can cause changes in sleeping, eating, and elimination patterns, as well as in libido and activity level.

● *Childhood traumas.* Failure in early social and educational activities may lead to low self-esteem and excessive feelings of guilt. Loss of a parent may predispose a child to depression as an adult. Intense fears early in life can result in unspecified anxiety during adulthood. A history of child abuse can predispose the victim to behave aggressively as an adult.

● *Parent-to-parent aggression.* Observing such behavior can cause a child to behave aggressively later in life.

● *Parental control.* If a parent inhibits a child's efforts to become independent, the child may develop excessively dependent relationships as an adult. Setting inconsistent limits for a child may lead to an inability to understand the needs and rights of others, which may reduce his capacity for intimacy later in life.

● *Family responsibilities. How will your present problems affect the responsibilities of other family members?* (For example, will the wife have to provide for the family, or will the husband have to keep house? Who'll care for the children?) The answers to these questions may indicate the extent to which the patient's mental illness is disrupting the family. Indirectly, you may learn how much support the family will be able to give the patient, how amenable the patient will be to long-term treatment or hospitalization, and how much stress the illness is causing within the family.

Psychosocial history

When you explore your patient's psychosocial history, one or more of the following areas may prove to be related to his present problems:

● *Values.* A conflict between parental and community values, perceived during childhood and later incorporated into the adult self, may interfere with the patient's ability to make decisions and can lead to antisocial behavior.

● *Goals.* Interference in achieving goals can cause anxiety.

● *Stress. How do you deal with stress?* When not managed successfully, stressful events, such as a marital or occupational crisis, can cause anxiety or depression, which the patient may try to relieve with cigarettes, alcohol, or drugs.

● *Life-style.* Frequent changes in life-style may produce anxiety. Social isolation may result in confusion.

● *Environment. Do you consider your home environment comfortable and stable? Have you just moved to a new home (new neighborhood, new town)?*

● *Sexual activity. Are you satisfied with the nature and frequency of your sexual activity? Has it recently changed?* Here you should also note whether the patient calls attention to his or her sexuality—by wearing tight, seductive clothing, for example.

● *Financial concerns. Are you worried about your finances? Will you be able to return to your job after you're discharged from the hospital?*

Activities of daily living

A patient's daily activities are especially pertinent to an accurate psychological assessment, because they can readily reflect underlying emotional problems. Explore the following areas with your patient:

● *Physical activity. How do you relax? Do you often feel fatigued?*

● *Sleeping. Do you have difficulty falling asleep? Do you use medication to help you sleep? How long have you had a problem sleeping?*

● *Appetite. Have your eating patterns changed recently? Have you experienced an unusual weight loss or gain? What are your favorite foods?*

Review of systems

Ask about the following signs and symptoms, which may be related to psychological disorders (psychophysiologic responses):

- **Skin.** Skin disorders may result from prolonged stress. And recent changes in facial appearance can precipitate feelings of worthlessness or guilt.
- **Cardiovascular.** Hypertension may also reflect prolonged stress.
- **Respiratory.** Asthma attacks can be precipitated by stress.
- **Gastrointestinal.** Overeating may be a method of coping with anxiety, anger, or stress. (Heartburn from hydrochloric acid may be another consequence of long-standing stress.) Diarrhea or constipation also may be a symptom of either anxiety or depression.
- **Endocrine.** Recent changes in body size or shape can result in feelings of worthlessness or guilt.
- **Female reproductive.** Dysmenorrhea, amenorrhea, or menorrhagia can be caused by stress, anxiety, or depression.

The mental status examination

Observing your patient

As you collect health history data for a psychological assessment, conduct a mental status examination by observing the following characteristics of your patient: general appearance and behavior, motor activity, affective reactions, thought flow and content, perceptions, orientation and level of consciousness, memory, intelligence and fund of information, and judgment and insight. (For a summary of psychological tests, see *Guide to Psychological Tests*, page 66.)

General appearance and behavior. Note whether your patient is well groomed and cooperative. Are his clothes neat and clean? Is his clothing appropriate to place, age, and weather conditions? If the patient is female, is her makeup applied properly?

Observe the patient's facial expressions, which can be important indicators of emotional status. Look for signs of anxiety, such as sweaty palms and a moist brow. Note whether the patient looks his stated age. Is he standing erect, or slumped over? Does he maintain eye contact? Is he communicative, or withdrawn and evasive? Are his actions flirtatious or exhibitionistic?

Motor activity. Carefully observe your patient's motor activity. Does he pace, or move about restlessly? These can be signs of anxiety. Does he use peculiar gestures, or mannerisms? Are his movements slow, or sudden and jerky? Is he agitated, impulsive, or assaultive? Is he physically handicapped?

Intellectual and emotional status

Affective reactions. Evaluate the appropriateness of your patient's emotional responses. (When assessing a patient's anxiety level, remember that the interview normally causes some tension.) Is he breathing heavily, laughing inappropriately, or wringing his hands? Does he appear sad, angry, or euphoric? Does he vacillate between crying and laughing? Is he unresponsive, or easily moved? Is his affect appropriate to the thoughts he expresses?

Investigate the patient's perception of his affect and mood. Ask questions such as, "How are your spirits?"

Thought flow and content. Assess the patient's speech patterns, the topics he discusses, and the coherence of his thoughts. Is his speech volume normal, soft, or loud—or is he mute? Is his speech slurred? Does he blurt out his answers to your questions? Does he talk excessively, or give short, incomplete answers? Does he repeat your words or phrases (echolalia)? Does he respond to different questions with the same answer (perseveration)?

Is his thought flow extremely slow or rapid? Does he move abruptly from one topic to another (flight of ideas), or are his thoughts logical and relevant? Does he use nonsensical words (neologisms)? Does he stop in midsentence, seemingly unable to recall what he was saying (blocking)?

What does the patient talk about? Does his conversation suggest that he's delusional? (For example, does he think he's God?) Does he express somatic complaints, feelings of hopelessness or worthlessness, or suicidal intent? (See *Suicide Potential*, page 67.)

Perceptions. Evaluate your patient's perceptions to determine if he's hallucinating.

Guide to Psychological Tests

TEST	TYPE	TO ASSESS	AGE-GROUP
Bender Visual-Motor Gestalt Test	Projective visual/motor development	• Personality conflicts • Ego function/structure • Organic brain damage	Ages 5 to adult
Benton Visual Retention Test	Objective performance	• Organic brain damage	Adult
Draw-a-Person (DAP) Test Draw-a-Family (DAF)-House-Tree-Person Test	Projective	• Personality conflicts • Ego functions • Visual/motor coordination • Self-image (DAP) • Intellectual functioning (DAP) • Family perception (DAF)	Ages 2 to adult
Gesell Developmental Schedules	Preschool development	• Cognitive, motor, language, and social development	Ages 1 month to 5 years
Minnesota Multiphasic Personality Inventory (MMPI)	Paper-and-pencil personality inventory	• Personality structure • Diagnostic classification	Adolescent to adult
Rorschach Test	Projective	• Personality conflicts • Ego function/structure • Defensive structure • Thought processes • Affective integration	Ages 3 to adult
Stanford-Binet Test	Intelligence	• Intellectual functioning	Ages 2 to adult
Thematic Apperception Test (TAT) Child's Apperception Test (CAT)	Projective	• Personality conflicts • Defensive structure	Child to adult
Vineland Social Maturity Scale	Social maturity	• Capacity for independent functioning	Birth to adult
Wechsler Adult Intelligence Scale (WAIS)	Intelligence	• Intellectual functioning • Thought processes • Ego functioning	Ages 16 to adult
Wechsler Intelligence Scale for Children (WISC)	Intelligence	• Intellectual functioning • Thought processes • Ego functioning	Ages 5 to 15

Adapted from A. James Morgan and Mary D. Morgan, *Manual of Primary Mental Health Care* (New York: Lippincott/Harper & Row, 1980) with permission of the publisher.

Suicide Potential

MISCONCEPTION	FACT
People who talk about suicide don't commit suicide.	Eight out of ten people who commit suicide have given definite warnings of their intentions. Almost no one commits suicide without first letting others know how he feels.
You can't stop a person who is suicidal. He's fully intent on dying.	Most people who are suicidal can't decide whether to live or die. Neither wish is necessarily stronger.
Once a person is suicidal, he's suicidal forever.	People who want to kill themselves are only suicidal for a limited time. If they're saved from feelings of self-destruction, they often can go on to lead normal lives.
Improvement after severe depression means that the suicidal risk is over.	Most persons commit suicide within about 3 months after the beginning of "improvement," when they have the energy to carry out suicidal intentions. They also can show signs of apparent improvement because their ambivalence is gone—they've made the decision to kill themselves.
If a person has attempted suicide, he won't do it again.	More than 50% of those who commit suicide have previously attempted to do so.

ASSESSING LETHALITY

Age and sex: Incidence of suicide is highest in young persons (ages 15 to 24) and in persons age 50 and over. Men succeed at suicide more often than women.
Plan: Remember these points:
Does the patient have a plan? Is it well thought out?
Is it easy to carry out (and be successful)?
Are the means available? (For example, does the patient have pills collected, or a gun?)
A detailed plan with availability of means carries maximum lethality potential.
Symptoms: What is the patient thinking and feeling?
Is he in control of his behavior? (Being out of control carries higher risk.)
Alcoholics and psychotics are at higher risk.
Depressed people are most at risk at onset and at decline of depression.
Relationships with significant others: Does the patient have any positive supports? Family, friends, therapist? Has he suffered any recent losses? Is he still in contact with people? Is he telling his family he's made his will? Is he giving away prized possessions?
Medical history: People with chronic illnesses are more likely to commit suicide than those with terminal illnesses. Incidence of suicide rises whenever a patient's body image is severely threatened—for example, after surgery or childbirth.

Does he feel safe, or threatened, in his environment? What does he perceive his problem to be? Are his perceptions realistic? Is he experiencing auditory or visual hallucinations? Does he grimace, or smile inappropriately?

Orientation and level of consciousness. Determine if your patient is oriented to time, place, and person. Does he know his name and where he is? Does he know today's date?

Is he alert, confused, or unresponsive? Does he respond to your questions, or touch? Does he respond to noxious stimulation, such as pain?

Memory. Assess your patient's memory by noting his attention span and recall of the immediate, recent, and remote past.
• *Immediate past.* Can he repeat a name or series of numbers immediately after you say it? Can he repeat it 5 minutes later?

• *Recent past.* Does he know why he's in the hospital? If he shows impairment of recent memory, does he try to fill in the gaps with imaginary details (confabulation)? Does he make up obviously false stories?

• *Remote past.* Can he name the town in which he grew up? Ask him to give a chronologic account of his life, with important dates.

Intelligence and fund of information. In assessing a patient's intelligence, consider his ability to comprehend and evaluate information and to think abstractly. Does he understand your questions and simple information? Can he do simple calculations?

Does he understand abstract concepts, or is his thinking strictly literal (concrete thinking)? For instance, ask him to explain "People who live in glass houses shouldn't throw stones." Does he interpret it correctly, or does he discuss it literally? Be careful not to overinterpret his answer. Keep in mind the patient's socioeconomic status and formal education level, which will influence his ability to think abstractly.

Test his fund of general information on such subjects as important current events and geography, making sure your questions are appropriate for his education and experience. Common questions you may use for most patients include: *What do we celebrate on the Fourth of July? Can you name the last four Presidents?*

Judgment and insight. A patient's judgment involves his ability to form a reasonable opinion by analyzing a situation or idea. For example, ask him what he would do if he saw a fire start in a crowded movie theater. Then test his insight (his ability to perceive cause-effect relationships, especially those concerning his own problems). Does he know he has problems, or that he's ill? Does he know what to do about his problems? Does he understand why he behaves the way he does?

Possible organic disorders

Thorough physical and neurologic examinations are required to substantiate findings that suggest a mental disorder (see Chapter 3, THE PHYSICAL EXAMINATION, and Chapter 15, NERVOUS SYSTEM).

To rule out such organic causes of psychological symptoms as tumors or temporal lobe epilepsy, the doctor may order a skull X-ray or special diagnostic tests, such as electroencephalography or computerized axial tomography (CT scan). Laboratory tests may detect such conditions as electrolyte imbalance, thyroid abnormalities, and the presence of excessive levels of alcohol in the blood.

Pediatric assessment

Normal behavioral variations

To assess a child's psychological status, you need to recognize normal variations in behavior that can occur during childhood.

Parents sometimes mistake normal psychological variations in their child for serious behavioral problems. This can have unfortunate repercussions for the child later in life. For example, a small child's appetite may diminish from time to time; this is perfectly normal. However, if the concerned parent force-feeds the child, real psychological problems may develop later.

Of course, parents should consider the possibility that unusual behavior in their child *is* a sign of serious emotional problems. For example, the child who doesn't regain his appetite may show signs of depression. In the case of such a child, psychological assessment would be advisable.

The anxious child

When taking a pediatric health history for a psychological assessment, examine both the parents' *and* the child's perceptions. A child's responses—or lack of response—may be revealing. For example, if the child refuses to give answers to questions, he may be feeling extreme anxiety. This could be caused by a lack of trust, inability to relate to others, or fear of being punished. To help him deal with this anxiety, phrase your questions so they convey empathy and understanding, yet still define the problem. You might say, "Your parents have brought you here because they're worried about you. It sounds like there may be a problem. What's going on?" You may be able to put an anxious young child at ease by relating a story about other children in similar circumstances. You might begin with, "Sometimes when children are unhappy, they...." As the child becomes involved in the story, ask him specific questions about his particular situation. (See pages 19 and 20.)

The parent-child relationship

While you're assessing the psychological status of a pediatric patient, evaluate the parents' relationship to the child—especially their understanding of his needs and their ability to meet these needs. Observe how they react when the child's upset. Do they try to comfort him? Do they comfort him effectively?

Observe how an infant's parents hold him and respond (verbally and nonverbally) to his body, when dressing him or changing his diaper. Pay careful attention to their responses to the less pleasant aspects of parenting, such as handling stool and vomitus. If they feel positive about their child, they won't be upset about these things.

Observe the parents' reaction to a toddler's normal developmental behavior. How do the parents of a 2-year-old respond to his temper tantrums? Do the parents of a 4-year-old respond appropriately to the child's interruptions and frequent demands for attention?

Also note if the parents show affection for the child and pride in his achievements. Most parents—even those who are having problems with their child—enjoy the positive elements of their relationship with him. If you observe no positive feelings at all, strongly suspect severe disturbance in the parent-child relationship.

Is the parents' behavior consistent with all their children (if the child has siblings)? Inquire about the parents' relationship with them. Ask about their ages, how well they behave, whether they get along well with the patient. What's the parents' biggest problem with the patient, and with his siblings? Parents who treat one or some of their children differently from the others will generally give some indication of this when answering your questions.

The child's mental status

Behavioral problems in a child may result from nutritional deficits, medications, visual or auditory impairments, or sudden changes in the child's home life—such as the mother's return to work or the birth of a sibling. Other problems require further psychological evaluation. You can conduct the same mental status examination that you use for an adult, rewording

the questions according to each child's age and developmental level.

Also, keep in mind that certain behavioral variations considered to be abnormal for an adult are normal for a child. For example, the guilt felt by a 4-year-old who, after wishing his mother ill, learns that she's actually sick is in keeping with his typical belief that his thoughts are responsible for subsequent events.

During the pediatric mental status examination, evaluate the child's fine and gross motor activities, visual perception, hand-eye coordination, right-left discrimination, and symmetry of movement. You might suggest games for the child (hopping on one foot, or finger-thumb movements, for example) that test these abilities. If you note any gross sensorimotor difficulties, perform a complete neurologic assessment (see pages 322 to 337).

Observing the child at play helps you assess his perceptions, concerns, self-concept, and preoccupations. When possible, provide games and toys (such as puppets, drawing material, or throwing games), and give the child time to play freely. Does the child initiate the play spontaneously or need direction? Notice whether he includes you or his parents in the games, or prefers to play alone. An abused child may act out his family situation when playing with dolls.

After the free-play period, suggest more structured activities, such as drawing pictures. Encourage the child to talk as much as he wants. For example, you might say, "Tell me about your drawing" or "What's going on in this picture?" To further assess how he relates to family members, suggest he draw a picture of himself and his family.

During these structured activities, assess the child's concepts of cause and effect, logic, and morality. You might ask him, "What would happen if a child were playing with his mother's vase and accidentally broke it?"

Identify sensitive issues. The child will let you know about these verbally (such as by not wanting to discuss certain issues) or nonverbally (such as by squirming, looking away, or playing with toys to cover his refusal to answer).

To overcome the child's resistance to discussing sensitive issues, you may want to use such communication techniques as fables,

Child Abuse Characteristics

Parent, child, and environment—all generally contribute to child abuse situations. The checklists below detail some observable characteristics of abusive parents and abused children. Of course, the presence of any of these factors doesn't automatically indicate child abuse, but it does suggest that you should investigate further.

Because child abuse occurs more frequently in high-crime areas and crowded urban communities, many people associate it only with poorly educated, socioeconomically disadvantaged families. Don't be blinded by this stereotype—child abuse also occurs in middle- and upper-income families, among seemingly well-adjusted parents and children.

Characteristics the abusive parent may exhibit:
● Lacks knowledge of infant developmental skills
● Has unrealistic expectations of the child's behavior
● Feels intensely anxious about the child's behavior
● Feels guilty and angry about inability to provide for the child
● Feels extremely lonely and isolated
● Relates poorly with spouse and own parents
● Has also been a victim of child abuse
● Believes physical punishment is the best discipline
● Lacks a strong emotional attachment to the child (for example, a mother who hasn't bonded well with her child).

Characteristics the abused child may exhibit:
● Has a history of behavior problems
● Is overactive, demanding, defiant
● Refuses to eat, violates rules, destroys parent's property and the property of others.

wishes, and projective questions. For example, ask the child what he'd wish for if he had three wishes. You may also find that wording your questions in the third person is an effective communication device. "How should a good mother act?" is an easier question for the child to answer than, "How do you feel about your mother?"

These techniques allow the child to tell you what he's feeling without fear of punishment or of betraying his parents. Remember, a child will usually protect his parents regardless of their behavior—even if they abuse him (see *Child Abuse Characteristics*).

Geriatric assessment

The stress of aging

When you assess the psychological status of an elderly patient, remember that he's probably dealing with complex and important changes at a time in his life when his ability to solve problems may be diminishing. If he tends to cope well with stress and views aging as a normal part of life, he should be able to adjust smoothly to the changes aging brings.

Common psychological problems among elderly patients include organic brain syndrome, depression, grieving, substance abuse, adverse drug reactions, paranoia, and anxiety. Of course, these problems aren't limited to elderly persons. Their incidence, however, is much higher in this age-group than in others.

Organic brain syndrome

Organic brain syndrome is the most common form of mental illness in elderly people. It occurs in both an acute form (reversible cerebral dysfunction) and a chronic form (irreversible cerebral cellular destruction). Characteristics of both types include impaired memory (especially recent memory), disorientation, confusion, and poor comprehension.

In the elderly patient, *acute organic brain syndrome* may result from malnutrition, cerebrovascular accident, drugs, alcohol, or head trauma. Restlessness and a fluctuating level of awareness, ranging from mild confusion to stupor, may signal this condition.

The causes of *chronic organic brain syndrome* are unknown. The major signs of this disorder include impaired intellectual functioning, poor attention span, memory loss using confabulation, and varying moods.

Depression in the elderly

Depression is the most common psychogenic problem found in elderly patients. Since the symptoms of depression span a wide range, consider it as a possibility in any elderly patient. Depression may appear as changes in behavior (apathy, self-deprecation, anger, inertia); changes in thought processes (confusion, disorientation, poor judgment), or somatic complaints (appetite loss, constipation, insomnia).

If you observe any of these signs, question your patient in detail about recent losses and find out how he's coping with them. Assess his feelings carefully. Remember that an elderly patient's attitude toward his own aging and death—and toward death and dying in general—will affect his chances for successful treatment of depression.

A common difficulty elderly patients face is adapting to loss, since the grieving process regularly intrudes on their lives. Your patient may have to deal with losing his job, income, friends, family, health, or even his home. These losses and the associated feelings of isolation and loneliness can cause stress that has physiologic and psychological consequences. For example, the loss of a spouse or other loved one can trigger profound sorrow, and resolution may be difficult. Unsuccessful resolution of grief can cause a pathologic grief reaction, which may take the form of physical or mental illness.

Many elderly people today are turning to substance abuse and suicide in response to severe stress. Suspect possible substance abuse or thoughts of suicide if your patient is taking an unusual number or amount of medications, or if you note such signs of alcohol abuse as jaundice and tremor.

Adverse drug reactions

When you assess an elderly patient, consider that his psychological problems may result from undetected adverse drug reactions. The incidence of these reactions increases in older people because they use more drugs and may not take medication in the prescribed manner. Physiologic changes related to the aging process also may alter a patient's reaction to a drug. Such routinely prescribed medications as tranquilizers and barbiturates can cause or increase depression. Other medications, including anticholinergics and diuretics, may cause confusion in elderly patients. Always include a detailed drug history in your psychological assessment.

Paranoia in the elderly

If you detect signs of paranoia during the mental status examination, try to determine whether they are a result of sensory-loss problems (which may be corrected by glasses or a hearing aid), psychological problems, or a realistic fear of attack or robbery.

Signs of possible paranoia include expressions of feeling alone and afraid; unpredictable behavior, affect, and thinking; difficulty relating to others; and feelings of being watched or threatened, especially by family members.

The effects of anxiety

In an elderly patient, the need to adjust to physical, emotional, and socioeconomic changes (such as hospitalization, loneliness, or moving to a new neighborhood) can cause acute anxiety reactions. These changes may raise his anxiety level to the point of temporary confusion and disorientation. Often an elderly person's condition is mislabeled senility or organic brain syndrome, when it should be considered a psychogenic disorder.

Guide to Psychological Disorders

DISORDERS	ANXIETY	DEPRESSION	
Amnesia, fugue states, somnambulism, and multiple personality	• Mild to moderate • Patient exhibits no observable hysterical reactions. • Patient uses repression as primary defense mechanism.	• Usually not observable	
Antisocial personality	• Usually lacking	• Not usually present	
Anxiety disorder (chronic or acute)	• Symptoms function to ward off free-floating anxiety. • Both psychological and physiologic responses occur in anxiety reaction	• May be present	
Bipolar affective disorder (depressive phase)	• Variable	• Severe • Patient may exhibit signs and symptoms of other depressions.	
Bipolar affective disorder (manic phase)	• Severe; manifested by increased activity	• Patient exhibits symptoms of mania to ward off depression • Patient exhibits labile affect (one moment happy, the next moment tearful)	
Borderline personality organization	• Moderate to severe • Patient lacks tolerance to anxiety; uses projection as primary defense mechanism.	• Moderate to severe	

PROBLEMS IN RELATING TO OTHERS	ANGER/AGGRESSION/ HOSTILITY	DISRUPTION IN THOUGHT PROCESS
• Is dependent on others • May act childishly or impulsively • Usually appears quite calm • Suffers amnesia	• Usually not observable	• Displays normal intellectual functioning that's unrelated to amnesia • Remains in contact with reality (aware of behavior but can't stop it)
• Appears superficially charming • Exhibits behavior patterns that cause repeated conflict with society • Acts impulsively and irresponsibly • Feels guilt infrequently • Doesn't learn from experience	• Patient can't tolerate frustration. • Patient may engage in delinquent or violent behavior.	• Lacks insight and uses poor judgment, despite great intelligence • Does not suffer delusions or irrational thoughts
• Remains in contact with reality (aware behavior occurs but can't stop it) • Is dependent on others • Feels impending doom • Doubts self • Displays indecision	• Usually not present	• Shows little or no impairment in intellectual function • Can't concentrate • Shows decreased ability to perceive and communicate as anxiety increases
• Loses interest in activities • Becomes isolated • May exhibit signs and symptoms of other depressions	• Patient hates self; thinks frequently of death and may attempt suicide. • Patient may exhibit signs and symptoms of other depressions.	• Exhibits delusions • Shows decreased thinking ability • May show signs and symptoms of other depressions
• Overinvolved in the activities of others; manipulative • Dresses and uses makeup inappropriately and bizarrely • Lacks normal inhibitions; may become sexually indiscreet and vulgar	• Patient may be angry and irritable, especially when behavior is controlled. • Patient may become violent.	• Rhymes, plays with words • Exhibits pressured speech • Exhibits delusions of grandeur and of persecution • Exhibits flight of ideas
• Acts impulsively and unpredictably • Engages in patterns of intense interpersonal relationships • Displays ongoing impaired social or occupational functioning • Exhibits identity disturbance	• Patient exhibits intense rage (anger/hostility is underlying cause). • Patient engages in self-harming acts (substance abuse; physical self-abuse).	• Uses poor judgment; shows lack of insight • Exhibits impaired intelligence • May exhibit brief episodes of psychosis *(continued)*

Guide to Psychological Disorders *(continued)*

DISORDERS	ANXIETY	DEPRESSION	
Catatonic schizophrenia	• Severe; possibly manifested by rapid pulse rate and darting eyes (suggesting fear) • *In catatonic excitement:* severe; manifested by ceaseless activity	• Severe; manifested by decreased motor activity, a blank look, and waxy flexibility (arms and legs remain in whatever position they're placed • *In catatonic excitement:* patient wards off depression through overactivity, according to some theorists	
Conversion disorder	• Anxiety not observable (la belle indifference)	• Usually not observable	
Depressive disorder (mild–severe but not psychotic)	• Mild, moderate, or severe	• May be mild, moderate, or severe	
Depressive disorder (severe and psychotic)	• Severe, especially in agitated form	• Severe; may or may not have precipitating environmental factors • Worst in early morning • Flat affect • Patient inactive, hopeless; acts helpless	
Disorganized schizophrenia (hebephrenic)	• Severe	• May be present; flat affect	
Drug abuse	• Moderate to severe; uses drugs or alcohol to relieve anxiety	• Moderate to severe	

PROBLEMS IN RELATING TO OTHERS	ANGER/AGGRESSION/ HOSTILITY	DISRUPTION IN THOUGHT PROCESS
• Permits direction of self • Exhibits personality disorganization • Experiences loosening of ego boundaries (confused over depersonalization or gender identity) • Withdraws from reality	• May be present • *In catatonic excitement:* patient thrashes wildly for no apparent reason and with no apparent target	• Exhibits negativism • Experiences delusions • Hallucinates • Imitates speech (echolalia) • Imitates movement (echophaxia) • Connects thoughts illogically (loose associations)
• Converts conflict into an observable symptom (conversion reaction) • Doesn't have voluntary control of symptom (it can't be explained by pathophysiologic mechanism) • Is dependent on others • Derives secondary gain from others' attention	• May be caused by underlying conflict centering around depression	• Shows little or no impairment in intellectual function; usually sees problem but can't stop behavior • Insight into signs and symptoms may create overwhelming anxiety, producing new symptoms. • Memory functions in impressions instead of specifics.
• Is dependent on others • Marginally able to meet commitments	• Mild to severe; turned inward • Patient contemplates and may attempt suicide	• Remains in contact with reality (aware of behavior but can't stop it) • Can't concentrate
• Speaks infrequently when in groups • Has poor self-image • Becomes severely withdrawn	• Patient feels anger toward self but usually doesn't have energy to act on feelings	• Experiences delusions of sinfulness, disease, or impending doom • Suffers from severely impaired judgment
• Regresses to a primitive, childlike state • Exhibits bizarre facial grimaces • Behaves in a silly manner • Exhibits inappropriate affect • Experiences loosening of ego boundaries • Withdraws from reality	• Patient exhibits angry outbursts	• Experiences delusions (bizarre and fragmentary) • Hallucinates • Giggles • Connects thoughts illogically (loose associations) • Exhibits garbled speech
• Can't decrease or stop use; tries without success • Exhibits impaired social and occupational functioning • Becomes involved in repeated legal difficulties	• Directed inward (misuse of substance) and toward others (verbal or physical)	• Exhibits mild-to-severe interference with perceptions and cognitive processes (caused by drugs or alcohol) *(continued)*

Guide to Psychological Disorders *(continued)*

DISORDERS	ANXIETY	DEPRESSION	
Hypochondriasis	• Mild to moderate • Patient displaces anxiety to body organ.	• Patient exhibits affective elements of depression.	
Obsessive compulsive disorder	• Mild to moderate • Signs and symptoms function to ward off intolerable anxiety.	• Patient may experience depression.	
Paranoid schizophrenia	• Severe; reduced through delusions	• May be present	
Phobias	• Anxiety is diffused by being transferred to an environmental object (anxiety changed into fear). • Patient uses displacement as defense mechanism.	• May be present	
Undifferentiated schizophrenia	• May be severe—reduced through delusions	• May be present; manifested by decreased motor activity; flat affect	

PROBLEMS IN RELATING TO OTHERS	ANGER/AGGRESSION/ HOSTILITY	DISRUPTION IN THOUGHT PROCESS
• Is dependent on others • Domineering, yet detached	• Patient is apathetic against aggressiveness.	• Tries to reason away signs and symptoms that may cause increased anxiety and new signs and symptoms • Uses illness to escape responsibilities • Is morbidly preoccupied with personal health
• Exhibits compulsion (repetitious performance of ritualistic acts to control anxiety) • Is obsessed (has thoughts that recur despite attempts to stop them) • Becomes anxious or panicky when acts or thoughts are interrupted • Domineering, yet detached	• Centers around aggressive or sexual thoughts or impulses (unacceptable to society) • Patient exhibits behavior that may have sadistic or masochistic elements. • Patient turns anger inward.	• May feel guilty and inadequate • Intellectualizes rigid thoughts (hampers creativity and alternatives) • May have difficulty concentrating • Has difficulty following directions that interfere with ritualistic activities
• Uses projection and denial pathologically • Acts suspicious • Exhibits inappropriate affect • Experiences loosening of ego boundaries • Withdraws from reality	• Patient may lash out physically or verbally in response to directions of auditory hallucinations	• Experiences systematized delusions (persecutory, grandiose, or somatic) • Connects thoughts illogically (loose associations) • Hallucinates
• Remains in contact with reality (aware behavior occurs but can't stop it) • Is dependent on others • May derive secondary gain from others' attention	• Patient displaces angry feeling to phobia target.	• Exhibits no thought disorder
• May exhibit characteristics of catatonic, paranoid, and disorganized schizophrenia	• Patient may exhibit angry outbursts in response to voices	• Experiences delusions, hallucinations, loose associations

5

Nutritional Assessment

Despite its obvious relationship to health, nutritional status is often evaluated superficially or completely overlooked in patient assessment. Complete nutritional assessment includes taking your patient's nutritional and health history, inspecting for signs of obvious malnutrition, performing anthropometric measurements, and evaluating results of laboratory tests, including those for immunocompetence.

Assessment can also help you differentiate primary malnutrition (insufficient nutrient intake) from malnutrition secondary to conditions that impair digestion, absorption, and utilization of nutrients or to conditions that increase nutrient requirements or excretion (see *Proteins, Vitamins, and Minerals: RDAs for Men*, page 79, and *Proteins, Vitamins, and Minerals: RDAs for Women*, page 80).

History data

Biographical data
Biographical data (especially your patient's age and sex) can help identify special nutritional risk factors. For example, elderly people need the same amounts of proteins, vitamins, and minerals as younger adults, but when their activity decreases, they require fewer calories. Also, iron deficiency anemia is more common in adolescent girls (because of their increased need for iron) than in adolescent boys.

History of present illness
Your patient's problems concerning nutrition will probably involve one or more of the following chief complaints: *weight loss, weight gain, asthenia* (weakness), *gastrointestinal disturbances, skin changes,* and *musculoskel-*

etal impairment (see *Guide to Nutritional Disorders,* pages 92 to 95).

Here are some questions you may want to ask about these complaints to explore fully the history of your patient's present illness:
● **Weight loss** (weight 20% or more below normal for height). *Was the weight loss intentional or unintentional? Has your appetite decreased lately? Have any changes occurred in your sense of taste or sense of smell?* (Obviously, diminished sense of taste makes food less appetizing; loss of sense of smell also affects the ability to taste.) Weight loss can accompany emotional disturbances, such as anxiety or depression, and pathologic disorders, such as cancer, hyperactive thyroid, infectious diseases, diabetes mellitus, chronic gastrointestinal (GI) disease, and renal failure. *Are you able to chew properly and comfortably?*
● **Weight gain** (20% or more above normal for height). *Was the weight gain intentional or unintentional? Has your appetite increased recently?*
● **Asthenia.** *Have you noticed any recent weakness or diminished strength or energy?* Asthenia may result from various nutritional deficiencies or from protein/calorie deficiency. Patients with emotional disorders and chronic illnesses may report asthenia. Further compromising of the patient's nutritional status may occur if his condition impairs his ability to prepare or obtain nutritious meals.
● **GI disturbances.** *Have you experienced loss of appetite, nausea, vomiting, dyspepsia, flatulence, diarrhea, or constipation lately? After eating? How often? Do you have this type of problem after you eat certain foods?*

Some specific physiologic and psychological conditions may produce GI disturbances that

Proteins, Vitamins, and Minerals: RDAs for Men

ELEMENT	AGES 19 TO 22 154 lb (70 kg) 70″ (178 cm)	AGES 23 TO 50 154 lb (70 kg) 70″ (178 cm)	AGE 51 + 154 lb (70 kg) 70″ (178 cm)
The recommended dietary allowances listed here are levels believed to maintain good nutrition in most healthy American men.			
Protein (g)	56	56	56
Vitamin A (mcg RE)	1,000	1,000	1,000
Vitamin D (mcg)	7.5	5	5
Vitamin E (mg or TE)	10	10	10
Vitamin C (mg)	60	60	60
Thiamine (mg)	1.5	1.4	1.2
Riboflavin (mg)	1.7	1.6	1.4
Niacin (mg NE)	19	18	16
Vitamin B_6 (mg)	2.2	2.2	2.2
Folacin (mcg)	400	400	400
Vitamin B_{12} (mcg)	3	3	3
Calcium (mg)	800	800	800
Phosphorus (mg)	800	800	800
Magnesium (mg)	350	350	350
Iron (mg)	10	10	10
Zinc (mg)	15	15	15
Iodine (mcg)	150	150	150

Courtesy National Research Council

lead to nutritional deficiencies. For example, anorexia, nausea, and vomiting in the hypermetabolic patient with cancer can result in decreased intake, leading to cachexia.

• *Skin changes.* Have you noticed any recent skin changes? Be sure to inspect the skin as well.

• *Musculoskeletal impairment.* Have you recently noticed muscle weakness or a change in muscle size? Inquire about other nutritionally related deformities. For example, vitamin D deficiency can result in rickets and other bone deformities.

Past history

When reviewing your patient's past history,

Proteins, Vitamins, and Minerals: RDAs for Women

ELEMENT	AGES 19 TO 22 120 lb (54 kg) 64" (163 cm)	AGES 23 TO 50 120 lb (54 kg) 64" (163 cm)	AGE 51 + 120 lb (54 kg) 64" (163 cm)
The recommended dietary allowances listed here are levels believed to maintain good nutrition in most healthy American women.			
Protein (g)	44	44	44
Vitamin A (mcg RE)	800	800	800
Vitamin D (mcg)	7.5	5	5
Vitamin E (mg or TE)	8	8	8
Vitamin C (mg)	60	60	60
Thiamine (mg)	1.1	1	1
Riboflavin (mg)	1.3	1.2	1.2
Niacin (mg NE)	14	13	13
Vitamin B_6 (mg)	2	2	2
Folacin (mcg)	400	400	400
Vitamin B_{12} (mcg)	3	3	3
Calcium (mg)	800	800	800
Phosphorus (mg)	800	800	800
Magnesium (mg)	300	300	300
Iron (mg)	18	18	18
Zinc (mg)	15	15	15
Iodine (mcg)	150	150	150

Courtesy National Research Council

focus on the following problems:
- **Increased metabolic demand.** This may result from *infection, cancer, trauma, pregnancy, surgery, long bone fractures,* and *major body burns,* as well as *regularly increased activity.*
- **Decreased metabolic requirements.** Examples are *decreased physical activity* and disorders such as *hypothyroidism.*
- **Chewing difficulty.** This may result from *trauma, lack of teeth, malocclusion,* or *improperly fitting dentures.*
- **Difficulty swallowing.** Many conditions may cause this symptom, including *cancer of the esophagus, neurologic impairment* (such as paralysis or Parkinson's disease), *esopha-*

geal stricture, or *radiation therapy* to the head and neck.

• **Increased nutritional loss.** Examples are *diarrhea, draining wounds, abscesses, gastrointestinal (GI) fistulas,* and *dialysis.*

• **Maldigestion or nutrient malabsorption.** These conditions may include *GI disease* (such as Crohn's disease, cancer, or ulcerative ileocolitis) or *GI surgery* (especially gastrectomy followed by dumping syndrome, massive small-bowel resection that results in decreased absorptive surface, or pancreatectomy with resulting pancreatic insufficiency).

• **Decreased nutritional intake.** Prolonged use of *I.V. fluids* or *withholding oral food and fluids* from a hospitalized patient for more than 10 days can severely compromise his nutritional status.

• **Chronic illnesses.** Examples are *cirrhosis, diabetes mellitus, chronic obstructive lung disease,* and *renal disease.*

• **Radiation therapy.** Radiation to any part of your patient's body may cause loss of appetite, nausea, and/or vomiting.

• **Allergy or intolerance.** Allergic reactions or intolerance to foods or drugs may cause your patient to experience symptoms, such as diarrhea, and to change his diet.

• **Medication interference.** Because many drugs adversely affect the bioavailability of nutrients, be sure to take an accurate drug and vitamin history.

• **Excessive alcohol use.** Excessive intake of alcoholic beverages increases magnesium excretion and interferes with utilization of folic acid, thiamine, vitamin B_6, and fats. Severe alcoholism may cause malnutrition, because many alcoholics don't eat properly.

Family history
Your patient's risk of becoming obese increases if *obesity* has affected members of his family. *Diabetes mellitus,* which tends to recur in families, causes disturbances in carbohydrate, protein, and fat metabolism.

Psychosocial history
Your review of the patient's psychosocial history should cover the following areas:

• **Financial status.** Limited income affects nutritional status if the person lacks the money to buy the type and quantity of food he needs. For instance, elderly people on fixed incomes,

faced with rising food prices, often must buy cheap food that doesn't provide sufficient nourishment. The number of family members also determines the amount of money available per person for food.

• **Inadequate housing.** Insufficient cooking or plumbing facilities, especially lack of running water or of proper food storage facilities, affect food quality and thus nutritional status.

• **Cultural background.** Religious preferences may affect food selection and preparation.

• **Living and work arrangements.** A person living alone may not bother to prepare nutritious meals for himself. Eating more than half the total meals away from home can affect nutrition, too. For example, a person with a busy schedule is apt to eat on the run or to skip meals entirely, and thus compromise his nutritional status.

• **Fad dieting.** Fad diets and quick-weight-loss methods are usually unsafe and nutritionally unsound. Besides possibly causing nutrient imbalance or toxicity, such a diet may cause a patient to delay seeking proper treatment for an illness, or terminate prescribed treatment.

• **Psychological conditions.** Both increased and decreased food intake may have a psychological stimulus. For example, in some persons, depression and anxiety cause disinterest in food; others may eat more to allay their anxiety or depression.

Activities of daily living
To review the patient's activities of daily living include these questions:

• **Impaired mobility.** Arthritis may interfere with self-feeding or with your patient's ability to obtain or cook food.

• **Lack of regular exercise.** Decreased energy requirements reduce nutritional requirements accordingly (see *Recommended Caloric Intake for Adults,* page 82).

Typical daily intake and 24-hour recall
You can determine how your patient's eating habits may affect his nutrition by using the 24-hour recall or recording his typical daily intake. When taking the 24-hour recall, ask the patient to describe all of the food and bev-

Recommended Caloric Intake for Adults

SEX	AGE	CALORIC NEEDS (kcal)
Men	19 to 22	2,500-3,000
(average: 154 lb [70 kg];	23 to 50	2,300-3,100
70″	51 to 75	2,000-2,800
[178 cm])	over 75	1,650-2,450
Women	19 to 22	1,700-2,500
(average: 120 lb [54 kg];	23 to 50	1,600-2,400
64″	51 to 75	1,400-2,200
[163 cm])	over 75	1,200-2,000

Here's a list of recommended caloric intake based on sex and age. Caloric need is measured in kcals, or kilocalories, a laboratory value that denotes how much heat is needed to raise the temperature of 1 kg of water 1° centigrade.

Energy needs for young adults are based on light work. Energy needs for older adults decrease in proportion to their presumed general decrease in activity. Pregnant women need an additional 300 kcals per day, and lactating women need an additional 500 kcals per day.

erage he has consumed in the past 24 hours (including amounts), how it was prepared, and when and where he ate it. This method describes the patient's intake only over the past 24 hours; to learn more about his usual eating habits, ask him about his typical daily intake: what food and beverage types he consumes and in what amounts, how the food is usually prepared, and when and where he usually eats. Also assess the degree to which your patient's answers may reflect his desire to please you or to appear affluent enough to eat well.

Food intake records (calorie counts)

Through food intake records, you can determine the protein, calorie, and other nutrient intake of malnourished patients or those at nutritional risk while hospitalized. You can then compare this information with each patient's basic nutritional requirements to assess his ability to maintain adequate nutrition. These records also help determine your patient's need for enteral/parenteral hyperalimentation, or let you monitor intake when weaning a patient from a tube feeding or a parenteral hyperalimentation regimen.

To compile a food intake record for your patient, record the types and amounts of all foods and beverages he consumes in a 24-hour period; calculate the consumed amounts of calories and proteins (and other nutrients, if warranted).

Physical examination

Inspection

Of the four assessment techniques—inspection, percussion, palpation, and auscultation—you'll use inspection most often in nutritional assessment, although its uses are limited. The signs and symptoms of nutritional deficiency (such as weight loss, asthenia, skin changes, musculoskeletal impairment, and gastrointestinal disturbances) are nonspecific for particular deficiencies, because obvious abnormalities appear only in advanced nutritional deficiency states.

Palpation

Although not as important as inspection in assessing nutritional status, palpation can be useful. For example, this technique can help you detect thyroid, parotid, liver, spleen, or other glandular enlargement, which may indicate a nutrition-compromising condition. Thyroid enlargement, for instance, is characteristic of iodine deficiency.

Height

Considering your patient's height together with his weight may give you clues to undernutrition or overeating.

Measure your patient's height yourself when possible by having him remove his shoes and stand on the height scale facing forward, with his back and heels against the bar and his head held erect. Measure and record his height to the nearest ½" (0.5 cm).

Body frame type

A person's body frame type—small, medium, or large—relates directly to his weight. For example, a large-framed patient may weigh more than a patient of the same height with a smaller frame and still be at his ideal weight.

To determine your patient's body frame type, measure his wrist at the smallest circumference distal to the styloid processes of the radius and the ulna. Then measure his height (without shoes), and compare his wrist circumference with his height on a standard chart to estimate body frame type.

Weight

Body weight is the total weight of lean body mass (extracellular fluid, protoplasm, and bone) and fat. When you compare your patient's weight, height, and body frame with standards and find he's above or below standard, investigate further to find out if he's obese or undernourished. Measured daily, your patient's weight reflects changes in hydration status, which can help you assess fluid retention or the effectiveness of diuretic therapy or dialysis.

Weigh your patient yourself, if possible, to obtain an accurate baseline for comparison of ideal body weight, usual weight, and future weight. If you rely on information from the patient, you may fail to identify significant weight changes.

If possible, weigh the patient at the same time each day. Make sure he's wearing lightweight clothing and no shoes. Use a beam or a lever scale, and record his weight to the nearest ½ lb (1.1 kg).

Sometimes a patient being admitted is too ill to be weighed or requires immediate medical care. In such circumstances, record what the patient tells you he weighs (always documented as *stated weight*) until you're able to weigh him. If accurate weight is essential to therapy and the patient can't stand up, weigh him using a bed scale.

You should be aware of the following limitations on the usefulness and validity of standard ideal weight charts:

● Ideal body weight for health maintenance has never been defined, so no such chart is completely authoritative.

● Body frame size, clothing weight, and heel height aren't defined.

● These figures were obtained at the turn of this century and may not represent current U.S. population standards.

The formula to express actual weight versus ideal weight as a percentage is *actual weight/ideal body weight multiplied by 100*. A weight-to-height ratio of about 80% or less usually indicates a significant deficit of protein and calorie reserves; a ratio of about 120% or more indicates obesity. Interpret these values carefully; edema may mask protein-calorie depletion or obesity.

Although weight loss can indicate loss of body cell mass or fluid, if your patient has experienced a recent unintentional loss of about 10% or more of his preillness weight, this usually indicates a decrease in body cell mass corresponding to a loss of protein or calorie reserves. A more useful measurement of nutritional status is the percentage of weight loss: *usual weight minus actual weight/usual weight, the result multiplied by 100*. For example, a patient who weighs 155 lb (70.3 kg) on admission may appear to be at an ideal weight for his height, but comparison with his usual weight of 200 lb (90.7 kg) indicates that he's lost about 22.5% of his body cell mass.

Triceps skinfold thickness

Measuring your patient's triceps skinfold (TSF) thickness with calipers helps you evaluate his subcutaneous fat stores, the main form in which energy is stored in the body. Although most widely used in assessing obesity, skinfold thickness measurements have recently proved helpful in assessing fat stores in undernourished hospitalized patients. The triceps area is most accessible for measurement (see *Common Arm Measurements,* page 84).

You can compare the TSF thickness measurement with standard measurements (adult standards for TSF thickness are 16.5 mm for

Common Arm Measurements

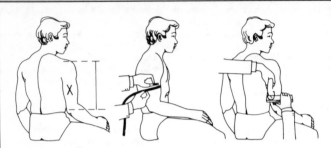

1 To take arm measurements, first locate the midpoint on your patient's upper arm using a nonstretch tape measure. Mark the midpoint with a felt-tip pen.
2 Then, measuring at the midpoint, use the tape measure to determine the patient's midarm circumference.
3 Next, determine the triceps skinfold thickness by grasping the patient's skin with your thumb and forefinger approximately 1 cm above the midpoint. Place the calipers at the midpoint and squeeze the calipers for about 3 seconds. Record the measurement registered on the handle gauge to the nearest 0.5 mm. Take two more readings, and average all three to compensate for any measurement error. Finally, calculate the midarm muscle circumference by multiplying the triceps skinfold thickness (in centimeters) by 3.143 and subtracting this figure from the midarm circumference.

women and 12.5 mm for men) and express them as a percentage of standard: *actual measurement/standard measurement multiplied by 100.* You can also compare these measurements with standards for obesity, which provide the minimum TSF measurement of obesity for males and females by age (see *Interpreting Obesity,* page 86).

Interpret these measurements cautiously; a measurement may indicate overabundant subcutaneous fat stores, but the fat may not be readily available as an energy source. (Metabolic aberrations secondary to stress, such as trauma and sepsis, may limit the availability of adipose stores for energy use.) Although skinfold thickness and midarm muscle circumference (another assessment technique) are important tools in assessment, they have the following limitations:

● Measurements assume that humeral size is the same for everybody.
● Measurements assume that bodily distribution of adipose and skeletal protein stores doesn't vary from one person to another.
● Edema may interfere with measuring skel-

etal protein (muscle mass) and adipose tissues.
● Measurements may not reflect acute body changes for approximately 3 to 4 weeks after those changes take place.

Subscapular skinfold thickness

This measurement, which is more reliable but less accessible than the measurement of triceps skinfold (TSF) thickness, also evaluates subcutaneous fat stores.

To measure your patient's subscapular skinfold thickness, position him so that he's sitting up or lying prone, with his arms and shoulders relaxed. With your thumb and forefinger, grasp the skinfold just below the angle of the right scapula, in line with the natural cleavage of the skin. (Note that the exact location of the measurement for subscapular skinfold thickness isn't as important as it is for a triceps measurement, since subcutaneous fat is evenly distributed in the subscapular area.) Apply the calipers and proceed as you would when you measure for TSF thickness.

Compare the subscapular skinfold thickness measurement directly with a chart, and express it as a percentage of standard according to the same formula used for TSF thickness measurement—and with the same limitations in mind.

Midarm circumference

Midarm circumference—also called *mid–upper-arm circumference*—reflects skeletal muscle and adipose tissue amounts and therefore helps indicate the extent of your patient's protein and calorie reserves. However, it doesn't differentiate the amount of muscle from the amount of fat present. (See *Common Arm Measurements,* page 84.)

Compare the actual measurement with a standard (see *Normal Arm Measurement Values*). You may also express the actual measurements as a percentage of standard: *actual measurement/standard measurement multiplied by 100.* Normal adult measurements are 29.3 cm for men and 28.5 cm for women. A measurement less than 90% of standard indicates caloric deprivation; if the measurement is greater than 90% of the standard, your patient has adequate or more than adequate muscle and fat.

Midarm muscle circumference

Midarm muscle circumference, also called *mid–upper-arm muscle circumference,* reflects the body's skeletal protein (muscle mass) reserves. Determine your patient's midarm muscle circumference by multiplying the triceps skinfold thickness (in centimeters) by 3.1413, then subtracting the resulting figure from the midarm circumference (in centimeters). Then, compare the midarm muscle circumference with a standard as both an actual measurement and as a percentage of standard: *actual measurement/standard measurement multiplied by 100.* Normal adult measurements are 25.3 cm for men and 23.2 cm for women. A measurement less than 90% of standard indicates protein depletion; a measurement greater than 90% indicates adequate or more than adequate protein reserves. Remember: Findings don't always correspond to actual protein stores available for use. Interpret findings cautiously.

Pediatric assessment

Children's nutrition

A child who deviates from expected growth rates and patterns requires further assessment. Assessment enables you to define nutritional problems, identify possible causes, and, possibly, obtain early intervention. Perform a

---

Normal Arm Measurement Values

When you measure your patient's triceps skinfold thickness, midarm circumference, and midarm muscle circumference, record them as percentages of the standard measurements listed here. Use this formula: actual measurement/standard measurement multiplied by 100. A measurement that's less than 90% of the standard indicates caloric deprivation; a measurement over 90% indicates adequate or more than adequate energy reserves.

TEST	STANDARD		PERCENTILE OF POPULATION			
			90%	80%	70%	60%
Triceps skinfold	Men	12.5 mm	11.3	10.0	8.8	7.5
	Women	16.5 mm	11.9	13.2	11.6	9.9
Midarm circumference	Men	29.3 cm	26.3	23.4	20.5	17.6
	Women	28.5 cm	25.7	22.8	20.0	17.1
Midarm muscle circumference	Men	25.3 cm	22.8	20.2	17.7	15.2
	Women	23.2 cm	20.9	18.6	16.2	13.9

Reprinted from G. Blackburn et al., *Manual for Nutritional/Metabolic Assessment* (Chicago: American College of Surgeons, 1976). Used with permission.

Interpreting Obesity

TRICEPS SKINFOLD MEASUREMENTS (MILLIMETERS)

Age	Women	Men
18	27	15
19	27	15
20	28	16
21	28	17
22	28	18
23	28	18
24	28	19
25	29	20
26	29	20
27	29	21
28	29	22
29	29	23
30 +	30	23

Compare your patient's triceps skinfold measurement to this chart. If his skinfold measurement is equal to or greater than the one indicated for his age, consider him clinically obese. *Note:* Use metal calipers, because plastic calipers generally won't have a large enough jaw face to measure an obese patient's skinfold.

complete nutritional assessment on any child at nutritional risk, especially one who's failed to thrive or has undergone surgery, in the same way you would for an adult. Additional techniques for assessing a child include plotting his development on a growth grid and, in infants, measuring head circumference.

The infant. The average full-term neonate weighs 7 lb (3.15 kg), is 20″ (50.8 cm) long, and has a head circumference of 13½″ to 14″ (34 to 36 cm). After birth, the neonate usually loses weight but regains it within 10 days. Most full-term infants double their weight within 5 months after birth and triple it within the first year. During the first year, an infant's length

increases by 10 to 12″ (25 to 30 cm). Head circumference increases about 5″ (13 cm) by the end of the first year. Keep nutritional guidelines in mind in your assessment, which should include the type of nourishment the infant is receiving.

The toddler. To adequately assess a toddler's nutrition, you should be familiar with normal growth and development changes in the first 3 years of life. Don't confuse normal changes with nutritional problems. For example, during a child's second year, his growth rate slows. Decreased appetite, which often begins about age 10 months, continues into the second year and results in decreased subcutaneous fat, giving the child a thinner, more muscular appearance. The second and third years of life are characterized by abdominal protuberance and mild lordosis, apparent when the child stands.

The preschool child. Throughout the preschool period, a child continues to grow and gain weight. By the fourth year, the abdominal protuberance and mild lordosis characteristic of the toddler's development usually disappear. The preschool child, therefore, develops a leaner appearance.

The school-age child. The school-age child's energy requirements, appetite and food intake increase as he grows. Consequently, he has few apparent feeding problems. Feeding problems that do occur may result from inattention to the child's food preferences, activities that interfere with mealtimes, and excessive discipline concerning table manners.

The adolescent. Adolescence is the second major period of rapid growth affecting every body system. This is also a time of major psychosocial and mental growth.

In your assessment of an adolescent's nutrition, look for indications of undernutrition, overeating, need to adjust his food intake to meet changing nutritional requirements, or nutritional problems resulting from the psychosocial pressures of adolescence. For example, adolescents' busy life-style and new independence often produce irregular eating patterns, such as skipping meals and increased snacking.

As a group, 10- to 16-year-olds have the most unsatisfactory nutrition. Common nutritional deficiencies among adolescents involve iron, calcium, and vitamins A and C.

Pediatric diet history

Obtain a child's diet history from the person who feeds him or from the child himself (if he's old enough) or from both. Because many parents may feel threatened by questions about their child's nutrition, explain the purpose of the interview beforehand. Be sure to ask how much milk an *infant* drinks. Is he breast-fed or bottle-fed? Is a bottle left in the crib at night? Does the child take vitamin supplements? Be sure to ascertain the type and dosage. How old was he when he began eating solid foods? Many authorities currently believe that introduction of semisolids before age 4 to 6 months predisposes a child to allergy and obesity. Does the infant have any problems sucking, swallowing, or chewing? Ask how often your pediatric patient eats snack foods and what kinds he likes.

In all pediatric age-groups, special considerations in a dietary history include:
• typical daily nutritional plan, including number and types of meals and snacks (see *Recommended Dietary Allowances for Children and Adolescents,* pages 88 and 89).
• any special or modified diet
• behavioral peculiarities associated with mealtimes or any feeding problems
• stress of illness or trauma, which can rapidly deplete nutrient stores
• sugar intake, because sugar is an *empty-calorie* food related to dental caries and obesity
• iron intake, since iron deficiency anemia is a major childhood problem
• protein intake, since it's essential for growth.

Growth grids

Growth grids allow you to screen for early signs of nutritional deficiencies. Include them in each young patient's chart.

Measure the child's height and weight, and plot your findings on a grid for comparison by age and sex. (Growth grids for children up to age 18, developed by the National Center for Health Statistics, are probably the most accurate source for evaluating these data.) These grids use percentiles rather than ideal weight for height. The 50th percentile represents average growth rates; consider findings below the 5th percentile or above the

95th percentile abnormal. Serial measurements can provide information that one measurement may not. For example, a child usually remains in the same percentile throughout his growth period, so you should consider a large deviation (such as a decrease from the 50th percentile to the 5th percentile) abnormal.

Skinfold thickness in children

Skinfold thickness (usually triceps skinfold thickness) measurements are useful for children older than age 3. Measure and express a child's skinfold thickness as you would an adult's.

Undernutrition

In any child, undernutrition can impair normal growth and development, affect body function, and (without proper intervention) have long-term deleterious effects. Undernutrition during the critical period for rapid brain growth—the prenatal period and the first 9 months of life—may cause permanent retardation. Possible clues that a child is undernourished include listlessness, apathy, pallor, dental caries, and decreased resistance to infection.

Undernutrition resulting from child neglect or abuse may accompany other signs, such as bruises, burns, and welts. The parents may act evasive or provide an implausible or contradictory explanation of the child's condition; this also makes accurate history-taking difficult.

Other factors that may cause, perpetuate, or complicate childhood undernutrition include:
• illnesses that impair digestion, absorption, or utilization of nutrients
• increased demand for nutrients due to growth
• presence of stress—such as from illness, trauma, surgery, or emotional upset.

Childhood obesity

Obesity is a major nutritional problem affecting children in all age-groups, including infancy. Because long-standing childhood obesity is less responsive to therapy than adult obesity, early detection and treatment are imperative. Also, psychological problems are more likely to trouble an obese child than an obese adult. Perhaps most important, child-

Recommended Dietary Allowances for Children and Adolescents (Male)

ELEMENT	AGES 1 TO 3 29 lb (13 kg) 35" (89 cm)	AGES 4 TO 6 44 lb (20 kg) 44" (112 cm)	AGES 11 TO 14 97 lb (44 kg) 63 " (160 cm)	AGES 15 TO 18 134 lb (61 kg) 68" (173 cm)
Kcal	1,300	1,700	2,700	2,800
Protein (g)	23	30	45	56
Vitamin A (mcg RE)	400	500	1,000	1,000
Vitamin A (IU)	2,000	2,500	5,000	5,000
Vitamin D (IU)	400	400	400	400
Vitamin E (mg or TE)	5	6.0	8.0	10
Ascorbic acid (Vitamin C) (mg)	45	45	50	60
Folacin (mcg)	100	200	400	400
Niacin (mg)	9	12	18	18
Riboflavin (B$_2$) (mg)	0.8	1.1	1.5	1.8
Thiamine (B$_1$) (mg)	0.7	0.9	1.4	1.4
Vitamin B$_6$ (mg)	0.9	1.3	1.8	2.0
Vitamin B$_{12}$ (mcg)	2	2.5	3.0	3.0
Calcium (mg)	800	800	1,200	1,200
Phosphorus (mg)	800	800	1,200	1,200
Iodine (mcg)	70	90	150	150
Iron (mg)	15	10	18	18
Magnesium (mg)	150	200	350	400
Zinc (mg)	10	10	15	15

hood obesity may foreshadow adult obesity.

Obesity standards in children are the same as in adults: weight-to-height ratio greater than 120% and triceps skinfold measurement indicating obesity.

Factors that may cause childhood obesity include:

• inactivity, or chronic illnesses that impair mobility

• overfeeding, common in bottle-fed infants and in situations where parents use food as a pacifier or insist that their child clean his plate

• genetic predisposition to obesity, although children may become obese by imitating their obese parents' eating patterns

• metabolic, endocrine, or neurologic abnormalities (rare).

Recommended Dietary Allowances for Children and Adolescents (Female)

ELEMENT	AGES 1 TO 3 29 lb (13 kg) 35" (89 cm)	AGES 7 TO 10 66 lb (30 kg) 54" (137 cm)	AGES 11 TO 14 97 lb (44 kg) 62" (157 cm)	AGES 15 TO 18 119 lb (54 kg) 68" (173 cm)
Kcal	1,300	2,400	2,200	2,100
Protein (g)	23	34	46	46
Vitamin A (mcg RE)	400	700	800	800
Vitamin A (IU)	2,000	3,300	4,000	4,000
Vitamin D (IU)	400	400	400	400
Vitamin E (mg or TE)	5	7.0	8.0	8.0
Ascorbic acid (Vitamin C) (mg)	45	45	50	60
Folacin (mcg)	100	300	400	400
Niacin (mg)	9	16	15	14
Riboflavin (B_2) (mg)	0.8	1.4	1.3	1.4
Thiamine (B_1) (mg)	0.7	1.2	1.1	1.1
Vitamin B_6 (mg)	0.9	1.6	1.8	2.0
Vitamin B_{12} (mcg)	2	3.0	3.0	3.0
Calcium (mg)	800	800	1,200	1,200
Phosphorus (mg)	800	800	1,200	1,200
Iodine (mcg)	70	120	150	150
Iron (mg)	15	10	18	18
Magnesium (mg)	150	250	300	300
Zinc (mg)	10	10	15	15

Iron deficiency anemia

In the United States, iron deficiency anemia is the most common nutritional disorder in young children. This disorder may affect a child's attention span and intellectual performance; if severe, the child may become irritable and lethargic.

Factors that may cause iron deficiency anemia include:

● limited iron reserves (at birth) in premature and low–birth-weight infants

● ingestion of large amounts of milk instead of solid foods (whole milk is a poor source of dietary iron, and the phosphate in milk combines with dietary iron and removes it). Human milk, although low in iron, is absorbed more efficiently.

● high-bulk diet (decreases iron absorption);

inadequate dietary intake of iron
• hemorrhage, or occult blood loss in stools (in some infants, gastrointestinal bleeding may result from protein in homogenized cow's milk; menstrual blood losses in adolescent girls
• increased iron requirements during growth periods, such as infancy and adolescence.

Characteristic clinical features of iron deficiency anemia include dyspnea on exertion, fatigue, listlessness, pallor, inability to concentrate, irritability, headache, and susceptibility to infection. Chronic iron deficiency anemia may cause spoon-shaped brittle nails, smooth tongue, dysphagia, cracked corners of the mouth, neuromuscular effects (such as numbness and tingling of the extremities), neurologic pain, and vasomotor disturbances. Elevated serum transferrin levels occur in severe iron deficiency; hemoglobin levels less than 11 g/100 ml, serum iron less than 70 mcg/dl for men and 80 mcg/dl for women, and hematocrit less than 33% confirm anemia.

Food allergies

Food allergies occur most frequently during early childhood but seldom persist into adulthood. True allergies usually result from production of antibodies to specific antigens; in food allergies, these are particular proteins in ingested food. Food allergies can result nonimmunologically, from enzyme deficiency. Food allergies can produce respiratory, gastrointestinal, and dermatologic signs and symptoms; excessive psychological or physiologic stress may exacerbate the allergic reaction.

Any food may cause an allergic reaction; some of the common reaction-producing foods are milk, eggs, chocolate, fish, shellfish, chicken, pork, beef, and wheat.

Testing for food allergies includes skin testing (with prepared food antigens to reveal IgE antibodies) and provocation and elimination testing (elimination of suspected food from the diet for 7 to 10 days; if signs and symptoms reappear after reintroduction of the food into the patient's diet, the food is confirmed as an allergen). Sometimes clinically irrelevant reactions lead to needless imposition of restricted diets. Misdiagnosis of food allergy may also lead to malnutrition in infants and children—and to anxiety and depression in their parents who may find that providing severely restricted diets is difficult.

Geriatric assessment

Normal aging changes

Aging is characterized by the loss of some body cells, and reduced metabolism in others. These conditions cause loss of bodily function and changes in body composition. Adipose tissue stores usually increase with age; lean body mass and bone mineral contents usually decrease.

A person's protein, vitamin, and mineral requirements usually remain the same as he ages, whereas caloric needs are lessened. Decreased activity may lower energy requirements about 200 calories/day for men and women aged 51 to 75, 400 calories/day for women over age 75, and 500 calories/day for men over age 75.

Other physiologic changes that can affect nutrition in an elderly patient include:
• decreased renal function, causing greater susceptibility to dehydration and formation of renal calculi
• loss of calcium and nitrogen (in patients who aren't ambulatory)
• decreased enzyme activity and gastric secretions
• decreased salivary flow and diminished sense of taste, which may reduce the person's appetite and increase his consumption of sweet and spicy foods
• decreased intestinal motility.

Patient history

Disabilities, chronic diseases, and surgical procedures (for example, gastrectomy) commonly affect an elderly patient's nutritional status, so be sure to record them in your patient history. Drugs or substances taken by your patient for his medical problem may also affect his nutritional requirements; for example, mineral oil, which many elderly persons use to correct constipation, may impair gastrointestinal (GI) absorption of vitamin A.

Some common conditions found in elderly persons, such as degenerative joint disease, paralysis, and impaired vision (from cataracts or glaucoma), can affect nutritional status by limiting the patient's mobility and therefore his ability to obtain and prepare food or feed himself.

GI complaints, especially constipation and stool incontinence, commonly occur in older patients. A decrease in intestinal motility characteristically accompanies aging; constipation may also be related to poor dietary intake, physical inactivity, or emotional stress or may occur as a side effect of certain drugs. Elderly patients often consume nutritionally inadequate diets consisting of soft, refined foods that are low in residue and dietary fiber. Laxative abuse, another common problem in elderly patients, results in the rapid transport of food through the GI tract and subsequent decreased periods of digestion and absorption.

Socioeconomic and psychological factors that affect nutritional status include loneliness, decline of the elderly person's importance in the family, susceptibility to nutritional quackery, and lack of money to purchase nutritionally beneficial foods.

Assessment techniques

Currently, the adult standards for nutritional assessment are used for the elderly, although they're not as reliable for this age-group. Further research is needed to develop tools for assessing the nutritional requirements of elderly persons. Measures you can use to assess such a patient's nutritional status include common sense, consideration of factors that place any patient at nutritional risk, the dietary history, your objective data (keeping their limitations in mind), and monitoring of the patient's intake (if he's hospitalized). Remember, protein-calorie malnutrition is a major nutritional problem in patients over age 75 and contributes significantly to this age-group's mortality.

Guide to Nutritional Disorders

DISORDER	CHIEF COMPLAINT	
Folic acid deficiency	• *Weight change:* Loss common • *Skin changes:* Severe pallor • *Asthenia:* Present • *Gastrointestinal problems:* Diarrhea • *Musculoskeletal impairment:* Absent	
Iodine deficiency	• *Weight change:* None • *Skin changes:* Dry, cold skin in severe stages • *Asthenia:* Present; may occur even in mild deficiency • *Gastrointestinal problems:* Anorexia • *Musculoskeletal impairment:* None	
Iron deficiency	• *Weight change:* None • *Skin changes:* Pallor • *Asthenia:* Present; may be extreme in severe cases • *Gastrointestinal problems:* Anorexia, flatulence, epigastric distress, constipation • *Musculoskeletal impairment:* Numbness, tingling of extremities; neuralgic pain possible	
Marasmus (calorie deficiency)	• *Weight change:* Loss may be profound • *Skin changes:* Dryness • *Asthenia:* Usually present; if severe, can result in profound weakness • *Gastrointestinal problems:* Frequent diarrhea • *Musculoskeletal impairment:* Growth retardation in children; muscular wasting	
Niacin deficiency	• *Weight change:* Loss possible, even in early stages • *Skin changes:* Mild eruptions in early stage, progressing to scaly dermatitis resembling severe sunburn • *Asthenia:* Present; fatigue even in early stages • *Gastrointestinal problems:* Anorexia, indigestion, nausea, vomiting, diarrhea possible • *Musculoskeletal impairment:* Muscle weakness in early stages; growth retardation in children in late-stage deficiency	
Obesity	• *Weight change:* Significant gain over time • *Skin changes:* Thickness, pale striae • *Asthenia:* May be present • *Gastrointestinal problems:* None obviously related • *Musculoskeletal impairment:* Possible joint strain or pain	

HISTORY	PHYSICAL EXAMINATION	DIAGNOSTIC STUDIES
• Inadequate intake of leafy vegetables, organ meats, beef, wheat. Most common in infants, pregnant women, chronic alcoholics, and patients with malabsorption	• Glossitis, cardiac enlargement, macrocytic megaloblastic anemia	• Serum value less than 100 ng/ml
• Insufficient intake (table salt, seafood); increased metabolic demands (growth, pregnancy, lactation) • Poor memory, chills, menorrhagia, amenorrhea	• Hoarseness, hearing loss, thick tongue bradycardia, lowered blood pressure, delayed relaxation phase in deep tendon reflexes	• Low T_4 with high ^{131}I uptake, low 24-hour urine iodine, and high TSH. T_3 or T_4 resin uptake test shows values 25% below normal.
• Inadequate dietary intake of iron as prolonged unsupplemented breast- or bottle-feeding or in periods of stress; iron malabsorption, such as in diarrhea, gastrectomy, celiac disease; blood loss	• In chronic form: nails become brittle spoon-shaped; corners of the mouth crack, tongue becomes smooth; in severe cases: tachycardia, dyspnea on exertion, listlessness, irritability; liver and spleen enlargement possible	• Low hemoglobin, less than 12 g/100 ml for males, less than 10 g/100 ml for females; low hematocrit, less than 47 ml/100 ml for males, less than 42 ml/100 ml for females; low serum iron levels with high binding capacity; low serum ferritin levels
• Inadequate intake of proteins and calories; may occur in hospitalized patients with conditions such as cancer, Crohn's disease, and cirrhosis	• Weight/height ratio 60% to 90% below standard; triceps skinfold thickness usually 60% below standard; mid–upper-arm circumference and mid–upper-arm muscle circumference, usually 60% to 90% below normal	• Creatinine height index decreased, possibly to 60% below normal; serum levels of albumin and transferrin are normal; one or more positive reactions to skin tests
• Inadequate intake, especially where corn is staple food; secondary to carcinoid syndrome or Hartnup disease; chronic alcoholism	• Mouth, tongue, and lips become reddened; atrophy of papillae; in late stages, confusion and disorientation	• Serum niacin levels less than 30 mcg/100 ml; headache, backache, sore mouth
• Commonly, pattern of overeating accompanied by decreased energy expenditure; less commonly, endocrine abnormality	• Weight/height ratio 20% or more above normal; triceps skinfold measurement indicating obesity	• None significant

(continued)

Guide to Nutritional Disorders *(continued)*

DISORDER	CHIEF COMPLAINT	
Riboflavin (B₂) deficiency	• *Weight change:* Less common • *Skin changes:* Seborrheic dermatitis in the nasolabial folds, scrotum, and vulva; generalized dermatitis • *Asthenia:* Usually present • *Gastrointestinal problems:* Not common • *Musculoskeletal impairment:* Possible growth retardation	
Thiamine (B₁) deficiency	• *Weight change:* Emaciated appearance in dry form • *Skin changes:* Pallor may occur, especially in infants; subcutaneous edema in extremities may occur in wet form • *Asthenia:* Apathy and confusion, loss of memory • *Gastrointestinal problems:* Anorexia, vomiting, constipation, abdominal pain may occur • *Musculoskeletal impairment:* Muscle cramps, paresthesias, polyneuritis; in severe cases, convulsions, paralysis of extremities, muscular atrophy	
Vitamin A deficiency	• *Weight change:* None • *Skin changes:* Dry, scaly, roughness with follicular hyperkeratosis; shrinking and hardening of mucous membranes • *Asthenia:* Vague apathy may be present • *Gastrointestinal problems:* None directly related • *Musculoskeletal impairment:* Possible failure to thrive	
Vitamin B₁₂ deficiency	• *Weight change:* Loss possible • *Skin changes:* Lemon-yellow pallor • *Asthenia:* Present • *Gastrointestinal problems:* Anorexia, vomiting, diarrhea • *Musculoskeletal impairment:* Hand and foot paresthesia; degeneration of spinal cord, decreased musculoskeletal innervation	
Vitamin C deficiency	• *Weight change:* Loss possible • *Skin changes:* Drying roughness and dingy brown color change; petechiae, ecchymosis, follicular hyperkeratosis • *Asthenia:* May be present • *Gastrointestinal problems:* Anorexia, diarrhea, vomiting possible in children • *Musculoskeletal impairment:* Limb and joint pain and swelling	
Vitamin D deficiency	• *Weight change:* None • *Skin changes:* None • *Asthenia:* Not present • *Gastrointestinal problems:* None • *Musculoskeletal impairment:* Chronic deficiency causes bone malformations from bone softening and retarded growth	
Vitamin K deficiency	• *Weight change:* None • *Skin changes:* Petechiae and ecchymosis possible • *Asthenia:* Present; may be related to blood loss • *Gastrointestinal problems:* Gastrointestinal bleeding, which can include massive hemorrhage, possible. • *Musculoskeletal impairment:* Hemorrhaging in muscles, joints	

HISTORY	PHYSICAL EXAMINATION	DIAGNOSTIC STUDIES
• Inadequate intake of milk, meat, fish, leafy green and yellow vegetables; chronic alcoholism; use of oral contraceptives	• Cheilosis, conjunctivitis in mild form; in late stages, moderate edema, neuropathy	• Riboflavin serum level less than 2 mcg/100 ml; prolonged diarrhea; complaints of photophobia and itching, burning, tearing eyes
• Increased need for B₁ during fever, pregnancy, etc.; infants on low-protein diets; inadequate intake, especially of whole or enriched breads or cereals, pork, beans, and nuts; malabsorption syndrome; chronic alcoholism	• In wet form, edema begins in legs and progresses upward. Cardiomegaly with tachycardia, dyspnea may occur; nystagmus possible; hyperactive knee-jerk reflex, followed by hypoactivity	• Serum values for thiamine less than 5 mcg/100 ml; elevated levels of pyruvic and lactic acid; low urine values for thiamine; nonspecific EKG changes
• Night blindness that may progress to permanent blindness; diet lacking in leafy green and yellow fruits and vegetables; fat malabsorption	• Dryness, roughness of conjunctiva; swelling and redness of lids; clouded cornea; ulcerations possible	• Serum values for vitamin A below 20 mcg/100 ml confirm deficiency
• Strict vegetarian; malabsorption resulting from gastrectomy or ileal resection	• Macrocytic megaloblastic anemia, bright red tongue, cardiovascular changes, dyspnea, chest pain, chronic congestive heart failure	• Serum value less than 100 pg/ml; resembles folic acid deficiency, with additional neural and mental changes
• Inadequate intake of fresh fruits and vegetables; overcooking; marginal intake during periods of stress. Groups at risk include infants fed processed cow's milk only, those on limited diets, and those with bizarre eating habits.	• Swollen and/or bleeding gums (early sign), loosening of teeth, pallor, ocular hemorrhages in the bulbar conjunctivas; delayed wound healing and tissue repair	• Serum ascorbic acid levels less than 0.4 mg/100 ml and WBC ascorbic acid levels less than 25 mg/100 ml (help confirm); poor wound healing; psychologic disturbances, such as hysteria, depression, anemia
• Inadequate dietary intake of vitamin D; malabsorption; inadequate exposure to sunlight; hepatic or renal disease	• Characteristic bone malformations	• Plasma calcium levels less than 7.5 mg/100 ml; inorganic phosphorus serum levels less than 3 mg/100 ml; serum citrate levels less than 2.5 mg/100 ml.
• Prolonged use of such drugs as anticoagulants and antibiotics; malabsorption of vitamin K (as in sprue, bowel resection, ulcerative colitis), biliary obstruction	• Bleeding tendencies	• Prolonged prothrombin time (25% longer than control)

6

Skin, Hair, and Nails

The skill you need to assess the integumentary system proficiently comes mainly from your experience with patients, since this system isn't covered in detail in the curricula of most professional schools. One reason for this is that skin assessment usually takes place during assessment of other body systems. Another reason is that—except for burn cases—you don't see many patients admitted primarily for the treatment of skin disorders, unless you work in the dermatologic inpatient unit of a large medical center (see *The Burn Patient*, pages 98 and 99).

Skin conditions may occur as primary disorders (resulting from changes in normal skin) or as secondary manifestations of dysfunction in other body systems. However, primary and secondary skin changes often exhibit a similar morphology and pattern.

Skin disorders are important in themselves (because they're so closely related to the patient's body image) and as indicators of other, possibly more serious, systemic dysfunctions. Skin assessment helps you to recognize these problems, determine your patient's needs, and plan most effectively to meet them.

History data

Biographical data
Biographical data can indicate whether your patient is likely to develop a particular type of skin disorder. For example, rosacea is more common in women than in men, keloid formation is more common in blacks, and psoriasis is more common in whites.

History of present illness
The most common chief complaints associated with skin disorders are *itching, rashes,* and *lesions* (see *Guide to Common Skin Disorders*, pages 110 to 113).

Here are some questions you may want to ask about these complaints to explore fully the history of your patient's present illness:
• *Itching: When did the itching begin?* If it started, for example, within 2 days after the patient began using a new dishwashing soap, this may indicate allergic contact dermatitis. *Has the itching spread? Does it get worse at a particular time of day?* Itching caused by scabies often worsens at night as the parasites become more active in the warm bedding. Itching from other disorders may also worsen at night. *Have you come in contact with anyone who has an itching problem?* Scabies can spread quickly, especially in places like dormitories or hospitals.

Have you tried creams, lotions, or special shampoos to relieve the itching? If so, which ones? Did they help, or make it worse? Some over-the-counter medicated shampoos relieve seborrheic dermatitis itching.
• *Rash: Where did the rash start? Have you had direct skin contact with known allergens? Is it spreading?* Both allergic reactions and viral exanthemas spread. *Does the rash burn or hurt?* Burning is characteristic of some vesicles, such as herpes zoster (shingles) and herpes simplex. *Have you ever had a similar rash? Do other signs and symptoms accompany the rash?* Fever and malaise may suggest that the rash has a viral origin.
• *Lesions* (see *Guide to Skin Lesions*, pages 100 and 101): *How long have you had this lesion? Has the color, size, or any other characteristic of the lesion changed? How long has it been changing?* Some lesions change in appearance over time. Herpes simplex, for ex-

ample, changes from red papules to vesicles to a crust. Some nevi may rise above the skin and enlarge. Always note the sequence of such changes. *Does anything irritate the lesion, for instance, clothing rubbing against it? Does the lesion limit or prevent activity?* For example, deep plantar warts can make walking painful.

Past history

Review the following areas of the past history of a patient with a skin disorder:

● **Related systemic conditions.** A skin disorder may signal the onset of a systemic disorder, such as systemic lupus erythematosus, or occur as a result of prolonged illness, such as malaria, syphilis, pulmonary tuberculosis, or coronary disease.

● **Immunosuppression therapy.** Such therapy—for cancer or collagen diseases, for example—may reduce the patient's resistance to herpes zoster. Alopecia often results from use of steroids and chemotherapeutic agents.

● **Allergens.** Common allergens that may cause skin disorders include plants (such as poison ivy, oak, sumac), pollens, foods, cosmetics and perfumes, soaps and laundry detergents, and preparations containing benzocaine, neomycin, or vitamin E. Skin conditions may also be precipitated by such metals as nickel and chrome, and by rubber (especially in elastic undergarments).

● **Medications.** Skin eruptions may result from the use of vitamins, cold remedies, laxatives, and prescription drugs, such as penicillin and sulfonamides. Some topical and systemic drugs can indirectly cause a photosensitivity reaction (see *Selected Drugs that Affect the Skin,* pages 107 and 108).

Family history

Certain skin disorders (such as psoriasis, acne vulgaris, vitiligo, and atopic dermatitis), as well as alopecia, may be hereditary. Atopic dermatitis is strongly associated with a family history of allergies, such as asthma and hay fever.

Psychosocial history

In your review of the patient's psychosocial history, include questions about the following:

● **Occupation and hobbies.** Exposure to chemicals containing a strong base or acid, like those used at some manufacturing plants

and in some hobbies, may predispose the patient to skin eruptions.

● **Recent travel.** Certain skin disorders are more likely to occur in particular geographic areas—for instance, parasitic diseases, such as cutaneous larva migrans, are more prevalent in tropical climates.

● **Housing.** A patient is more likely to contract pediculosis corporis in an unclean or crowded home.

● **Personal contact.** Pediculosis capitis and pediculosis pubis, as well as scabies, may be transmitted through close personal contact.

Activities of daily living

Outdoor activities in very hot or cold weather may cause skin disorders or aggravate an existing condition. For instance, cold weather usually aggravates dry skin. Known as *winter itch,* this condition is especially prevalent in elderly persons. Overexposure to sunlight can cause a direct photosensitivity reaction, which may be immediate or delayed.

Review of systems

Primary skin disorders don't usually affect other body systems, but secondary skin eruptions may indicate pathology in other body systems. For example, skin symptoms (such as rashes and itching) may appear during allergic reactions, along with symptoms (such as itchy eyes and dyspnea) related to other systems. The respiratory, cardiovascular, gastrointestinal, urinary, immune, and endocrine systems may be affected.

Pigmentation and nevi may change during pregnancy, and reversible hair loss is common after delivery. Stretch marks (striae) from distention of the skin (especially of the abdomen) may result from pregnancy, obesity, ascites, tumors, or subcutaneous edema.

Physical examination

Preparation and positioning

For skin inspection, overhead fluorescent lighting or strong natural light is best. Avoid using incandescent lighting, because it may produce a transilluminating effect. Check that the room isn't too cold (which may cause cyanosis or blanching) or too hot (which may cause flushing).

The Burn Patient

To assess the patient who's been burned, you must first obtain complete information about the accident. If the patient can't communicate, see if the family or rescue personnel can supply the information you need. Why is this information important? If, for example, the fire occurred indoors, or if the patient's clothing was burned, you should suspect smoke inhalation as well.

Airway: Whether your patient suffered smoke inhalation or not, examine his airway closely. Suspect airway injury if the patient's nose hairs are singed, if you find soot particles in his mouth and pharynx or in his sputum, or if he drools or salivates excessively. Look for signs of laryngeal stridor and upper airway irritation and inflammation.

Respirations: Next, assess his respirations. Observe him for signs of alveolar collapse, pulmonary edema, hypoxemia, and pneumonia. You may hear rales, rhonchi, or wheezes on auscultation. Estimate his level of ventilation (rate and depth of expansion). Note any cough, and describe his sputum. If the patient's suffered circumferential chest burns, his chest expansion may be impaired because of eschar formation, and he may require escharotomy. You should also draw blood for arterial blood gas analysis of carbon dioxide, partial pressures, and pH.

Vital signs: You'll need to take the patient's vital signs and monitor urinary output to establish a baseline for assessing fluid loss. With burn wounds, fluid moves from the intravascular area into the interstitium. This may cause hypovolemia and shock.

Level of consciousness: Determine the patient's level of consciousness. Watch for symptoms of carbon monoxide poisoning: headache, weakness, dizziness, nausea, vomiting, and in severe poisoning, syncope and collapse. Elevated carboxyhemoglobin levels may also indicate carbon monoxide poisoning.

Burn size: Estimate the size of the burn wound. To do this, use the assessment method known as the Rule of Nines, discussed on the opposite page.

Burn depth: Estimating burn depth is difficult in the first few hours after the accident. Once this time has elapsed, you can determine burn depth by answering these questions:
* Is the burned area pink or red, with minimal edema?
* Is it sensitive to temperature change?

If the answers are yes, your patient has a first-degree burn, involving one or two skin layers.
* Is the burned area pink or red, and does it blanch when touched?
* Does the patient have large, thick-walled blisters, with subcutaneous edema?
* Is the burned area firm or leathery?
* Does touching the burn cause the patient severe pain?

If the answers are yes, your patient has a second-degree burn, involving at least two skin layers.
* Is the burned area waxy white, red, brown, or black?
* If red, does it remain red and not blanch when touched?
* Is it leathery, with extensive subcutaneous edema?
* Is it insensitive to touch?

If the answers are yes, your patient has a third-degree burn, involving all skin layers.

Electrical burns: If your patient has suffered an electrical burn, follow the same basic procedure outlined above. Note these special considerations:
* If an electrical current has passed through the brain or the heart, the patient will probably be unconscious or in cardiac and respiratory arrest.
* If the current passed through an extremity, assess pulses—peripheral and distal—and extremity color and temperature. Intravascular coagulation may impair his circulation.
* If your patient's in shock, note that the condition may not result from fluid loss; it may be caused by the injury or by accompanying abdominal or thoracic injury.
* If, on auscultation, your patient's bowel sounds are absent, suspect paralytic ileus. Look for an exit wound from the electrical current. If present, it can give you a general idea of the current's pathway and the blood vessels and nerves it damaged.

Chemical burns: If your patient has suffered a chemical burn, he'll probably have a localized lesion (unless other systems are injured simultaneously). You can define the injury's extent by assessing erythema, blistering, ulceration, necrosis, and sloughing.

The Burn Patient

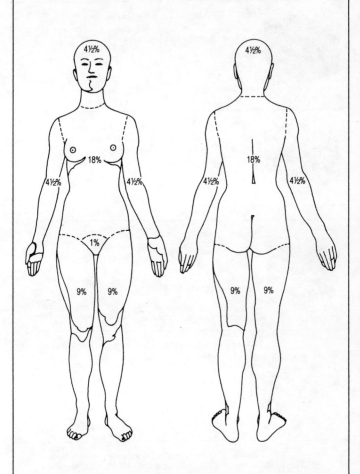

The Rule of Nines divides body surface area into percentages that, when totaled, equal 100%. To use this technique, mentally transfer your patient's burn to the body chart shown here. Add the percentages assigned to the sections in which the burn falls. This total is a rough estimate of the burn size and serves as a guide in initial fluid replacement. In nonemergency situations, you'll use more involved methods to assess burn size.

Guide to Skin Lesions

	TYPE	DESCRIPTION	EXAMPLE
	Crust	Dried serous or purulent exudate	Impetigo
	Fissure	Linear cracking of the skin	Hand dermatitis
	Macule	Flat, pigmented, circumscribed area	Freckle
	Nodule	Firm, raised lesion; deeper than a papule	Intradermal nevus
	Papule	Firm, inflammatory, raised lesion up to 1 cm in diameter	Acne papule, lichen planus

Guide to Skin Lesions *(continued)*

	TYPE	DESCRIPTION	EXAMPLE
	Plaque	Circumscribed, solid, elevated lesion greater than 1 cm in diameter. Elevation above skin surface occupies larger surface area in comparison with height.	Psoriasis
	Scale	Thin, dry flakes of shedding skin	Psoriasis
	Ulcer	Epidermal and dermal destruction	Decubitus ulcer
	Vesicle	Raised, circumscribed, fluid-containing lesion less than 0.5 cm in diameter	Chicken pox, herpes simplex
	Wheal	Raised, firm lesion with intense localized skin edema, varying in size and shape, and transient in occurrence. Disappears in hours.	Hive

Have the patient stand or sit for the examination unless he's ill or injured, in which case you should place him in the supine position or prone position.

Skin inspection and palpation

Color and pigmentation. Observe the general color and pigmentation of the skin. The characteristics of normal skin vary with the patient's racial, ethnic, and familial background. Note any paleness, jaundice, or cyanosis.

Also, note the location of any *hypopigmentation:* Is the lack of color partial or total? Hypopigmentation usually occurs in patches, especially on the face and arms. Dry skin commonly causes patches of peeling hypopigmented skin, especially on the arms and legs.

Darkened areas of skin *(hyperpigmentation)* may occur on any part of the patient's body but occurs most often on the face (chloasma and melasma). Note the location of any hyperpigmented areas you find on inspection. *Trauma* is a common cause of *postinflammatory discoloration.*

Skin hydration. Inspection and palpation readily identify dry skin. Skin dryness can vary from mild to the rare, severe form known as *ichthyosis.* Persons of all ages can have dry skin; you'll usually see more patients with this condition during cold weather. Almost all elderly patients have dry skin.

If your patient's skin looks oily, inspect his body for acne, especially on areas where the sebaceous glands are concentrated—the face, neck, back, chest, and buttocks.

Exertion, anxiety, or fear can cause increased perspiration (hyperhidrosis). In some persons, however, excessive perspiration has no demonstrable relationship to stress. Inspect the areas most commonly affected: the patient's palms, soles, and axillary and groin areas.

Skin texture and thickness. Feel your patient's skin. Is it rough or smooth? If you see scaling, note whether it occurs in large patches or as individual lesions. Also observe the general thickness of your patient's skin— whether it looks and feels normal or whether it's thin and fragile, as in the elderly or in patients with debilitating diseases. Check for the thickened plaques of chronic eczema and psoriasis. Inspect palms and soles for calluses.

Turgor and elasticity. Test turgor and elasticity by picking up a fold of the patient's skin over a bony prominence and then releasing it. Normal skin immediately returns to its previous state. Elasticity is greatly reduced in scleroderma. To test for mobility, see if the skin moves back and forth smoothly over the same bony prominence.

Vascularity, erythema, and edema. Observe your patient's skin for vascular abnormalities, such as *purpuric disorders,* characterized by purple or brown-red petechiae (pinpoint lesions) or *bruises (ecchymoses),* caused by hemorrhage into the cutaneous tissues. *Telangiectasias* (formed by the dilatation of small blood vessels) are also common. Telangiectasias blanch when pressure is applied; petechiae do not.

Note whether your patient's skin has any red areas (erythema) and whether the erythema is generalized, localized, or diffuse. Erythema is the outstanding symptom of some systemic diseases, especially measles, rubella, and scarlet fever, and numerous dermatologic conditions. Also note the erythema's distribution pattern because certain dermatologic conditions characteristically occur in specific anatomic areas. To observe overall distribution of your patient's skin lesions (for instance, the Christmas-tree pattern of pityriasis rosea), view him from a distance of 2′ to 3′ (0.6 to 0.9 m). Finally, check for any local lymphadenopathy.

If you note any edema, record its location and whether it's associated with erythema, rash, or any type of lesion.

Hair and scalp examination

The color of your patient's hair has no relationship to his health status except when the color has changed suddenly.

Note any dryness, brittleness, or fragility, which may be the result of trauma (usually from cosmetic causes) or a body system dysfunction. Examine the quantity, quality, and distribution of the hair, and observe the pattern (generalized or patchy) of any hair loss. (Keep in mind that a person normally loses up to 100 head hairs a day.) If hair loss seems excessive, gently pull on the patient's hair to see if it comes out easily. Look for regrowth in patchy hair-loss areas. If you see any erythema, scaling, or crusting on the patient's scalp, along with excessive hair loss, darken the room and examine the patient's scalp under a Wood's light (a specially filtered ultraviolet light). Certain dermatophytes, such as those causing tinea capitis (ringworm), appear fluorescent green under a Wood's light. This may be a sign of ringworm infestation.

An excess of body and facial hair (hypertrichosis) or sparsity of such hair (hypotrichosis) is not necessarily abnormal; neither is hair in moles or birthmarks (evaluate such areas for malignancy).

If you see inflammation or pustular eruption on your patient's scalp, observe whether the condition occurs only around hair follicles or is more widespread. Also observe for other lesions that can occur on the scalp, such as cysts, warts, moles, and bites.

Distinguish between the mild flaking of ordinary dandruff; heavy scaling, as in psoriasis; and the greasy scaling of seborrheic dermatitis. Seborrheic dermatitis is commonly accompanied by scaling in the eyebrows, in creases (such as the nasolabial and postauricular folds), and in hairy areas, such as a man's chest.

If the patient is scratching his head and you suspect pediculosis, wear gloves when examining his scalp or use two tongue depressors to separate the hairs for inspection. You can usually see the live adult lice. If you don't see them but still suspect pediculosis, ask the patient to bend over a large piece of white paper or a sheet and to shake his head vigorously; the lice should fall onto the paper or sheet. Also check clothing seams, especially near the collar, for nits (louse ova) or lice. Then check for erythematous papules on the nape of the neck. Detecting nits is harder than detecting lice, because the nits resemble dandruff. Nits exude a sticky substance that fastens them to the hair shaft, so you can't pull them off as you can dandruff flakes.

To estimate how long your patient's been infested with lice, measure the distance between the nits and the base of the hair shaft. Because nits are laid on the scalp, and hair grows approximately 10 mm/month, the distance indicates when the infestation began.

Nail inspection
Observe the color of your patient's nails. Normally, they're pink in Caucasians and black

and brown (possibly with a pattern of longitudinal lines) in blacks. Note if the nails appear blue-black or purple, brown or yellow-gray.

Inspect the shape and texture of his nails, noting any irregularities, such as brittleness, cracking, or peeling. If any nails are missing, note whether the loss is partial or total. If the nail and its nail bed have separated (onycholysis), examine the nail for discoloration, debris accumulated under the nail, and thickening. (Remember, onycholysis is often a sign of psoriasis.)

Your inspection of the patient's nails may also reveal striations, vertical or horizontal ridges, or tiny depressions (*thimble pits*). The paronychial tissue folds around the nail may be swollen, erythematous, or oozing pus or serous fluid. Paronychial warts and ingrown nails (especially ingrown toenails) are also common. (See *Nail Abnormalities,* pages 104 to 105.)

Pediatric assessment

Skin problems in infants
Common infant skin problems are diaper rash, cradle cap, newborn rash (erythema neonatorum toxicum), infant acne, impetigo, and roseola. If you see diaper rash, ask the patient's parents about the diaper-changing procedures they use. Do they wash the diaper-covered area with each change? Keeping the rash area clean and dry usually helps healing; if it doesn't, suspect monilial dermatitis.

Bacterial or monilial infection may occur with diaper rash: Check for papules, pustules, or vesicles. Monilial rashes are severely erythematous and pustular, with vesicular and satellite lesions. Culturing is recommended to identify the infectious agent.

The scaling and crusting of cradle cap may cover an infant's entire scalp. Ask about a family history of atopic dermatitis, which is inherited. Check for accumulations of soap residue and hair that's been shed. If an infant has severe cradle cap with diaper rash just to the diaper borders, he may have true seborrheic dermatitis.

For any skin problem, ask the parents how often they bathe the infant since excessive bathing can dry an infant's skin, and what kinds

Nail Abnormalities

	DISORDER	DESCRIPTION	POSSIBLE ASSOCIATED DISORDERS
	Beau's lines	Transverse depressions in all nails	Severe acute illness, malnutrition, anemia
	Clubbing	Early clubbing: soft, cushiony nail base; late clubbing: swollen nail base	Cardiopulmonary disorders
	Mees' lines	Crescent-shaped transverse lines in the nail plate	Arsenic poisoning
	Onycholysis	Partial separation of distal nail edge	Heart disease, chronic diseases
	Paronychia	Erythema, swelling, and thickening of skin surrounding the nail edges, with possible severe pain and infection	Monilia (most common), diabetes, bacterial infections, third-stage syphilis, leprosy
	Pigment band	Line of discoloration in the nail plate	Junction nevus
	Pterygium	Inflammatory lesion involving the nail matrix, accompanied by fusing of the proximal nail fold to the nail bed	Peripheral vascular disease, trauma, lichen planus

Nail Abnormalities (continued)

	DISORDER	DESCRIPTION	POSSIBLE ASSO-CIATED DISORDERS
	Splinter hemorrhage	Small, stripelike, brown discoloration of the nail plate	Subacute bacterial en-docarditis, minor trauma
	Striated nails	Longitudinal ridges, usually accompanied by fragile nails	Variable
	Subungual hematoma	Mass of blood under the nail	Trauma, jogger's toe; requires biopsy to rule out melanoma

Photos courtesy of the American Academy of Dermatology

of soap, lotions, powders, and oils they use since some may produce a skin reaction.

Young children's skin

Preschool and school-age children are susceptible to such common skin disorders as allergic contact dermatitis (from poison ivy, oak, or sumac, or rubber in shoes or clothing), atopic dermatitis, warts (especially on the hands), viral exanthemas, impetigo, ringworm, scabies, and skin reactions to food allergies.

For the child with any kind of rash, obtain a thorough history. Asking about how and where the rash began, its evolution pattern, and its preceding symptoms may help differentiate between rubella, rubeola, scarlet fever, viral exanthemas, and drug reactions. (See *Distribution Patterns of Common Pediatric Skin Disorders,* page 109.)

Adolescent skin disorders

When a child enters puberty, hormonal changes affect his skin and hair. Androgen levels increase, causing sebaceous glands to secrete large amounts of sebum, which can clog hair follicle openings. Pubic and axillary hair begin to grow. Common dermatoses occurring during adolescence include acne, warts, sunburn, scabies, atopic dermatitis, and pityriasis rosea. Also common in adolescents are allergic contact dermatitis (especially from jewelry and cosmetics) and fungal infections (especially tinea pedis, tinea cruris, and tinea versicolor). Examine an adolescent for these disorders, using the same procedures as for an adult.

If an adolescent has severe acne, observe his speech and behavior for possible signs of depression. Remember, an adolescent is usually very concerned with his appearance, so skin problems can affect his self-image.

Distribution Patterns of Common Skin Disorders

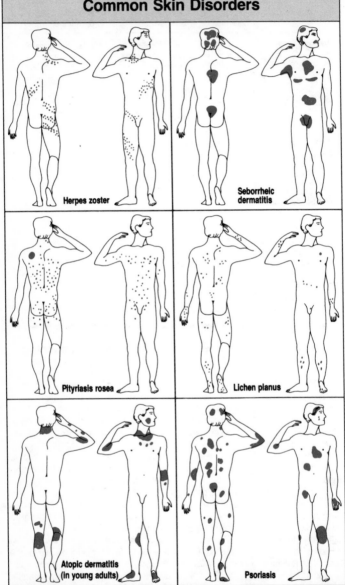

Herpes zoster

Seborrheic dermatitis

Pityriasis rosea

Lichen planus

Atopic dermatitis (in young adults)

Psoriasis

Selected Drugs that Affect the Skin

CLASSIFICATION	POSSIBLE SIDE EFFECTS
Pituitary hormones corticotropin (ACTH)	• Impaired wound healing, thin fragile skin, petechiae, ecchymoses, facial erythema, increased sweating, acne, hyperpigmentation, hirsutism, purpura
Antipsychotics chlorpromazine hydrochloride (Thorazine)	• Mild photosensitivity, dermal allergic reactions (such as exfoliative dermatitis)
haloperidol (Haldol*)	• Rash
Barbiturates pentobarbital sodium (Nembutal sodium*)	• Rash, urticaria
Antidiarrheals diphenoxylate with atropine (Lomotil*)	• Pruritus, urticaria, rash
Antiarrhythmics phenytoin sodium (Dilantin*)	• Scarlatiniform or morbilliform rash, exfoliative or purpuric dermatitis, erythema multiforme (Stevens-Johnson syndrome), lupus erythematosus
propranolol hydrochloride (Inderal*)	• Rash
Sulfonamides sulfadiazine (Microsulfon)	• Erythema multiforme (Stevens-Johnson syndrome), generalized skin eruption, epidermal necrosis, exfoliative dermatitis, photosensitivity, urticaria, pruritus
Estrogens dienestrol (AVC/Dienestrol Creme)	• Erythema multiforme, chloasma, melasma
Tetracyclines tetracycline hydrochloride (Achromycin*, Sumycin*)	• Maculopapular and erythematous rashes, urticaria, photosensitivity, increased pigmentation
Anticonvulsants bromides (Lanabrom, Neurosine)	• Acneiform, morbilliform, and granulomatous eruptions; erythema nodosom; Stevens-Johnson syndrome
diazepam (Valium*)	• Rash; urticaria
trimethadione (Tridione)	• Acneiform and morbilliform rash, exfoliative dermatitis, erythema multiforme, petechiae, alopecia

(continued)

Selected Drugs that Affect the Skin

CLASSIFICATION	POSSIBLE SIDE EFFECTS
Antituberculars isoniazid [INH] (Hyzyd)	● Eruptions (types vary)
Tranquilizers meprobamate (Equanil, Miltown*)	● Pruritus, urticaria, erythematous maculo-papular rash
Oral contraceptives estrogen with progestogen (Brevicon, En-ovid)	● Rash, chloasma or melasma, acne, sebor-rhea, oily skin
Penicillins penicillin G potassium (Pentids)	● Rash, urticaria, maculopapular eruptions, exfoliative dermatitis
Nonnarcotic analgesics phenolphthalein (Azolid, Butazoldin*)	● Petechiae, pruritus, purpura, various der-matoses from rash to toxic necrotizing epi-dermolysis
Expectorants codeine	● Pruritus
Anticoagulants dicumarol (Dufalone**)	● Dermatitis, urticaria, rash, alopecia
Skeletal muscle relaxants dantrolene sodium (Dantrium*)	● Eczematoid eruption, pruritus, urticaria
Antifungals griseofulvin (Fulvicin, Grifulvin V)	● Rash, urticaria, photosensitive reactions (may aggravate lupus erythematosus)
Gold compounds gold sodium thiomalate (Myochrysine*)	● Rash and dermatitis
Diuretics chlorothiazide (Diuril)	● Dermatitis, photosensitivity, rash
Uncategorized agents allopurinol (Zyloprim*)	● Rash, usually maculopapular; exfoliative, urticarial, and purpuric lesions; erythema multiforme; severe furunculosis of nose; ichthyosis; toxic epidermal necrolysis

*Available in U.S. and Canada. **Available in Canada only. All other products (no symbol) available in U.S. only.

Distribution Patterns of Common Pediatric Skin Disorders

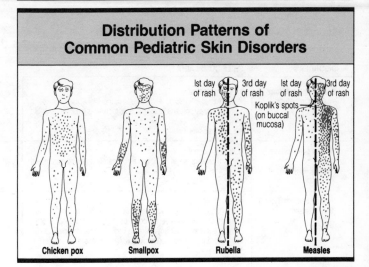

Chicken pox Smallpox Rubella Measles

1st day of rash 3rd day of rash 1st day of rash 3rd day of rash

Koplik's spots (on buccal mucosa)

Geriatric assessment

Effects of aging on the skin

In the elderly, subcutaneous fat loss, dermal thinning, decreasing collagen, and increasing elastin result in the development of facial lines (crow's feet) around the eyes, mouth, and nose, increased prominence of the supraclavicular and axillary regions, the knuckles, and the hand tendons and vessels, as well as fat pads over bony prominences. Mucous membranes become dry, and sweat gland output lessens as the number of active eccrine sweat glands is reduced. Very elderly persons' skin loses its elasticity until it may seem almost transparent. Although melanocyte production decreases as a person ages, localized melanocyte proliferations are common and cause brown spots to appear, especially in areas regularly exposed to the sun.

Hair pigment decreases with aging, so a person's hair turns gray or white (and also thins as he ages). Hormonal changes cause pubic hair loss. Facial hair often increases in postmenopausal women and decreases in aging men.

Many people's nails change significantly with aging. They may grow at different rates, and longitudinal ridges, flaking, brittleness, and alterations in form may increase. Toenails may discolor.

Geriatric skin disorders

As a person ages, susceptibility to certain skin disorders increases. For example, actinic keratoses and basal cell epitheliomas from past sun exposure commonly occur in elderly persons. Xerosis, capillary hemangiomas, pedunculated fibromas, and seborrheic keratoses are extremely common. Other characteristic geriatric skin conditions include xanthelasma, plantar keratosis, seborrheic dermatitis, and pigmented nevi. If your elderly patient's mobility has decreased and his circulation is impaired, he may develop stasis dermatitis and possibly stasis ulcers.

Guide to Common Skin Disorders

DISORDERS	CHIEF COMPLAINT	
Exanthema subitum (roseola infantum)	• *Itching:* absent • *Rash:* present; begins with macular or maculopapular eruption on trunk; *rarely* spreads to arms, neck, face, and legs; fades within 24 hours • *Lesion:* absent	
Herpes progenitalis Type 2 (herpes simplex)	• *Itching:* absent • *Rash:* present; small grouped vesicles around genital and mouth areas • *Lesion:* present	
Herpes simplex Type 1 (fever blister)	• *Itching:* absent • *Rash:* present; single group of vesicles ruptures, leaving a painful ulcer, followed by a yellow crust; usually occurs around mouth or nose but may occur anywhere on body; healing begins 7 to 10 days after initial onset, is complete within 3 weeks • *Lesion:* present	
Impetigo	• *Itching:* present • *Rash:* rarely present; small, very fragile vesicles; when broken, exudes liquid that dries and forms honey-colored crusts; usually occurs on face but may occur anywhere on body • *Lesion:* present	
Pediculosis (lice)	• *Itching:* present; mild to severe • *Rash:* present; inflamed papules caused by scratching • *Lesion:* absent	
Rubella (German measles)	• *Itching:* absent • *Rash:* present; begins with maculopapular rash on face, which spreads to trunk • *Lesion:* absent	
Rubeola (measles)	• *Itching:* absent • *Rash:* present; begins with faint macules on hairline, neck, and cheeks; increases to maculopapular rash on entire face, neck, and upper arms; spreads to back, abdomen, arms, thighs, and lower legs; appears 2 to 4 days after onset of other symptoms; lasts 4 or 5 days • *Lesion:* absent	
Scabies	• *Itching:* present, especially at night, because mites are more active in the warm environment of a bed • *Rash:* present; excoriated and sometimes erythematous papules, 1 cm long, caused by scratching • *Lesion:* present; burrows about ⅜″ long in straight or zigzag line, with a black dot at end	

HISTORY	PHYSICAL EXAMINATION AND DIAGNOSTIC STUDIES
• Exposure to infected person 7 to 17 days previously • Sudden high fever 3 or 4 days prior to rash • Usually affects infants and children age 6 months to 3 years	• Inflamed pharynx
• *In infants:* delivered vaginally with infected mother • *In adolescents and adults:* sexual contact with infected person	• No other physical characteristics • Culture shows herpes simplex virus
• Cold, fever, trauma, menstruation, or over-exposure to sunlight may occur prior to sores. • Recurrences common	• No other physical characteristics • Culture shows herpes simplex virus
• Most common in children during hot weather • Predisposing factors: overcrowded living quarters, poor skin hygiene, anemia, malnutrition, minor skin trauma	• No other physical characteristics • Culture and sensitivity tests show *Streptococcus pyogenes* and *Staphylococcus aureus*
• Exposure to infected persons • Predisposing factor: overcrowded living conditions	• Lice sometimes observable • *Pediculosis capitis:* on scalp • *Pediculosis pubis:* primarily found in pubic hairs but may extend to eyebrows, eyelashes, or axillary or body hairs
• Exposure to infected person 14 to 21 days previously • *In children:* usually no symptoms prior to rash • *In adolescents:* headache, malaise, anorexia may occur prior to rash	• *In adolescents and adults:* conjunctivitis, low-grade fever, posterior cervical and post-auricular lymphadenopathy, joint pain
• Exposure to infected person 10 to 14 days previously • Cold, conjunctivitis, fever, and cough prior to rash • Greatest communicability 11 days after exposure, lasting 4 or 5 days	• Koplik's spots (white patches on oral mucosa) • Generalized lymphadenopathy, conjunctivitis
• Exposure to affected person	• May affect interdigital webs on hands, wrists, elbows, breasts, buttocks, and penis • Mites and nits can be seen with a microscope in scraping from intact lesion. • Resembles contact dermatitis, atopic dermatitis

(continued)

Guide to Common Skin Disorders *(continued)*

DISORDERS	CHIEF COMPLAINT
Scarlet fever	• *Itching:* absent • *Rash:* present; bright red, finely papular in skin creases of axillae, groin, and neck; spreads rapidly to trunk, extremities, and face; lasts 1 or 2 days • *Lesion:* absent
Tinea capitis (scalp ringworm)	• *Itching:* present on scalp; very mild • *Rash:* present; small spreading papules on scalp, causing patchy hair loss with scaling • *Lesion:* present; papules may become inflamed, pus-filled lesions
Tinea corporis (smooth skin ringworm)	• *Itching:* present; intense • *Rash:* absent • *Lesion:* present; round, red, scaly lesions, with slightly raised borders; central area heals while lesion continues outward; may be anywhere on body
Tinea cruris (jock itch)	• *Itching:* present; more severe than in seborrheic dermatitis • *Rash:* absent • *Lesion:* present; bilateral, fan-shaped red scaly patches, with slightly raised borders in groin, upper thighs, and gluteal folds
Tinea pedis (athlete's foot)	• *Itching:* present in interdigital webs, palms, and soles; accompanied by burning, stinging • *Rash:* absent • *Lesion:* present; in acute form, blisters; in chronic form, dry, scaly skin
Tinea versicolor	• *Itching:* present; mild • *Rash:* present; tawny, small, irregularly shaped, slightly scaly lesion on upper chest and back • *Lesion:* absent
Varicella (chicken pox)	• *Itching:* present; urticaria around vesicle • *Rash:* present; begins with crops of small red papules and clear vesicles on red base; vesicles break and then dry, causing crust formation; begins on trunk and spreads to face and scalp • *Lesion:* present; may leave scars
Verrucae (warts)	• *Itching:* absent • *Rash:* absent • *Lesion:* present; slightly raised papules, with fingerlike projections; usually on hands or feet but may occur anywhere on body; black specks that appear within warts are coagulated blood, the result of wart abrasion and subsequent bleeding
Viral herpes zoster (shingles)	• *Itching:* absent • *Rash:* present; grouped vesicles or crusted lesions along nerve root, usually unilateral • *Lesion:* present

HISTORY	PHYSICAL EXAMINATION AND DIAGNOSTIC STUDIES
• Exposure to infected person 1 or 2 days previously • Accompanied by sore throat, headache, vomiting	• Red pharynx, with exudate • Strawberry-red tongue • Fever • Peeling skin on hands and feet possible after several days.
• Exposure to infected people	• Patchy hair loss • Infected areas sometimes appear green under Wood's light. • Hyphae can be seen with a microscope.
• Exposure to infected animals or people • Most common in children	• No other physical characteristics • Potassium hydroxide diagnoses condition. • Hyphae can be seen with a microscope.
• Males more susceptible than females • Previous history of tinea cruris, obesity, chafing • Usually occurs concurrently with tinea pedis	• No other physical characteristics • Potassium hydroxide diagnoses condition.
• Previous history of tinea pedis • Males more susceptible than females	• Blisters or scaly skin on feet and between toes • Potassium hydroxide diagnoses condition. • Skin scrapings examined microscopically may reveal fungus.
• Previous history of tinea versicolor • More common in summer	• No associated discomfort • White patches on tanned body • Spots prominent under Wood's light • Hyphae can be seen with a microscope.
• Exposure to infected person 13 to 21 days previously • Malaise, anorexia prior to rash • In temperate areas, higher incidence in late fall, winter, and spring	• Slight fever
• Previous history of warts	• No other physical characteristics
• Chicken pox (condition caused by reactivation of chicken pox virus) • Persistent postherpetic neuralgia possible	• No other physical characteristics • Culture shows varicella

7

Eyes and Vision

People rely mainly on vision to give them accurate information about their environment. It has been estimated that about 90% of the information sent to a person's brain enters the nervous system through his eyes. Because of this, sight is the physical sense the majority of people value most.

You should assess a patient's eyes and vision—not only to recognize signs and symptoms of primary ophthalmologic disorders but also of disorders in other body systems that may have eye manifestations.

You can also teach your patients about prevention of eye disease and accidents, the importance of regular eye examinations, and the need for prompt treatment of eye disorders. The National Society for the Prevention of Blindness has estimated that at least 50% of all cases of sight loss are preventable.

History data

Biographical data
Biographical data have limited significance in assessing patients with eye and vision disorders. Strabismus is usually associated with the young patient and macular degeneration with the older patient.

History of present illness
Four groups of signs and symptoms constitute the most common chief complaints regarding the eyes and vision: pain/discomfort, vision changes, tearing/secretion, appearance changes (see *Guide to Eye Disorders*, pages 126 to 135).

Vision changes include complaints about decreased or absent vision as well as blurred or double vision. Also in this category are reports of seeing distorted images, colors or lights, and floating particles. Complaints of pain and discomfort include tenderness or pressure. Changes in eye appearance include the presence of a lump or foreign body.

Here are some questions you may want to ask about these complaints to explore fully the history of your patient's present illness:
● **Decreased or absent vision.** *Is your vision clearer in one eye than in the other?* Gradual visual loss usually indicates a chronic problem that may be correctable. Sudden visual loss is an ocular emergency that may indicate retinal artery or vein occlusion (see *Ocular Trauma,* page 115). *Do you see a blind spot? If so, does it move with eye movement? Is the problem in the center of your field of vision, or at the side? Does it occur only at night?* Visual loss in one specific area (scotoma) results from retinal or optic pathway damage. Reduced night vision can be from retinal degeneration.
● **Blurred or double vision.** *Does a shade, or curtain, seem to be covering your field of vision?* Find out whether the condition is constant or can be relieved by an action such as squinting. *Is it related to fatigue or eyestrain? Is it worse in the morning, or in the evening? In the dark, or in the light?*
● **Distorted images, colors, or lights.** *Does what you see look bent or warped? Is it difficult to differentiate colors, or do the colors blend together?* Positive responses to these questions may indicate retinal disease. *Do you see lights or halos?* These symptoms may indicate acute glaucoma, cataracts, or corneal disease.
● **Floating particles.** *Do you see many particles, or only a few?* Seeing only a few spots is usually not significant. The sudden occurrence of many floaters, commonly described

Ocular Trauma

The patient with ocular trauma needs your immediate help. Notify the doctor, then quickly follow these emergency steps:

● Identify the nature and extent of the injury. Is it a blunt trauma—for example, from a cosmetic applicator; a penetrating injury—for example, from a BB gun pellet; or a chemical burn—for example, from lye in a drain cleaner? (Remember, he may also have other injuries that require immediate attention.)

● In a case of blunt trauma or a penetrating injury, have the patient lie down. Place a plastic or metal shield over the eye to prevent further injury until the doctor arrives. Then help the doctor treat and bandage the eye.

● In the case of a chemical burn, irrigate the eye with at least 1 qt (950 ml) of water. Be careful not to touch the eye with the irrigating catheter's tip. Also, never direct the irrigation flow toward the nasal cavity. To check the effectiveness of the irrigation, test the pH level of the inferior cul-de-sac by inserting litmus paper. Irrigate until the pH level returns to normal.

● Ask the patient about his past medical history. Especially note any allergies, current medications, and the date of his last tetanus shot.

● Following treatment, you'll want to test the patient's visual acuity. He'll need a complete eye examination, including a dilated fundus examination performed by an ophthalmologist.

---

as *sooty vision,* may indicate vitreous detachment—a possible precursor of retinal detachment or intraocular inflammation.

● *Pain and discomfort. Is the pain on the eye, or does it seem to be in the eye? Is it worse at night?* Glaucoma and intraocular infections cause deep-seated pain that worsens at night. *Does it feel better when you keep your eyes closed? Does blinking make it better or worse?* Keeping the eyes closed relieves pain caused by infections, foreign bodies, or corneal injuries. Blinking makes it worse. *Does bright light cause pain in your eyes?* Photophobia may indicate an inflammation or injury involving the eye's external structures. *Do you sense pressure behind or around the eyes? Do your eyes feel as if they're bulging?* Brain tumors can cause pressure behind the eye, whereas diseases of the orbit can cause pressure around it. Thyroid disease can cause exophthalmos (bulging eyes), which may produce discomfort from conjunctival or corneal irritation.

● *Lump or foreign body. Does the lump or foreign body seem to be on the eyeball, or on the lid? Does it move with eye movement?* A stye (hordeolum) can feel like a lump or foreign body in one area of the eye or eyelid. A foreign body will move with blinking, unless it's imbedded in the cornea.

● *Discharge. What color is the discharge? Is*

it thick or watery? Do you wake up with your eyelids stuck together?

● *Itching or redness. Does the itching occur in a particular circumstance or environment? Do other parts of your body itch at the same time?* Itching is usually a symptom of allergy. *When did you first notice the redness—under what conditions? Did it seem to relate to a particular incident?* Redness may result from infection, trauma, or allergy.

● *Excessive tearing or dryness. Do your eyes tear a great deal?* Excessive tearing can result from chemical irritation, allergies, inflammation, or obstruction of the lacrimal drainage system. *Are your eyes excessively dry? How long have they felt dry?* Dryness occurs with aging and in several collagen disorders. Some people taking tranquilizers will report that their eyes feel dry.

Past history

Ask about the following health considerations and problems:

● *Vision care. Do you normally wear glasses or contact lenses? If so, who prescribed them, and how long ago? How many pairs do you have? What type of correction is involved? When did you have your last eye examination? Were you tested for glaucoma?* Visual symptoms, such as blurred vision, headaches, and eyestrain, can result from wearing improperly prescribed lenses.

• **Allergies.** *Has any allergy ever affected your eyes? Have you ever had a reaction to eye medications? If so, what happened, and what relieved it?* Both local allergies and systemic allergies can cause symptoms of eye disorders.

• **Medications.** *Do you use eye drops, ointments, or washes regularly? Why do you use them? How do your eyes react?* Repeated use of unprescribed eye medications sometimes can precipitate, rather than relieve, visual signs and symptoms. *What other medications are you using?* Note any regular use of systemic medications that can cause visual changes.

• **Neurologic disorders.** Visual changes may be seen in some neurologic disorders (see page 305).

• **Endocrine disorders.** Long-standing diabetes causes degenerative changes in the retinal vasculature that, if untreated, can lead to blindness. Thyroid disorders can also damage eye structures and affect eye function.

• **Circulatory disorders.** Damage to the retinal vasculature or the optic nerve can result from hypertension, hyperviscosity syndromes, or impaired circulation that decreases the oxygen and nutrient supply. Cerebrovascular accident may cause vision problems, such as diplopia.

• **Hepatic and renal disorders.** Disturbances of the liver's ability to detoxify chemicals (such as cirrhosis or liver failure) or of the kidney's ability to eliminate wastes (such as pyelonephritis or glomerulonephritis) can affect both neural and vascular eye structures.

Family history

Note any family history of *early vision loss, retinitis pigmentosa, strabismus, chronic glaucoma,* or *cataracts.* Also note if the patient's mother had an illness, such as *rubella,* during pregnancy.

Psychosocial history

Your patient's *occupation* is the main aspect of the psychosocial history. Ask whether he's routinely exposed to dust, smoke, chemical spraying, flying debris, or other irritants or hazards. If so, does he wear safety goggles or take any other precautions?

Activities of daily living

When you review your patient's activities of daily living, cover these areas:

• **Smoking.** *Do you smoke cigarettes? How many packs a day, and for how many years?* Nicotine causes arterial constrictions that can produce visual symptoms.

• **Alcohol.** *Do you drink alcoholic beverages? At what age did you first begin drinking? How much do you drink?* A type of amblyopia can result from heavy consumption of alcoholic beverages, especially in conjunction with heavy cigarette smoking. At times an alcoholic may suffer acute transient periods of blindness.

• **Recreation.** *Do you participate in sports that pose a hazard to your glasses or contact lenses, or that make you susceptible to eye injury?* Eye injuries are common in racquet sports. Swimming can cause eye infections.

• **Cosmetics.** *Do you regularly wear eye makeup?* Containers for eye make-up are excellent culture media for bacteria. Also ask if the patient uses lotions near the eyes.

• **Self-care.** *Do you sometimes burn yourself when cooking? Do you bump into things often?* A patient may be able to best describe his visual problem in terms of how it alters his activities.

Review of systems

Focus your questions on the following relevant areas:

• **General.** *Fever* that causes eye burning and tenderness can result from an infectious process.

• **Skin.** *Scabbing* and *crusting* result from infections and dermatoses.

• **Cardiovascular.** *Hypertension* and *arteriosclerosis* cause vascular changes in the eye.

• **Gastrointestinal.** *Nausea* and *vomiting* may occur with prolonged, elevated intraocular pressure.

• **Nervous.** *Motor disturbances from myasthenia gravis or multiple sclerosis can affect the eyes. Headache* can be caused by increased intraocular pressure, extraocular muscle imbalances, or space-occupying lesions (which may also cause visual disturbances).

• **Musculoskeletal.** *Muscle weakness, joint pain,* and *stiffness* may indicate a dystrophic or autoimmune disorder that can affect eye musculature.

● **Hematopoietic and immune.** Anemias can cause retinal changes.

Physical examination

Preparation and equipment

The best environment for an eye examination is a quiet room, free of distractions, in which you can control the lighting and make the patient comfortable. Be sure you have the following equipment on hand:

● Snellen or E chart (to test distance vision)
● Jaeger or Lebensohn card (to test near vision)
● hand light or penlight
● cover card or eye cover
● direct ophthalmoscope
● cotton-tipped applicator (to evert eyelids).

Testing distance vision

With most patients, use the Snellen chart to test distance vision (see *The Snellen Chart*). Make sure the chart is well-lighted and without glare.

Seat the patient 20′ (6 m) away from the chart. If he's wearing glasses or contact lenses, ask him to remove them so you can test his uncorrected vision first. Begin with the right eye. Have the patient occlude the left eye. Then, ask him to read the smallest line of letters he can see on the chart.

Visual acuity is recorded as a fraction: The numerator is the distance from the chart, and the denominator is the distance at which a normal eye can read this line. Record the fraction assigned to the smallest line your patient can read. A person who can read the 20/20 line on the Snellen chart is considered to have normal distance vision. If your patient's distance vision tests at less than 20/20, use a pinhole occluder and perform the test again; his tested vision may improve if it's a refractive error.

Now repeat the test for the patient's left eye, with the right eye occluded. If your patient wears glasses or contact lenses, use the same procedure to test his corrected vision.

If your patient can't read the largest letter on the Snellen chart from a distance of 20′, ask him to approach the chart until he *can*

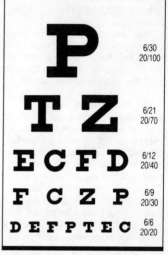

The Snellen Chart

You'll use a Snellen chart like the one shown here to test your patient's distance vision.

P	6/30 20/100
T Z	6/21 20/70
E C F D	6/12 20/40
F C Z P	6/9 20/30
D E F P T E C	6/6 20/20

read it. Then record the distance between him and the chart. For example, if the patient can see the 20/200 line of the eye chart from a distance of 3′ (1 m), record the test result as *3′/200*.

Your patient's distance vision may be so poor that he can barely count the number of fingers you hold up in front of him. If he can count fingers (CF) at 2′ (61 cm), record his distance vision as *CF at 2′*. If the patient can't see your fingers, try hand movements (HM) at a distance of 2′. Move your hand up and down or from side to side, and ask him which way your hand is moving. If he responds correctly, record the result as *HM at 2′*. (Sometimes a patient may be able to see better if he turns his head slightly.)

A patient may have only light perception in his eyes from such disorders as trauma, dense cataracts, retinal degeneration, or hemorrhage. To test light perception (LP), first occlude the patient's left eye. Then darken the room, position an ophthalmoscope in front of the patient's right eye, and begin switching the instrument's light on and off. Ask the patient if he sees the light; if he does, ask when he first sees it and when he stops seeing it, and if he can tell you the direction from which the light is coming. Then vary the quadrants of the light. If he responds correctly, record the result as *LP with projection.* If he can't see the light at all, record *NLP* (no light perception).

If your patient is illiterate, you can use an E chart to test his distance vision. Ask him which way the legs of the E are pointing. Record the results of this visual acuity test as you would with the Snellen chart.

Near vision testing

If the patient wears glasses or bifocals, he should wear them throughout this test. Ask him to hold a well-lighted Jaeger or Lebensohn card at a comfortable distance—about 14″ (35 cm)—from his eyes. (If you don't have a near vision card, use a newspaper page with different type sizes on it.) Then ask him to cover his left eye and read the smallest paragraph he can see clearly on the card. After recording the results, have the patient cover his right eye and repeat the test.

Color vision testing

Using color plates, such as the Ishihara and the Hardy-Rand-Ritter plates, is the preferred method for determining a patient's ability to distinguish reds, greens, and blues. You can also ask your patient to distinguish between the red and green lines on the Snellen chart.

External eye inspection

Begin by standing directly in front of the patient. Inspect his eyes for symmetry in size, shape, contour, and movement of the eyes and surrounding structures (see *External Eye Structures,* page 119). Observe their alignment: Do the eyes look alike? Normally, the upper quarter of the iris can't be seen on frontal view because the eyelid covers it. Are the eyes entirely exposed? Or, do the lids droop (ptosis)? Ask the patient to close his eyes gently; check for complete lid closure. Inadequate lid closure may expose the cornea during sleep and cause drying and ulceration.

Next, examine the patient's eyelids for edema, inflammation, or masses. A *stye* (hordeolum) is a staphylococcal infection of the eyelid glands characterized by a localized red, swollen, acutely tender area on the lid margin. Located deep in the eyelid, a *chalazion* is a sterile inflammation of the meibomian glands (or the glands of Zeis) that's swollen but, unlike a stye, is painless. The inflammation is chronic and doesn't subside spontaneously.

Yellow plaques on the skin of the lids *(xanthelasma)*—usually at the medial canthal area—indicate increased lipid deposits in the patient's blood. Note the turgor of the lids, and any extra skin folds. Do the lids appear to have lost elasticity? Are the changes bilateral?

Note whether the lid margins turn inward *(entropion),* causing the lashes to scrape against the eyeball, or outward *(ectropion),* at times preventing complete closure of the eye. Examine the lid margins closely for erythema and scales. Are the lashes clean and free of debris? (Note whether the patient wears eye makeup.)

Palpate both the preauricular and submandibular lymph nodes. Then, palpate each bony orbit for pain, edema, and masses, noting the eye's size and shape. The eyeballs shouldn't protrude excessively from their orbits *(exophthalmos)* or appear abnormally sunken *(enophthalmos).* Eye position should be the same bilaterally.

Inspect the skin around the patient's eyes for plaques, moles, discoloration, redness, and scaliness. Carefully observe any growths, such as moles, for color, shape, and contour.

Examine the inside of the patient's lower lid. You'll notice an initial blanching from this maneuver; the normal pink color should reappear promptly. (If the lid remains pale, your patient may be anemic.) Inspect also for foreign bodies, such as lashes or traces of eye makeup. Evert the upper lid to check for infection, swelling, or foreign bodies. To do this, have the patient look down, then gently pinch the lashes of the upper lid and bend the lid back over a cotton-tipped applicator.

Inspect the conjunctiva and sclera by separating the patient's eyelids widely, avoiding excessive pressure on the eyeball by holding the lids against the ridge of the bony orbit. Then, ask him to look right and left, then up and down.

The conjunctiva should be clear and transparent, free of cloudiness and redness.

The normal sclera is white and quiescent.

External Eye Structures

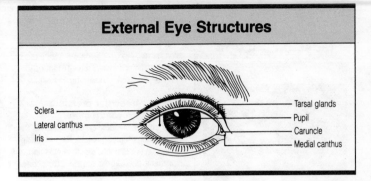

Sclera

Lateral canthus

Iris

Tarsal glands

Pupil

Caruncle

Medial canthus

Black patients may show scattered areas of brown pigment—a normal finding. Blue discoloration may indicate scleral thinning.

Note any change from normal in the sclera's color or vascular bed. Often such changes are among the first symptoms of a systemic disorder (for example, the yellow sclera that is suggestive of jaundice).

Extraocular muscle function

Assessing extraocular muscle function involves three tests: the corneal reflex, the cover-uncover test, and checking the six cardinal fields of gaze. (See *Extraocular Muscle Function,* page 120.)

To test your patient's corneal light reflex, stand directly in front of him, and hold a penlight or small flashlight at his eye level and 12″ to 15″ (30 to 38 cm) away. Ask him to stare straight ahead. Then shine the light directly between his eyes. You'll see a dot of light on each cornea; the dots should be in the same spot on the cornea and equidistant from his nose. If they are, your patient's reflex is symmetrical. An asymmetrical reflex indicates a deviating eye—possibly from a muscle imbalance.

This finding is your cue to perform the cover-uncover test to see if the patient can maintain parallel gaze, necessary for binocular vision. To perform this test, have him fixate on a distant object. Cover his left eye, and watch the right eye to see if it moves to remain fixed on the distant object. Next, uncover the left eye: If it jerks into position to fix on the object the eye has drifted while resting, which indicates a muscle imbalance.

Repeat this procedure, in reverse, covering the right eye.

You can test extraocular muscle function further by checking the fields of gaze. Hold a pencil or tongue depressor in front of your patient. Ask him to keep his head still and follow the object with his eyes as you move it clockwise, tracing the six cardinal fields of gaze. Stop at each field, and observe the patient's eyes. Note if they drift away from a fixed position and jerk back *(nystagmus).* Minor nystagmus is normal only in the extreme lateral gaze. Consider all other nystagmus findings abnormal. Also note any *eye deviation.* If one of the patient's eyes deviates nasally, record the movement as *esotropic (ET).* Record temporal deviation as *exotropic (XT).* Record an upward deviation as *hypertropic (HT).*

Peripheral vision

Confrontation visual field testing provides gross estimates of your patient's peripheral vision and also serves as a useful screening procedure for partial vision loss. (To perform this test, *you* must have normal peripheral vision.) Sit directly opposite the patient at a distance of about 2′ (60 cm). Have the patient cover his left eye while you cover your right eye. Then ask the patient to fixate on your nose or uncovered eye. Hold a brightly colored object, pencil, or penlight in your left hand, and extend your left arm to the side. Ask the patient to maintain his gaze while you slowly move the object into his line of vision, and to tell you when he first sees it. Use your own visual field as the normal for this test. Examine all quadrants of the patient's right eye (both

Extraocular Muscle Function

When performing the corneal light reflex test, watch the dots of light for symmetrical or asymmetrical positioning.

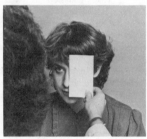

Use the cover-uncover test to evaluate your patient's eye muscles for weakness or imbalance.

When testing the six cardinal fields of gaze, note normal and abnormal nystagmus.

directions horizontally, from above and from below); then examine his left eye in the same way.

If your patient's visual field is significantly constricted, more sophisticated testing (such as perimetry or a tangent screen examination) may be required to obtain further data.

Intraocular pressure measurement

Two kinds of tonometers are available: the indentation (Schiøtz) tonometer and the applanation (Goldmann) tonometer. As part of a general physical examination, the Schiøtz tonometer—which measures the depth of indentation produced on the cornea—is most commonly used.

For this test, have the patient lie on his back. Explain that he must keep both eyes open for this test and must fixate on a target (use a spot on the ceiling, positioned directly above his eyes). Reassure him that although you'll be touching his eye with an instrument, he won't feel any discomfort.

Then, instill a topical eye anesthetic, such as 0.5% tetracaine hydrochloride, and wait 15 to 20 seconds.

Now, gently retract the patient's upper and lower lids and, holding the tonometer vertically, rest the curved footplate gently on the center of the cornea. Don't put pressure on the eyeball. Note the position of the pointer on the scale. To determine the tension, refer to the table of measures that accompanies the tonometer. An average reading falls between 5 and 6 units on the tonometer scale and translates to a tension of between 12 and 20 mm Hg. Generally, the lower the reading on the tonometer scale, the higher the tension.

If the patient squeezes his eyelids together, it will falsely elevate the tension. Instruct him repeatedly to look at the fixation point with his other eye. This will distract him, relieve the tension in the eyelids, and enable him to be more cooperative. If the tonometer scale reads 3 units or less, use the 7.5-g weight or the 10-g weight and repeat the test.

After testing the right eye, repeat the procedure with the left eye.

Corneal Inspection

Inspect your patient's corneas for haziness, abnormal light reflex, and blood vessels. Direct a penlight beam slowly over all corneal areas. You should observe the light reflecting evenly across each cornea.

During corneal inspection, you can easily assess the anterior chamber of the eye—which should be clean, deep, shadow-free, and filled with clear aqueous humor (see *Anatomy of the Eye*).

If your patient's blink reflex is not obvious, test his corneal reflex. Ask the patient to look up. Then, touch the cornea of one eye lightly with the tip of a piece of cotton. If the reflexes are normal, the patient should blink both eyes repeatedly.

Iris and pupillary inspection

When inspecting the iris, note its color, size, shape, texture, and pattern. Look for evidence of previous surgery—such as sector iridectomy, which may appear as a wedge-shaped or roughly circular dark opening. Also inspect for evidence of trauma; for example, iris prolapse may be signaled by hyphema or a ragged, irregular pupil.

Your patient's pupils should be of equal size and roundness (although about 25% of the population have unequally sized pupils). Normal pupil size (which varies at different ages and from patient to patient) generally ranges from 3 to 4 mm. Note any change from round in the shape of the pupils.

To test the pupils, stand directly in front of the patient. Ask him to stare straight ahead as you shine a penlight into one of his eyes. (The light should come from the side, because direct light makes the pupil constrict before you can look at it.) The pupil should constrict quickly. Repeat this procedure on the patient's other eye. You should also notice a *consensual pupillary response:* The pupil of one eye constricts simultaneously when the opposite pupil is exposed to light. This response should occur even if the other eye is blind. (If only the blind eye is exposed to light, neither pupil will react.)

Ophthalmoscopic examination

The direct ophthalmoscope lets you examine the interior of the patient's eyes. This handheld instrument is equipped with a strong light

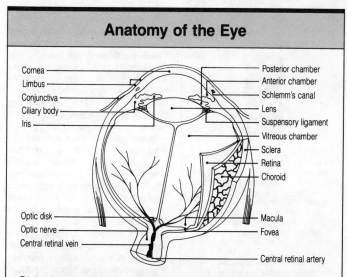

Anatomy of the Eye

Cornea
Limbus
Conjunctiva
Ciliary body
Iris

Posterior chamber
Anterior chamber
Schlemm's canal
Lens
Suspensory ligament
Vitreous chamber
Sclera
Retina
Choroid

Optic disk
Optic nerve
Central retinal vein

Macula
Fovea

Central retinal artery

This lateral cross section shows the three layers of the eye: the external or *fibrous* layer, which contains the sclera and cornea; the middle or *vascular* layer, which contains the choroid, ciliary body, and iris; and the internal or *nervous* layer, which contains the retina.

The Ophthalmoscope

An ophthalmoscope consists of three parts: the handle, the battery housing, and the head. Note that the ophthalmoscope head has two dials on it: one on the back for aperture regulation and one on the side for lens selection. The ophthalmoscope shown here is a Welch Allyn ophthalmoscope. Your ophthalmoscope may come with an interchangeable otoscope, throat illuminator head, or nasal illuminator head, but it's basically similar to the one shown here.

To assemble the ophthalmoscope, screw the handle onto the battery housing. Next, align the base of the head with the lugs on the top of the handle, push down, and rotate the head until you hear it click into place.

source and various lenses that enable you to view the lens, the anterior chamber, and retinal structures and blood vessels. (See *The Ophthalmoscope*.)

You can regulate the amount of light you shine into your patient's eyes by using the aperture selection dial, located on the back of the ophthalmoscope head. You can select the lens you need (to focus the image you're looking at) using the lens selection wheel, which is located on the side of the ophthalmoscope head. To examine the patient's right eye, hold the ophthalmoscope up to your right eye with your right hand. Reverse the procedure to examine the left eye.

Flash the circle of light on the patient's pupil from a distance of about 1′ (30 cm) and also at a slight angle (about 25° to 30°), lateral to the patient's line of vision. You should notice a bright orange glow in the pupil—the *red reflex*. In some patients, an opacity may obscure your view of it. Keeping the red reflex in sight, instruct the patient to keep both eyes open and to maintain his gaze on a distant object. Then approach the patient slowly, until the ophthalmoscope is close to his pupil. This prevents eye rotation and encourages dilatation of the pupils.

Look next at the anterior chamber, which should be clear and free of particles. To do this, sit close to your patient, looking through his pupil with the ophthalmoscope, until some retinal structure, such as a blood vessel or the disk, comes into view. Focus the image. If the disk is not apparent, follow the vessels toward the midline until the optic disk comes into view. Focus the disk image.

To distinguish between arteries and veins in your patient's eye, remember that veins have a larger caliber and are dark red, with little or no light reflex. Arteries are small and bright red, with a bright light reflex. Note the normal light reflex present on the vessel. Vessels should appear regular in configuration and emanate from the optic disk into the vitreous.

Look for color differences in the blood vessels; copper or silver coloring can indicate arteriosclerosis. Also note the presence of any white blood vessels, called *ghost vessels*. These indicate previous vascular events. Note the general color, configuration, tortuosity, and course of the vessels. Are the veins beaded or sausage-shaped? Vascular irregularities may indicate systemic as well as ocular disorders.

Look at the background of the retina. Ask the patient to gaze upward, downward, and to each side. Its color may vary according to your patient's race and skin pigmentation, but normally you won't see areas of hemorrhage or small red dots (microaneurysms).

Next, observe the optic disk directly. Note its size and shape, as well as how distinct its margins are. The nasal edge of the disk is normally not as distinct as the temporal edge, especially when the patient is myopic. The overall color of the optic disk is also important. It should be pink. Next, note the shape of the *physiologic cup*—the depressed central area of the disk—which is normally yellow-white. It should occupy one third of the optic disk diameter. If it's larger than this, or asymmetrical, consider the possibility that your patient has glaucoma.

Finally, examine the macula. Because this is the center of most acute vision, avoid directing the ophthalmoscope's light on it for long periods; the light can be uncomfortable for the patient. Instead, to find the macula, locate the disk and look temporally about two disk diameters away. The macula should appear darker than the rest of the retina, with a bright spot of light reflected from its center—the fovea. If you can't find it this way, ask the patient to look directly at the light. The macula is light reflective and should come into view.

Pediatric assessment

The child's health history

When taking a child's history, be alert for clues to familial eye disorders, such as refractive errors or retinoblastoma. A child whose family history includes relatives with glaucoma should be referred to an ophthalmologist, even if he has no obvious symptoms.

Ask if the child has been hurt during play. Children may suffer blows to the eye or head during play that can cause ocular trauma, such as hyphema. (Although you may detect the hemorrhage on external examination, it may not be readily visible to the parents, and the child may not complain of pain or discomfort.) If the child's history indicates he may have been hurt during play, ask the parents if the child has been unusually lethargic or drowsy. And because nausea and vomiting usually occur with hyphema, question the parents about these signs. Refer the child to an ophthalmologist if you suspect ocular trauma.

Often a school nurse or teacher will be the first to notice a child's vision problems and refer him for further evaluation. Behavior problems in school are often related to a child's having trouble seeing the chalkboard.

Visual acuity tests

Because 20/20 visual acuity and depth perception are fully developed by age 7, you can test vision in school-age children as you would for adults. To test toddlers and preschoolers, you'll need to use different techniques. No accurate method is available to test visual acuity in children under age 3, but testing with Allen cards may give you some useful data. The Allen cards can make the eye examination seem like play and help reduce the child's anxiety.

Each Allen card is illustrated with a familiar object, such as a Christmas tree, birthday cake, or horse. Show the child the cards, and give him time to become familiar with them. Ask if he can identify the objects. Then test his right eye first (cover his left eye). As you flash the cards one by one, ask the child to identify each picture. Next, gradually back away from the child, and record the maximum distance at which he identifies at least three pictures. Record this distance as the numerator of the measure of visual acuity. (The denominator of 30′ [9 m] represents the maximum distance at which a child with normal vision can differentiate the cards; it's the standard for measuring children in this age-group.) For example, if the child identifies three pictures at a maximum of 15′ (4.5 m), you would record his visual acuity as *15/30*.

Normal visual acuity for children ages 2 to 3 ranges from 12/30 to 15/30. Children ages 3 to 4 normally have a visual acuity ranging from 15/30 to 20/30.

Test a child age 4 with the E chart, which is composed entirely of capital Es, their legs variously pointing up, down, right, or left. The child identifies what he sees by indicating with his hands or fingers the position of each E.

Visual fields and color vision

Seat the child on his parent's lap, and have the parent hold the child's head straight forward (or ask the child to look at your nose) while you move an object, such as a small toy, into the child's visual field, following the same procedure you'd use for an adult.

Another way to perform this test is to have a co-worker or parent stand in front of the child and serve as the object for the child to fixate on; you stand behind the child and move the toy.

Color blindness is uncommon in girls, so you'll generally assess only boys' color vision. If a child can identify colors and is over age 4, perform color screening by asking the child to distinguish colored wools or to trace numbers on color-vision charts with his fingers.

Strabismus

For a child to develop normal vision, both his eyes must work in unison. One of the most commonly seen abnormalities in preschool-age children is *strabismus,* caused by the misalignment of each eye's optic axis. As a result, one or both of the child's eyes turn in (crossed eyes), up, down, or out. Irreversible vision loss may occur if this condition is not detected early.

A child with a deviating eye usually develops double vision (*diplopia*) first, and then his brain compensates for the double vision by suppressing one image. Continued disuse of the deviating eye leads to *amblyopia*—an irreversible loss of visual acuity in the suppressed eye.

If the infant or toddler appears to have a deviating eye, refer him to an ophthalmologist for further evaluation. In older children, you can perform the *cover-uncover test.* Ask the child to fixate on an attractive distant target, such as a stuffed animal, a lollipop, or a cartoon figure. Cover his left eye with an occluder (but don't touch it), and observe his right eye. It shouldn't move or change position to view the object. And when the occluder is removed, the other eye shouldn't jerk back into position. If you don't see any movement, the eye is straight. Cover the right eye and repeat the test. To detect more subtle deviations, repeat the test in all fields of gaze. Have the patient look up, down, right, and left.

The *light reflection test* (Hirschberg's test)

also helps to detect strabismus. Shine a penlight into the child's eyes. The light reflection should appear in the same position on each pupil. A slight variation indicates strabismus.

Dilating a child's pupils

A complete ophthalmoscopic examination of a child, like that for an adult, frequently necessitates pupillary dilatation (mydriasis). Dilating drops sting, and you may have difficulty maintaining the child's cooperation. Some health-care professionals advocate instilling a topical anesthetic before the dilating drops, but anesthetic drops also sting. Generally, you'll need to use gentle force and perhaps enlist assistance from the parents or coworkers.

Geriatric assessment

Some effects of aging on eyes and vision

When you examine an elderly patient's eyes, keep in mind that ocular manifestations of aging can affect the entire eye. As you begin your inspection, you may note that his eyes sit deeper in the bony orbits. This normal finding results from fatty-tissue loss, which occurs with age.

Your patient's *eyelids* probably also show evidence of aging. Look for excess skin on the upper lid that results from normal loss of tissue elasticity. Entropion and ectropion are common in elderly persons. You may note drooping of the upper eyelids (blepharochalasis). When it results from normal aging changes, blepharochalasis usually occurs gradually and bilaterally. It may be so severe that it obscures vision. If sudden or unilateral, it may indicate a more serious problem.

When you inspect the *conjunctiva,* be aware that its luster may appear dimmed, and it may be drier and thinner than in younger patients. This dryness may trigger frequent episodes of conjunctivitis.

Aging can also affect the *lacrimal apparatus.* For example, the delicate *canaliculi* and *nasolacrimal ducts* may become plugged or kinked, resulting in constantly watering eyes. Such a blockage can also decrease tear production, causing dryness of an elderly person's eyes.

When you inspect the patient's *corneas,* you

may note lipid deposits on the periphery, known as *arcus senilis*. In persons who are at least age 50, these deposits usually have no pathologic effect. The cornea also flattens with age, sometimes causing astigmatism.

You may see bilateral irregular *iris* pigmentation, with the normal pigment replaced by a pale brown color. After iridectomy to treat glaucoma, the iris may be irregular.

An elderly patient's *pupils* may be unusually small if he's taking medication to treat glaucoma. If an intraocular lens was implanted in the pupillary space after cataract removal, the pupil may be irregularly shaped.

Normally, when you examine an elderly patient's *macula* with an ophthalmoscope, you may find that the *foveal light reflex* is not as bright as in younger patients.

Effects of drugs on the eyes

Because an elderly patient is likely to be taking medications for a systemic disease, remember that certain drugs used to treat such conditions as hypertension and congestive heart failure may have ocular sequelae. Make sure you've questioned your patient thoroughly about such medications in the history interview.

Certain ocular medications can cause systemic side effects that affect elderly patients more often than the general population. One example of this is scopolamine hydrobromide eye drops—a cycloplegic used in the treatment of uveitis and postoperatively in patients who have had cataract surgery. It may cause dizziness and disorientation.

Presbyopia

Gradual loss of accommodation because of decreased lens elasticity is an early indication of aging known as *presbyopia*. This condition usually begins during the fourth decade of life. The patient complains of near-vision blurring and fatigue from close work. Characteristically, he holds reading material farther and farther away, as presbyopia advances, in an attempt to focus clearly. Presbyopia is easily corrected with reading glasses or bifocals.

Cataracts

Cataracts are lens opacities that arise from changes in the physical and chemical state of the lens. These changes occur very slowly and can cause painless vision loss.

Cataracts occur in different forms. They may occur on the lens peripherally—similar in appearance to the spokes of a wheel—or centrally. A cataract may be dense, occluding the lens, or appear as crystals in the lens, causing little (or no) vision loss. A dense, mature cataract (totally opaque and white) gives the pupil an obvious light-colored or white appearance. If your patient's cataract causes severe visual impairment, the lens can be surgically removed and replaced with an intraocular lens implant or contact lens.

Other geriatric vision disorders

Retinal detachment, in which the sensory portion of the retina separates from the pigment layer, most commonly affects persons over age 45. Many of these patients report recent eye trauma or have a history of nearsightedness. Patients with retinal detachment complain of vision loss (sometimes a cloud over part of the visual field) and the sudden appearance of *floaters*—spots flashing in their field of vision. If untreated, blindness may result.

Glaucoma, a slowly progressive disease characterized by abnormally increased intraocular pressure, may begin in a patient's early years, but its long-term effects are more readily seen in an elderly patient. Caused by overproduction of aqueous humor or obstruction of its outflow, glaucoma may produce pain, blurred vision, and eventual optic nerve damage, or it can progress to blindness with *no* discomfort.

Senile macular degeneration, a bilateral condition of unknown etiology, frequently occurs in persons age 60 and older. This untreatable condition is a leading cause of blindness in the United States and is characterized by the presence of *drusen,* small, yellow defects in the retinal epithelium. Drusen result from breaks in the integrity of the retinal pigment. They may be scattered throughout the retina, causing no vision loss, or may coalesce in the macular area, causing significant central vision loss.

Pterygium (an encroachment of a fold of conjunctiva onto the cornea) is a degenerative and hyperplastic process that progresses slowly and may eventually cover the cornea. The patient may complain of irritation or even vision loss.

Guide to Eye Disorders

DISORDERS	CHIEF COMPLAINT	
Blepharitis	• *Pain/Discomfort:* itching; burning; foreign-body sensation • *Vision changes:* none • *Tearing/Secretion:* crusted lids after awakening • *Appearance changes:* red-rimmed lids from unconscious rubbing; with seborrheic blepharitis, greasy scales on lashes; with ulcerative blepharitis, flaky scales on lashes, ulcerated areas on lid margins, loss of lashes	
Cataract	• *Pain/Discomfort:* none • *Vision changes:* photophobia; gradual blurring and loss of vision; misty vision; changes in color value (particularly loss of blue and yellow); halos around lights; difficulty with night driving from scattering of light • *Tearing/Secretion:* none • *Appearance changes:* none	
Chalazion	• *Pain/Discomfort:* none • *Vision changes:* astigmatism or distorted vision, depending on size of chalazion • *Tearing/Secretion:* none • *Appearance changes:* localized swelling of affected lid	
Conjunctivitis	• *Pain/Discomfort:* varying degrees of pain and discomfort; itching; foreign-body sensation • *Vision changes:* photophobia when cornea affected • *Tearing/Secretion:* increased tearing; discharge (may be purulent) • *Appearance changes:* reddened cornea and conjunctiva; lids may be crusty or have sticky mucopurulent discharge; pseudoptosis, especially apparent in early morning	
Corneal abrasion	• *Pain/Discomfort:* severe pain, despite size of injury; foreign-body sensation • *Vision changes:* decreased acuity, depending on size and location of injury • *Tearing/Secretion:* increased tearing • *Appearance changes:* reddened conjunctiva	
Corneal ulcers	• *Pain/Discomfort:* pain aggravated by blinking • *Vision changes:* blurred vision, especially in central corneal ulceration • *Tearing/Secretion:* increased tearing; purulent discharge if bacterial infection present • *Appearance changes:* injected cornea	

HISTORY	PHYSICAL EXAMINATION AND DIAGNOSTIC STUDIES
• Seborrhea of scalp, eyebrows, or ears; recent *Staphylococcus aureus* infection; conjunctivitis; superficial keratitis on lower third of cornea; chronic meibomianitis in early morning	• Inspection reveals red-rimmed lids; scales, ulcers, or nits on lashes. • Loss of lashes possible. • Further diagnostic studies include culture of ulcerated lid.
• Mostly affects older persons; also result of lens trauma from foreign body, or intraocular diseases; exposure to cataractogenic drugs, such as ergot, dinitrophenol, naphthalene • Diabetes	• Inspection with penlight reveals visible white area behind pupil. • Ophthalmoscopic examination reveals lens opacification. • Slit-lamp examination shows dark area or shadow in otherwise homogenous red reflex. • Vision acuity tests reveal decreased acuity often proportionate to density of cataract.
• Inflammation developed over a period of weeks	• Inspection reveals lump on upper or lower lid, pointing toward conjunctival side of lid; red-yellow raised arch inside lid. • Palpation reveals small lump on lid. • Further diagnostic studies include biopsy if chalazion recurs persistently.
• Allergic reactions; infection; recent onset; in children, recent fever or sore throat	• Inspection may reveal enlarged regional nodes; reddened conjunctiva; sticky, crusty lids, with mucopurulent discharge; increased tearing. • Vision acuity tests reveal photophobia, with corneal involvement. • Further diagnostic studies include culture and sensitivity tests and stained smears of conjunctival scrapings.
• Sudden onset of symptoms after eye trauma—such as from a piece of dust, metal, dirt, or grit embedded under the eyelid—or prolonged contact lens wear	• Inspection reveals reddened cornea and conjunctiva; foreign body (possibly visible with light); green affected area, after instilling 2% fluorescein. • Slit-lamp examination reveals depth of abrasion. • Vision acuity tests reveal decreased acuity.
• Trauma • Contact lens wear	• Inspection reveals possibly injected cornea; irregular corneal surface apparent with light; outline of ulcer apparent with fluorescein dye instilled. • Vision acuity tests reveal decreased acuity in varying degrees. • Further diagnostic studies include culture and sensitivity tests.

(continued)

Guide to Eye Disorders *(continued)*

DISORDERS	CHIEF COMPLAINT	
Dacryocystitis	• *Pain/Discomfort*: in acute form, pain, tenderness over nasolacrimal sac; in chronic form, discomfort from tearing • *Vision changes*: none • *Tearing/Secretion*: constant tearing; in acute form, purulent discharge from punctum, with pressure over nasolacrimal sac; in chronic form, mucoid discharge, with pressure over nasolacrimal sac • *Appearance changes*: in acute form, inflammation over nasolacrimal sac; in chronic form, none	
Diabetic retinopathy	• *Pain/Discomfort*: none • *Vision changes*: glaring of vision; decreased acuity in later stages; dark spots, floaters • *Tearing/Secretion*: none • *Appearance changes*: none	
Extraocular motor nerve palsies	• *Pain/Discomfort*: may have pain, depending on cause of palsy • *Vision changes*: diplopia, depending on muscles innervated • *Tearing/Secretion*: none • *Appearance changes*: none	
Eyeball trauma resulting in hyphema	• *Pain/Discomfort*: varying degree of pain and discomfort • *Vision changes*: may have loss of vision (if injury caused retinal damage) • *Tearing/Secretion*: none • *Appearance changes*: blood obscuring iris; may have associated swelling of eyelid, ecchymosis (black eye)	
Glaucoma (acute closed-angle)	• *Pain/Discomfort*: sudden onset of severe unilateral inflammation, pain, and pressure • *Vision changes*: sudden onset of blurring; decreased acuity; halos around lights; photophobia; if untreated, can produce blindness in 3 to 5 days • *Tearing/Secretion*: none • *Appearance changes*: cornea may appear hazy	

HISTORY	PHYSICAL EXAMINATION AND DIAGNOSTIC STUDIES
• Severe trauma to midface or nasal disease	• Inspection reveals evident tearing; in acute form, inflammation over affected lacrimal sac. • Palpation reveals lump over area; discharge, with pressure over affected area. • Further diagnostic studies include conjunctival smear.
• Adult or juvenile diabetes	• Slit-lamp examination reveals thickened retinal capillary walls. • Indirect ophthalmoscopic examination shows retinal changes, such as venous dilation and twisting, exudates, microaneurysms, hemorrhages, or edema. • Further diagnostic studies include fluorescein angiography to differentiate between microaneurysms and true hemorrhages, and BUN and serum creatinine for renal function.
• Tumors, diabetes, or recent sixth cranial nerve infection • Trauma • Aneurysm • Meningitis	• Inspection reveals, with third nerve palsy, ptosis, exotropia, dilated and unresponsive pupil, no eye movement, no accommodation; with fourth nerve palsy, head tilted to opposite shoulder to compensate for vertical diplopia (ocular torticollis); with sixth nerve palsy, eye unable to abduct beyond midline, esotropia. • Skull X-rays and scan performed to diagnose tumors; culture and sensitivity tests performed if caused by infection.
• Recent injury, such as being struck by a ball or fist	• Slit-lamp examination reveals blood in anterior chamber, obscuring the iris. • Tonometer examination reveals increased intraocular pressure. • Dilated fundus examination reveals retinal damage possibly. • Vision acuity tests reveal decreased acuity, depending on extent of injury.
• Sudden increase in volume of posterior chamber from hemorrhage, congestion or edema of uveal tract • Use of mydriatics	• Inspection reveals shallow or absent anterior chamber; corneal edema; hazy, fixed, and moderately dilated pupil; ciliary injection. • Ophthalmoscopic examination reveals pale optic disk. • Palpation reveals one eye harder than other.

(continued)

Guide to Eye Disorders *(continued)*

DISORDERS	CHIEF COMPLAINT	
Glaucoma (chronic closed-angle)	• *Pain/Discomfort:* none, unless left untreated until final stage • *Vision changes:* transient blurred vision; halos around lights • *Tearing/Secretion:* none • *Appearance changes:* none	
Glaucoma (chronic open-angle)	• *Pain/Discomfort:* mild aching or dull headache; usually no pain • *Vision changes:* gradual, bilateral loss of peripheral vision; halos around lights; decreased acuity, especially at night • *Tearing/Secretion:* none • *Appearance changes:* none	
Hordeolum (stye)	• *Pain/Discomfort:* acute pain and tenderness, depending on extent of swelling • *Vision changes:* none • *Tearing/Secretion:* pus formation within lumen of affected gland • *Appearance changes:* red and swollen lid gland	
Hypertensive retinopathy	• *Pain/Discomfort:* none • *Vision changes:* mild-to-severe decreased acuity • *Tearing/Secretion:* none • *Appearance changes:* none	
Keratitis	• *Pain/Discomfort:* irritation or mild pain • *Vision changes:* photophobia; blurred vision if infection occurs in center of cornea • *Tearing/Secretion:* increased tearing • *Appearance changes:* reddened cornea and conjunctiva; decreased corneal luster	
Keratoconjunctivitis	• *Pain/Discomfort:* burning, scratching, or sandy sensation • *Vision changes:* photophobia • *Tearing/Secretion:* diminished tear production, excess mucus secretion • *Appearance changes:* none	

HISTORY	PHYSICAL EXAMINATION AND DIAGNOSTIC STUDIES
• Family history • Increase in volume of posterior chamber from hemorrhage, congestion, or edema of uveal tact • Gradual narrowing of angle	• Ophthalmoscopic examination reveals cupping and atrophy of optic disk late in disease. • Vision acuity tests reveal loss of peripheral vision.
• Familial; genetically determined • Changes in the lens or uveal tract from systemic disorders • Family history of glaucoma	• Ophthalmoscopic examination reveals cupping and atrophy of optic disk. • Vision field tests reveal loss of peripheral vision. • Tonometer examination reveals increased intraocular pressure.
• Gradual onset of pain and swelling	• Inspection reveals red and swollen lid gland; outward-pointing lash possible. • With internal hordeolum, swollen lid gland points into conjunctival side of lid. • With external hordeolum, swollen lid gland points to skin side of lid margin. • Further diagnostic studies include culture and sensitivity tests of purulent matter.
• High blood pressure	• Ophthalmoscopic examination reveals hard, shiny deposits (in early stages); tiny hemorrhages; elevated arterial blood pressure; cotton-wool patches (in late stages); exudates; retinal edema; papilledema; hemorrhages and microaneurysms. • Vision acuity tests reveal decreased acuity.
• Exposed cornea; bacterial conjunctivitis; with dendritic keratitis, recent upper respiratory tract infection with herpes virus cold sores; with interstitial keratitis, congenital syphilis • Allergies to pollens, dusts, and some foods	• Inspection reveals reddened conjunctiva and decreased corneal luster. • Slit-lamp examination with fluorescein staining reveals one or more small dendritic lesions, ciliary injection, and reduced corneal sensation. • Visual acuity slightly decreased.
• Sjögren's syndrome, rheumatoid arthritis, or other autoimmune diseases characterized by hypofunctioning lacrimal glands, excessive evaporation of tears, or a mucin deficiency	• Slit-lamp examination reveals interrupted or absent tear meniscus at lower lid margin; tenacious, yellow mucous strands in conjunctival fornix; thickened, edematous, and hyperemic bulbar conjunctiva; diminished luster. • Further diagnostic studies include Schirmer tearing test, tear film breakup time to test mucin deficiency, conjunctiva and corneal stain with rose bengal.

(continued)

Guide to Eye Disorders *(continued)*

DISORDERS	CHIEF COMPLAINT	
Keratoconus	• *Pain/Discomfort:* none • *Vision changes:* blurred vision; acuity decreases as disorder progresses • *Tearing/Secretion:* none • *Appearance changes:* indentation of lower lid by cornea when patient looks down (Munson's sign); corneal hydrops may occur	
Optic atrophy	• *Pain/Discomfort:* none • *Vision changes:* decreased acuity; visual fields altered • *Tearing/Secretion:* none • *Appearance changes:* none	
Orbital cellulitis	• *Pain/Discomfort:* dull to extreme pain • *Vision changes:* eye may be closed; visual loss from optic nerve compression or double vision from ocular muscle involvement • *Tearing/Secretion:* possibly purulent discharge from affected area • *Appearance changes:* unilateral lid edema, chemosis (swelling of conjunctiva at cornea), reddened eyeball, matted lashes, hyperemia of orbital tissues, impaired eye movement	
Retinal artery occlusion	• *Pain/Discomfort:* none • *Vision changes:* sudden unilateral loss of vision, partial or complete • *Tearing/Secretion:* none • *Appearance changes:* none	
Retinal detachment	• *Pain/Discomfort:* none • *Vision changes:* shade or curtain spreads across visual fields; floating spots or recurrent flashes of light; gradual loss of vision as detachment progresses • *Tearing/Secretion:* none • *Appearance changes:* none	

HISTORY	PHYSICAL EXAMINATION AND DIAGNOSTIC STUDIES
• Progressively decreased vision; uncorrectable (mostly affects females entering puberty)	• Inspection reveals cone-shaped cornea in later stages. • Placido's disk examination reveals distorted corneal reflection; unclear fundus. • Keratometer reveals abnormal readings. • Ophthalmoscopic examination with high plus lens reveals round, shadowlike reflex in central cornea. • Visual acuity tests reveal decreased acuity that worsens as disorder progresses.
• Central nervous system disorder, such as multiple sclerosis, intraorbital or intracranial tumors; other intraocular disorders • Ingested methanol • Arteriosclerotic changes; systemic degenerative diseases (such as multiple sclerosis); papilledema; metabolic diseases • Syphilis	• Ophthalmoscopic examination reveals nerve head pallor. • Slit-lamp examination reveals optic disk pallor and loss of pupillary reaction. • Vision acuity tests reveal decreased acuity, visual field changes (scotoma possible). • Further diagnostic studies include serology.
• Sudden onset of symptoms; recent streptococcal, staphylococcal, or pneumococcal infection of surrounding areas; recent orbital trauma, such as insect bite; recent history of sinusitis	• Inspection reveals lid edema, reddened eyeball, matted lashes, purulent discharge from affected areas. • Range-of-motion exercises reveal limited movement. • Further diagnostic studies include culture and sensitivity tests.
• Unilateral loss of vision lasting several seconds to a few minutes; mostly affects older persons	• Ophthalmoscopic examination shows emptying of retinal arteries through transient attack; visible segmentation of blood column within 2 hours of occlusion; pale, opaque posterior retina; choroid seen as cherry-red spot; absent direct pupillary response. • Vision acuity tests show decreased acuity or complete loss of vision in affected eye. • Further diagnostic studies include carotid angiography and ultrasonography, to test condition of blood vessels.
• Gradual loss of vision; vitreous detachment	• Ophthalmoscopic examination shows—with dilation—gray, opaque retina, with an indefinite margin; in severe detachment, inward-bulging, gently rippled or folded retina; almost black arteriole and venules; one or more retinal holes possible • Vision acuity tests reveal decreased acuity corresponding to portion of retina detached.

(continued)

Guide to Eye Disorders *(continued)*

DISORDERS	CHIEF COMPLAINT	
Retinitis pigmentosa	• *Pain/Discomfort:* none • *Vision changes:* night blindness first symptom—usually occurs in adolescence; progressively decreased peripheral vision (gun-barrel vision leading to eventual blindness) • *Tearing/Secretion:* none • *Appearance changes:* none	
Strabismus	• *Pain/Discomfort:* none • *Vision changes:* with binocular strabismus, diplopia; with monocular strabismus, amblyopia in deviated eye • *Tearing/Secretion:* none • *Appearance changes:* eyes crossed or deviated	
Trachoma	• *Pain/Discomfort:* pain • *Vision changes:* photophobia, decreased acuity (if untreated, blindness may occur) • *Tearing/Secretion:* increased tearing during early infection; dry eyes if lacrimal ducts become obstructed; exudate • *Appearance changes:* early in disease, lids appear red and edematous, conjunctival follicles visible; 4 to 6 weeks after onset—hard, densely packed conjunctival papillae are beefy-red; later turn yellow or gray; late in disease, lids appear deformed and shortened, and conjunctival and corneal scarring occur.	
Uveitis	• *Pain/Discomfort:* moderate-to-severe pain • *Vision changes:* photophobia; blurred vision; with granulomatous uveitis, floating spots and loss of vision • *Tearing/Secretion:* none • *Appearance changes:* with nongranulomatous uveitis, none; with granulomatous uveitis, affected eye becomes diffusely red with circumcorneal flush	
Vitreous hemorrhage	• *Pain/Discomfort:* none • *Vision changes:* sudden unilateral, loss of vision; may see floaters or dark streaks • *Tearing/Secretion:* none • *Appearance changes:* none	

HISTORY	PHYSICAL EXAMINATION AND DIAGNOSTIC STUDIES
• Hereditary disorder	• Ophthalmoscopic examination shows, with early stage, degenerated retinal pigment epithelium, attenuated retinal arteries, gray or yellow atrophied disk; with final stage, posterior subcapsular cataracts, choroidal sclerosis, macular degeneration. • Vision acuity tests reveal decreased acuity, narrowing visual field. • Further diagnostic studies include electroretinography and electro-oculography.
• Family history indicates strabismus; amblyopia at early age; severe central nervous system disorders, such as Down's syndrome, cerebral palsy, or mental retardation	• Inspection: deviated, uncoordinated eye movements; ptosis; abnormal head position. • Vision acuity tests reveal decreased acuity and eccentric fixation.
• Poor hygiene; lack of water, especially in desert areas or poverty settings; patient may live (or recently have lived) in Africa, Asia, or Latin America, or among Southwest American Indians	• Inspection reveals excessive tearing; red and edematous lids; conjunctival follicles visible, possibly red, gray, or yellow, depending on stage of disease; exudates; conjunctival scarring and lid deformities late in disease. • Visual acuity tests reveal photophobia; possibly decreased acuity. • Further diagnostic studies include Giemsa-stained smears of conjunctival epithelial scrapings.
• May have history of tuberculosis, arthritis, exposure to toxoplasmosis, histoplasmosis, syphilis, arthritis, or genitourinary infection • With nongranulomatous uveitis, acute onset • With granulomatous uveitis, gradual onset	• *Nongranulomatous uveitis:* Inspection reveals small nonreactive pupils, severe injection, and sluggish pupil response to light. *Granulomatous uveitis:* Inspection reveals redness and distorted pupils. • Opthalmoscopic examination reveals active choroid and retina lesions appearing yellow-white through a cloudy vitreous. • Slit-lamp examination reveals keratitic precipitates; Koeppe nodules (cluswhite cells) in iris. • Vision acuity tests reveal decreased acuity and photophobia. • Further diagnostic studies include skin tests for tuberculosis and histoplasmosis, and chest X-ray.
• Diabetes, contusion, concussion, sickle cell anemia	• Slit-lamp examination reveals blood in vitreous chamber and retinal neovascularization. • Ophthalmoscopic examination reveals loss of fundus detail and floating red debris. • Vision acuity tests reveal decreased acuity. • Further diagnostic studies include ultrasonography.

8

Ears and Hearing

Hearing's importance derives from the basic human need to communicate, which colors every aspect of personal growth and development. Unimpaired hearing helps a person communicate with others by enabling him to receive oral messages accurately and hear himself speak. Language retardation in children is commonly caused by undetected deafness—proof of the causal relationship between auditory system functioning and development of language skills.

Assess your patient's ears thoroughly and methodically. A detailed health history is especially important in assessing the auditory system, because many symptoms of ear disorders, such as dizziness and tinnitus, are subjective.

As part of the routine physical examination, you'll perform several procedures, involving all three parts of the ear, including: inspecting the auricle, palpating the pinna and tragus, examining the external ear canal and eardrum, using an otoscope, testing hearing with voice, watch, or a tuning fork.

The causes of ear disorders are numerous, but the most common are fluid behind the eardrum, bacterial or viral infections, trauma, excessive wax buildup or a foreign body in the ear canal, and neurologic dysfunction (see *Hearing Pathways,* page 137).

History data

Biographical data

Acute ear disorders, conductive hearing loss, and reversible hearing loss occur most commonly in children. Otosclerosis most commonly affects females in their late teens and

early 20s. The incidence of presbycusis increases with age.

History of present illness

The most common chief complaints associated with ear or hearing disorders are *pain, discharge, hearing loss, tinnitus,* and *dizziness/ vertigo* (see *Guide to Ear Disorders,* pages 150 to 155). Here are some questions you may want to ask about these complaints to explore fully the history of your patient's present illness:

● **Pain.** *Does the pain occur only when the ear is touched or pulled?* Ear pain that occurs with manipulation usually indicates an external ear problem. *Is the pain deep and throbbing?* Such pain may indicate an acute middle ear disorder. *Does the ear feel blocked?* If your patient's external ear is severely inflamed, the canal may be swollen or completely blocked. Sensations of pressure or blockage may be from eustachian tube dysfunction, which creates negative pressure in the middle ear, or from muscle spasm or temporomandibular joint arthralgia. *Did other health problems precede the ear pain?* Ear pain can be referred from adjacent areas of your patient's body, such as the nose, mouth, paranasal sinuses, and hypopharynx.

● **Discharge.** *Was there a feeling of fullness, followed by a popping sound, before the discharge?* Discharge from your patient's ear can indicate an infection of the external canal or the middle ear. A feeling of fullness may indicate pus or fluid accumulation behind the eardrum. Discharge after a popping sound usually indicates a perforated eardrum caused by a middle ear disorder. *What color is the drainage?* If the drainage is a mixture of blood and pus, the patient's eardrum may have rup-

Hearing Pathways

Sound waves are conveyed through the ear by two pathways—air conduction and bone conduction.

The air conduction pathway operates by transmitting sound waves in the *air* through the external and middle ear to the inner ear. The bone conduction pathway operates by transmitting sound waves through *bone* to the inner ear.

Both bone- and air-transmitted vibrations stimulate nerve impulses in the inner ear. The cochlear branch of the auditory nerve (eighth cranial nerve) transmits these vibrations to the brain so that sound can be heard.

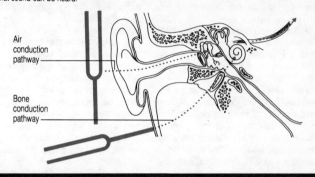

Air
conduction
pathway

Bone
conduction
pathway

tured from a middle ear infection.

● **Hearing loss.** *Do you sometimes shout during a conversation, or ask others to repeat what they've said? Do you often have to turn up the television or radio volume? Is loss of hearing present to some degree in both ears?* Hearing loss resulting from an immobile stapes usually affects both ears. It typically begins to develop—most often in females—when the patient is in her late teens or early 20s. *Do voices sound as though your head is in a bucket?* This is a common complaint of patients with a blocked eustachian tube.

● **Tinnitus.** *Is the noise unilateral or bilateral? Does it seem to pulse?* Pulsations usually accompany middle ear inflammation. *Have you noticed that your own voice sounds hollow and other sounds are muffled?* Tinnitus may result from wax buildup in the ear canal, eardrum perforation, or fluid in the middle ear. *Is the tinnitus high-pitched and ringing?* Such tinnitus usually accompanies acoustic trauma and use of such medications as aspirin and quinine.

● **Dizziness/vertigo.** *Do you feel the room is turning when your eyes are open, and that you are moving when your eyes are closed?* These are the classic symptoms of vertigo. If your patient feels light-headed and unsteady, and *doesn't* have a sensation of turning, he's probably experiencing dizziness. *Does the vertigo come and go, or is it continuous?* Each of these types of vertigo is characteristic of specific diseases. Negative middle ear pressure may produce either set of symptoms. *Does the dizziness/vertigo cause nausea and vomiting?* Labyrinthine disease is the most common cause of severe vertigo or dizziness in a patient who doesn't have central nervous system disease. Dizziness that is less severe and doesn't follow a pattern may be caused by a disease or disorder anywhere in the body. *When did the vertigo begin? Is it associated with other symptoms?* Vertigo of several months' duration, accompanied by ringing tinnitus and hearing loss in one or both ears, is characteristic of edema of the membranous labyrinth in the inner ear. To help identify vertigo, you may also ask: *Does the condition force you to lie down or has it made you fall?*

Past history

Focus on the following health problems and related matters when reviewing your patient's past history:

● *Allergies.* Allergic reactions to cosmetic preparations, such as hair dyes and sprays, can cause chronic dermatitis. Acute serous otitis media may also follow an allergic episode.

● *Chronic ear discharge.* Recurrent ear infections with persistent discharge can become chronic. If untreated, they may cause permanent perforation of the eardrum and eventual hearing loss.

● *Upper respiratory tract infections.* Complications of a common cold, such as sinusitis or bronchitis (usually with fever), can lead to infection of the middle ear through the eustachian tube.

● *Endocrine disorders.* Because patients with diabetes generally don't respond quickly to treatment of infections, ear disorders must be diagnosed and treated promptly to prevent complications. Hypothyroidism can cause hearing loss, usually reversible. Dizziness caused by endocrine dysfunction may occur during menstruation or pregnancy, or hormone (particularly estrogen) treatment.

● *Hypertension.* Hypertension, or a condition in which hypertension occurs (such as arteriosclerosis), causes a high-pitched tinnitus from vascular changes in the patient's central nervous system. Tinnitus fluctuates with blood pressure rise and fall.

● *Drugs.* Many drugs produce cochlear and vestibular toxicity, resulting in related inner ear signs and symptoms, such as dizziness, gait disturbances, or hearing loss.

● *Recent head trauma or injury.* Head injuries can cause tinnitus, vertigo, or hearing loss. A cupping blow to the external ear may rupture the eardrum. A sudden loud noise, such as an explosive blast, can cause acoustic trauma.

● *Previous hearing tests.* The results of previous hearing tests give you baseline information about the progress of your patient's hearing loss.

● *Recent head, facial, or dental surgery.* Because your patient's ear pain may be referred from adjacent body areas, note evidence of any recent surgery involving these regions. For example, tonsillectomy commonly causes referred ear pain within 24 to 48 hours after surgery. Infected tonsils can also cause this type of pain.

Family history

Congenital syphilis can cause hearing loss. *Waardenburg's syndrome* may also cause deafness that's familial in origin but sometimes not until several generations have passed. Individuals born in intervening generations, although not deaf, may exhibit other characteristics of Waardenburg's syndrome, such as heterochromia, widely spaced eyes, or an epicanthal fold.

Psychosocial history

Your patient's occupation may cause, or contribute to, an ear or hearing disorder. Therefore, when you take his psychosocial history, ask if he works in a factory, an airport, or a place where he's frequently exposed to loud noise (for example, from motorcycles, trucks, loud music, or heavy industry). Exposure to loud noise may produce hearing loss that can become permanent if exposure continues.

Activities of daily living

Review of your patient's activities of daily living should include questions about the following:

● *Cosmetics.* Use of cosmetics, hair spray or other hair products, or earrings can irritate the earlobe or the ear canal. Ear piercing, if not done under sterile conditions, can cause an infection in the lobe.

● *Recreation.* Swimming in contaminated water can result in an ear infection, partly because the wax in the patient's ear can cause harmful microorganisms in the water to be retained in the ear canal. If your patient scuba dives or flies frequently, remember that failure to equalize pressures between the environment and the middle ear can cause barotrauma. Ask about hobbies—such as frequently listening to excessively loud music or taking part in skeet shooting—that may expose the patient to loud noises.

● *Self-care.* Using cotton-tipped applicators or bobby pins to clean the ears can irritate your patient's ear canal, introduce infectious organisms, or rupture his eardrum. Regular use of earplugs, earphones, or earmuffs can trap moisture in the ear canal, creating a favorable culture medium for bacteria.

Review of systems

Disorders of the labyrinthine apparatus in the inner ear, such as Ménière's disease, may cause nausea and vomiting. Except for complications resulting from the spread of ear infections, no other body system is significantly affected by ear or hearing disorders.

Physical examination

Preparation and equipment

When examining a patient with an ear or hearing disorder, you inspect and palpate the auricles and surrounding tissues, use an otoscope to inspect the external ear canal and eardrum, and perform appropriate hearing and equilibrium tests. You'll need an otoscope with various-sized specula, cotton-tipped applicators to clear away soft wax, a wristwatch with an audible second hand, and a tuning fork of 512 or 1,024 cycles/second. You may also need a curette or cerumen spoon to remove dry wax or debris from your patient's ear canal.

Before you begin, make sure the examining room is well lighted and quiet. Seat the patient on an examining table or chair, depending on his size, so his head is level with or slightly below yours.

The auricles

Begin examining your patient's ears by inspecting the auricles for bilateral symmetry, angle of attachment (a deviation of more than 10° from the vertical is abnormal), and size in proportion to the patient's head. Normally, the top of each auricle aligns with the canthi of the eye on the same side. Ears vary considerably in size and shape, however; so ignore any minor variations you see and note only striking deformities or deviations.

Next inspect the auricles for appearance (see *The External Ear,* page 140). The taut skin of a healthy auricle is intact and unblemished. Note any discolorations or lesions. (Of course, the color of the auricle depends on your patient's skin color.) If discharge is present in the auricle, note its color, consistency, and odor, and obtain a specimen for culturing.

Palpate all surfaces of each auricle for warmth and tenderness, as well as for swelling, deformities, nodules, skin lesions, or cysts. Press lightly on the tragus, then gently pull

the auricle backward, observing the patient for any sign of discomfort.

Next press firmly on the mastoid area behind each auricle, noting any swelling or tenderness. Then, as your patient opens and closes his mouth, palpate the temporomandibular joint in front of the tragus. Note any crepitation or malalignment, because ear pain can be referred from temporomandibular joint pain. Another way to perform this test is to place the tips of your index fingers in the ear openings while the patient opens and closes his mouth.

Otoscopic examination

After inspecting and palpating the auricles and surrounding tissues, use the otoscope to inspect the ear canal and eardrum. Before beginning, make sure the otoscope is in working order (see *The Otoscope,* page 141). Inspect the entrance to the ear canal to rule out obstruction by a foreign body. Note any irritation or discharge. With a cotton-tipped applicator or suction device, carefully remove any secretions near the ear canal entrance.

Select the largest speculum that will fit comfortably into the ear canal without hurting your patient. To insert the speculum easily, stand to the adult patient's side and tilt his head away from you. Then gently pull his auricle up, back, and slightly out, to better align the S-shaped ear canal with his eardrum.

Before inserting the speculum into the ear canal, brace the hand holding the otoscope against your patient's head (see illustration on page 141) to avoid direct pressure on the canal. Then, while continuing to hold the auricle, carefully insert the speculum into the canal, moving it first downward, then forward. Remember that Arnold's nerve, the auricular branch of the vagus nerve, lies near the entrance to the ear canal. If you stimulate this nerve, you may cause your patient to cough or feel nauseated.

As you insert the speculum, observe the ear canal through the eyepiece, being careful not to insert the speculum too far. (If excessive hair in the ear canal is blocking your view, moisten the speculum with water or a water-soluble lubricant.) Note the width of the canal, as well as any swelling, redness, or obstructions. If you see wax in the canal, note its color. In a light-skinned patient, fresh wax is usually yellow or pink except when dry or impacted,

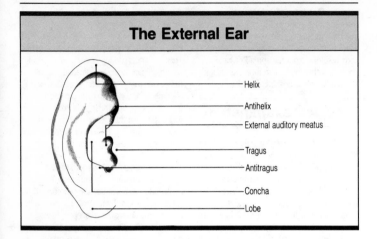

The External Ear

- Helix
- Antihelix
- External auditory meatus
- Tragus
- Antitragus
- Concha
- Lobe

when it's usually yellow brown. Normally, in a dark-skinned patient, earwax may be black or brown. If so much wax has accumulated in the ear canal that you can't see the eardrum, it must be removed.

Eardrum inspection
Looking at your patient's eardrum through the otoscope requires that you manipulate the instrument skillfully, usually with some turning of the patient's head and a gentle tug on the auricle. With this technique, you should be able to see all the eardrum except the anterior inferior quadrant, which normally remains hidden from view because of the membrane's unique angle and the curvature of the anterior canal wall (see *Anatomy of The Eardrum,* page 142). Record the approximate percentage of the eardrum that you can see.

Once you have the eardrum in view, observe its color (see *The Eardrum: Normal and Abnormal Findings,* pages 144 and 145). A healthy eardrum is pearl gray, with a distinctive luster or translucence to its concave surface. The cone of light should stand out clearly between 4 o'clock and 6 o'clock in the right ear, and between 6 o'clock and 8 o'clock in the left ear, assuming your patient is sitting upright. (If he's in any other position, allow for the corresponding rotation of the cone of light.) Now, look for the malleus, which is creamy white; you should locate it easily. Its short process separates the anterior and pos-

terior mallear folds; you'll see the umbo, the tip of the long process, at the vertex of the cone of light. The manubrium (handle) of the malleus, the most prominent landmark, appears as an opaque, narrow band starting at the drum's center. If your patient has an ear disorder, any of these landmarks may be affected, as well as the eardrum's integrity, thickness, vascularity, and symmetry.

Hearing loss tests
Once you've inspected your patient's ear canal and eardrum with the otoscope, you're ready to test his hearing. But remember: The screening tests described here are qualitative and can only suggest that your patient has a hearing disorder; they can't determine the exact type or degree of his hearing loss. Depending on test results, you may have to refer the patient for further evaluation, including audiometry.

Actually, your assessment of a patient's hearing should begin—informally, at least—during the health history interview. At this time, note how he responds. If he seems to watch your lips when you talk, suspect he's lipreading. Test this suspicion by walking behind him and asking him a question. Does he reply inappropriately or fail to answer? Poor articulation may also indicate hearing loss, because speech is learned through hearing.

The *watch-tick* and *whispering* tests provide a gross measurement of your patient's hearing.

The Otoscope

1. Shown here are the basic parts of the otoscope: the battery housing and handle (also used with ophthalmoscope attachments), a light source and magnifying lens, and various-sized specula.

2. Here's how to assemble the parts: Screw the battery housing to the handle, as shown here. Attach the otoscope head to the handle by aligning the lugs on the head with the notches on the handle. Push down firmly, and twist the head clockwise until it clicks into place.

Attach an ear speculum—the largest one comfortable for your patient—by aligning the notch inside the speculum with the notch on the otoscope head. Gently snap the speculum into place.

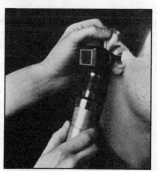

3. Hold the otoscope so the speculum's at the top. Insert the speculum into your patient's ear. Extend the third and fourth fingers of the hand holding the otoscope so that they rest against your patient's head. This will help you brace the otoscope and prevent any damage to your patient's ear. If your patient's uncooperative, try holding the otoscope so the speculum's at the bottom and the entire side of your hand rests against your patient's head, as shown on the right.

Anatomy of the Eardrum

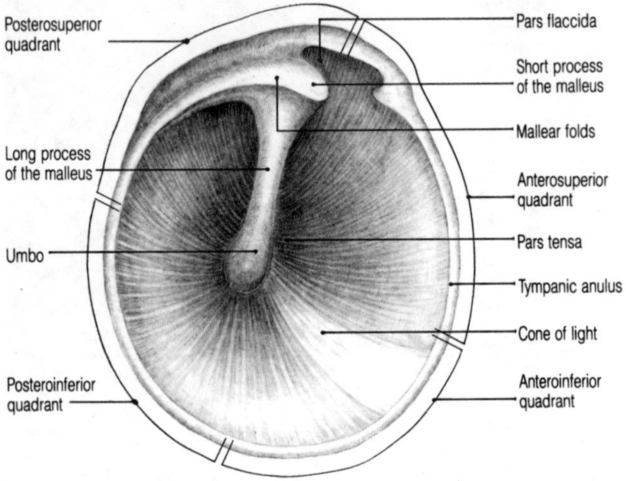

Posterosuperior quadrant

Pars flaccida

Short process of the malleus

Mallear folds

Long process of the malleus

Anterosuperior quadrant

Pars tensa

Umbo

Tympanic anulus

Cone of light

Posteroinferior quadrant

Anteroinferior quadrant

If the findings are abnormal, he'll need further testing. While you're performing these tests, ask your patient to rapidly—but gently—move the tip of his index finger back and forth within the canal entrance of the ear not being tested. This creates a masking effect: The patient hears a different-frequency sound in this ear than he hears in the ear you're testing, so you can be sure he's responding only to what he hears in the tested ear. The same effect may be accomplished by having your patient fold the earlobe over the canal or simply cover his ear with his hand. If he can't do this properly, do it for him; then proceed with one or both of the following tests:

Hold a ticking watch close to the patient's ear. Then move it away from his ear until he says he can't hear the ticking anymore. Record this distance in your notes.

Another version of this test involves whispering, or speaking softly, at a distance of 1' to 2' (30 to 60 cm) from the patient's ear. Exhale fully (to minimize the intensity of your voice), then softly whisper common two-syllable words (such as *airplane*, *watchman*, or *blackboard*) or numbers (*14, 18, 30*)—or a series of monosyllabic numbers (*2, 5, 10*). Usually two or three words or numbers are enough. Then ask the patient to repeat what you said. When you test his other ear, use different words or numbers. If your patient can't understand a low whisper, increase the intensity of your voice to a loud whisper. If he still can't hear you, try soft, medium, and loud speech until he responds correctly. To prevent lipreading, ask him to cover his eyes (or do this for him) or simply mask your mouth with your hand.

The tuning fork

To perform the Weber, Rinne, and Schwabach tests, use a tuning fork with a frequency of 512 or 1,024 cycles/second, which corresponds to the frequency range of normal human speech (see *Tuning Fork Tests,* page 146). The results of these tests help differentiate *conductive, sensorineural* (perceptive), and *mixed* hearing loss, which is a combination of conductive and sensorineural hearing loss (see *Weber, Rinne, and Schwabach Tests,* page 147). Conductive hearing loss is caused by a blockage of sound conduction to the inner ear; sensorineural hearing loss results from disorders of the inner ear, auditory nerve, or brain.

Abnormal results of any of these tests require further quantitative testing.

The Weber test

To perform the Weber test, place the base of a vibrating tuning fork at the vertex of your patient's head or in the center of his forehead. As an alternate site, you may choose the bridge of his nose, his central incisors, or his mandibular symphysis. Ask him if he hears the tone equally well in both ears. (Don't bias his answer by asking which ear he hears it in.) If he does, record the results as *Weber negative,* a normal finding.

If the patient doesn't hear the tone equally well in both ears, ask him to point to the ear in which he hears the *louder* tone. Record the result as *Weber right* or *Weber left,* depending on which ear the patient points to. This is an abnormal finding, possibly indicating conductive hearing loss in this ear. The reason for this seemingly paradoxical conclusion is simple: The tone lateralizes to the affected ear through bone conduction, while background noise prevents similar detection of the tone by the unaffected ear.

The Weber test isn't as specific for sensorineural hearing loss. But if one ear is normal and sensorineural loss exists in the other, the tuning fork is heard louder in the normal ear.

The Rinne test

The Rinne test compares your patient's responses, in both ears, to bone conduction and air conduction of sound. For this test, hold the tuning fork by the stem and strike it against your hand. Then place the vibrating fork against the patient's mastoid process. Hold it there until he no longer hears the tone. Note how many seconds this takes. Then quickly move the tuning fork, still vibrating, to a position in front of his ear canal, with the prongs parallel to the auricle's vertical axis. Hold the tuning fork in this position, without touching the auricle, until the patient no longer hears the tone. Again, note how long this takes. Then repeat the test on his other ear.

If your patient's hearing is normal, he'll hear the air-conducted tone twice as long as the bone-conducted tone (*Rinne positive*). If he hears the bone-conducted tone for as long as he hears the air-conducted tone or longer, it may indicate conductive hearing loss (*Rinne negative*). The Rinne test also produces a positive response in a patient with sensorineural hearing loss, because the inner ear's perception of sound waves by air or bone conduction is compromised.

The Schwabach test

The Schwabach test compares your perception of bone-conducted sound with the patient's. (If your hearing isn't normal, don't perform this test; the results will be inaccurate.) Hold the tuning fork by the stem and strike it against your opposite hand, then place it on the patient's mastoid process. If he hears the tone, quickly place the tuning fork against *your* corresponding mastoid process. Listen for the tone, as you occlude your other ear. If you can hear the tone, place the tuning fork back against the patient's mastoid process. If he can still hear the tone, again place the tuning fork against your mastoid process to see if *you* can still hear it.

Repeat this back-and-forth procedure until neither of you can hear the tone. In most cases, the tone will become inaudible to both of you at the same time. If the patient continues to hear the tone after it's become inaudible to you, note for how many seconds he can still hear it. This abnormal finding indicates possible conductive hearing loss: The patient continues to hear the bone-conducted sound because he is less able to hear the air-conducted background noise that's made the

The Eardrum: Normal and Abnormal Findings

FINDING	COLOR	CONCAVITY/CONVEXITY
Normal	Shiny pearl gray to pale pink	Slightly conical
Inflammation (mild to severe)	Bright pink to bright red	Ranges from loss of conical shape to convex bulging
Bubble, pus, or serum behind tympanic membrane	Yellow to white	Convex bulging
Blood	Blue	Convex bulging
Perforation	Pearl gray, with dark areas	Varies; normal if perforation is small
Obstructed eustachian tube	Normal	Concave
Plaque formation	Pearl gray, with dense white plaques throughout	Conical

bone-conducted tone inaudible to you. Conversely, the patient with sensorineural hearing loss won't hear the tone for as long as you do. Repeat this test on the other ear.

Testing equilibrium

Three common equilibrium tests that you should know how to conduct are the past-pointing test, the falling test, and Hallpike maneuvers. A fourth test—caloric testing—is usually done by physicians.

For the past-pointing test, sit across from the patient, and ask him to close his eyes, extend his arms in front of him, and point with his index fingers. Extend your arms in the same manner, placing your index fingers under and touching the patient's fingers. Ask the patient to raise his arms a few inches, then lower them so his fingers come down on top of yours. A patient with normal equilibrium can do this easily. If the patient misses your fingers (past-pointing), he may have a vestibular apparatus dysfunction.

To conduct the falling test, ask the patient to stand with his feet together, his eyes closed, and his arms at his sides. Normally, the patient

remains erect or sways only slightly, but he shouldn't sway significantly—or fall (Romberg's sign). Make sure you stand close enough to the patient to stop him from falling if he does lose his balance.

Hallpike maneuvers evaluate (and also treat) benign paroxysmal positional vertigo. With the patient lying on his back, gently move his head to the right and hold it there for 1 minute. Positive signs (center and left nystagmus) usually occur within 5 to 10 seconds.

Pediatric assessment

History considerations

A child may be having his ears examined and hearing tested because his parents have noticed that he seems less talkative or less responsive to sounds than usual. A school nurse may refer a child for further testing if he fails a hearing test in school or seems unusually restless or inattentive in class. Such situations are commonplace because of the high incidence of acute ear disorders among children.

As a rule, an infant can localize the direction

LIGHT REFLECTION	APPEARANCE OF LANDMARKS
Bright to dim	Well defined; umbo appears regressed
Dim to lacking	Indistinguishable to lacking definition
Lacking	Variable (depending on fluid, pus, or serum levels)
Lacking	*Umbo and anulus:* not visible; *malleus:* variable (depending on amount of blood in the affected area)
Present *unless* perforation involves the anteroinferior quadrant	Defined *unless* perforation involves specific landmark area
Bent or lacking	Defined but smaller
Present *unless* plaque formation involves the anteroinferior quadrant	Defined *unless* plaques involve specific landmark area

of sound by age 6 months, and a child's hearing is fully developed by age 5. Interview one or both of the parents to obtain history data. Investigate the child's speech development by listening to him carefully. Speech development reflects hearing acuity during childhood. By age 7, for example, most children can speak clearly enough to be understood by most adults. Also observe the child's nonverbal behavior for apparent signs of ear disorders. Does the child rub his ear as though it hurts? Does he tilt his head when listening?

Congenital disorders

If your patient's an infant or very young child, consider possible congenital causes of ear or hearing disorders. Obtain a detailed birth history, including precise information on the mother's health during pregnancy. Prenatal causes of congenital hearing defects include maternal infection (especially rubella during the first trimester), maternal use of ototoxic drugs, and fetal exposure to X-rays. Events at birth that may cause hearing loss include hypoxia (or anoxia), jaundice, and trauma. If your patient has a congenital deformity, such as a cleft palate, he's more at risk for otitis media than normal children.

Also investigate the possibility of an inherited hearing disorder. Ask the parents of an infant or young child about inherited conditions, such as Waardenburg's syndrome, that predispose the patient to hearing loss.

Daily activities

Ask the mother of an infant with an ear or hearing disorder how she feeds him. If the infant drinks regularly from a bottle while lying down (especially on his back), the liquid may leak into his eustachian tubes when he coughs or cries. This happens because an infant's eustachian tube runs more horizontally from his pharynx to his middle ear, as opposed to its more vertical course in adults. As a result, fluid entering the child's eustachian tube tends to stagnate, creating a perfect growth medium for the infectious organisms that cause otitis media.

Listen carefully to what the mother says. She may relate observations about her child that indicate possible hearing loss: for example, that he doesn't startle or wake up in response

Tuning Fork Tests

1 For the Weber test, place a vibrating tuning fork firmly midline on your patient's forehead (as the examiner is doing here) or midline on the top of his head.

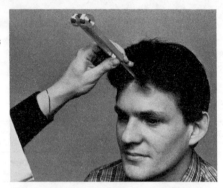

2 For the Rinne test, hold a vibrating tuning fork against the patient's mastoid process, as shown here, until the patient indicates he no longer hears the tone. This tests bone conduction. Then, quickly move the vibrating fork in front of his ear canal, as shown in the inset. This tests air conduction.

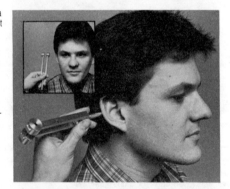

3 For the Schwabach test, position a vibrating tuning fork against the patient's mastoid process, as shown here. Then, place the tuning fork against *your* mastoid process, as shown in the inset. Alternate these positions until you or the patient no longer hears the tone. *Remember:* You must have normal hearing to conduct this test.

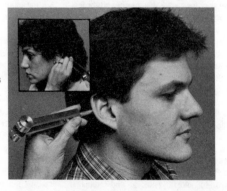

Weber, Rinne, and Schwabach Tests

TEST	NORMAL HEARING	CONDUCTIVE HEARING LOSS	SENSORINEURAL (PERCEPTIVE) HEARING LOSS
Weber (bone)	• Patient hears same tone (intensity and volume) in both ears. Document result as *Weber negative: no* lateralization.	• Patient hears the tone louder in the affected ear. Document result as *Weber lateralizes to right* or *Weber lateralizes to left.*	• Weber test is inconclusive in this particular condition. However, you may expect the patient to hear the tone equally or louder in the ear you suspect is *unaffected.*
Rinne (air/bone)	• Patient hears an air-conducted tone twice as long as a bone-conducted tone. Document result as *+ R* (Rinne positive): *AC>BC.*	• Patient hears a bone-conducted tone for as long or longer than he hears an air-conducted tone. Document result as *− R* (Rinne negative): *BC=AC* or *BC>AC.*	• Patient hears air-conducted tones longer than bone-conducted tones. Document result as *+ R* (Rinne positive): *AB>BC.*
Schwabach (bone)	• Patient and nurse hear tone for equal amounts of time. Document result as *Time equal to examiner.*	• Patient hears tone longer than nurse. Document result as *Time more than examiner.*	• Patient hears tone shorter time than nurse. Document result as *Time less than examiner.*

to a loud stimulus, or that (for a child's old enough to understand commands) he has to be told several times to do something. In fact, any report of generally inattentive or unresponsive behavior should raise your suspicion of a hearing disorder. Remember that clues to hearing loss in children may be subtle, because the deficit may affect only one ear, and the child may compensate well with his good ear.

Always investigate external causes of hearing loss in children, such as ear damage from firecrackers, a cap pistol, or lead poisoning. Also ask if the child habitually puts things in his ears, because eardrum damage may result from foreign-body mechanical irritation in the ear canal.

The child's auricles
Pay special attention to how a child's auricles are positioned. As in the adult, the top of the auricle should align with the inner and outer canthi of the eye. If a child's ears are low set,

it may mean he has one or more birth defects, such as renal agenesis or anomalies.

Observe for other external ear deformities that may be associated with abnormalities. For example, in a child with Down's syndrome, you'll see hyperplasia of the superior crus of the antihelix, which causes the auricle to fold over. Microtia—an uncommon developmental anomaly in which the auricle is grossly undersized and the external ear canal is either blind or absent—can be associated with renal disease.

The otoscope examination
Because inserting an otoscope may make a child uncomfortable, postpone this part of your assessment until the end of the physical examination, if possible. To help alleviate the child's fears, let him hold and look at the otoscope before the examination. You can also place the instrument at the opening of his ear canal (not *into* it), and then remove it, to show him that insertion doesn't hurt. When restraint

is necessary, have the child sit or lie on his parent's lap. Instruct the parent to hold the child firmly.

To begin the examination, gently pull the child's auricle down, *but not back,* before inserting the otoscope. Remember that in an infant or young child the ear canal slants upward, and in an older child or adult the ear canal slants downward. Because the child's canal is also shorter, take care to insert the otoscope only about ¼" to ½" (6 to 13 mm). For maximum control of the otoscope, hold it upside down to insert it, with your hand braced against the child's head. This minimizes displacement of the otoscope if the child squirms or moves his head.

When you look through the otoscope, expect the cone of light on a normal child's eardrum to be indistinct, in contrast to its clear outline in a normal adult. Remember that a red eardrum in a crying child is often normal.

Pneumatic otoscopy may be used to evaluate a child's eardrum further.

Hearing tests

You can't perform tuning fork tests on an infant or young child, but you can test his hearing with simpler procedures. For example, with an infant, make a sudden loud noise, such as clapping your hands or snapping your fingers, about 12" (30 cm) from his ear. He should respond with the startle reflex or by blinking. (If you clap your hands, be careful not to create an airstream that would cause the infant to blink.) Both these responses are normal, but they suggest only that the child did perceive the noise you made, not that he doesn't have some degree of hearing loss. Be sure to test both ears.

A 6-month-old infant normally reacts expectantly if he hears his mother's voice before she comes into view, so this is a good way to test hearing in such a young child. To evaluate hearing in a child between ages 2 and 5, use play techniques, such as asking him to put a peg in a board when he hears a sound transmitted through earphones. For an older child, try the whisper test, but be sure to use words he knows, and take care to prevent him from lipreading. The child should hear a whispered question or simple command at 8' (2.5 m).

Recurrent otitis media, a major cause of hearing loss in young children, can block nor-

mal development of speech and socialization skills. For this reason, be sure to test the hearing of every child you examine who has a history of recurrent middle ear infections.

Pediatric ear disorders

Acute otitis media is one of the most common childhood diseases, and many children have recurrent middle ear infections. A foreign body in the ear canal is another common problem in children.

Eustachian tube malfunction is commonly associated with middle ear disease in children. Consider it whenever you see a child with recurrent ear infections, enlarged adenoids, a history of allergies, or a cleft palate.

A child who's had a myringotomy tube inserted may develop a middle ear infection, because the tube allows organisms normally present in the ear canal to enter the middle ear space. Usually the child experiences a significant discharge of pus and blood, but no pain.

Geriatric assessment

Hearing loss in the elderly

Many elderly patients have some degree of hearing loss, most often caused by *presbycusis,* the slowly progressive deafness that often accompanies aging. Aging results in degenerative structural changes in the entire auditory system. The incidence of hearing loss in elderly persons is probably higher than statistics indicate. Often an older person isn't immediately aware of a hearing defect's onset or progression. He may recognize the problem but, accepting it as a natural aspect of aging, may not seek medical help.

Because hearing loss in an elderly patient may interfere significantly with his individual pursuits and social interactions, you must periodically assess each geriatric patient thoroughly to rule out conditions that can be treated by surgery or medication.

Interviewing an elderly patient who has a hearing defect requires patience, understanding, and the use of special techniques (see pages 23 and 24). Be alert for signs that he's experiencing social isolation because of a hearing loss. Typical comments are, "I don't use the telephone anymore—it's too low," "I don't go to meetings—all the noise is too confusing," or "My family gets tired of talking to me."

Observe him, too, for behavioral patterns directly related to hearing loss. Insecurity and anxiety, perhaps coupled with disturbances in sleep patterns, may be manifestations of the feelings of loss and depression often experienced by an elderly person whose hearing is impaired. He may also be disorganized or unreasonable because of his inability to understand what is being said to him—and around him. Ask an elderly patient if he'd like to have a family member or a close friend remain with him during the health history interview and the physical examination.

Presbycusis

The most common cause of hearing loss in the elderly is presbycusis. Sometimes called *senile deafness,* presbycusis is irreversible, bilateral, sensorineural (perceptive) hearing loss that usually starts during middle age and slowly progresses. Four distinct forms of presbycusis are recognized. The most common form is *sensory presbycusis,* caused by atrophy of the organ of Corti and the auditory nerve.

Suspect presbycusis if your elderly patient complains of gradual hearing loss over many years but has no history of ear disorders or severe generalized disease. In most patients, the physical examination shows no abnormalities of the ear canal or eardrum. The Rinne test is positive—that is, the patient hears the air-conducted tone longer than the bone-conducted tone, with air conduction about equal in both ears. If your patient has a positive history of vertigo, ear pain, or nausea, suspect some pathology other than presbycusis. Any hearing or vestibular function abnormality requires immediate referral for audiometric testing.

Examination considerations

During the physical examination, stand close to an elderly patient with a hearing disorder in case he experiences dizziness or vertigo. Try to make the examination as thorough as possible, without tiring him. If necessary, complete the examination later rather than accept inappropriate responses that may be prompted by fatigue.

As much as possible, combine interviewing techniques and examination procedures. For example, if your history interview elicits a particular complaint, ask the patient to elaborate on the symptom as you look for corresponding signs during the physical examination.

Inspection and palpation of the auricles and surrounding areas should yield the same findings as in the younger adult, with the exception of the normally hairy tragus in an older man. Examination with the otoscope yields similar results. Remember that the eardrum in some elderly patients may normally appear dull and retracted instead of pearl gray, but this can also be a clinically significant sign.

For early detection of hearing loss in an elderly patient, always perform tuning fork tests. Be particularly careful when you perform the Weber test, because the geriatric patient may become confused if he hears the tone better in his affected ear. As a result, he may falsely report that he hears the tone better in his other ear. Also evaluate the patient's ability to hear and understand speech, in case you need to recommend rehabilitative therapy. Use the past-pointing and falling tests to evaluate patients who complain of vertigo, dizziness, or light-headedness.

If your patient wears a hearing aid, inspect it carefully for proper functioning. Check how well the aid fits. Examine the earpiece, sound tube, and any connecting tubing for cracks and for the presence of dust, wax, or other sound-obstructing matter. Check that the batteries are installed correctly. Suspect that the aid isn't functioning properly if your patient reports that what he hears through it sounds fluttery or garbled.

Guide to Ear Disorders

DISORDER	CHIEF COMPLAINT	
Benign paroxysmal spinal postural vertigo	• *Pain/Discomfort:* none • *Discharge:* none • *Hearing loss:* none • *Vertigo/Dizziness:* sudden vertigo; lasts seconds to minutes with positional head changes • *Tinnitus:* present in both ears	
Bullous myringitis (viral otitis media)	• *Pain/Discomfort:* severe in canal; fullness • *Discharge:* none • *Hearing loss:* conductive; mild • *Vertigo/Dizziness:* present • *Tinnitus:* present	
Eustachian tube block	• *Pain/Discomfort:* intermittent; sensation of canal blockage • *Discharge:* none • *Hearing loss:* conductive • *Vertigo/Dizziness:* occasional • *Tinnitus:* may be present	
Acute otitis externa	• *Pain/Discomfort:* mild-to-severe pain, which may be aggravated by jaw motion or pressure on the pinna or on the tragus; may be a throbbing ache over entire affected side of head • *Discharge:* usually yellow but may be serous, bloody, or cheesy; foul-smelling; tenacious • *Hearing loss:* may be mild, depending on degree of occlusion; conductive, low pitch • *Vertigo/Dizziness:* uncommon • *Tinnitus:* may be mild; low pitch	
Chronic otitis externa	• *Pain/Discomfort:* severe itching of entire ear • *Discharge:* usually present • *Hearing loss:* none, unless discharge accumulates in the ear canal; then loss depends on the degree of occlusion; conductive • *Vertigo/Dizziness:* may be mild • *Tinnitus:* may be mild; low pitch	
Otomycosis	• *Pain/Discomfort:* severe itching in canal often aggravated by scratching • *Discharge:* none except in severe cases; then foul-smelling, serous, or whitish secretion, with cheesy appearance • *Hearing loss:* may be mild, depending on degree of occlusion; conductive • *Vertigo/Dizziness:* may be mild • *Tinnitus:* may be mild; low pitch	
Otosclerosis	• *Pain/Discomfort:* none • *Discharge:* none • *Hearing loss:* conductive; progressive • *Vertigo/Dizziness:* little or none • *Tinnitus:* commonly present	

HISTORY	PHYSICAL EXAMINATION AND DIAGNOSTIC STUDIES
• Easily fatigued	• Otoscopy normal • Hearing tests normal • Nylen-Bárány maneuver positive for nystagmus
• Recent illness or exposure to virus • Recent upper respiratory tract infection	• Eardrum blood-filled, or blood in adjacent canal • Fine vascularity to diffuse hemorrhage • Numerous bubbles on tympanic membrane
• Pressure change, such as during air travel	• Eardrum retracted; may be red • Air bubbles may be present in middle ear space.
• Summer swimming • Moist, hot climate • Cleaning ears with sharp object • Allergy to hair spray • Lymphadenopathy	• Tragus, acoustic meatus, and canal may be edematous. • May be unable to insert otoscope because of pain or occlusion • Possibly fever
• Repeated episodes of dermatoses (psoriasis, dermatoses) • Allergy to hair spray and dyes, nail polish • Lymphadenopathy	• Eardrum normal • Auricle and canal red, thick, excoriated; often crusted • Canal and tympanic membrane insensitive
• Often asymptomatic • Recent infection by candida, aspergillus, tinea organisms or actinomycosis • Moist, hot climate • No signs or symptoms unless ear tissues invaded by fungus	• Eardrum whitish gray with black dots; may be cottony • Canal edema and debris
• Positive family history • Gradually worsening • Made worse with pregnancy • Monohybrid autosomal dominant inheritance (25% to 40% incidence)	• Eardrum normal • Schwartz's sign (faint pink blush seen behind eardrum) may be present. • Canal normal • Soft speaking despite hearing loss

(continued)

Guide to Ear Disorders *(continued)*

DISORDER	CHIEF COMPLAINT	
Furunculosis	• *Pain/Discomfort:* severe; localized in outer cartilaginous half of ear canal • *Discharge:* after furuncle breaks, bloody or purulent for brief time • *Hearing loss:* may be moderate to severe, depending on degree of occlusion; conductive • *Vertigo/Dizziness:* may be mild • *Tinnitus:* may be mild; low pitch	
Acute labyrinthitis	• *Pain/Discomfort:* none • *Discharge:* none • *Hearing loss:* sensorineural • *Vertigo/Dizziness:* severe vertigo; gradual onset, reaching maximum in 1 to 2 days; lasts 3 to 6 weeks; caused by head motion • *Tinnitus:* none	
Acute mastoiditis	• *Pain/Discomfort:* dull aching behind ear; deep, with pressure on mastoid process • *Discharge:* thick, foul-smelling, creamy, profuse • *Hearing loss:* none, unless complications occur • *Vertigo/Dizziness:* occasional • *Tinnitus:* may be mild	
Ménière's disease	• *Pain/Discomfort:* none • *Discharge:* none • *Hearing loss:* fluctuating low-frequency sensorineural loss; present usually in only one ear • *Vertigo/Dizziness:* sudden vertigo; lasts from minutes to hours; occurs weeks to months apart • *Tinnitus:* low buzz; fluctuates; present in one ear	
Ototoxicity	• *Pain/Discomfort:* none • *Discharge:* none • *Hearing loss:* sensorineural; usually in one ear • *Vertigo/Dizziness:* sudden or gradual vertigo; minimal • *Tinnitus:* mild to severe; present in one ear	
Perilymph fistula	• *Pain/Discomfort:* none • *Discharge:* none • *Hearing loss:* present; permanent deafness possible • *Vertigo/Dizziness:* sudden or gradual vertigo; duration depends on cause • *Tinnitus:* present in both ears; usually high pitched	
Acute serous otitis media	• *Pain/Discomfort:* little or none; pressure (as with nose-blowing, sneezing) • *Discharge:* none • *Hearing loss:* usually reversible; occasional sensation of canal blockage; conductive • *Vertigo/Dizziness:* occasional, slight dizziness, not true vertigo • *Tinnitus:* may be mild	

HISTORY	PHYSICAL EXAMINATION AND DIAGNOSTIC STUDIES
• Otitis media, with discharge	• Eardrum normal unless otitis media present • Furuncles visible in canal
• Recent acute febrile disease, drugs, alcohol, allergy, fatigue, upper respiratory tract infection, otitis media • Nausea and vomiting when severe • Fever, headache, nystagmus	• Otoscopy normal • Hearing tests indicate sensorineural loss • Nystagmus and past-pointing may be present.
• Previous acute suppurative otitis media (especially with adequate treatment) • Two weeks prior to onset of otitis media, fever, pinna displaced laterally or inferiorly	• Eardrum swollen, lusterless, dull, thick, edematous
• Episodes recurrent • Asymptomatic between attacks • Altered activities of daily living • Audiography abnormal	• Sensorineural hearing loss in one ear • Fluctuating hearing loss
• Stapedectomy • Pressure charge, such as during air travel • Round window rupture • Recent ear trauma	• Otoscopy normal unless trauma; then perforation of tympanic membrane and blood are seen.
• Ototoxic medication use • Ataxia • Symptoms depend on drug	• Otoscopy normal • Hearing tests normal
• Gradual onset; lasts several weeks or months • Recent upper respiratory tract infection, barotrauma; occasional fever, with upper respiratory tract infection present	• Eardrum retracted with prominent mallear folds • Yellow or blue fluid, or bubble line, behind tympanic membrane • Dark line lying horizontally across eardrum (sign of fluid level in eardrum) may be visible.

(continued)

Guide to Ear Disorders *(continued)*

DISORDER	CHIEF COMPLAINT	
Acute suppurative otitis media	• *Pain/Discomfort:* severe, deep in head; throbbing; none with external ear motion • *Discharge:* purulent, if tympanic membrane is pierced • *Hearing loss:* conductive; moderate to severe • *Vertigo/Dizziness:* may be mild; accompanied by nausea • *Tinnitus:* may be present	
Chronic suppurative otitis media	• *Pain/Discomfort:* little or none • *Discharge:* thick, purulent • *Hearing loss:* conductive; moderate to severe • *Vertigo/Dizziness:* none unless complications, such as irritation of labyrinth, occur • *Tinnitus:* none	

HISTORY	PHYSICAL EXAMINATION AND DIAGNOSTIC STUDIES
• Progressive • Recent upper respiratory tract infection or measles, allergies, adenoid hypertrophy, barotrauma, fever, or chills • Sudden cessation of pain when tympanic membrane ruptures	• Eardrum hyperemic; minimal retraction, with dull red landmarks obscured • Perforation possible, accompanied by discharge • Canal normal or pus-filled
• Untreated acute suppurative otitis media; occasional fever	• Eardrum perforated and covered with drainage

9

Respiratory System

Respiratory assessment is essential on hospital admission, at regular intervals during illness, and during routine health evaluation and screening. Perform respiratory assessment daily for ambulatory patients and more frequently for patients who are acutely ill or particularly susceptible to disease (pediatric and geriatric patients, for example) or those whose activities are limited by medication, surgery, or debilitating diseases.

The two vital functions of the respiratory system are maintenance of oxygen and carbon dioxide exchange in the lungs and tissues, and regulation of acid-base balance. Any changes in the functions of this system affect all the other body systems. Using correct assessment techniques, you can detect changes in a patient's respiratory system early and intervene quickly, perhaps preventing serious complications.

History data

Biographical data

When assessing a patient's respiratory system, remember that his age and sex can affect his thoracic configuration. When you note the area where a patient lives and what he does for a living, be alert to possible environmental or occupational hazards that can affect his lungs and breathing.

History of present illness

The most common chief complaints for respiratory disorders are *cough*—with or without sputum production or hemoptysis—*dyspnea*, and *chest pain* (see *Guide to Respiratory Disorders*, pages 174 to 183). Here are some questions you may want to ask about

these complaints to explore fully the history of your patient's present illness:

● **Cough.** *Does your cough usually occur at a specific time of day? How does it sound— dry, hacking, barking, congested?* Try to determine whether the patient's cough is related to cigarette smoking or irritants. (The most common causes of coughing are smoking and chronic bronchitis.) *Please describe any medication you're using or treatment you're receiving to clear the cough. How frequently do you take the medication or receive treatment? Have you recently been exposed to anyone with a similar cough? Was this person's cough caused by a cold or flu?*

● **Sputum production.** *How much sputum are you coughing up per day?* Remember, the tracheobronchial tree can produce up to 3 oz (90 ml) of sputum per day. *What time of day do you cough up the most sputum?* Smokers cough when they get up in the morning; nonsmokers generally don't. Coughing from an irritant occurs most often during exposure to it—for example, at work. *Is sputum production increasing?* This may result from external stimuli or from such internal causes as chronic bronchial infection or a lung abscess. Excess production of sputum that separates into layers may indicate bronchiectasis. *Does the sputum contain mucus, or look frothy? What color is it? Has the color changed? Does it smell bad?* Foul-smelling sputum may result from an anaerobic infection, such as an abscess. Blood-tinged or rust-colored sputum may result from trauma caused by coughing or from such underlying pathology as bronchitis, pulmonary infarction or infections, tuberculosis, and tumors. A color change from white to yellow or green indicates infection.

● **Dyspnea.** *Are you always short of breath*

or do you have attacks of breathlessness? Onset of dyspnea may be slow or abrupt. For example, a patient with asthma may experience acute dyspnea intermittently. *What relieves the attacks—positioning, relaxation, medication? Do the attacks cause your lips and nail beds to turn blue? Does body position, time of day, or a certain type of activity affect your breathing?* Paroxysmal nocturnal dyspnea and orthopnea are commonly associated with chronic lung disease, but they may be related to cardiac dysfunction. *How many stairs can you climb or blocks can you walk before you begin to feel short of breath? Do such activities as taking a shower or shopping make you feel this way?* Dyspnea from activity suggests poor ventilation or perfusion, or inefficient breathing mechanisms. *Do you experience associated signs and symptoms, such as cough, diaphoresis, or chest discomfort? Does the breathlessness seem to be stable or getting worse? Is it accompanied by external sounds, such as wheezing or stridor?* Wheezing results from small-airway obstruction (for example, from an aspirated foreign body, from a tumor, from asthma, or from congestive heart failure). Stridor results from tracheal compression or laryngeal edema.

● *Chest pain. Is the pain localized? Is it constant or do you experience attacks? Have you ever had a chest injury? Does a specific activity (such as movement of the upper body, or exercise) produce pain?* Chest pain may be associated with cardiovascular disorders, but respiratory disorders usually cause musculoskeletal chest pain (the lungs have no pain-sensitive nerves). However, the parietal pleura and the tracheobronchial tree are sensitive to pain. *Is the pain accompanied by other signs and symptoms, such as coughing, sneezing, or shortness of breath? Does the pain occur when you breathe normally or only when you breathe deeply?* This distinction is important in determining whether your patient's pain is pleuritic. *Does splinting relieve the pain?* (See *Chest Pain Assessment*, pages 186 to 187.)

Past history

Focus on the following body systems, procedures, and conditions when reviewing your patient's past history:

● *Respiratory system.* Ask if your patient's ever had *pneumonia, pleurisy, asthma, bron-*

chitis, emphysema, or *tuberculosis.* Also ask him how often he gets colds.

● *Cardiovascular system.* Ask if your patient's ever had *high blood pressure, heart attack,* or *congestive heart failure.* A history of such a disorder is particularly significant, because of the close relationship between the cardiovascular system and the respiratory system.

● *Chest surgery.* Find out if the patient has had lung surgery or other chest surgery. Remember that physical examination findings differ for patients who've undergone such procedures as *thoracoplasty* or *pneumonectomy.*

● *Invasive medical procedures.* Ask the patient if he's undergone any chest- or lung-related procedures, such as *bronchoscopy* or *thoracocentesis.*

● *Chest deformities.* Note that *congenital* or *trauma-related deformities* may distort cardiac and pulmonary structures.

● *Laboratory tests.* Ask your patient for the dates and results of his last chest X-ray, pulmonary function test, electrocardiogram, arterial blood gas analysis, sputum culture, and skin test for tuberculosis.

● *Allergies.* Ask whether the patient reacts to such common allergens as medications, foods, pets, dust, or pollen. Also ask if he has any allergic signs and symptoms, such as coughing, sneezing, sinusitis, or dyspnea. Chronic allergies may predispose him to other respiratory disorders. Has he ever been treated for an allergy?

● *Medications.* Ask the patient if he takes any prescription or over-the-counter drugs for cough control, expectoration, nasal congestion, chest pain, or dyspnea. Also note any other medications the patient is taking.

● *Vaccinations.* Ask the patient if he's ever been vaccinated against pneumonia or flu.

Family history

When reviewing your patient's family history, ask if anyone in his family has ever had *asthma, cystic fibrosis,* or *emphysema,* all of which may be genetically transmitted. Other important disorders to ask about include *lung cancer* and *infectious diseases,* such as tuberculosis. Also inquire about *chronic allergies* in the family, *cardiovascular disorders* (such as hypertension, myocardial infarction, and congestive heart failure), and *respiratory disturbances* (such as frequent colds or episodes of flu, pneumonia, asthma, or emphysema). Disorders involving other body systems may be associated with pulmonary dysfunction, so ask about a family history of such conditions as *kyphosis, scoliosis, obesity,* and *neuromuscular dysfunction.*

Psychosocial history

Focus your questions about the patient's psychosocial history on the following aspects of his life:

• *Home conditions.* Persons living near a constant source of air pollution, such as a chemical factory, may develop respiratory disorders. Exposure to cigarette smoke in the home may aggravate respiratory symptoms. Crowded living conditions facilitate the transmission of communicable respiratory diseases.

• *Work.* Exposure on the job to cigarette smoke or to other substances that may be irritating to the respiratory system may be significant.

• *Pets.* Exposure to animals may precipitate allergic or asthmatic attacks.

• *Hobbies.* Seemingly innocent pastimes, such as building model airplanes or refinishing old furniture, may expose the patient to harsh chemical irritants.

• *Stress.* Some respiratory conditions, such as asthma and infection, can be aggravated by stress.

Activities of daily living

When reviewing your patient's activities of daily living, ask if he smokes cigarettes, cigars, pipe tobacco, or marijuana. If he smokes cigarettes, find out how many packs he smokes each day, and how long he's been smoking at this rate. If the patient doesn't smoke now, ask if he used to smoke, and how much. Learning about a patient's smoking habits is vital to completing a comprehensive respiratory history. Smoking can be associated with numerous and varied pathologies, such as lung cancer, chronic bronchitis, and emphysema.

The risk of lung disease is higher among smokers exposed to respiratory irritants either near their homes or on the job. So when asking your patient about his daily activities, be especially alert to a history of exposure to chemicals, noxious fumes, chromium, and dust

containing nickel, uranium, or asbestos.

Your patient's daily routine is also important, because respiratory signs and symptoms can interfere with such activities as climbing stairs or traveling to work.

Review of systems

Complete your patient's health history by asking about the following signs and symptoms:

• *General. Fever, chills,* and *fatigue* may occur in association with respiratory symptoms.

• *Skin. Nocturnal diaphoresis* may be associated with tuberculosis.

• *Blood-forming. Anemia* decreases the blood's oxygen-carrying capacity; *polycythemia* may occur in response to chronic hypoxemia.

• *Nose. Nasal discharge, sinus pain or infection,* or *postnasal drip* may result from seasonal allergies or chronic sinus problems.

• *Mouth and throat. Halitosis* may result from a pulmonary infection, such as an abscess or bronchiectasis.

• *Cardiovascular. Ankle edema, paroxysmal nocturnal dyspnea, orthopnea,* or *chest pain that worsens with exercise, eating, or stress* may reflect a cardiovascular disorder rather than a respiratory one.

• *Gastrointestinal. Weight loss* suggests possible deterioration from disease, such as from lung cancer.

• *Nervous. Confusion, syncope,* and *restlessness* may be associated with cerebral hypoxia.

• *Musculoskeletal.* Chronic hypoxia may cause *fatigue* and *weakness.*

• *Psychological.* Some respiratory signs and symptoms (for example, *wheezing* and *hyperventilation*) may be associated with emotional problems.

Physical examination

Environment and equipment

Before assessing your patient, be sure the examining area is quiet so you can auscultate his lungs accurately. Make sure the lighting is adequate to detect skin color variations. (If possible, use natural light, because fluorescent light doesn't show true skin color.)

You'll need a nasal speculum, a tongue depressor, a penlight, a cotton-tipped applicator or swabstick, and a stethoscope. You may also wish to use a marking pen and a centimeter stick to mark points of reference on the patient's body.

Preparation and positioning

Tell the patient to undress to the waist and to put on a loose-fitting examining gown. (If the patient's a woman and she's wearing a bra, ask her to remove it.) Be sure the patient is adequately draped for privacy and warmth.

Place the patient in a comfortable position that allows you access to his posterior and anterior chest. If he experiences shortness of breath, elevate his head. If the patient's condition permits, have him sit on the edge of a bed or examining table or in a chair, leaning slightly forward, with his arms folded across his chest. If this isn't possible, place him in the semi-Fowler's position for the anterior chest examination. Then ask him to lean forward slightly, using the side rails or mattress for support, so you can examine his posterior chest. If the patient can't lean forward for posterior chest examination, place him in a lateral position.

Remember that when you use the lateral position to examine your patient's posterior chest, the bed mattress and the organ displacement involved distort sounds and lung expansion. To offset these effects, examine the uppermost side of your patient's chest first; then roll him on his other side and repeat the examination, for comparison.

When you assess the patient's thorax, keep in mind the three thoracic portions to be examined—posterior, anterior, and lateral. You can examine any of these areas first and perform the lateral examination during the posterior or anterior assessment. The most important point is to *proceed systematically*, always comparing one side of the patient's thorax with the other side. (In this way, the patient serves as his own control.) Remember to examine the apices during the posterior and the anterior examinations. For a list of diagnostic tests useful in assessing pulmonary problems, see this page.

Overview of respiratory status

Before starting your detailed pulmonary assessment, quickly observe the patient for the following signs and symptoms of severe hy-

---

Essential Diagnostic Tests

Here are several essential diagnostic tests that help you assess pulmonary function:
- *Arterial blood gas analysis* helps detect ventilation and perfusion abnormalities by measuring oxygenation (Pao_2), arterial carbon dioxide pressure ($Paco_2$), and pH.
- *Hemoglobin* measurement can help support clinical findings. As you know, hemoglobin's the primary carrier of oxygen and carbon dioxide. Long-standing hypoxia causes hemoglobin to *rise. Low* hemoglobin (caused by anemia or primary bleeding) may produce such symptoms of hypoxemia as fatigue, tachycardia, and shortness of breath.
- *Hematocrit* measurement determines red blood cell (RBC) concentration. A decrease in RBC concentration causes a decrease in hemoglobin, because hemoglobin is the principal protein in the cytoplasm of circulating RBC.
- *Chest X-rays* help to further differentiate significant clinical findings. However, pulmonary changes aren't always apparent on X-ray films. Don't distrust clinical findings just because they're not immediately proven or disproven by X-ray.
- *Spirometry* is another reliable measure of pulmonary function. It helps determine maximum breathing capacity, forced vital capacity, and inspiratory and expiratory reserve volume. Changes in these sensitive indicators suggest the degree of dysfunction and your patient's capacity for normal activities.

---

poxia or other acute respiratory difficulty:
- low level of consciousness
- shortness of breath when speaking
- rapid, very deep or very shallow, or depressed respirations (see *Common Respiratory Patterns,* page 160)
- use of accessory muscles when breathing
- intercostal and sternal retractions
- cyanosis
- external sounds (such as crowing, wheezing, or stridor)
- diaphoresis
- nasal flaring
- extreme apprehension or agitation.

A patient exhibiting most or all of these signs and symptoms requires immediate intervention. Position him appropriately to re-

Common Respiratory Patterns

To determine the rate, rhythm, and depth of your patient's respirations, observe him at rest. Make sure he's unaware that you're counting his respirations. Why? A person conscious of his respirations may alter his natural pattern.

Always count respirations for at least 1 minute. If you count for only a fraction of a minute and then multiply, your count may be off by as much as four respirations per minute.

Your patient's respiratory rhythm should be even, except for an occasional deep breath. Use this chart as a guide for noting differences in respiratory rates, rhythms, and depths.

Eupnea

Normal respiration rate and rhythm. For adults and teenagers, 12 to 20 bpm; ages 2 to 12, 20 to 30 bpm; newborns, 30 to 50 bpm. Also, occasional deep breaths at a rate of 2 or 3 bpm.

Tachypnea

Increased respirations, as seen in fever. Respirations increase about four bpm for every degree Fahrenheit above normal.

Bradypnea

Slower but regular respirations. Can occur when the brain's respiratory control center is affected by opiate narcotics, tumor, alcohol, a metabolic disorder, or respiratory decompensation. Normal during sleep.

Apnea

Absence of breathing; may be periodic.

Hyperpnea

Deeper respirations; rate normal.

Cheyne-Stokes

Respirations gradually become faster and deeper than normal, then slower, over a 30- to 170-second period. Periods of apnea for 20 to 60 seconds alternate.

Blot's

Faster and deeper respirations than normal, with abrupt pauses in between. Each breath has same depth. May occur with spinal meningitis or other CNS conditions.

Kussmaul's

Faster and deeper respirations without pauses; in adults, over 20 bpm. Breathing usually sounds labored, with deep breaths that resemble sighs. Can occur from renal failure or metabolic acidosis.

Apneustic

Prolonged gasping inspiration, followed by extremely short, inefficient expiration. Can occur from lesions in the brain's respiratory center.

lieve distress, then notify the doctor. (See also *Respiratory Emergencies*).

Skin color and condition

Begin your detailed respiratory examination by inspecting your patient's skin color. Look for central *cyanosis* in highly vascular areas:

the lips, the nail beds, the tip of the nose, the ear helices, and the underside of the tongue. For a patient with dark brown or black skin, inspect those areas where cyanotic changes would be most apparent: the nose, the cheeks, and the mucosa inside the lips. Facial skin may

---

Respiratory Emergencies

Respiratory assessment of the emergency patient is critical because life-threatening problems may impair oxygen delivery to tissues.
Begin your assessment by simultaneously checking airway patency and adequate ventilation.
- Observe the chest for rise and fall.
- Listen to the sound of air movement near your patient's mouth and nose.
- Feel for air movement over his mouth and nose.
Use this chart to assess the emergency situation properly.

CONDITION	ASSESSMENT	INTERVENTION
Acute respiratory arrest	• No respiratory movement • No air felt over mouth and nose	• Position airway, using the head-tilt or jaw-thrust method. • Start mouth-to-mouth resuscitation immediately. • Once you've accomplished ventilation, continue until no longer needed. • Use endotracheal intubation and manual (or mechanical) ventilation, as ordered, for long-term support.
Complete airway obstruction	• No respiratory movement • No air felt over mouth and nose • If conscious, patient attempts to speak but fails, and typically reaches for his throat	• Administer four rapid blows between the scapulae, followed by the abdominal thrust or compression of the midchest, as is done in external cardiac massage. • If airway remains obstructed, manual clearing may locate and remove obstruction. • Anticipate cricothyrotomy or tracheotomy if other attempts fail. Perform cricothyrotomy only in life-threatening emergency when a doctor is unavailable. Usually a doctor performs a tracheotomy in the operating room.
Partial airway obstruction	• Increased respiratory effort (orthopnea in conscious patients) • Noisy respirations (whistling, wheezing, crowing) • Use of accessory muscles, including abdominals, sternocleidomastoid, and internal intercostals, to try to breathe • Possible intercostal retractions along with nasal flaring	• Administer back blows in succession. (This condition is unlikely to be relieved by an abdominal thrust or by chest compression.) • Administer oxygen until direct laryngoscopy becomes available.

be pale gray in a cyanotic dark-skinned patient.

Central cyanosis, which affects all body organs, results from prolonged hypoxia. Its presence helps you gauge the severity of a patient's illness. (Remember, though, that severely anemic patients with respiratory difficulty don't appear cyanotic.) Be sure you know how to distinguish central cyanosis from *peripheral cyanosis,* which is caused by local vasoconstriction and is only apparent in the nail beds and sometimes the lips.

For all patients, examine the skin for dryness—a possible sign of dehydration—or for diaphoresis, which may be associated with fever and infection. Bright cherry-red mucous membranes may result from carbon monoxide poisoning. While inspecting the skin, observe the fingers for clubbing, a sign of chronic respiratory dysfunction as well as certain cardiovascular and gastrointestinal disorders.

Upper respiratory tract

Inspect your patient's facial structures, observing for symmetry, deformities, and inflammation. Check his nasal septum for deviation and perforations. Using a nasal speculum, examine his nostrils for discharge, for the condition and color of their mucosa (it should be slightly redder than oral mucosa), for swelling and bleeding, and for any obstructions.

Next, palpate his nose to detect any swelling, pain, or fractures. Palpate the maxillary sinuses for tenderness and swelling by pressing the patient's cheeks over the maxillary areas. Palpate his frontal sinuses by placing your thumbs just below the patient's eyebrows and pressing upward. While observing and palpating these facial structures, listen for external sounds of moisture or mucus, and for stridor or wheezing.

If the patient wears dentures, ask him to remove them. Then, using a tongue depressor, a cotton-tipped applicator (or swabstick), and a penlight, examine his oropharynx for color changes, inflammation, white patches, ulcerations, bleeding, exudate, and lesions. Be sure to check his soft palate, anterior and posterior pillars of fauces, uvula, tonsils, posterior pharynx, teeth, gums, tongue, mouth floor, mucous membranes, and lips. Remember that a dark-skinned patient has dark patches on his mucous membranes.

Using a tongue depressor, bring the patient's pharynx into view and ask him to say "eh." Observe for symmetrical rise and fall of the soft palate. Next, touch both sides of his posterior pharynx with the applicator to check his gag reflex. (This test is particularly helpful when you're assessing an older patient with decreased sensitivity to touch, or one who has suffered a cerebrovascular accident [CVA]; it helps you determine such a patient's ability to swallow oral secretions and food.) To determine the patient's ability to clear his respiratory tract of accumulated secretions, ask him to cough. If your patient is debilitated by CVA or other cerebral trauma or by drug or alcohol ingestion, elicit a cough by gently touching his posterior oropharynx with a swabstick.

Inspect the patient's trachea for midline position, and observe again for any use of accessory neck muscles in breathing. If you can't see his trachea, palpate for it at the midline position, using the fingertips of one hand. Starting at the middle base of the patient's lower jaw, gently slide your fingertips down the center of his neck. After locating his larynx, you should be able to feel his trachea in the area of the sternal notch. Any deviation of the trachea to either side indicates deformity and necessitates further investigation. Also, observe and palpate the patient's neck over the trachea for swelling, bruises, tenderness, and masses that might obstruct breathing.

Posterior chest inspection

Instruct the patient to sit and lean forward, with his shoulders rounded and his arms crossed on his chest. (Always note the patient's tolerance of position changes.) After checking his posterior chest for wounds, lesions, masses, or scars, observe the rate, rhythm, and depth of his respirations. The normal respiratory rate for an adult is 12 to 20 breaths/minute. Respirations should be regular and inaudible, with the sides of the chest expanding equally. Normal respirations consist of inspiration, a slight pause, and a slightly longer expiration. Prolonged expiratory time suggests air outflow impedance.

Next, observe the patient's chest for local lag or impaired movement. Normally, the chest moves upward and outward symmetrically on inspiration. Impairment may result from pain, exertion from poor positioning, or obstruction from abdominal distention. Paradoxical movement of the chest wall may result from fractured ribs or flail chest.

Note the slope of the patient's ribs. Check for retraction of intercostal spaces during inspiration and for abnormal bulging of intercostal spaces during expiration. Then observe for such spinal deformities as lordosis, kyphosis, and scoliosis.

Posterior chest palpation

Palpate the patient's posterior chest to assess his thorax, to identify thoracic structures, and to check chest expansion and vocal or tactile fremitus. Begin by feeling for muscle mass with your fingers and palms (use a grasping action of the fingers to assess position and consistency). Normally, it feels firm, smooth, and symmetrical. As you palpate muscle mass, also check skin temperature and turgor. Be sure to note the presence of crepitus (especially around a wound site). Then palpate the thoracic spine, noting tenderness, swelling, or such deformities as lordosis, kyphosis, and scoliosis.

Next, using your metacarpophalangeal joints and fingerpads, gently palpate the patient's intercostal spaces and ribs for abnormal retractions, bulging, and tenderness. Normally, the intercostal spaces delineate a downward sloping of the ribs. In a patient with an increased anteroposterior diameter caused by obstructive lung disease, you'll feel ribs that are abnormally horizontal.

Now palpate the thoracic landmarks to identify underlying lobe structures (see *Thoracic Landmarks*, page 164). To help you identify the division between the patient's upper and lower lobes, instruct him to raise his arms above his head; then palpate the borders of his scapulae. The inner edges of the scapulae should line up with the divisions between the upper and lower lobes (see *Lung Lobe Positions*, page 165).

The inferior border of the lower lobes is usually located at the 10th thoracic spinous process and may descend, on full inspiration, to the 12th thoracic spinous process. To locate the lower lung borders in a patient lying laterally, palpate the visible free-floating ribs or costal margins; then count four intercostal

spaces upward for the general location of the lower lung fields.

Palpate for symmetrical expansion of the patient's thorax (respiratory excursion) by placing your palms—fingers together and thumbs abducted toward the spine—flat on the bilateral sections of his lower posterior chest wall. Position your thumbs at the 10th-rib level, and grasp the lateral rib cage with your hands. As the patient inhales, his posterior chest should move upward and outward, and your thumbs should move apart; when he exhales, your thumbs should return to midline and touch each other again. Repeat this technique on his upper posterior chest.

Palpate for vocal or tactile fremitus by using the top portion of each palm and following the palpation sequence illustrated on the opposite page. To check for vocal fremitus, ask your patient to repeat "99" as you proceed. Palpable vibrations will be transmitted from his bronchopulmonary system, along the solid surfaces of his chest wall, to your palms and fingers.

Note the symmetry of the vibrations and the areas of enhanced, diminished, or absent fremitus. (Remember, fremitus should be most pronounced in the patient's upper chest where the trachea branches into the right and the left mainstem bronchi, and less noticeable in the lower regions of the thorax.)

You can estimate the level of your patient's diaphragm on both sides of his posterior chest by placing the ulnar side of your extended hand parallel to the anticipated diaphragm level. Instruct the patient to repeat "99" as you move your hand downward. The level where you no longer feel fremitus corresponds approximately to the diaphragm level.

Posterior chest percussion

To learn the density and location of such anatomic structures as the patient's lungs and diaphragm, you must identify five percussion sounds: flat, dull, resonant, hyperresonant, and tympanic (see *Percussion Sounds*, page 166). Start by percussing across the top of each shoulder. The area overlying the lung apices—approximately 2″ (5 cm)—should be resonant. Then percuss downward toward the patient's diaphragm, at 2″ intervals, comparing right and left sides as you proceed (see *Percussion and Auscultation Sequences*, page 167). Re-

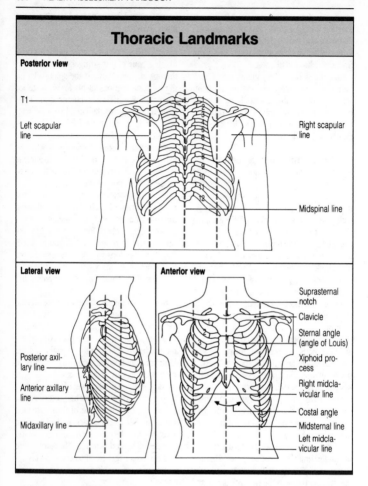

Thoracic Landmarks

Posterior view

T1

Left scapular line

Right scapular line

Midspinal line

Lateral view

Posterior axillary line

Anterior axillary line

Midaxillary line

Anterior view

Suprasternal notch

Clavicle

Sternal angle (angle of Louis)

Xiphoid process

Right midclavicular line

Costal angle

Midsternal line

Left midclavicular line

member to avoid his scapulae and other bony areas. The thoracic area (except over the scapulae) should produce resonance when you percuss. At the level of his diaphragm, resonance should change to dullness. A dull sound over the lungs indicates fluid or solid tissue. Hyperresonance or tympany over a patient's lung suggests pneumothorax, or large emphysematous blebs. A marked difference in diaphragm level from one side to the other is an abnormal finding.

Next, measure diaphragmatic excursion. Instruct the patient to take a deep breath and hold it while you percuss downward until dullness identifies the lower border of the lung field. Mark this point. Now ask the patient to exhale and again hold his breath, as you percuss upward to the area of dullness. Mark this point, too. Repeat this entire procedure on the opposite side of the patient's chest. Now measure the distances between the two marks on each side. Normal diaphragmatic excursion measures about 1¼″ to 2¼″ (3 to 6 cm). (A person's diaphragm is usually slightly higher on his right side.)

Lung Lobe Positions

To locate lung lobes, you'll need to know the common chest wall landmarks shown in these illustrations.

In the posterior view, the oblique fissures divide the upper lobes from the lower lobes of both lungs. Externally, you can approximate the location of these fissures by imagining bilateral lines drawn laterally and inferiorly from the third thoracic spinous process to the inferior border of the scapula. You should remember that unlike the other views shown here, where all lobes can be identified, you can identify only two lobes in each lung in the posterior view.

In the left lateral view, the left oblique fissure divides the left upper lobe (LUL) from the left lower lobe (LLL). Externally, you can approximate the location of this fissure by imagining a line drawn anteriorly and inferiorly from the third thoracic spinous process to the sixth rib, midclavicular line.

In the right lateral view, you can determine the location of the right oblique fissure as you did for the left oblique fissure. But the right oblique fissure divides the upper *portion* of the lung (both upper and middle lobes) from the right lower lobe (RLL). To approximate the division of the right upper lobe (RUL) and the right middle lobe (RML), imagine a line drawn medially from the fifth rib, midaxillary line, to the fourth rib, midclavicular line.

In the anterior view, you can locate the apices and the inferior borders of both lungs using external landmarks on the chest. The apices lie ¾" to 1½" (2 to 4 cm) above the inner portion of the clavicle. The inferior borders run from the sixth rib, midclavicular line, to the eighth rib, midaxillary line.

The horizontal fissure divides the right upper lobe from the right middle lobe. Externally, you can approximate the location of this fissure by imagining a line drawn anteriorly and superiorly from the fifth rib, midaxillary line, to the fourth rib, midclavicular line.

The right and left oblique fissures divide the lower lobe from the upper and middle lobes. Externally, you can approximate the location of these fissures by imagining bilateral lines drawn medially and inferiorly from the fifth rib, midaxillary line, to the sixth rib, midclavicular line.

Locating both chest wall landmarks and the imaginary lines noted above will help you perform a complete thoracic assessment of your patient.

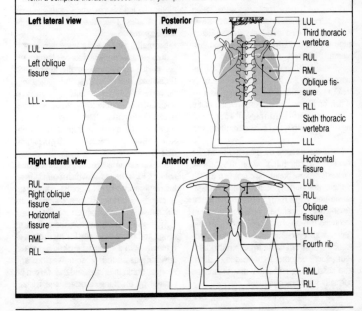

Left lateral view
- LUL
- Left oblique fissure
- LLL

Posterior view
- LUL
- Third thoracic vertebra
- RUL
- RML
- Oblique fissure
- RLL
- Sixth thoracic vertebra
- LLL

Right lateral view
- RUL
- Right oblique fissure
- Horizontal fissure
- RML
- RLL

Anterior view
- Horizontal fissure
- LUL
- RUL
- Oblique fissure
- LLL
- Fourth rib
- RML
- RLL

Percussion Sounds

SOUND	PITCH	INTENSITY	QUALITY	INDICATION
Flatness	High	Soft	Extreme dullness	*Normal:* sternum; *abnormal:* atelectatic lung
Dullness	Medium	Medium	Thudlike	*Normal:* liver area, cardiac area, diaphragm; *abnormal:* pleural effusion
Resonance	Low	Moderate to loud	Hollow	*Normal:* lung
Hyperresonance	Lower than resonance	Very loud	Booming	*Abnormal:* emphysematous lung or pneumothorax
Tympany	High	Loud	Musical, drumlike	*Normal:* stomach area; *abnormal:* air-distended abdomen

Posterior chest auscultation

To assess the flow of air through the patient's respiratory system, auscultate his lungs and identify normal and abnormal (adventitious) breath sounds (see *Normal and Abnormal Breath Sounds,* page 168). Lung auscultation helps detect abnormal fluid or mucus, as well as obstructed passages. You can also determine the condition of the alveoli and surrounding pleura.

Before auscultating the posterior chest, remove clothing and bed linen from the body area to be examined. If the patient has a lot of hair on his posterior chest, wet and mat it with a damp washcloth to prevent it from causing rubbing sounds that can be confused with rales.

When auscultating the patient's chest, instruct him to take full, slow breaths through his mouth. (Nose breathing changes the pitch of the lung sounds.) Listen for one full inspiration and expiration before moving the stethoscope. Remember, a patient may try to accommodate you by breathing quickly and deeply with every movement of the stethoscope—which can cause hyperventilation. If your patient becomes light-headed or dizzy, stop auscultating and allow him to breathe normally for a few minutes.

Using the diaphragm of the stethoscope, be-gin auscultating above the patient's scapulae. Move to the area between the scapulae and the vertebral column. Then move laterally beneath the scapulae, to the right and left lower lobes. Move the stethoscope's diaphragm methodically, and compare the sounds you hear on both sides of the chest before moving to the next area.

Normally, you'll hear vesicular breath sounds—soft, low-pitched sounds lasting longer during inspiration—at the lung bases. Bronchovesicular breath sounds—medium-pitched sounds that are equal in duration on inspiration and expiration—can be heard between the scapulae. Decreased or absent breath sounds may result from bronchial obstruction, muscle weakness, obesity, or pleural disease.

If you hear an adventitious breath sound, note its location and at which point during the respiratory process it occurs—during inspiration, for example. Then continue auscultating the patient's posterior chest.

After auscultating, instruct the patient to cough and breathe deeply. Let him rest, and listen again to the area where you heard the adventitious sound or sounds. Note any changes. Sometimes rales and rhonchi can be cleared by coughing; wheezes and friction rubs can't be cleared this way.

Percussion and Auscultation Sequences

Follow the percussion and auscultation sequences shown here to help you identify abnormalities in your patient's lungs.

Remember to compare sound variations from one side to the other as you proceed. Document any abnormal sounds you hear and describe them carefully, including their location.

Posterior

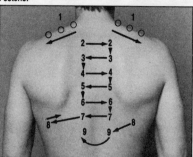

Anterior

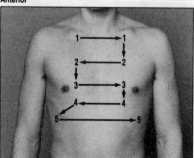

Left lateral   **Right lateral**

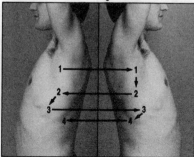

Normal and Abnormal Breath Sounds

Breath sounds are produced by air moving through the tracheobronchoalveolar system. Normal breath sounds are labeled *bronchial, bronchovesicular,* and *vesicular.* They're described according to location, ratio of inspiration to expiration, intensity, and pitch.

Abnormal (adventitious) breath sounds occur when air passes either through narrowed airways or through moisture, or when the membranes lining the chest cavity and the lungs become inflamed. These sounds include *rales, rhonchi, wheezes,* and *pleural friction rub.* You may hear them superimposed over normal breath sounds.

Use this chart as a guide to assess both normal and abnormal breath sounds. Document your findings.

NORMAL BREATH SOUNDS

TYPE	LOCATION	RATIO	DESCRIPTION
Bronchial	Over trachea	I ⟋⟍ E 2:3	Loud, high pitched, and hollow, harsh, or coarse
Bronchovesicular	Anteriorly, near the mainstem bronchi in the first and second intercostal spaces; posteriorly, between the scapulae	I ⟋⟍ E 1:1	Soft, breezy, and pitched about two notes lower than bronchial sounds
Vesicular	In most of the lungs' peripheral parts (cannot be heard over the presternum or the scapulae)	I ⟋⟍ E 3:1	Soft, swishy, breezy, and about two notes lower than bronchovesicular sounds

ABNORMAL BREATH SOUNDS

TYPE	LOCATION	CAUSE	DESCRIPTION
Rales	Anywhere. Heard in lung bases first with pulmonary edema, usually during inspiratory phase	Air passing through moisture, especially in the small airways and alveoli	Light crackling, popping, nonmusical; can be further classified by pitch: high, medium, or low
Rhonchi	In larger airways, usually during expiratory phase	Fluid or secretions in the large airways or narrowing of large airways	Coarse rattling, usually louder and lower pitched than rales; can be described as sonorous, bubbling, moaning, musical, sibilant, and rumbly
Wheezes	Anywhere. Occurs during expiration	Narrowed airways	Creaking, groaning; always high-pitched, musical squeaks
Pleural friction rub	Anterolateral lung field, on both inspiration and expiration (with the patient in an upright position)	Inflamed parietal and visceral pleural linings rubbing together	Superficial squeaking or grating

If you've detected any respiratory abnormality during palpation, percussion, and auscultation, assess your patient's voice sounds for vocal resonance. The significance of vocal resonance is based on the principle that sound carries best through a solid, not as well through fluid, and poorly through air. Normally, you should hear vocal resonance as muffled, unclear sounds, loudest medially and less intense at the lung periphery. Voice sounds that become louder and more distinct signal *bronchophony,* an abnormal finding except over the trachea and posteriorly over the upper right lobe. To elicit bronchophony, ask your patient to say "99" or "one, two, three" while you auscultate his thorax in the systematic way described above.

Whispered pectoriloquy reveals the presence of an exaggerated bronchophony. Ask your patient to whisper a simple phrase like "one, two, three." Hearing the words clearly through the stethoscope is an abnormal finding.

Egophony is another form of abnormal vocal resonance. Ask your patient to say "ee-ee-ee." Transmission of the sound through the stethoscope as "ay, ay, ay" is an abnormal finding possibly indicating compressed lung tissue, as in a pleural effusion.

You may hear increased vocal resonance, whispered pectoriloquy, and egophony in any patient with consolidated lungs.

Anterior chest inspection

To inspect your patient's anterior chest, place him in semi-Fowler's position. Begin by inspecting the anterior chest for draining, open wounds, bruises, abrasions, scars, cuts, and punctures, as well as for rib deformities, fractures, lesions, or masses. Then inspect the rate, rhythm, and depth of respirations. Remember that men, infants, and children are normally diaphragmatic (abdominal) breathers, as are athletes, singers, and persons who practice yoga. Women are usually intercostal (chest) breathers.

Your patient's face should look relaxed when he breathes. Abnormal findings include nasal flaring, pursed-lip breathing, use of neck or abdominal muscles on expiration, and intercostal or sternal retractions. Inspect for local lag and impaired chest wall movement. Observe for thoracic deformities, such as pectus

excavatum (funnel chest) and pectus carinatum (pigeon chest) (see *Chest Deformities,* page 170). Check the patient for barrel chest by noting the ratio between the anteroposterior diameter of his chest and its lateral diameter; the normal ratio ranges from 1:2 to 5:7.

Anterior chest palpation

Begin palpating your patient's anterior chest, using your fingers and palms. Feel for areas of tenderness, muscle mass, and skin turgor and elasticity. Note any crepitus during your palpation, especially around wound sites, subclavian catheters, and chest tubes.

Palpate his sternum and costal cartilages for tenderness and deformities and then, using your metacarpophalangeal joints and fingerpads, palpate his intercostal spaces and ribs for abnormal retractions, bulging, and tenderness. Remember to proceed to the lateral aspects of the thorax.

Next, palpate the thoracic landmarks used to identify underlying structures.

To assess for symmetrical respiratory expansion, place your thumbs along each costal margin, pointing toward the xiphoid process, with your hands along the lateral rib cage. Ask the patient to inhale deeply, and observe for symmetrical thoracic expansion.

Now palpate for vocal or tactile fremitus, remembering to examine the lateral surfaces and to compare symmetrical areas of the patient's lungs (see *Palpation Sequences,* page 171). (If your patient is a woman, you may have to displace her breasts to examine her anterior chest.) Remember that fremitus will usually be decreased or absent over the patient's precordium.

Anterior chest percussion

Percussing the patient's anterior chest allows you to determine the location and density of his heart, lungs, liver, and diaphragm. Begin by percussing the lung apices (the supraclavicular areas), comparing right and left sides. Then percuss downward in 1¼" to 2" (3- to 5-cm) intervals. You should hear resonant tones until you reach the third or fourth intercostal space (ICS), to the left of the sternum, where you'll hear a dull sound produced by the heart. This sound should continue as you percuss down toward the fifth ICS and laterally

Chest Deformities

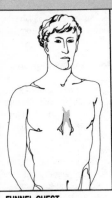 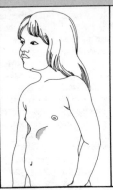 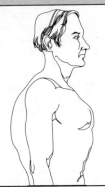

FUNNEL CHEST
Physical characteristics
• Sinking or funnel-shaped depression of lower sternum
• Diminished anteroposterior chest diameter
Signs and associated conditions
• Postural disorders, such as forward displacement of neck and shoulders
• Upper thoracic kyphosis
• Protuberant abdomen
• Functional heart murmur

PIGEON CHEST
Physical characteristics
• Projection of sternum beyond abdomen's frontal plane. Evident in two variations: projection greatest at xiphoid process; projection greatest at or near center of sternum
Signs and associated conditions
• Functional cardiovascular or respiratory disorders

BARREL CHEST
Physical characteristics
• Enlarged anteroposterior and transverse chest dimensions; chest appears barrel-shaped
• Prominent accessory muscles
Signs and associated conditions
• Chronic respiratory disorders
• Increasing shortness of breath
• Chronic cough
• Wheezing

toward the midclavicular line. At the sixth ICS, at the left midclavicular line, you'll hear resonance again. As you percuss down toward the rib cage, you'll hear tympany over the stomach. On the right side, you should hear resonance, indicating normal lung tissue. Near the fifth to seventh ICS you'll hear dullness, marking the superior border of the liver.

To percuss his lateral chest, instruct the patient to raise his arms over his head. Percuss laterally, comparing right and left sides as you proceed. These areas should also be resonant.

Anterior chest auscultation

In the same way you auscultated the patient's posterior chest, auscultate his anterior and lateral chest, comparing sounds on both sides before moving to the next area.

Begin auscultating the anterior chest at the trachea, where you should hear bronchial (or tubular) breath sounds.

Next, listen for bronchovesicular breath sounds where the mainstem bronchi branch from the trachea (near the second intercostal space, ¾" to 1¼" or 2 to 3 cm to either side of the sternum). Bronchial and bronchovesicular sounds are abnormal when heard over peripheral lung areas.

Now, using the standard chest landmarks, listen over the patient's peripheral lung fields for vesicular sounds. Be sure to auscultate his lateral chest walls, comparing right and left sides as you proceed. On the left side, heart sounds diminish breath sounds; on the right side, the liver diminishes them.

If you hear adventitious breath sounds, de-

Palpation Sequences

Use the palpation sequences illustrated here to palpate the posterior and anterior chest. It will help you detect any areas of increased or decreased fremitus.

When following the sequence, use the top portion of your palm to palpate. You'll also find using only *one* hand is best. Remember to avoid bony areas.

Carefully document your findings, including location and description of any abnormalities.

Posterior

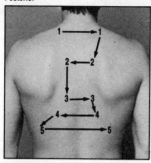

Anterior

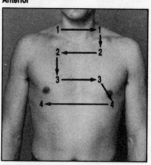

scribe them and note their location and timing. After you've listened to several respirations in the area of the adventitious sound, instruct the patient to cough and breathe deeply. Then, using the technique described on page 167 for the posterior chest, auscultate the area producing the abnormal sound and, if necessary, auscultate for bronchophony, whispered pectoriloquy, and egophony.

Pediatric assessment

Pediatric history data

Ask the parents how often the child has had upper respiratory tract infections. Remember that a history of more than six nose or throat infections a year necessitates further evaluation of the child, because colds in preschool children are often a sign of streptococcal infection. Find out if the child has had other respiratory signs and symptoms, such as dyspnea, wheezing, rhinorrhea, or a stuffy nose. Ask if these appear related to the child's activities or to seasonal changes.

Also, ask if the child has had a cough that

interrupts his sleep or causes vomiting. If so, does it produce sputum? Is the sputum blood-tinged? Ask if anyone in the family has ever had cystic fibrosis or other major respiratory diseases, such as asthma.

Examination considerations

Positioning a child for a respiratory examination depends, of course, on his age, condition, and disposition. The sitting position offers you easiest access to his thorax, and usually a parent can help by holding the child in his lap. You and the parent can also form a mock examining table by sitting opposite each other, placing your knees together, and allowing the child to sit on the parent's lap.

If the child is quiet, auscultate his lungs first. If you hear fluid, place the stethoscope's diaphragm over his nose to determine if the fluid is in the nose or upper respiratory tract. This is important in children, because the sound of fluid in the nose can be transmitted through the short distance between nose and lungs.

To examine the child's nostrils for patency, occlude one, put the stethoscope's diaphragm over the other, and listen and watch for condensation on the diaphragm. With infants and young children, perform this procedure (which may provoke crying) after auscultating the lungs, because crying can cause an unnatural respiration rate and interfere with breath sound auscultation. Also, crying usually elicits mouth breathing, which can make determining the nostrils' patency difficult. To quiet a crying child and relax his breathing, hand him a plastic windmill and ask him to blow on it, or have him pretend to blow out a candle.

The procedure you should use for inspecting the child's mouth and throat also depends on his age and disposition. Position the *infant* on his back and ask the parent to hold him still. If the patient's a *young child,* have the parent hold the child on his lap, restraining the child's head with one arm and his arms with the other. Or, the parent can raise and hold the child's arms over his head, immobilizing the head between the arms. A child age *6 or older* will probably sit on the examining table without restraint. (To ease his anxiety, you might allow him to handle the equipment.)

Use a flashlight and tongue depressor to examine the child's mouth and throat. You can also use the tongue depressor to elicit the gag reflex in infants, but *remember, you should never test this reflex or examine the pharynx in a child suspected of having epiglottitis,* because these procedures can cause complete laryngeal obstruction, which could be fatal.

While examining the posterior thorax of the older child, be sure to check for scoliosis. If you observe an abnormality, refer him for treatment. Also, remember that Harrison's groove (a horizontal ridge at the diaphragm level, accompanied by some flaring of the ribs below the groove, as by rickets or congenital syphilis) is considered normal in infants and young, thin children—if other pathologic signs aren't present.

Childhood respiratory disorders

You may see laryngotracheobronchitis (croup)—the most common cause of respiratory distress in children over age 3—in a child with a history of upper respiratory tract infections, a hacking cough, fever, stridor, and diminished breath sounds with rhonchi. Signs and symptoms of this usually benign disease are similar to those for epiglottitis. Usually, a chest X-ray determines the cause of respiratory distress in children.

Epiglottitis, a bacterial infection preceded by a minor respiratory illness, sometimes may be present in a child with sudden respiratory distress and a high fever, so-called seal bark, hoarseness, and anoxia. *Remember: Excitement or stress that causes the child to cry can produce immediate airway obstruction.* Epiglottitis is more common in children between ages 3 and 8; croup, which has similar signs and symptoms, is more common in children between ages 2 and 5.

Intracostal, subcostal, and suprasternal retractions and expiratory grunts are always serious signs in children. Refer an infant or child with any of these signs for treatment immediately. He may have pneumonia, respiratory distress syndrome, or left-sided heart failure. An infant with untreated pneumonia can die within hours.

When a child's symptoms and signs include retractions, nasal flaring, cyanosis, restlessness, and apprehension—primarily on inspiration—the trachea or mainstem bronchi may be obstructed. If these signs and symptoms occur on expiration, his bronchioles may be obstructed, as seen with asthma or bronchitis. Foreign body aspiration is another major cause of respiratory distress in children. These signs and symptoms indicate serious respiratory distress.

Geriatric assessment

Health history concerns

During the health history interview, remember that the elderly patient may be confused or his mental function may be slow, especially if he has hypoventilation and hypoperfusion from respiratory disease. Also, keep in mind that because an elderly patient has reduced sensations, he may describe his chest pain as heavy or dull, whereas a younger patient would describe the same pain as sharp. When recording a retired patient's psychosocial history, be sure you ask about his former occupation, because it may have caused exposure to harmful substances.

Examination findings

As you inspect an elderly patient's thorax, be

especially alert for degenerative skeletal changes, such as kyphosis. Palpating for diaphragmatic excursion may be more difficult in the elderly patient because of loose skin covering his chest. Therefore, when you position your hands, slide them toward his spine, raising loose skin folds between your thumbs and the spine.

When you percuss his chest, remember that loss of elastic recoil capability in an elderly person stretches the alveoli and bronchioles, producing hyperresonance. Pulmonary function also decreases in the elderly. During auscultation, carefully observe how well your patient tolerates the examination. He may tire easily because of low tolerance to oxygen debt.

Also, taking deep breaths during auscultation may produce light-headedness or syncope faster than in a younger patient. You may hear diminished sounds at the lung bases because some of his airways are closed.

Risk of illness

Elderly persons are subject to the same respiratory disorders and diseases as younger adults. However, in cold, damp weather, the incidence of chronic respiratory disease, colds, and flu rises more steeply among the elderly. Also, geriatric patients run a greater risk of developing pneumonia because their weakened chest musculature reduces their ability to clear secretions.

Guide to Respiratory Disorders

DISORDER	CHIEF COMPLAINT	
Adult respiratory distress syndrome (ARDS)	• *Cough:* dry, progressing from rusty and frothy to burgundy red sputum • *Dyspnea:* tachypnea, progressing to dyspnea • *Chest pain:* absent	
Asthmatic attack	• *Cough:* dry and minimal; progresses to thick and productive • *Dyspnea:* severe, with audible wheezing • *Chest pain:* absent	
Atelectasis	• *Cough:* present • *Dyspnea:* sudden; wheezing • *Chest pain:* absent or pleuritic	
Bacterial pneumonia	• *Cough:* present, productive, with mucoid, purulent sputum; hemoptysis • *Dyspnea:* present on exertion • *Chest pain:* present, pleuritic	
Bronchiectasis (advanced)	• *Cough:* chronic, with copious, foul, purulent sputum; hemoptysis • *Dyspnea:* present in severe and extensive disease • *Chest pain:* absent, except in pneumonia or second-degree chronic cough	

HISTORY	PHYSICAL EXAMINATION AND DIAGNOSTIC STUDIES
• Shock (septic, hemorrhagic, cardiogenic, anaphylactoid), direct chest trauma, aspiration, fat emboli, massive viral pneumonia	• Tachycardia; cyanosis; diffuse scattered rales, progressing to poor respiratory excursion; normal fremitus; normal percussion; normal breath and voice sounds • Chest X-ray abnormal; arterial blood gas analysis abnormal
• *Allergic asthma:* history of taking aspirin or other nonsteroidal anti-inflammatory agents; exposure to feathers, dander, molds, or certain foods; family history of allergies • *Idiosyncratic asthma:* attacks common following respiratory infection; no family history of allergies • *Precipitating or exacerbating asthma:* environment, stress, occupation, exercise, respiratory infection	• Tachycardia; pale and slightly cyanotic appearance; tendency to sit or lean forward; difficult speech; diaphoresis; nasal flaring on expiration; bulging neck veins; use of accessory muscles in retraction of intercostal, supraclavicular, and suprasternal spaces; markedly distended and fixed chest in inspiratory position; tactile fremitus decreased; hyperresonant percussion; diaphragm low on percussion; voice sounds decreased; breath sounds distant; expiration greater than inspiration; sibilant rhonchi (wheezing) throughout lung fields on expiration • Chest X-ray normal; arterial blood gas analysis abnormal during attack • Hyperinflation may be present.
• *Mild or chronic:* no signs or symptoms • *Acute:* sudden signs or symptoms; recent surgery	• Tachycardia; tracheal shift to affected side; respiratory excursion limited on affected side; tactile fremitus decreased or absent; dull to flat percussion over collapsed lung; hyperresonance over remaining portion of affected lung; decreased or absent breath and voice sounds; adventitious sounds high pitched with rales, especially on inspiration • Abnormal chest X-ray possible
• Predisposing conditions include depressed cough and glottis reflexes; altered consciousness from alcoholism, drug abuse, seizure, head trauma, general anesthetic, cerebrovascular disease, old age; painful breathing; muscle weakness; neuromuscular diseases; obstructive diseases; impaired mucus transport; possibly aspiration of vomitus or oil; respiration or immunosuppressive drug therapy	• Fever, chills, tachycardia, tachypnea, cyanosis, hypotension, guarding and decreased excursion on affected side • *With adventitious sounds:* crepitant inspiratory rales, pleural friction rub with pleural involvement • *With consolidation:* tactile fremitus increased; percussion dull or flat; breath sounds tubular or bronchial; voice sounds increased, including bronchophony, egophony, and whispered pectoriloquy • *With bronchial plug and consolidation:* tactile fremitus absent; percussion dull; voice, breath sounds decreased or absent • Increased white blood cell count; chest X-ray abnormal; sputum examination abnormal
• Recurring pneumonia or sinusitis; congenital defects in bronchial system; hereditary predisposition; deficient immunities; local bronchial	• Cyanosis; clubbing; fever; night sweats; weight loss; sibilant or sonorous rhonchi and rales over lower lobes; in progressive advanced bronchiectasis, lung findings similar to Type A chronic ob- *(continued)*

Guide to Respiratory Disorders *(continued)*

DISORDER	CHIEF COMPLAINT	
Bronchiectasis (advanced) *continued*		
Chest wall deformities (including pectus excavatum, kyphoscoliosis, thoracoplasty, and trauma)	• *Cough:* absent or productive, depending on severity or tendency toward infection • *Dyspnea:* present only in severe deformity • *Chest pain:* absent	
Chronic obstructive pulmonary disease (COPD) Type A (pink puffer)	• *Cough:* present, with scant mucoid production • *Dyspnea:* insidious onset; slowly progresses to severe dyspnea on exertion • *Chest pain:* absent	
Chronic obstructive pulmonary disease (COPD) Type B (blue bloater)	• *Cough:* chronic and productive cough occurring most often in the morning, for at least 3 months of the year for 2 consecutive years; possibly hemoptysis • *Dyspnea:* first occurs only during chest infections; less severe than Type A • *Chest pain:* absent, except in second-degree chronic cough	
Connective tissue disease affecting the lungs (such as systemic lupus erythematosus)	• *Cough:* may be present, with or without production • *Dyspnea:* present • *Chest pain:* pleuritic or dull sensation, with pleural effusion	

HISTORY	PHYSICAL EXAMINATION AND DIAGNOSTIC STUDIES
obstruction; general weakness and fatigue	structive pulmonary disease ● Chest X-ray abnormal; bronchography abnormal; pulmonary function test normal or abnormal; arterial blood gas analysis abnormal
● Possibly asymptomatic; signs and symptoms occur gradually; past history of chest trauma or congenital deformity	● Physical deformities; accessory muscle changes; lung distortion, making interpretation of findings difficult; flail chest (paradoxical movement of region of wall and local bulging during expiration, and retraction during inspiration); consolidation may be present; no adventitious sounds ● Chest X-ray and pulmonary function test normal or abnormal, depending on severity of deformity; chronic deformity may cause increase in hematocrit and hemoglobin (polycythemia)
● Genetic predisposition; cigarette smoking; acute recurring respiratory illness (more common in Type B); exposure to environmental hazards; under age 60	● Reddish complexion; weight loss; neck veins distended on expiration, collapsed on inspiration; increased anteroposterior diameter; use of accessory muscles; decreased respiratory excursion bilaterally; decreased tactile fremitus; hyperresonant percussion; decreased diaphragmatic excursion; breath sounds distant with prolonged expiration; pursed lips when breathing; decreased voice sounds; adventitious sounds; occasionally sonorous or wheezing ● Chest X-ray abnormal; pulmonary function test abnormal; arterial blood gas analysis abnormal; hematocrit abnormal
● Exposure to air pollution, inorganic and/or organic dusts, or noxious gases; cigarette smoking; genetic predisposition; increased frequency of respiratory infections	● Red or blue complexion; cyanosis; overweight; increased anteroposterior chest diameter (barrel chest); hyperresonance on percussion; prolonged expiratory phase; sibilant and sonorous rhonchi and rales may be present; cor pulmonale may occur as complication ● Chest X-ray normal or abnormal (may show evidence of past inflammatory disease); pulmonary function test abnormal; arterial blood gas analysis abnormal; hematocrit abnormal
● Past history of connective tissue disease	● Signs of specific suspected disease; fibrosis; clubbing; decreased respiratory excursion; trachea deviates toward more affected side; resonant to dull percussion; decreased breath and voice sounds, especially in diffuse fibrosis; rales audible on inspiration and expiration; pleural friction rub ● Chest X-ray abnormal; pulmonary function tests abnormal; specific tests to identify disease include antinuclear antibody and Rh factor

(continued)

Guide to Respiratory Disorders *(continued)*

DISORDER	CHIEF COMPLAINT	
Lung abscess	● *Cough:* present, productive with large amounts of bloody, purulent sputum ● *Dyspnea:* present, frequent ● *Chest pain:* present, pleuritic	
Lung tuberculosis	● *Cough:* present, productive, purulent; hemoptysis ● *Dyspnea:* present only in advanced disease ● *Chest pain:* present, occasionally pleuritic	
Lung tumor	● *Cough:* absent, mild, or change in pattern of chronic cough ● *Dyspnea:* absent or on exertion ● *Chest pain:* absent	
Mycoplasmal pneumonia (atypical pneumonia)	● *Cough:* prolonged history of dry, hacking, possibly persistent cough; no hemoptysis ● *Dyspnea:* absent ● *Chest pain:* present, possibly from secondary musculoskeletal cough	
Neuromuscular disorders	● *Cough:* absent ● *Dyspnea:* possible ● *Chest pain:* absent	
Obesity, pickwickian syndrome	● *Cough:* absent or productive, depending on severity or tendency toward infection ● *Dyspnea:* absent, or present only on exertion ● *Chest pain:* absent	
Pleural effusion (large, chronic)	● *Cough:* absent ● *Dyspnea:* usually present ● *Chest pain:* possibly pleuritic or dull	

HISTORY	PHYSICAL EXAMINATION AND DIAGNOSTIC STUDIES
• Recurrent dental infections; history similar to that of bacterial pneumonia but more insidious; history of altered mental status	• Fever, weight loss, fetid breath, poor dentition; respiratory findings may appear normal or similar to consolidation in bacterial pneumonia • Chest X-ray normal or abnormal; sputum culture should identify organism; increased white blood cell count (leukocytosis)
• Possibly asymptomatic; malaise, irritability at end of day; night sweats; exposure to active pulmonary tuberculosis; associated with uncontrolled diabetes, alcoholism, undernutrition, institutionalization, long-term treatment with corticosteroids	• Fever; weight loss; decreased respiratory excursion; in early stages, respiratory findings may appear normal; extensive fibrosis may cause consolidation: apical dullness, bronchial breath sounds, coarse rales • Chest X-ray abnormal; sputum culture positive for tubercle bacillus; positive tuberculin test
• May be asymptomatic; cigarette smoking; possibly anorexia, weight loss, nausea, vomiting, weakness	• Possibly weight loss, consolidation, or atelectasis • Possibly abnormal chest X-ray, sputum cytology, bronchoscopy, and fiberoscopy
• Between ages 5 and 20; family history of disease; onset of signs and symptoms resembles that of viral respiratory tract infection (malaise, myalgia, sore throat, headache, mild cough, earache)	• Fever during first 2 weeks; in about 15% of cases, inflamed tympanic membrane, with bullae; fine crepitant rales at end of inspiratory cycle possible; dullness on percussion; rhonchi; coarse or musical wheezes; normal chest findings possible • Chest X-ray abnormal; complement fixation test shows level of specific antibody to *Mycoplasma;* no leukocytosis
• *Neuromuscular disorders:* medulla or spinal cord dysfunction, bulbar poliomyelitis, cervical cord trauma, Guillain-Barré syndrome, muscular dystrophy, myasthenia gravis • *Respiratory center depression:* brain tumor, sedation, industrial or carbon monoxide poisoning, polymyxin or other antibiotic therapy, encephalopathy, high-flow uncontrolled oxygen therapy	• Shallow or absent respiration, requiring artificial ventilation; distant breath sounds; symptoms of neuromuscular disease; respiratory muscle atrophy; adventitious sounds caused by underlying pathology • Pulmonary function test abnormal; arterial blood gas analysis may be abnormal
• Possibly asymptomatic; history of weight gain; daytime somnolence	• Distant breath sounds; reduced respiratory excursion • Possible abnormal pulmonary function test
• Possibly asymptomatic; same history as small, acute pleural effusion	• Trachea deviates toward normal side; tactile fremitus absent; dull or flat percussion; voice sounds absent or decreased; breath sounds absent; adventitious sounds caused by underlying pathology and lung consolidation • Chest X-ray abnormal

(continued)

Guide to Respiratory Disorders *(continued)*

DISORDER	CHIEF COMPLAINT	
Pleural effusion (small, acute)	● *Cough:* absent ● *Dyspnea:* possible ● *Chest pain:* possibly pleuritic or dull	
Pneumonectomy	● *Cough:* absent ● *Dyspnea:* absent, unless remaining portion of lung is unable to compensate ● *Chest pain:* absent	
Pneumothorax closed	● *Cough:* absent ● *Dyspnea:* moderate ● *Chest pain:* pleuritic; may be sudden and sharp	
Pneumothorax open	● *Cough:* absent ● *Dyspnea:* severe ● *Chest pain:* severe, pleuritic; sudden and sharp	
Pulmonary edema	● *Cough:* dry at first, progressing to productive, with pink, frothy sputum ● *Dyspnea:* in acute form: wheezing; in chronic form: paroxysmal nocturnal dyspnea; orthopnea ● *Chest pain:* absent	
Pulmonary embolism	● *Cough:* hemoptysis ● *Dyspnea:* sudden, unexplained tachypnea ● *Chest pain:* pleuritic, but only if infarction occurs	
Pulmonary fibrosis, chemical (irritant gases, chemicals)	● *Cough:* present, hemoptysis ● *Dyspnea:* present, wheezing ● *Chest pain:* present	

HISTORY	PHYSICAL EXAMINATION AND DIAGNOSTIC STUDIES
• Possibly asymptomatic; history of neoplasms, congestive heart failure, rheumatoid arthritis, subphrenic abscess, pancreatitis	• Limited respiratory excursion may be present; tactile fremitus decreased or absent; dull percussion; decreased breath and voice sounds; adventitious sounds caused by underlying pathology • Chest X-ray abnormal
• Possibly asymptomatic; history of lung surgery; fatigue	• Breath sounds absent; in partial pneumonectomy, remaining portion of lung may overexpand, causing hyperresonance; in total pneumonectomy, decreased respiratory excursion occurs on affected side • Chest X-ray and pulmonary function test normal or abnormal, depending on severity of deformity
• Dizziness, emphysema, tuberculosis	• Crepitus; if small, no trachea deviation; *on affected side:* limited respiratory excursion; tactile fremitus absent; resonant or hyperresonant percussion; breath and voice sounds absent or decreased; no adventitious sounds • Chest X-ray abnormal
• Dizziness	• Crepitus; trachea deviates to normal side; *on affected side:* limited respiratory excursion; tactile fremitus absent; hyperresonant or tympanic percussion; breath and voice sounds absent or decreased; no adventitious sounds; cyanosis • Chest X-ray abnormal
• May be sudden or chronic; history of heart disease	• *Acute:* must sit up and lean forward to breathe; cyanosis; resonant percussion; normal voice sounds; breath sounds reveal prolonged expiratory phase; adventitious sounds reveal dry, fine rales usually at base, progressing to moist, bubbling rales throughout chest; sibilant rhonchi; rattle sound • *Chronic:* enlarged heart, peripheral edema, hepatomegaly, bilateral diffuse butterfly density from hilum • Chest X-ray abnormal
• Previous thromboemboli, recent surgery, dehydration, pregnancy, congestive heart failure, chronic pulmonary disease, use of oral contraceptives, leg fracture, deep venous insufficiency, extended inactivity, such as bed rest or prolonged air travel	• Tachycardia; may be normal except for rales and localized wheezing; pleural effusion and pleural friction rub possible if infarction occurs; atelectasis and pneumonia may occur as complications • Chest X-ray inconclusive; arterial blood gas analysis abnormal; pulmonary angiography abnormal. Ventilation/perfusion lung scan abnormal
• Exposure to irritant gases or chemicals	• Burning and irritation of eyes, nose, throat, trachea; nausea and vomiting; cyanosis on exertion; fine metallic crepitant basilar rales; decreased chest excursion in advanced disease • Chest X-ray abnormal; pulmonary function test abnormal *(continued)*

Guide to Respiratory Disorders *(continued)*

DISORDER	CHIEF COMPLAINT	
Pulmonary fibrosis, non-chemical (dust, industrial irritants, allergens)	• *Cough:* present, dry, irritable, progressing to productive hemoptysis • *Dyspnea:* present, progressive, exertional; wheezing; tachypnea • *Chest pain:* present	
Tension pneumothorax	• *Cough:* absent • *Dyspnea:* severe • *Chest pain:* severe, pleuritic; sudden and sharp	
Tumor	• *Cough:* present; cardinal symptom of bronchial tumor or of tumor compressing bronchus • *Dyspnea:* usually present if tumor is large • *Chest pain:* possibly pleuritic or dull	

HISTORY	PHYSICAL EXAMINATION AND DIAGNOSTIC STUDIES
• Inhalation of dust, industrial irritants, or allergens; malaise; weight loss; anorexia	• Cyanosis on exertion; fine metallic crepitant basilar rales; decreased chest excursion in advanced disease • Chest X-ray abnormal; pulmonary function test abnormal
• Acute symptoms	• Cyanosis; shock; possible tympanic percussion; other physical findings same as those of open pneumothorax • Chest X-ray abnormal
• Presence of signs and symptoms depends on tumor's size and location	• In large tumor, physical findings same as those of chronic pleural effusion • Chest X-ray abnormal

10

Cardiovascular System

The phenomenally high incidence of heart disease and the seriousness of its complications continually reaffirm your need to know how to assess the complex cardiovascular system. No body system wears out, breaks down, or otherwise malfunctions so often, in so many people. Heart disease affects people of all ages and takes many forms. It can be congenital or acquired, and it can develop suddenly or insidiously. Mastering cardiovascular assessment skills is therefore essential to your development as a member of the professional health-care team.

History data

Biographical data

Age, sex, and race are all essential considerations in identifying patients with cardiovascular disorders. For example, coronary artery disease most commonly affects white men between ages 40 and 70; hypertension occurs most often in blacks.

History of present illness

The most common chief complaints in cardiovascular disorders are *chest pain* or *discomfort, dyspnea, fatigue and weakness, irregular heartbeat,* and *peripheral changes such as edema, dry skin,* and *extremity pain* (see *Guide to Cardiovascular Disorders,* pages 208 to 219).

Here are some questions you may want to ask about these complaints to explore fully the history of your patient's present illness:

• **Chest pain.** *How would you characterize the pain? For example, does it burn or produce a squeezing sensation? Where in your chest do you feel the pain? Can you point to*

the area? Does it radiate? Ischemic pain usually affects a large chest area, and the patient has difficulty localizing it. If he can circumscribe the painful area, the pain probably isn't ischemic. *How long have you been having this chest pain? How long does an attack last? Is it related to emotional stress or physical exertion?* Prinzmetal's angina usually occurs while at rest (see *Chest Pain Assessment,* pages 186 and 187).

• **Dyspnea.** *When do you experience the shortness of breath?* This symptom may indicate transient congestive heart failure or left ventricular failure. If the dyspnea occurs with exertion, ask specifically how much activity is required to cause it. Dyspnea at rest suggests advanced disease; increasing dyspnea with less exertion may indicate progressive pathology and failing compensatory mechanisms.

• **Paroxysmal nocturnal dyspnea (PND).** A classic symptom of left ventricular failure, PND occurs at night when the patient is sleeping. He awakens with a feeling of suffocation. Maneuvers that cause gravity to drain fluid from the lungs to the feet—for example, sitting on the edge of the bed or walking to the window for fresh air—relieve PND. The attack usually subsides in a few minutes.

• **Orthopnea.** *How many pillows do you use to make breathing easier? Do you use more now than you used to?* An increase in the number of pillows indicates developing orthopnea. The number of pillows the patient uses helps determine the degree of left ventricular failure. Record your patient's response as *two-pillow orthopnea, three-pillow orthopnea,* and so on.

• **Unexplained weakness and fatigue.** *Do you tire easily? What type of activity causes you to feel tired? How long can you perform* *this activity before becoming tired? When did you first notice the feeling of weakness and fatigue? Is it getting worse? Is the feeling relieved by rest?* Fatigue and weakness on mild exertion, especially if relieved by rest, may be a sign of heart disease. Such a patient's heart can't provide sufficient blood to meet the body's metabolic needs. These symptoms are often the hallmark of early progressive heart failure.

● **Irregular heartbeat.** *Does your heart pound or beat too fast?* Palpitations may reflect arrhythmias, especially tachyarrhythmias. *Does your heart ever skip a beat or seem to jump?* Skipped beats often indicate premature atrial or ventricular contractions. *Do you ever experience dizziness or faint? When?* These symptoms may be related to transient arrhythmias, sometimes caused by underlying heart disease or by intake of certain beverages, such as coffee, tea, and cola.

● **Weight change with edema.** *Does your weight fluctuate or have you gained weight recently?* Weight changes are common in cardiovascular disease, especially weight gain from sodium and water retention secondary to congestive heart failure and hypertension. *Are your ankles or feet swollen? Do your shoes feel tight or uncomfortable at the end of the day? Is the swelling relieved by elevating your feet or lying down?* Edema associated with cardiovascular disease is readily mobilized.

● **Dry skin.** *Have you noticed any skin dryness or scaliness, especially on your legs?* Dry skin may be associated with peripheral vascular disease.

● **Extremity pain.** *Have you experienced any pain or discomfort in your arms or legs?* Ischemia from peripheral vascular disease can cause aches or cramps when the patient moves the affected arm or leg. *Do you feel pain or cramps in your legs when you walk? Is the pain relieved by rest? Does elevating the leg cause pain that's relieved by dangling or lowering the leg?* Intermittent claudication results from advanced atherosclerosis of the femoral arteries. *How many stairs or city blocks can you walk before the symptoms begin? Is the pain associated with walking over any particular kind of terrain, in certain temperatures, or at a particular pace?* These factors affect the intensity of exertion. *Does the pain increase with prolonged standing or sitting?* Pain

that's most severe during prolonged standing or sitting indicates venous insufficiency. Venous pain located in the calf and lower leg, usually described as an aching, tired, or full feeling, is commonly accompanied by leg edema and obvious varicosities.

Past history

Explore the following relevant areas when reviewing your patient's history:

● **Hypertension.** *Have you ever had your blood pressure taken? Can you recall what it was? Have you ever been told you had high blood pressure? Have you ever taken medication for blood pressure?* Pressure above 160/90 correlates positively with ischemic heart disease, renal failure, cerebrovascular accident, and an accelerated rate of coronary artery disease (CAD).

● **Hyperlipoproteinemia.** *Have you ever been told by your doctor that you have high cholesterol or triglyceride levels?* Elevated serum levels of cholesterol, triglycerides, and free fatty acids probably correlate directly with a higher incidence of CAD, although this relationship is still disputed. The two most common hyperlipoproteinemia patterns in patients with premature atherosclerosis are Type II—elevated cholesterol with normal or slightly elevated triglycerides—and Type IV—elevated triglycerides with normal or slightly elevated cholesterol.

● **Diabetes mellitus.** *Have you ever been told you had sugar in your urine? Have you ever had a test for blood sugar? Was it normal?* The relationship between diabetes mellitus and CAD is still controversial, but patients with the most common types of hyperlipoproteinemia usually show abnormal carbohydrate metabolism. Patients with CAD also have a high incidence of diabetes mellitus, and patients with diabetes seem to have a tendency toward atheroma formation. Such atherosclerosis occurs not only in the coronary artery system, but also in the arteries of the systemic circulation, particularly in the aorta and in the femoral and carotid arteries.

● **Rheumatic fever.** *Did you ever have rheumatic fever? Were you ever told you had a heart murmur?* Many people have so-called innocent or functional heart murmurs unrelated to rheumatic fever or structural congenital heart disease. The effect of rheumatic fever

Chest Pain Assessment

CONDITION	LOCATION AND RADIATION	CHARACTER
Myocardial ischemia (angina pectoris)	• Substernal or retrosternal pain spreading across chest • May radiate to inside of either or both arms, the neck, or jaw	• Squeezing, heavy pressure, aching, or burning discomfort
Myocardial infarction	• Substernal or over precordium • May radiate throughout chest and arms to jaw	• Crushing, viselike, steady pain
Pericardial chest pain	• Substernal or left of sternum • May radiate to neck, arms, back, or epigastrium	• Sharp, intermittent pain (accentuated by swallowing, coughing, deep inspiration, or lying supine)
Pulmonary embolism	• Inferior portion of the pleura • May radiate to costal margins or upper abdomen	• Stabbing, knifelike pain (accentuated by respirations)
Spontaneous pneumothorax	• Lateral thorax • Does not radiate	• Tearing, pleuritic pain
Infectious or inflammatory processes (pleurisy)	• Pleural • May be widespread or only over affected area	• Moderate, sharp, raw, burning pain
Aortic aneurysm (dissecting)	• Anterior chest • May radiate to thoracic portion of back	• Excruciating, knifelike pain
Esophageal pain	• Substernal • May radiate around chest to shoulders	• Burning, knotlike pain (simulating angina)
Chest wall pain	• Costochondral or sternocostal junctions • Does not radiate	• Aching pain or soreness

ONSET AND DURATION	PRECIPITATING EVENTS	ASSOCIATED FINDINGS
• Sudden onset • Usually subsides within 5 minutes	• Mental or physical exertion; intense emotion • Hot, humid weather • Heavy food intake; especially in extreme temperatures or high humidity	• Feeling of uneasiness or impending doom
• Sudden onset • More severe and prolonged than anginal pain	• Occurs spontaneously, with exertion, stress, or at rest	• Dyspnea • Profuse perspiration • Nausea and vomiting • Dizziness, weakness • Feeling of uneasiness or impending doom
• Severe, sudden onset • Usually relieved by bending forward • May occur intermittently over several days	• Upper respiratory tract infection • Myocardial infarction • Rheumatic fever • Pericarditis	• Distended neck veins • Tachycardia • Paradoxical pulse possible with constrictive pericarditis • Pericardial friction rub
• Sudden onset • May last a few days	• Anxiety (associated with coughing)	• Dyspnea; tachypnea • Tachycardia • Cough with hemoptysis
• Sudden onset • Relieved by aspiration of air	• Trauma • Ruptured emphysematous bleb • Anxiety	• Dyspnea; tachypnea • Mediastinal shift • Decreased or absent breath sounds over involved lung
• Occurs on inspiration • Relief usually occurs several days after effective treatment	• Underlying disease of lung, such as pneumonia	• Fever • Cough with sputum production
• Sudden onset • Unrelieved by medication or comfort measures • May last for hours	• Hypertension	• Lower blood pressure in one arm than in other • May have paralysis • May have murmur of aortic insufficiency or pulsus paradoxus • Hypotension and shock
• Sudden onset • Relieved by diet or position change, antacids or belching • Usually brief duration	• May occur spontaneously • Eating	• Regurgitation
• Often begins as dull ache, increasing in intensity over a few days • Usually long lasting	• Chest wall movement	• Symptoms and physical findings vary with specific musculoskeletal disorder

or of repeated streptococcal infections, however, can permanently damage heart valves—especially the mitral and aortic—leaving them insufficient (unable to close) or stenosed (scarred, rigid, and unable to open fully). Knowing whether the patient has had these conditions will help you interpret heart murmurs common in patients with post–rheumatic fever heart disease.

● *Medications.* Have you ever taken diuretics (water or fluid pills)? Do you know why the doctor prescribed the medication you took? Have you ever taken any drugs for your heart or circulation? Knowledge of medications the patient is taking or has taken in the past can provide valuable information on past or present cardiovascular disorders.

Family history

Note any family history of the following conditions:

● *Cardiovascular disease.* Ask the patient specific questions about any family history of angina, acute myocardial infarction, hypertension, cerebrovascular accident, diabetes, or renal disease. The incidence of coronary artery disease (CAD) is higher in patients with a family history of advanced atherosclerotic disease or of one or more deaths from a CAD-related event.

● *Acquired behavior.* Genetic predisposition to cardiovascular disease may exist, but acquired behavior—including diet (high sodium intake, high lipid levels, obesity), personality, and a stressful life-style—is a significant contributing factor.

Psychosocial history

Explore the following areas in your patient's psychosocial history:

● *Personality.* How does the patient view himself? Your patient's personality is the most significant aspect of his psychosocial history.

● *Occupation.* The physical and emotional demands of a person's occupation can place him under a great deal of stress, a factor that may be important in the diagnosis of cardiovascular disease. Commuting long distances can also be stressful.

● *Domestic problems.* Problems at home can be more stressful than occupational problems and may also predispose a person to cardiovascular disease.

Activities of daily living

Examine the following aspects of your patient's daily life for patterns that may predispose him to cardiovascular problems:

● *Physical activity.* A healthy person should engage in aerobic activity at least three times a week. Exercise is beneficial to general cardiovascular conditioning.

● *Smoking.* If your patient smokes cigarettes, determine the duration of his habit and the amount he smokes, and record this data as *pack years.* (Calculate pack years by multiplying the number of years by the number of packs per day.) Nicotine, a sympathetic nervous system stimulator, increases heart rate, stroke volume, cardiac output, cardiac work, and vasoconstriction. Smoking is a significant risk factor for peripheral vascular disease, and the mortality for patients with coronary artery disease is about 70% higher in middle-aged men who smoke one pack a day than in those who don't smoke. The percentage decreases for older men, and the correlation isn't as clear for women. Further, this risk doesn't apply to pipe and cigar smokers, probably because they generally don't inhale as much as cigarette smokers.

● *Diet.* A brief history of your patient's eating habits, particularly his intake of carbohydrates and fats, may help determine his potential for CAD. A high-sodium diet can aggravate the development of edema and may be one of the factors associated with the development of hypertension.

Review of systems

Ask the patient about the following signs and symptoms, which may indicate cardiovascular dysfunction (see *Cardiac Emergency Assessment,* page 189):

● *Skin.* Diaphoresis usually reflects strong sympathetic nervous system stimulation and is commonly associated with myocardial ischemia.

● *Respiratory.* Painful breathing may be pericardial or pleural in origin. Nocturnal or bloody coughing may indicate pulmonary edema, pulmonary embolism, pneumonia, or worsening congestive heart failure. Pain accompanying wheezing is most commonly associated with such bronchospastic obstructive diseases as asthma and bronchitis.

● *Gastrointestinal.* Nausea and vomiting are

often associated with severe myocardial ischemia and myocardial infarction.

• **Genitourinary.** Nocturia can result when edema occurs during the day and renal perfusion increases at night, causing increased diuresis. In the absence of genitourinary disorders, nocturia is commonly associated with congestive heart failure.

• **Nervous.** Light-headedness, dizziness, or fainting may be related to hypotension, transient arrhythmias, or rapid heartbeat.

Physical examination

Positioning and equipment

After ensuring privacy, instruct your patient to change into a hospital gown that allows for thorough examination of his neck, chest, arms, and legs. Then ask him to assume the supine position, with his head and thorax comfortably supported at about a 45° angle. Make sure the bed or table height allows inspection of the patient in this and other positions—sitting forward, as well as in the left lateral recumbent position.

Make sure the lighting is adequate. Position the light source so the light *crosses* the areas you'll inspect—the neck and precordium—and doesn't shine directly on them. Also make sure the environment is quiet—particularly during your auscultation of cardiac sounds, which are usually subtle and low pitched.

Normally, the only equipment you'll need is a stethoscope, a blood pressure cuff, and a ruler. After inspecting the patient for overt signs of cardiac risk factors (such as xanthelasma) and recording his vital signs, you'll examine him from head to toe using inspection, palpation, and auscultation. In cardiovascular assessment, percussion has limited value, because inspection, palpation, and chest X-rays more accurately determine heart size and borders as well as liver size (see *Diagnostic Tests,* page 190).

During the examination, stand on the patient's right side. This allows you to reach comfortably across the precordium for palpation and auscultation and to palpate the liver area on the right side correctly.

General inspection

During your general inspection, record your

Cardiac Emergency Assessment

If your patient's in a state of cardiac emergency, you'll want to assess his condition quickly and accurately. If your patient's *unconscious,* check his respiration and pulse. If necessary, institute cardiopulmonary resuscitation. Assess the *conscious* cardiac emergency patient as follows:

Assess central pulse
• Assess the patient's central pulse by palpating his carotid or femoral arteries. Check his pulse for regularity and rate. *Note:* A weak, rapid pulse may precede cardiac arrest.
• Assess for chest pain. If present, note its location, duration, and severity.

Assess cardiac rhythm
• Assess his cardiac rhythm by instituting cardiac monitoring. Suspect impaired perfusion if the patient has tachyarrhythmias or bradyarrhythmias.

Assess perfusion status
• Assess his perfusion status by comparing central and peripheral pulses. Suspect impaired perfusion if the patient's peripheral pulse is weaker and/or slower than his central pulse.
• Measure his blood pressure. Remember, don't rule out shock just because hypotension's not evident.
• Determine his level of consciousness, and suspect shock if it's reduced.
• Check his skin; if it's cool and clammy, suspect impaired perfusion.
• Measure his urinary output. Consider shock confirmed if, along with the above findings, your patient's urinary output is severely decreased or absent.

initial impressions of the patient's body type, posture, gait, and movements as well as his overall health and basic hygiene. Also note observable cardiac risk factors, such as cigarette smoking, obesity, and fatty skin deposits (xanthomas). Observe his facial expressions and gestures for signs of pain or anxiety (clenching the front of the chest while describing discomfort—Levine's sign—strongly indicates ischemic heart pain). During conversation, assess his mental status, particularly the appropriateness of his responses and the clarity of his speech. Determine his apparent

Diagnostic Tests

The tests listed here may prove helpful when assessing the patient with a cardiac problem:
• *Blood gas tests:* determine acidity or alkalinity of the blood, partial pressure of oxygen, and carbon dioxide levels in the blood.
• *Cardiac enzyme and isoenzyme tests:* (CPK-MB, LDH_1 and LDH_2, HBD, SGOT): aid in identifying such cardiac disorders as myocardial infarction.
• *Electrolyte analysis:* may aid in identifying causes of some cardiac conduction disorders.
• *Electrocardiography:* records the conduction, magnitude, and duration of the electrical activity of the heart.
• *Chest X-rays:* permit visualization of the position, size, and contour of the heart and great vessels.
• *Fluoroscopy:* permits visualization of the pulsations of the heart and great vessels and helps detect and confirm malfunctions of prosthetic heart valves.
• *Ultrasonography* (echocardiography): helps evaluate cardiac structure and function and can reveal valve deformities.
• *Thallium imaging:* evaluates myocardial blood flow.
• *Technetium pyrophosphate scanning:* reveals damaged myocardial tissue as hot spots (areas where radioisotopes accumulate).
• *Cardiac catheterization:* permits visualization of cardiac contraction and cardiac structures, and measurement of intracardiac pressure and cardiac output.
• *Pulmonary artery catheterization:* permits measurement of pulmonary capillary wedge pressure (PCWP) and reflects both left atrial and left ventricular end-diastolic pressure.

Measurement of cardiac output (the amount of blood ejected from the right and left ventricles every 60 seconds) and estimation of the cardiac index (the cardiac output divided by the figure obtained from the patient's nomogram) are derived by using the four-lumen thermodilution catheter.

mood. Is he cooperative or withdrawn, fearful, or depressed?

Obtain some general information about the patient's cardiovascular system. Assess his skin color and condition and further assess his level of consciousness, if appropriate. Skin color, especially in the face, mouth, earlobes, and fingernails, helps determine the adequacy of cardiac output. Pallor or cyanosis may indicate poor cardiac output and tissue perfusion. (Remember, a dark-skinned patient with a cardiac disorder may appear gray. Inspect his lips and nail beds for cyanosis and his conjunctivas and mucous membranes for pallor, which may indicate anemia.)

Feel the patient's arm to assess its warmth and dryness. Dry, warm skin indicates adequate cardiac output and tissue perfusion. If the skin of the arm is perspiring and feels cool or cold, suspect peripheral vasoconstriction; this can be an early compensatory response in shock.

While assessing your patient's skin, you can also palpate his radial artery pulse to determine if the pulse rate, quality, and volume are within normal limits. Generally, the rate should be between 60 to 100 beats/minute; the quality should be strong and regular. This gross determination indicates whether your patient's cardiovascular system is stable or seriously compromised and requires immediate intervention.

When checking your patient's vital signs, remember that factors such as age, activity level, and physical and emotional status can affect them (see pages 31 to 36, and *How Age Affects Pulse and BP,* page 191). To complete the general inspection phase of cardiovascular assessment, record the patient's vital signs.

Venous pulse inspection

Blood from the jugular veins flows directly into the superior vena cava and the right heart. Thus, you can assess the adequacy of your patient's circulating volume, right heart function, and venous pressure by examining external and internal jugular vein pulsations. External jugular veins, which lie superficially, are visible above the clavicle. Internal jugular veins are larger, lie deeper along the carotid arteries, and transmit their pulsations outward to the skin covering the neck.

Normally, a person's neck veins are visible when he lies down; they're flat when he stands up. The semi-Fowler's position is best for inspection, because at a 45° elevation, the height of distended neck veins should be less than 3-4 cm above the sternal angle if right heart function is normal. Position the patient properly, and turn his head slightly away from you.

Use a small pillow to support the head, but don't flex the neck sharply. Remove clothing around the neck and thorax to prevent constriction. Arrange the lighting to cast small shadows along the neck.

You can learn about right heart dynamics by analyzing the venous waveform of your patient's right internal jugular vein. Use his carotid pulse or heart sounds to time the venous pulsations with the cardiac cycle.

The jugular venous pulse consists of five waves. The three ascending waves—a, c, and v—produce an undulating pulsation normally seen ⅜″ to ¾″ (1 to 2 cm) above the clavicle, just to the medial side of the sternocleidomastoid muscle, as follows:

• The a wave is the initial pulsation of the jugular vein, produced by right atrial contraction and retrograde transmission of the pressure pulse to the jugular veins. It occurs just before the first heart sound. You can time the atrial contraction by placing your index finger on the patient's opposite carotid, to feel the carotid pulse, or by listening for the first heart sound at the apex. The first jugular pulsation you see just before feeling the carotid pulse or hearing S_1 is the a wave. Remember that this wave won't appear in arrhythmias lacking atrial contraction, such as in atrial fibrillation and junctional rhythm. Also, the a wave may be exaggerated in chronic obstructive pulmonary disease, pulmonary embolism, and pulmonic or tricuspid stenosis—conditions causing elevated right atrial pressure. *Cannon wave* is a giant a wave occurring when the atrium contracts against a closed tricuspid valve during ventricular systole. This condition results from ectopic heartbeats, especially premature ventricular contractions, atrioventricular (AV) dissociation, or complete AV block.

• The c wave begins shortly after the first heart sound and may result from backward bulging of the tricuspid valve during right ventricular systole or from the carotid artery's impact on the adjacent jugular vein or pressure transmission. This wave may be hard to see.

• The v wave results from passive atrial filling during ventricular systole.

Two descending waves complete the jugular venous pulse:

• x descent, the descent of the a and c waves,

How Age Affects Pulse and BP

ARTERIAL PULSE

Age	Pulse Rate (beats per minute)
Under 1 month	90 to 170
Under age 1	80 to 160
Age 2	80 to 120
Age 6	75 to 115
Age 10	70 to 110
Age 14	65 to 100
Over age 14	60 to 100

ARTERIAL BLOOD PRESSURE

Age	Average Reading
Under 1 year	63 mean
Age 2	96/30
Age 4	98/60
Age 6	105/60
Age 10	112/64
Ages 11 to 18	120/75
Over age 18	130/80

results from right atrial diastole, as well as from the tricuspid valve's being pulled down during ventricular systole, reducing right atrial pressure.

• y descent is the fall in right atrial pressure from the peak of the v wave after tricuspid valve opening. It occurs during rapid atrial emptying into the ventricle in early diastole.

Venous pressure measurement

You can obtain more information about the right side of your patient's heart by determining his venous pressure level. (Venous pressure, the force exerted by the blood in the venous system, normally ranges from 6 to 8 cm of water.) Factors affecting venous pressure include circulating blood volume, vessel wall tone, vein patency, right heart function, respiratory function, pulmonary pressures, as well as the force of gravity.

Examples of alterations in venous pressure due to respiration include Kussmaul's sign and the hepatojugular reflux. *Kussmaul's sign,* a paradoxical rise in the height of jugular pressure during inspiration, may be seen in patients with chronic constrictive pericarditis. The *hepatojugular reflux* is increased venous pressure from abdominal compression during normal respirations. Although compressing the abdomen increases right heart volume, venous pressure shouldn't rise significantly. If it does (a positive hepatojugular reflux), the patient may have congestive heart failure.

You can describe jugular venous pressure by characterizing the neck veins as mildly, moderately, or severely distended and by measuring pressure levels in fingerbreadths of distention above the clavicle. Such a report might read: "The patient's neck veins are moderately distended to a level of three fingers above the clavicle, at a level of 45° from the horizontal." Generally, you should observe the veins bilaterally to confirm true venous distention. (Unilateral jugular venous distention may be caused by a local obstruction.)

Carotid pulse examination

Carefully inspect and palpate your patient's carotid arteries. This is essential, because the carotid pulse correlates with central aortic pressure and reflects cardiac function more accurately than peripheral vessels. During diminished cardiac output, a patient's peripheral pulses may be difficult or impossible to feel, but his carotid pulse should be easy to palpate.

Examine your patient's carotid pulse for rate, rhythm, equality, contour, and amplitude. Observe the carotid area for excessively large waves, indicating a hypervolemic or hyperkinetic state of the left ventricle, as in aortic regurgitation.

Before palpating both carotid pulses, auscultate them in this fashion:

● Turn the patient's head slightly away from you to allow space for the stethoscope.

● Auscultate only one carotid artery at a time.

● Place the bell of the stethoscope on the skin overlying the carotid artery.

● Ask the patient to hold his breath. (Avoid Valsalva's maneuver—forced exhalation against a closed glottis—which may initiate arrhythmias in some patients.)

Blood flow through the arteries is silent except in a patient with occlusive arterial disease. Auscultation of the blood flow in such a patient usually produces a blowing sound called a *bruit.* Murmurs, arteriovenous fistula and various high cardiac output conditions, such as anemia, hyperthyroidism, and pheochromocytoma, may also cause bruits. If you hear a bruit, gently repalpate the artery with the pads of your fingers to detect the *thrill* (a vibrating sensation similar to the one you perceive by feeling a purring cat's throat) that frequently accompanies it. A thrill results from turbulent blood flow caused by arterial obstruction.

With the patient in the semi-Fowler's position and his head turned toward you, use these techniques to palpate the carotid arteries:

● To prevent possible cerebral ischemia, palpate *only one* carotid artery at a time.

● Feel the trachea and roll your fingers laterally into the groove between it and the sternocleidomastoid muscle (below and medial to the angle of the jaw).

● Don't exert too much pressure or massage the area; this may induce excessive slowing of the heart rate.

The carotid pulse correlates with S_1. To gain information about heart rate and rhythm in a patient with a regular rhythm, palpate the pulse for 30 seconds. Remember, you can't determine the presence of an apical-radial pulse deficit until you analyze the precordium and apical pulse.

Describe the amplitude of the carotid pulse as increased (hyperkinetic) or decreased (hypokinetic). Increased pulses are large and bounding, with wide pressures. You'll feel a rapid upstroke, a brief peak, and a fast downstroke. This is common during exercise and when a person feels anxious or afraid. Increased amplitude may also accompany hyperthyroidism, anemia, aortic regurgitation, complete heart block, extreme bradycardia, and hypertension. A bounding carotid pulse may indicate that the left ventricle is generating excessive pressures to accomplish adequate cardiac output.

Decreased amplitude is characterized by small, weak pulsations that demonstrate diminished pressure and a slow, gradual, or normal velocity of upstroke, a delayed systolic peak, and a prolonged downstroke. This type of pulse results from left heart failure, severe shock, constrictive pericarditis, or aortic stenosis.

Precordium inspection

Begin inspecting the patient's precordium by identifying anatomic landmarks. The critical landmarks for cardiovascular assessment are the suprasternal notch and the xiphoid process (see *Cardiac Landmarks,* this page). Other important landmarks include the midsternal line, the midclavicular line (MCL), and the anterior axillary, midaxillary, and posterior axillary lines.

Place the patient in the supine position, and elevate his upper trunk 30° to 45°. Remember, you can examine the precordium best by standing to the right of the patient and using lighting that casts shadows across the chest area.

Inspect the patient's entire thorax for shape, size (including thickness), symmetry, obvious pulsations, and retractions. (Certain congenital heart diseases can cause left-chest prominence.)

Next observe the apical impulse, which is normally located in the fifth intercostal space (ICS) at about the MCL and is about 2 cm by 2 cm in size. You can see this apical beat as a pulsation produced by the thrust of the contracting left ventricle against the chest wall during systole. This apical beat is evident in about half the normal adult population. Because it occurs almost simultaneously with the carotid pulse, simultaneous palpation of a carotid pulse helps you identify it.

The apical impulse reflects cardiac size, es-

Cardiac Landmarks

The heart's base (the superior portion, where the ascending aorta and pulmonary trunk emerge and the superior vena cava enters) corresponds to a horizontal line at the third costal cartilages. This line begins about 1 cm from the right sternal margin and ends about 2 cm from the left sternal margin.

The heart's apex (the inferior portion that points down and to the left) is normally located at the fifth left intercostal space, about 8 to 9 cm to the left of the midsternal line. The right end of the inferior surface lies under the sixth or seventh chondrosternal junction.

You can determine the approximate size and shape of your patient's heart by identifying these points, marking them on his chest with a felt-tip pen, and connecting them with slightly convex lines.

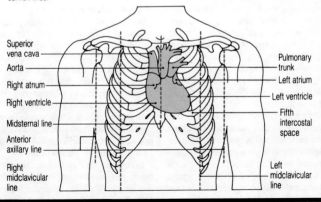

Superior vena cava — Aorta — Right atrium — Right ventricle — Midsternal line — Anterior axillary line — Right midclavicular line — Pulmonary trunk — Left atrium — Left ventricle — Fifth intercostal space — Left midclavicular line

pecially left ventricular size and location. In a patient with left ventricular hypertrophy, the impulse is sustained and forceful. In left ventricular enlargement, the impulse is laterally displaced. You'll see left ventricular hypertrophy in patients with hypertension, mitral regurgitation, aortic stenosis, and hypertrophic cardiomyopathy. A rocking motion at the apex is commonly associated with left ventricular hypertrophy.

Inspect the patient's right and left lower sternum for excessive pulsation and any bulging, lifting, heaving, or retraction. A slight retraction of the chest wall just medial to the MCL in the fourth ICS is a normal finding, but retraction of the rib is abnormal and may result from pericardial disease. When the work and force of the right ventricle increase markedly, a diffuse and lifting pulse can usually be seen or felt along the left sternal border. This impulse is called a *parasternal lift* and indicates right ventricular hypertrophy.

Precordium palpation

To palpate the patient's precordium, start at the apex and move methodically to the left sternal border and the base of the heart. (You may also palpate the epigastrium, the right sternal border, and the clavicular and left axillary areas.) Begin by placing your right palm over the apex area—the midclavicular line at the fifth intercostal space (ICS)—to locate the apical impulse (the point on the patient's anterior chest wall where the tip of the left ventricle hits during ventricular systole). Using light palpation, you should feel a tap with each heartbeat over an area the size of a nickel. The apical impulse correlates with the first heart sound and carotid pulsation. To be sure you're feeling it, you can use your left hand to palpate the patient's carotid artery. If you have difficulty palpating the apical impulse, turn the patient to the left lateral decubitus position, which brings the heart closer to the left chest wall.

The apical impulse may be abnormal in size, strength, and location. Generally, a weak apical impulse indicates poor stroke volume and a weakened contractile state, such as decompensated congestive heart failure from increased lung volume. Remember that the apical impulse may be imperceptible in a patient who's muscular or obese, or whose chest

wall is enlarged (as in emphysema) or deformed. (Occasionally, in a patient with left ventricular hypertrophy, you may feel a lifting sensation under your examining hand in the apical impulse area.) An apical impulse that's sustained, forceful, and diffuse over a large area or that's displaced toward the axillary line usually indicates left ventricular enlargement. Generally, the degree of apical impulse displacement correlates with the degree of left ventricular enlargement. Displacement can indicate left ventricular dilatation. Conditions associated with volume overload, such as mitral and aortic regurgitation, left to right shunts (septal defects), and acute myocardial infarction, usually produce such dilatation and hypertrophy. Conditions that produce hypertrophy without dilatation include aortic stenosis, hypertrophic cardiomyopathy, and systemic hypertension. Hypertrophy without dilatation results in an apical impulse that's increased in force and duration but not necessarily displaced laterally.

After assessing the patient's apical impulse, palpate the apex for thrills resulting from turbulent blood flow (possibly due to mitral regurgitation and stenosis) in the following circumstances:

- across a damaged valve
- through a partially obstructed valve
- through artificial changes between arteries and veins, such as atrioventricular shunts or fistulas
- through abnormal openings between heart chambers, such as ventricular or atrial septal defects
- because of high flow rates.

Next, place your right palm on the patient's left sternal border area. A diffuse, lifting systolic impulse indicates right ventricular hypertrophy, which occurs in fewer patients than left ventricular hypertrophy. It may be associated with a systolic retraction at the apex, resulting from posterior displacement and rotation of the left ventricle posteriorly by the enlarged right ventricle. Pulmonic valve disease, pulmonary hypertension, and chronic lung disease may underlie this finding. Palpate for thrills along the left sternal border.

To continue the examination, palpate the base of your patient's heart, located at the second left and right ICS at the sternal borders. (Keep in mind that the sternal notch, or angle of Louis, marks the exact location of the second ICS.) Normally, you won't feel any pulsations at the base of the heart. Detection of pulsations or thrills may indicate excessive systemic or pulmonary pressures, as well as aortic or pulmonary valve disease. When your hand is over the base, the aortic valve area is under your palm and the pulmonic valve area is under your fingertips. Remember that these areas don't correspond to the valves' exact locations, but to the sites where their sounds are normally transmitted.

A thrill in the second ICS or in the first and third right ICS may indicate aortic stenosis. In a patient with systemic hypertension, you may palpate an exaggerated vibration, indicating aortic valve closure, during the second heart sound. A thrill in the second and third left ICS may indicate pulmonic valve stenosis; pulsations in this area suggest pulmonary hypertension. The most common cause of abnormal pulsations in the pulmonary artery–pulmonic valve area is increased pulmonary artery pressure and flow, associated with pulmonary hypertension and atrial septal defect.

Heart sounds and murmurs

Listening over the precordium with a stethoscope remains the most useful examination technique for learning about your patient's heart function. While auscultating, listen selectively for each cardiac cycle component, and move the stethoscope slowly over the five main topographic areas (see *Chest Auscultation for Heart Sounds,* pages 196 and 197, and *Cardiac Rate, Rhythm, and Sound,* pages 198 and 199). Remember that acquiring expertise in identifying heart sounds and murmurs takes a great deal of practice. Follow the same procedure sequence every time you listen.

First, using the stethoscope's diaphragm, listen to your patient's heart at the apex—the fifth intercostal space (ICS) at the midclavicular line—for the two normal heart sounds, S_1 and S_2. (S_1 is the *lub* and S_2 the *dub* of the *lub-dub* sound made by the normal heart.) You can hear S_1 best by listening as you palpate the carotid pulse, because the sound and the beat occur simultaneously. S_1 splitting is significant only if very pronounced.

S_2 immediately follows S_1. You'll hear it best at the heart's base (at the second ICS, right and left sternal borders). S_2 normally splits

into an aortic and a pulmonic component when pulmonic valve closure is delayed during inspiration. This physiologic split is most distinct at the second ICS, left sternal border. In systemic hypertension and dilatation of the ascending aorta, the aortic component is usually loud and sharp; in severe aortic stenosis, it may be diminished or absent. In pulmonary hypertension resulting from such conditions as mitral stenosis, left ventricular failure, pulmonary emboli, or pulmonary heart disease, the pulmonic component is louder; in severe pulmonic stenosis, it's diminished. Always identify S_1 and S_2 first, because you can only recognize abnormal sounds by their relationship to diastole and systole.

Now, use the stethoscope's bell to listen at the apex of your patient's heart for the abnormal S_3 and S_4 sounds. (Apply the bell lightly, because exerting pressure makes it work like a diaphragm.) S_3, a low-pitched sound immediately following S_2, is probably caused by abrupt limitation of left ventricular filling. Called *ventricular gallop* because of its triple sound, S_3 is an important early sign of heart failure and indicates more serious pathology than S_4. Learning to detect this extra sound takes practice and patience. But you should develop your skill, because S_3 often appears before other significant symptoms of congestive heart failure, such as rales, dyspnea, and elevated jugular venous pressure. This means that your skill in detecting it may contribute significantly to early identification of your patient's problems. In fact, S_3 is such an important indicator of congestive heart failure that many doctors begin drug therapy as soon as it's detected. (Remember: Effective treatment for heart failure makes this sound disappear.)

S_4 occurs just before S_1 and can be more difficult to hear than S_3. Called an *atrial gallop* because of its triple sound, S_4 results from atrial contraction during diastolic ventricular filling. Normally, atrial systole is silent, but when ventricular filling pressure is high and the ventricle is stiffer than normal (as in heart disease), the atria produce an extra sound as they contract against this greater ventricular resistance. (This explains why S_4 occurs just before S_1.) Although not as specific as S_3 for congestive heart failure, S_4 is a key sign for other forms of heart disease, including hy-

Chest Auscultation for Heart Sounds

SOUNDS	TIMING	PHYSIOLOGY
S_1	Beginning of systole	Mitral and tricuspid valves close almost simultaneously, producing a single sound; S_1 corresponds to the carotid pulse.
Accentuated S_1	Beginning of systole	Mitral valve is still open wide at the beginning of systole, so the valve slams shut from an open position.
Diminished S_1	Beginning of systole	Mitral valve has time to float back into an almost closed position before ventricular contraction forces it shut, so it closes less forcefully. Softer closure may also be from an immobile, calcified valve.
Split S_1	Beginning of systole	Mitral valve closes slightly before the tricuspid valve.
S_2	End of systole	Pulmonic and aortic valves close almost simultaneously.
Physiologic split S_2 (split on inspiration but not on expiration)	End of systole	During inspiration, the pulmonic valve closes later than the aortic valve. (Pulmonic valve closure is normally delayed during inspiration, which causes decreased thoracic pressure and allows more blood into the right side of the heart, delaying pulmonic valve closure.)
Persistent wide split S_2 (split on both inspiration and expiration, but more widely split on inspiration)	End of systole	Pulmonic valve closes late or (less commonly) the aortic valve closes early.
Fixed split S_2 (equally split on inspiration and expiration)	End of systole	Pulmonic valve consistently closes later than aortic valve. Right side of heart is already ejecting a larger volume, so filling cannot be increased during inspiration. The sound remains fixed.
Paradoxical (reversed) S_2 split (widely split on expiration)	End of systole	On expiration, aortic valve closes after the pulmonic valve, from delayed or prolonged left ventricular systole. On inspiration, the normal delay of the pulmonic valve closure causes the two sounds to merge.
S_3 (ventricular gallop)	Early diastole	Ventricles fill early and rapidly, causing vibrations of the ventricular walls.
S_4 (atrial gallop)	Late diastole	Atrium makes an extra effort to fill against increased resistance.

INDICATION	WHERE TO AUSCULTATE
• Normal	Apex
• During rapid heart rate • Mitral stenosis • After mitral valve disease, such as mitral prolapse	Apex
• First degree heart block • Mitral regurgitation • Severe mitral stenosis with calcified immobile valve	Apex
• Normal in most cases • Right bundle-branch heart block (wide splitting of S_1) • Pulmonary hypertension	Beginning at mitral area and moving toward tricuspid area
• Normal	Aortic and pulmonic areas (base); heard best at aortic area
• Normal; a physiologic S_2 split corresponds to the respiratory cycle.	Aortic and pulmonic areas; heard best at pulmonic area on inspiration
Late pulmonic valve closure: • Complete right bundle-branch heart block, which delays right ventricular contraction. As a result, the pulmonic valve closes later. • Pulmonary stenosis, which prolongs right ventricular ejection	Pulmonic area
• Severe right ventricular failure, which prolongs right ventricular systole • Atrial septal defect, which causes blood return to the right ventricle from lungs, prolonging the ejection	Pulmonic area
• Left bundle-branch heart block (most common cause) • Aortic stenosis • Patent ductus arteriosus • Severe hypertension • Left ventricular failure, disease, or ischemia	Aortic area
• Early congestive heart failure • Ventricular aneurysm • Common in children and young adults	Mitral area and right ventricular area using stethoscope bell, with patient on his left side
• Hypertensive cardiovascular disease • Chronic coronary artery disease • Aortic stenosis • Hypertrophic cardiomyopathy • Pulmonary artery hypertension	Apex

Cardiac Rate, Rhythm, and Sound

CLASSIFICATION	RATE	RHYTHM	SOUND
Normal sinus rhythm	*Atrial:* 60 to 100 *Ventricular:* 60 to 100	Regular	Normal (S_1 is of constant intensity; normal S_2 splitting)
Sinus bradycardia	*Atrial:* less than 60 *Ventricular:* less than 60	Regular	Normal
Sinus tachycardia	*Atrial:* 100 to 180 *Ventricular:* 100 to 180	Regular	Normal
Premature atrial contraction (PAC)	*Atrial:* 60 to 100 *Ventricular:* 60 to 100 Rate varies, depending on number of PACs.	Irregular	Normal, although S_1 and S_2 intensities may vary
Paroxysmal atrial tachycardia	*Atrial:* 150 to 200 *Ventricular:* 150 to 200	Regular, except at onset and termination	Normal but rapid
Atrial fibrillation	*Atrial:* 400 to 600 (controlled *and* uncontrolled) *Ventricular:* under 100 (with controlled atrial fibrillation) *Ventricular:* over 100 (with uncontrolled atrial fibrillation)	Very irregular	S_1 intensity varies; normal S_2 splitting
Nodal rhythm	*Atrial:* 40 to 60 *Ventricular:* 40 to 60 (Atrial arrhythmia may also exist *or* atria may be captured retrogradely)	Fairly regular	S_1 intensity varies; normal S_2 splitting

CLASSIFICATION	RATE	RHYTHM	SOUND
Premature ventricular contraction (PVC)	*Atrial:* 60 to 100 *Ventricular:* 60 to 100 (Rates vary depending on the number of PVCs)	Irregular	Normal
Ventricular tachycardia	*Atrial:* variable *Ventricular:* 100 to 270	Fairly regular	S_1 intensity varies; abnormal S_2 splitting. If atria are captured retrogradely, may be constant.
Ventricular fibrillation	*Atrial:* cannot be determined *Ventricular:* 400 to 600	Irregular	Absent
First degree heart block	*Atrial:* 60 to 100 *Ventricular:* 60 to 100	Regular	Decreased S_1 intensity; normal S_2 splitting; S_4 heard with conduction delay
Type I second degree heart block	*Atrial:* 60 to 100 *Ventricular:* 30 to 100 (Atrial rate greater than ventricular)	Regular, although ventricular may be irregular, contraction not occurring with every atrial contraction.	S_1 intensity decreases cyclically, then increases after pause; normal S_2 splitting; S_4 heard with conduction delay
Type II second degree heart block	*Atrial:* 60 to 100 *Ventricular:* 30 to 100 (Atrial rate twice that of ventricular rate)	Regular, although ventricular may be irregular	Constant S_1 intensity; abnormal S_2 splitting
Complete atrioventricular block	*Atrial:* 60 to 100 *Ventricular:* less than 40	Regular	S_1 intensity varies; abnormal S_2 splitting

pertension, cardiomyopathies, and aortic stenosis. In adults with severe myocardial disease and tachycardia, summation (a cumulative effect) of S_3 and S_4 may occur, producing a *summation gallop.*

The *systolic click* is an extra sound best heard with the diaphragm of the stethoscope at the apex. It occurs at early, mid-, or late systole and may be accompanied by a systolic murmur. The systolic click is heard most commonly in young females with mitral valve prolapse.

Pericardial friction rub is an extra cardiac sound resembling squeaking leather or a grating, scratching, or rasping sound. These sounds seem close to the ear and have a "to and fro" rhythm. You can hear it best between the apex and the sternum; it may be loud enough to mask other heart sounds. Inflammation of the pericardial sac causes the parietal and visceral surfaces to rub together.

Finally, listen carefully for *heart murmurs,* which result from turbulent blood flow produced by valvular or septal wall pathology (see *Heart Murmurs,* page 201). Murmur loudness is classified in six grades, with Grade 1 the softest audible murmur and Grade 6 the loudest—audible even when the stethoscope isn't touching the patient's chest. Murmurs can be classified as systolic or diastolic. Systolic murmurs occur during ventricular systole and may result from turbulent flow through a stenotic aortic or pulmonic valve, regurgitant flow through an incompetent mitral or tricuspid valve, or flow through a ventricular septal defect. Diastolic murmurs occur during ventricular diastole and may result from turbulent flow through stenotic mitral or tricuspid valves or regurgitant flow through an incompetent aortic or pulmonic valve. Listen for a pansystolic murmur during the acute stage of myocardial infarction. A murmur of this type may indicate the presence of a ventricular septal defect or mitral regurgitation. (The synonymous terms *pansystolic* and *holosystolic* indicate that the murmur occurs during the entire systolic cycle; you'll hear it as a whooshing sound between S_1 and S_2.)

Remember that identifying murmurs, like identifying heart sounds, is difficult. Developing this skill may take years of study and practice.

Auscultation sequence

Positioning your patient properly can help you hear heart sounds better. For the apex area, begin auscultation with the patient supine. Then turn him on his left side and listen with the bell to identify low-pitched filling sounds or murmurs (as in mitral stenosis). Finally, listen to the base with the patient sitting up. To hear high-pitched diastolic murmurs (as in aortic or pulmonic insufficiency), press the diaphragm firmly against the chest wall while the patient leans slightly forward.

Use the following auscultation sequence (see *Cardiac Auscultation Areas,* page 203):
● With the patient in the supine or semi-Fowler's position, begin auscultating with the diaphragm at the *apex* to identify rate, rhythm, S_1 (the loudest sound at this location), and S_2. Then listen for extra sounds, such as murmurs, clicks, S_3, S_4, or pericardial friction rubs.
● Turn the patient on his *left side,* and listen with the bell to identify mitral valve murmurs and the filling sounds of S_3 and S_4.
● Position the patient on his back and inch the diaphragm up the *left sternal border* to the third intercostal space (ICS)—Erb's point. (Murmurs caused by tricuspid valve dysfunction and pulmonic valve disorders radiate to Erb's point.) Then proceed to the second ICS (pulmonic) area, where you can identify S_1 and S_2, and note the physiologic split of S_2 on inspiration. (S_2 is the more prominent sound in this base location.)
● Proceed to the second ICS at the right sternal border (aortic area), using the diaphragm. Note S_1 and S_2 (still the most prominent sound in this area). Then ask the patient to sit forward. Press the diaphragm firmly against his chest wall and listen for the high-pitched murmurs of aortic regurgitation and, possibly, aortic stenosis.

Epigastric examination

Assess your patient's upper abdominal area for evidence of cardiovascular disease. A normal patient may have visible or palpable pulsations in the epigastric area (upper central abdominal region). Abnormally large aortic pulsations may result from an aneurysm of the abdominal aorta or from aortic valvular regurgitation. To distinguish right ventricular hypertrophy—which can exaggerate epigastric pulsations—from an aortic pathology,

Heart Murmurs

When you listen for heart sounds, you may hear more than the sounds identified as S_1 through S_4. You may hear a murmur, or audible vibration, when blood flow is obstructed or abnormal.

To help in identifying types of murmurs, carefully note the following indicators. Then, study the chart to learn about the different types of murmurs.

● *Timing:* Note the occurrence—is it in the systolic phase or the diastolic phase? A midsystolic murmur is also called an ejection murmur; a murmur heard throughout the systolic phase is called a pansystolic, or holosystolic, murmur.

● *Quality:* Describe the quality or sound of the murmur—is it blowing, harsh, musical, or rumbling?

● *Pitch:* Identify the pitch or frequency of the murmur—is it high, medium, or low?

● *Location:* Name the auscultation location where you hear the murmur best—is it aortic, pulmonic, tricuspid, or mitral?

● *Radiation:* List the bordering structures where the murmur is also heard.

● *Loudness:* Employ this rating system to describe the volume of the murmur: 1–barely heard; 2–faint but distinct; 3–moderately detectable; 4–loud; 5–very loud; 6–heard before stethoscope comes in contact with the chest.

● *Pattern:* Refers to the configuration of the murmur much as it would appear on a phonocardiogram. This indicates the approximate relationship of the murmur to the normal heart sounds, in timing and intensity. *Crescendo* means the murmur begins softly and gets louder. *Decrescendo* means the opposite. *Crescendo-decrescendo* (diamond-shaped) is a combination of the two patterns. *Plateau* means the murmur is fairly constant, not appreciably altering in intensity.

TIMING	QUALITY	PITCH	LOCATION	RADIATION	PATTERN
Midsystolic (systolic ejection)	Harsh, rough	Medium to high	Pulmonic	Toward left shoulder and neck	S_1 S_2
Midsystolic (systolic ejection)	Harsh, rough	Medium to high	Aortic and suprasternal notch	Toward carotid arteries or apex	Crescendo-decrescendo
Holosystolic	Harsh	High	Tricuspid	Precordium	
Holosystolic	Blowing	High	Mitral, lower left sternal border	Toward left axilla	S_1 S_2
Holosystolic	Blowing	High	Tricuspid	Toward apex	Plateau (constant)
Early diastolic	Blowing	High	Midleft sternal edge (not aortic area)	Toward sternum	S_1 S_2 S_1
Early diastolic	Blowing	High	Pulmonic	Toward sternum	Decrescendo
Mid- to late diastolic	Rumbling	Low	Apex	Usually none	S_1 S_2 S_1
Mid- to late diastolic	Rumbling	Low	Tricuspid, lower sternal border	Usually none	Crescendo

place your palm on the epigastric area, and slide your fingers under the rib cage. You'll feel the aortic pulsations with your palm and the right ventricular impulses with your fingertips. Next, use the bell to auscultate the abdominal aorta from the epigastric area in the abdominal midline to the umbilicus, listening for bruits—which may indicate obstruction of the aorta by plaques.

Evaluating your patient's liver size by percussion or palpation can help determine the presence and extent of right-sided heart disease (for more information, see *Estimating Liver Size,* page 229). Remember to note whether liver percussion or palpation causes the patient discomfort, because tenderness is characteristic of right heart failure resulting from excessive venous congestion with swelling of the liver.

Palpating peripheral pulses

Your evaluation of the rate, rhythm, amplitude, and symmetry of peripheral pulsations, along with your auscultation of the femoral pulses for bruits, reveals important information about your patient's cardiac function and peripheral perfusion. Using your dominant hand, palpate his peripheral pulses lightly with the pads of your index, middle, and (when appropriate) ring fingers. Use three fingers where space permits and two fingers when the area you're palpating is small or angled (for example, the femoral pulses).

To determine *rate,* count all pulses for at least 30 seconds (60 seconds when recording vital signs). The normal rate is between 60 and 100 beats/minute. If you detect an irregular radial pulse, use the technique for apical-radial pulses.

To estimate the pulse's *volume* or *amplitude,* palpate the blood vessel during ventricular systole. Pulse amplitude reflects the adequacy of the circulating volume, the vessel tone, the strength of left ventricular contraction, and the elasticity and distensibility of the arterial walls. Normal arteries are soft and pliable. Sclerotic vessels are more resistant to occlusion by external pressure; when you palpate them, they feel beaded and cordlike. Characterize your patient's pulse volume using this scale:
- 3 + : bounding, increased
- 2 + : normal
- 1 + : weak, thready, decreased

- 0: absent.

Palpate pulses on both sides of the patient's body simultaneously (except the carotid pulse) to determine *symmetry;* inequality is diagnostically significant. Always assess peripheral pulses methodically, moving from the patient's head (temporal, facial) to his arms (brachial, radial, ulnar) to his legs (femoral, popliteal, posterior tibial, pedal). For the *temporal pulse,* feel the ear immediately in front of the tragus, where the artery passes over the root of the temporal bone's zygomatic process. Then palpate the *facial pulse* where the artery passes over the mandible's lower border, at the anterior border of the masseter muscle.

Feel the patient's *brachial pulse* medial to the biceps tendon. Palpate the *radial pulses* on the palmar surface of the patient's relaxed, slightly flexed wrist, medial to the radial styloid process. (Remember, the radial pulse is the most frequently used indicator of pulsation rate and rhythm.) Feel the *ulnar artery* by pressing it against the ulna on the palmar surface of the patient's wrist. Be sure to note rate, amplitude, and symmetry for both of the patient's arms.

To assess the patient's *femoral pulses,* use the pads of your fingers to deep-palpate the area below the inguinal ligament, midway between the anterior superior iliac spine and the symphysis pubis. Then, auscultate the pulsation sites on both sides of the patient's body for bruits, which indicate arteriosclerotic changes.

To locate the patient's *popliteal* arteries, which are relatively deep in the soft tissues behind the knee, flex his knee slightly while he's supine or in the semi-Fowler's position. Use both hands to deep-palpate the pulsation. You may locate the pulse more easily by placing both thumbs on the patient's knee and palpating behind it with the first two fingers of both hands.

Assess the patient's *pedal pulses* by using the pads of your fingers to palpate the dorsum of the foot. To prevent excessive traction on the artery, dorsiflex the foot, preferably to 90°, and palpate where the vessel passes over the dorsum. To locate the pulsation, place your palm on the dorsum until you feel the dorsalis pedis pulse point. (Remember, the pedal pulse is a superficial pulse that can be obscured by

Cardiac Auscultation Areas

To perform cardiac auscultation, you'll need to know the locations of the five areas shown here.

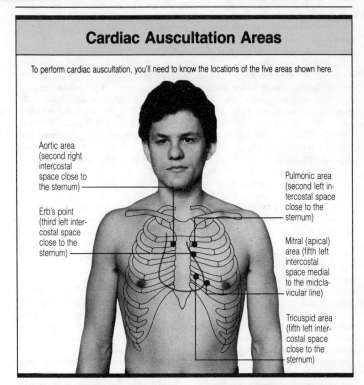

Aortic area (second right intercostal space close to the sternum)

Erb's point (third left intercostal space close to the sternum)

Pulmonic area (second left intercostal space close to the sternum)

Mitral (apical) area (fifth left intercostal space medial to the midclavicular line)

Tricuspid area (fifth left intercostal space close to the sternum)

heavy palpation.) Keeping the patient's foot in the dorsiflexed position, use the pads of your fingers to locate the posterior tibial pulsation on the posterior or inferior medial malleolus of the ankle. Always check the pedal pulse in patients with intermittent claudication or gangrene.

Remember that in some patients the dorsalis pedis may occupy a different position or be difficult to palpate; failure to find the pulse doesn't necessarily indicate arterial disease.

Perfusion status

Inspect the skin color of your patient's hands and feet. You can describe skin color as *normal, cyanotic, mottled,* or *excessively pale.* Note if the patient has any petechial hemorrhages, evidence of Osler's nodes in his fingers or on his palms, or Janeway spots on his palms.

To assess arterial flow adequacy, have the patient lie down and raise his legs or arms

12″ (30 cm) above heart level; then ask him to move his feet or hands up and down briskly for 60 seconds. Next, tell the patient to sit up and dangle his legs or arms—which should show mild pallor, with the original color returning in about 10 seconds and the veins refilling in about 15 seconds. Significant arterial insufficiency may be present if one or both of the patient's feet or hands show marked pallor, delayed color return ending with a mottled appearance, or delayed venous filling— or if you note marked redness of his arms or legs.

Next, assess the adequacy of the patient's venous system by inspecting and palpating his legs for superficial veins. When the legs are in a dependent position, venous distention, nodular bulges at venous valves (bifurcations of veins), and collapsing veins are normal. Evidence of venous insufficiency (dilated, tortuous veins with poorly functioning valves) includes peripheral cyanosis, peripheral edema that pits with pressure, unusual ankle pigmentation, skin thickening, and ulceration—especially around the ankles.

To test capillary refill, squeeze a small area of the patient's foot or toe between your fingers to cause blanching, then release the pressure and observe how rapidly normal color returns. Immediate return indicates good arterial supply.

Test the patient's arms and legs for normal sensations to both light and deep palpation. Also note symmetry, areas of tenderness, and increased warmth or coolness.

Examine the patient's fingernails and toenails for quantitative changes, including decreased or increased thickness, and such qualitative changes as color, contour, consistency, and adherence to the nail bed. Also check for clubbed nails, which are associated with lung and heart disease. In patients with long-standing heart disease, nail changes may result from hypoxemia. In these patients, you'll note chronic nail thickening and enlargement, as well as bulbous enlargement of the ends of fingers or toes. Inspection also reveals exaggerated curves in the nails, with obscuring of the obtuse angle between the distal portion of the finger or toe and the nail. The end root feels spongy or soft.

Now, inspect and palpate the patient's skin for texture and hair patterns. In a patient with chronic poor circulation, the skin appears thick, waxy, fragile, and shiny; normal body hair on the arms and legs is absent. These changes, characteristic of arterial insufficiency, also accompany long-standing diabetes mellitus. Also observe the patient for areas of unusual pigmentation that may indicate new skin lesions, rashes, or scarring from past injury or ulceration.

Inspect the patient's arms, hands, legs, feet, and ankles for edema caused by increased hydrostatic pressure and vascular fluid exudation into the tissue interspaces. (If the patient has been confined to bed, also check for edema in his buttocks and sacral areas, because edema occurs in the most dependent body parts.) Palpate for edema against a bony prominence and describe its characteristics:

• type (pitting or nonpitting)

• extent and location (ankle-foot area, foot-knee area, hands, or fingers)

• degree of pitting (described in terms of depth): 0″ to ¼″ is mild (1 +); ¼″ to ½″, moderate (2 +); and ½″ to 1″, severe (3 +)

• symmetry (unilateral or symmetrical).

Inspect and palpate for evidence of deep vein inflammation or clot formation. Determine the presence of pain, tenderness, or a sense of fullness in the calf, which may be aggravated when your patient stands or walks. Next, assess for local redness, foot edema, or cyanosis of the foot, especially when it's dependent. Gently press the calf muscle with your palm; pain indicates possible thrombophlebitis. To test for Homans' sign, firmly and abruptly dorsiflex the patient's foot while supporting the entire leg, which must be extended or slightly bent (deep calf pain may indicate thrombophlebitis); then palpate the foot.

Pediatric assessment

Pediatric history questions

Ask if the child has frequent upper respiratory tract infections. Then determine if he experiences shortness of breath. For an infant, ask the parents if their child has ever turned blue or had a bluish cast to his skin—especially on his face and around his mouth. Determine if the infant has trouble finishing a bottle without gasping or drinks only about 2 to 4 oz (60 to 120 ml) of milk at a time. Ask if other symptoms—such as increased breathing, rapid heartbeat, dyspnea, and diaphoresis—occur during feeding. Does the infant seem to tire easily and need rest? Also determine if the infant's breathing is greatly labored during bowel movements. Is loss of appetite, profuse sweating, or vomiting a problem?

Ask an older child if he can keep up physically with children his age. Next, determine if the child experiences cyanosis on exertion, dyspnea, or orthopnea. Ask the parents if he constantly assumes a squatting position or sleeps in the knee-chest position; either sign may indicate tetralogy of Fallot or other cyanotic heart disease. Finally, find out if he bleeds excessively when cut.

Check the family history for indications of possible congenital heart defects. If the child is old enough, talk with him to obtain a profile of his life-style and daily activities. What he tells you can provide important information about his symptoms, including whether they've affected his activities.

Inspection

Examine the child for retarded growth or development. This condition may indicate significant chronic congestive heart failure or complex cyanotic heart disease. Then inspect his skin. Pallor can indicate a serious cardiac problem in an infant or anemia in an older child; in an infant or child, cyanosis may be an early sign of a cardiac condition. Cyanosis of the extremities (acrocyanosis) is a common and usually normal finding in neonates, but you should evaluate it when present. Acrocyanosis decreases when the infant is warm and active; cyanosis from decreased tissue oxygenation increases when the infant is crying and active.

Check for clubbed fingers, a sign of cardiac dysfunction. (Clubbing does not ordinarily occur before age 2.) Also, remember that dependent edema (a late sign of congestive heart failure in children) appears in the legs only if the child can walk; in infants, it appears in the eyelids. If the child is bedridden, also check his sacrum and buttocks.

Although it's difficult to do, you must measure blood pressure in children and infants, because it provides important diagnostic information—for instance, it can help confirm coarctation of the aorta. First, select an appropriate cuff size. It shouldn't be more than two thirds or less than one half of the upper arm length, and it should be about 20% wider than the arm's diameter. Pediatric cuff sizes are 2½", 5", 8", and 12". Remember, blood pressure may be inaudible in children under age 2. A Doppler stethoscope provides a more accurate measurement of blood pressure in children under age 2 than a regular stethoscope.

Before beginning, allow the child to handle the cuff and stethoscope to allay his fears. When you take his blood pressure, have him seated with his arm at heart level. Take an infant's blood pressure when he's supine. Also take an infant's thigh blood pressure, because lower diastolic readings in the legs than in the arms may indicate a coarctation of the aorta.

For children under age 1, the systolic thigh reading should equal the systolic arm reading; for older children, it may be 10 to 40 mmHg higher, but the diastolic thigh value should equal the diastolic arm value. If thigh readings are below normal, suspect coarctation.

Next, simultaneously palpate the child's radial and femoral pulses. If you feel the radial pulse before the femoral, suspect coarctation.

Palpation, percussion, and auscultation

In judging cardiac enlargement, remember that in children under age 8 the heart is proportionately smaller and the apical impulse is higher. Palpate or percuss the liver for enlargement, such as occurs in right ventricular failure, or for systolic pulsations, such as in tricuspid regurgitation.

Before auscultating, try to obtain a young child's cooperation by letting him listen to his own heart. For infants, use a smaller bell on the stethoscope. If your stethoscope doesn't have interchangeable bells, remove the bell and use the base.

An S_3 sound is more common and more likely to be a normal finding in a child. Sinus arrhythmia (a variation in which the heart accelerates on inspiration and decelerates on expiration) is also more common and is normal in children. To confirm this variation in an older child, tell him to hold his breath; a true sinus arrhythmia will disappear.

Split sounds are significant in children. Carefully evaluate an S_2 split, which is easier to hear in a child than in an adult. Heard over the pulmonic area, this split occurs when the aortic valve closes slightly before the pulmonic valve. The difference in timing between the valve closures results in the S_2 split, which should increase during inspiration and decrease during expiration. A split that doesn't change during respiration or that changes paradoxically is abnormal.

So-called innocent murmurs (functional murmurs) are those which don't reflect underlying pathology. Usually such a murmur is Grade I or Grade II early systolic, without transmission, and you'll hear it at the pulmonic area. Some organic murmurs have the same characteristics as innocent ones, so until you have considerable experience, refer every child with a murmur to a doctor for further evaluation.

Childhood heart problems

The two primary cardiac conditions of childhood are congenital heart problems and rheumatic fever. Of every 1,000 full-term infants, 5 to 8 experience congenital heart problems, and this rate increases two to three times in premature infants. Neonates suffer the highest morbidity and mortality from congenital conditions—most deaths occur during the first week of life. Early detection and surgery could prevent at least 50% of these deaths.

The most common congenital cardiac conditions include atrial and ventricular septal defects, patent ductus arteriosus, tetralogy of Fallot, coarctation of the aorta, aortic stenosis, pulmonic stenosis, and transposition of the great vessels. Rheumatic fever (a complication of Group A streptococcal infection), unlike these conditions, most commonly strikes children between ages 5 and 15. Children in this age-group should always be given a thorough cardiac examination 2 weeks after a streptococcal infection.

Geriatric assessment

Geriatric history questions

As you begin the interview, assess your patient's *level of consciousness*, noting confusion or slowed mental status—occasionally, these are early signs of inadequate cardiac output. Remember that poor memory and generalized cerebral atherosclerosis may make it difficult for your patient to understand and respond to your questions.

Ask your elderly patient about *chest pain,* which could be interpreted as angina pectoris. Remember, however, that his chief complaint may be dyspnea or palpitations rather than chest pain, because although aging contributes to coronary artery plaque development, it also promotes collateral circulation to areas deprived of perfusion. Also keep in mind that these signs and symptoms in the elderly may indicate pathology in many systems other than cardiovascular, including the urinary, endocrine, musculoskeletal, and respiratory systems.

Ask your patient about his *activities of daily living,* any signs or symptoms associated with these activities, and his response to physical and emotional exertion. Reduced cardiac reserve limits the elderly patient's ability to respond to such conditions as infection, blood loss, hypoxia-induced arrhythmias, and electrolyte imbalance. Combine the information on your patient's daily activities with your assessment of his mental status, and try to correlate these signs and symptoms with any eating and sleeping difficulties he has.

Determine if the patient has a history of smoking, frequent coughing, wheezing, or dyspnea, which may indicate *chronic lung disease.* Pulmonary hypertension resulting from pulmonary disease is a chief cause of right-sided heart failure.

Ask, too, about *medication side effects.* Weakness, bradycardia, hypotension, and confusion may indicate elevated potassium levels; weakness, fatigue, muscle cramps, and palpitations may indicate inadequate levels of potassium. A patient's anorexia, nausea, vomiting, diarrhea, headache, rash, vision disturbances, and mental confusion may indicate an overdose of digitalis or antiarrhythmic medications.

Physical examination guidelines

In an elderly patient who may have *chronic lung disease,* check for evidence of cor pulmonale and advanced right-sided congestive heart failure: large, distended neck veins; hepatomegaly with tenderness; hepatojugular reflux; and peripheral dependent edema. Check, too, for evidence of chronic obstructive pulmonary disease.

Carefully assess your elderly patient for signs and symptoms associated with *cerebral hypoperfusion*—such as dizziness, syncope, confusion or loss of consciousness, unilateral weakness or numbness, aphasia, and occasionally slight clonic, jerking movements. Cerebral hypoperfusion may result in transient ischemic attacks caused by cerebrovascular spasm, carotid stenosis, microembolic phenomena, or transient bradyarrhythmias resulting from degenerative disease of the heart's conduction system (Stokes-Adams attack). Check the carotid artery or femoral pulse when these signs and symptoms occur to help you differentiate between transient ischemic attacks and Stokes-Adams attack. An extremely slow or absent pulse followed by rapid return of consciousness and a slightly increased or normal heart rate may indicate Stokes-Adams attack.

Record baseline blood pressures bilaterally and use them carefully to determine if pressures are consistently above 150 mmHg systolic. Because aging causes a person's arterial walls to thicken and lose elasticity, readings—especially systolic readings—may be higher than normal.

Measure the patient's heart rate for 60 seconds, apically and radially. (Remember that as a person ages, increased vagal tone slows the heartbeat.) If the apical rate is below 50 beats/minute in a hospitalized patient, monitor his vital signs frequently. Determine if the patient has palpitations or symptoms of inadequate cardiac output.

When palpating the carotid pulse, be alert for hyperkinetic pulses and bruits over the carotids, which are common in older patients with advanced arteriosclerosis.

Kyphosis and scoliosis, common in the elderly, distort the chest walls and may displace the heart slightly. Thus, your patient's apical impulse and heart sounds may be slightly displaced. According to some authorities, S_4 sound is common in the elderly population and results from decreased left ventricular compliance. Diastolic murmurs indicate pathology; soft, early systolic murmurs may be associated with normal aortic lengthening, tortuosity, or sclerotic changes and may not indicate serious pathology. Check for signs of peripheral arterial insufficiency.

Guide to Cardiovascular Disorders

DISORDER	CHIEF COMPLAINT	HISTORY	
Abdominal aortic aneurysm	• *Chest pain:* absent • *Peripheral changes:* none	• Most common in men over age 50	
Acute myocardial infarction	• *Chest pain:* sudden but not instantaneous onset of constricting, crushing, heavy weightlike chest pain occurring at any time—not relieved by nitroglycerin; located centrally and substernally, although not usually in left chest; may build rapidly or in waves to maximum intensity in a few minutes; may be accompanied by nausea and vomiting • *Dyspnea:* present; may be accompanied by orthopnea, cough, and wheezing • *Fatigue:* present; indicated by weakness and apprehension • *Irregular heartbeat:* may be present; patient complains of palpitations or skipped beats • *Peripheral changes:* peripheral cyanosis, with decreased perfusion	• Risk factors same as in angina pectoris. • Past medical history may include episodes of angina pectoris.	
Angina pectoris	• *Chest pain:* may be dull or burning, or described as pressure, tightness, heaviness; builds and fades gradually; may be in abdomen; may radiate to jaw, teeth, face, or left arm • *Dyspnea:* possible, with sense of constriction around larynx or upper trachea • *Fatigue:* absent • *Irregular heartbeat:* may be present; patient complains of palpitations or skipped beats • *Peripheral changes:* none	• Risk factors include family history of coronary artery disease, arteriosclerotic heart disease, cerebrovascular accident, diabetes, gout, hypertension, renal disease, obesity caused by excessive carbohydrate and saturated fat intake, smoking, lack of exercise, stress (Type A personality). • Higher incidence in men over age 40; lower incidence in women prior to menopause • Precipitating factors include exertion, stress, cold or hot weather, and emotional excitement.	
Aortic regurgitation (incompetence)	• *Chest pain:* angina pectoris • *Dyspnea:* on exertion early in disease; paroxysmal noctur-	• Past medical history includes Reiter's syndrome, rheumatoid arthritis, psoriasis,	

PHYSICAL EXAMINATION	DIAGNOSTIC STUDIES
• Inspection reveals subcutaneous ecchymosis in flank or groin. • Palpation reveals pulsating midabdominal and upper abdominal mass.	• Aortography shows size of aneurysm. • EKG, urinalysis, BUN evaluate renal and cardiac function.
• Fever after 24 hours • Inspection reveals anxiety, tenseness, sense of impending doom, nausea, vomiting, and possibly distended neck veins, sweating, pallor, cyanosis, and shock. • Palpation reveals tachycardia or bradycardia and weak pulse. • Auscultation reveals normal or decreased blood pressure (less than 80 mmHg), significant murmurs that may preexist or occur with ruptured septum or ruptured papillary muscle, diminished gallop rhythm, pericardial friction rub and rales. • In severe attack, shock, decreased urinary output, pulmonary edema.	• EKG at onset shows elevated ST segment, which then returns to baseline; T waves become symmetrically inverted; abnormal Q waves present; may also show arrhythmias. • WBC count shows leukocytosis on second day (lasts 1 week); erythrocyte sedimentation rate normal at first, rises on second or third day. • Enzyme testing shows elevated creatine phosphokinase (CPK) and CPK-MB initially; then increased SGOT.
• Inspection reveals patient anxiety and diaphoresis. • Palpation reveals tachycardia. • Auscultation reveals change in blood pressure, possibly hypertension, especially during anginal attack; transient rales associated with congestive heart failure; paradoxical splitting of S_2 possible.	• EKG may show depressed ST segments during ischemia attack but may be within normal limits; atrioventricular conduction defect. • Thallium stress imaging or stress EKG may show ischemic areas.
• Inspection reveals generalized skin pallor; strong, abrupt carotid pulsations; forceful apical impulse to left of left midclavicular line	• EKG shows evidence of left ventricular hypertrophy. • X-ray shows enlarged left ventricle. *(continued)*

Guide to Cardiovascular Disorders *(continued)*

DISORDER	CHIEF COMPLAINT	HISTORY	
Aortic regurgitation (incompetence) *(continued)*	nal dyspnea; orthopnea and cough signal beginning of decompensation • *Fatigue:* present; weakness if left ventricular failure present • *Irregular heartbeat:* palpitations (signal beginning of decompensation) • *Peripheral changes:* none	rheumatic fever, syphilis, subacute bacterial endocarditis.	
Aortic stenosis	• *Chest pain:* present in severe stenosis • *Dyspnea:* present, with coughing, on exertion; paroxysmal nocturnal • *Fatigue:* usually present; syncope • *Irregular heartbeat:* present, as palpitations occasionally	• Most common in males • Usually asymptomatic unless severe	
Cardiomyopathies	• *Dyspnea:* paroxysmal nocturnal, accompanied by orthopnea • *Fatigue:* present • *Irregular heartbeat:* palpitations; Stokes-Adams attacks with conduction defects • *Peripheral changes:* dry skin, extremity pain, edema and ascites with right-sided failure	• Past medical history includes viral illness, alcoholism, chronic debilitating illnesses.	
Dissecting thoracic aortic aneurysms	• *Chest pain:* present; sudden and severe, radiating to back, abdomen, and hips • *Peripheral changes:* paralysis of legs possible	• Recent history may include convulsions. • Past medical history includes hypertension, arteriosclerosis, congenital heart disease, Marfan's syndrome, pregnancy, trauma	
Idiopathic hypertrophic subaortic stenosis (IHSS) or asymmetric septal hypertrophy	• *Chest pain:* present; similar to angina pectoris; but unrelieved by nitroglycerin • *Dyspnea:* present on exertion	• Symptoms may be induced by high temperatures, pregnancy, exercise, standing suddenly, Valsalva's maneuver.	

PHYSICAL EXAMINATION	DIAGNOSTIC STUDIES
and downward; capillary pulsations. • Palpation reveals sustained and forceful apical impulse, displaced to left and downward; rapidly rising and collapsing pulses. • Auscultation reveals normal heart sounds; soft, blowing, diastolic murmur (heard over aortic area and apex; usually loudest along left sternal border); in advanced aortic insufficiency, Austin Flint murmur that may be heard at apex; with diastolic pressure less than 60 mmHg, possibly wide pulse pressure.	• Echocardiography helps establish aortic valve incompetence. • Cardiac catheterization and angiocardiography performed to exclude complicating lesions and to assess left ventricular function and magnitude of leak.
• Inspection reveals apical impulse localized and heaving, usually not laterally displaced. • Palpation reveals sustained localized forceful apical impulse; systolic thrill over aortic area and neck vessels; small, slowly rising plateau pulse, best appreciated in carotid pulse. • Auscultation reveals harsh, rough, systolic ejection murmur in aortic area, radiating to the neck and apex; possibly systolic ejection click at aortic area just before murmur; paradoxical splitting of second sound with significant stenosis; normal or high diastolic blood pressure.	• EKG shows criteria for left ventricular hypertrophy; possibly complete heart block. • X-rays and fluoroscopy may show calcified aortic valve, poststenotic dilatation of ascending aorta (hyperactivity evident with fluoroscopy), left ventricular hypertrophy. • Echocardiography may identify level of obstruction and a bicuspid aortic valve. • Cardiac catheterization indicates the severity and location of the obstruction as well as left ventricular function.
• Fever • Signs of right and/or left heart failure • Palpation reveals displaced cardiac impulse to left; tachycardia. • Auscultation reveals systolic murmur, S_3 sound, and postural hypotension.	• EKG reveals nonspecific ST-T changes, decreased height of R wave; may show arrhythmias and conduction defects (especially atrial fibrillation). • Echocardiography and chest X-ray may help determine heart size.
• Fever • Palpation reveals unequal or diminished peripheral pulses. • Auscultation reveals aortic diastolic murmur and murmurs over arteries.	• Aortography shows size and extent of aneurysm.
• Palpation reveals peripheral pulse with characteristic double impulse. • Auscultation reveals systolic ejection murmur.	• EKG reveals left ventricular hypertrophy, ST segment, and T wave abnormalities. • Echocardiography shows increased thickness of the interventricular system and ab- *(continued)*

Guide to Cardiovascular Disorders *(continued)*

DISORDER	CHIEF COMPLAINT	HISTORY
Idiopathic hypertrophic subaortic stenosis (IHSS) or asymmetric septal hypertrophy *(continued)*	• *Fatigue:* present; accompanied by dizziness and syncope • *Irregular heartbeat:* may be present; patient may complain of palpitations or skipped beats • *Peripheral changes:* peripheral edema (uncommon)	
Left ventricular failure	• *Chest pain:* usually absent • *Dyspnea:* present on exertion, accompanied by cough, orthopnea, paroxysmal nocturnal dyspnea; in advanced disease, present at rest • *Fatigue:* present on exertion, accompanied by weakness • *Irregular heartbeat:* may be present; patient may complain of rapid heart rate and skipped beats	• Patient uses pillow to prop self up for sleep; wakes up gasping for breath; must sit or stand for relief. • History of present illness includes wheezing on inspiration and expiration (cardiac asthma), right upper abdominal pain or discomfort on exertion, daytime oliguria, nighttime polyuria, constipation (uncommon), anorexia, progressive weight gain, generalized edema, progressive weakness, fatigue, decreased mentation. • Past medical history includes severe chronic congestive heart failure.
Mitral regurgitation (incompetence)	• *Chest pain:* absent • *Dyspnea:* present, progressive with exertion; orthopnea, paroxysmal dyspnea • *Fatigue:* present, progressive with exertion • *Irregular heartbeat:* present as palpitations • *Peripheral changes:* none	• Past medical history includes rheumatic fever, endocarditis, congenital mitral valve defect, papillary muscle dysfunction or rupture, chordae tendineae dysfunction or rupture, heart failure associated with left ventricular dilation, blunt injury to the chest.
Mitral stenosis	• *Chest pain:* usually absent • *Dyspnea:* present; induced by exertion; may also occur during rest; orthopnea; paroxysmal nocturnal dyspnea; hemoptysis • *Fatigue:* present; increased with decreased exercise tolerance • *Irregular heartbeat:* usually absent	• Most common in women under age 45 • Recent bronchitis or upper respiratory tract infection may worsen symptoms. • Past medical history includes rheumatic fever, congenital valve disorder, tumor (myxoma).

PHYSICAL EXAMINATION	DIAGNOSTIC STUDIES
• In advanced stage, signs of mitral insufficiency (such as systolic murmur), congestive heart failure, and sudden death possible.	normal motion of the mitral valve.
• Inspection reveals profuse sweating, pallor or cyanosis, frothy white or pink sputum, heaving apical impulse, hand veins that remain distended when patient puts hands above level of right atrium. • Palpation reveals enlarged, diffuse, and sustained left ventricular impulse at precordium, displaced to left; pulsus alternans at peripheral pulses. • Percussion reveals pleural fluid (indicated by dullness at lung bases) and decreased tactile fremitus. • Auscultation reveals S_3 and S_4 sounds, possibly mitral and tricuspid regurgitation murmurs, accentuated pulmonary component of second sound, decreased or absent breath sounds, rales (basilar) that don't clear on cough.	• Pulmonary artery and pulmonary capillary wedge pressures elevated. • Central venous pressure elevated if condition has advanced to right ventricular failure, or hypervolemia from increased sodium and water retention. • EKG reflects heart strain or left ventricular enlargement, ischemia, and arrhythmias. • X-ray shows left atrial enlargement and pulmonary venous congestion.
• Inspection reveals forceful apical impulse to left of left midclavicular line. • Palpation reveals forceful, brisk apical impulse; systolic thrill over apical impulse; normal, small, or slightly collapsing pulse. • Auscultation reveals blowing, high-pitched, harsh, or musical pansystolic apical murmur maximal at apex and transmitted to axilla; abnormally wide splitting of S_2; possibly S_3 present; normal blood pressure.	• EKG shows P waves broad or notched in standard leads; with pulmonary hypertension, tall peaked P waves, right axis deviation, or right ventricular hypertrophy; possibly atrial fibrillation. • X-ray shows enlargement of left ventricle and moderate aneurysmal dilatation of left atrium. • Echocardiography shows dilated left ventricle and left atrium; pattern of contraction of left ventricle suggests diastolic overload. • Cardiac catheterization and ventriculography help determine amount of regurgitation and identify prolapsing cusps.
• Inspection reveals malar flush; in young patients, precordial bulge and diffuse pulsation. • Palpation reveals tapping sensation over area of expected apical impulse, middiastolic and/or presystolic thrill at apex, small pulse, overactive right ventricle with elevated pulmonary pressure. • Auscultation reveals localized, delayed, rumbling, low-pitched, diastolic murmur at or	• EKG shows notched and broad P waves in standard leads; inverted P in V_1 lead; atrial fibrillation common. • X-ray and fluoroscopy show left atrial enlargement. • Echocardiography helps assess severity of stenosis. • Cardiac catheterization and angiocardiography help determine amount of regurgitation that may also be present. *(continued)*

Guide to Cardiovascular Disorders *(continued)*

DISORDER	CHIEF COMPLAINT	HISTORY	
Mitral stenosis *(continued)*	• *Peripheral changes:* extremity pain		
Pericarditis	• *Chest pain:* sudden onset; precordial or substernal, pleuritic, radiating to left neck, shoulder, back, or epigastrium; worsened by lying down or swallowing • *Dyspnea:* usually absent; breathing may cause pain • *Fatigue:* usually absent • *Irregular heartbeat:* absent • *Peripheral changes:* none	• Past medical history includes viral respiratory infection, recent pericardiotomy or myocardial infarction, disseminated lupus erythematosus, serum sickness, acute rheumatic fever, trauma, uremia, lymphoma, dissecting aorta. • Most common in men between ages 20 and 50	
Pericarditis with effusion	• *Chest pain:* may be present as dull, diffuse oppressive precordial or substernal distress; dysphagia • *Dyspnea:* present; associated with cough that causes patient to lean forward for relief • *Fatigue:* usually absent • *Irregular heartbeat:* absent • *Peripheral changes:* none	• Past medical history includes uremia, malignancy, connective tissue disorder, viral pericarditis.	
Pulmonic regurgitation (incompetence)	• *Chest pain:* absent • *Dyspnea:* present • *Fatigue:* present; patient tires easily; weakness • *Irregular heartbeat:* absent • *Peripheral changes:* peripheral edema	• Pulmonary hypertension • Congenital defect	
Pulmonic stenosis	• *Chest pain:* usually not present • *Dyspnea:* present on exertion • *Fatigue:* present • *Irregular heartbeat:* absent • *Peripheral changes:* peripheral edema possible	• Congenital stenosis or rheumatic heart disease, associated with other congenital heart defects, such as tetralogy of Fallot	
Raynaud's disease and Raynaud's phenomenon	• *Chest pain:* absent • *Peripheral changes:* with Raynaud's disease: attacks of cyanosis, followed by pallor in fingers (rarely in thumbs or toes); redness, swelling, throbbing, and paresthesia during	• Most common in females between puberty and age 40 • Precipitating factors include emotional upsets or a cold. • Past history includes immunologic abnormalities. • Family history of vasospastic	

	PHYSICAL EXAMINATION	DIAGNOSTIC STUDIES
	near apex (duration of murmur varies depending on severity of stenosis; onset of murmur at opening snap early in diastole); possibly loud S_2 with elevated pulmonary pressure; normal blood pressure.	
	● Fever: 100° to 103° F. (37.8° to 39.4° C.) ● Palpation reveals tachycardia. ● Auscultation reveals pericardial friction rub.	● EKG shows ST-T segment elevation in all leads; returns to baseline in a few days, with T wave inversion. ● Possibly atrial fibrillation
	● Inspection reveals distended neck veins. ● Palpation and percussion reveal tachycardia, enlarged area of cardiac dullness, apical beat that's within dullness border or not palpable. ● Auscultation reveals abnormal blood pressure and possibly pericardial friction rub, and acute cardiac tamponade (inspiratory distention of neck veins, narrow pulse pressure, paradoxical pulse); may progress to shock.	● EKG shows T waves flat, low diphasic or inverted leads, QRS voltage uniformly low.
	● Inspection reveals jugular vein distention. ● Palpation reveals hepatomegaly. ● Auscultation reveals diastolic murmur in pulmonic area.	● EKG shows right ventricular or right atrial enlargement.
	● Inspection reveals jugular vein distention. ● Palpation reveals hepatomegaly. ● Auscultation reveals systolic murmur at left sternal border and split S_2 sound, with delayed or absent pulmonic component.	● EKG shows right ventricular hypertrophy, right axis deviation, right atrial hypertrophy.
	● Inspection reveals atrophy of terminal fat pads of fingers.	● None usually performed.

(continued)

Guide to Cardiovascular Disorders *(continued)*

DISORDER	CHIEF COMPLAINT	HISTORY	
Raynaud's disease and Raynaud's phenomenon *(continued)*	recovery, occurring when areas are warmed; numbness, stiffness, diminished sensation; with Raynaud's phenomenon: usually unilateral cyanosis, which may involve only one or two fingers	diseases • Raynaud's phenomenon may accompany cervical rib, carpal tunnel syndrome, scleroderma, systemic lupus erythematosus, frostbite, ergot poisoning.	
Rheumatic fever (acute)	• *Chest pain:* absent • *Dyspnea:* may be present • *Fatigue:* malaise • *Irregular heartbeat:* absent • *Peripheral changes:* weight loss	• Recent history includes streptococcal infection of upper respiratory tract (in previous 4 weeks), anorexia. • Past medical history includes migratory, gradually beginning arthritis; recurrent epistaxis; "growing pains" in joints (arthralgia). • Increased clumsiness	
Right ventricular failure, acute	• *Chest pain:* usually absent • *Dyspnea:* respiratory distress secondary to pulmonary disease or advanced left ventricular failure • *Fatigue:* in severe cases, weakness and mental aberration • *Irregular heartbeat:* atrial arrhythmias common • *Peripheral changes:* dependent edema: begins in ankles but progresses to legs and genitalia; initially subsides at night, later does not; ascites; weight gain	• History of present illness includes anorexia, right upper abdominal pain or discomfort during exertion, nausea, and vomiting. • Past medical history includes left ventricular failure, mitral stenosis, pulmonic valve stenosis, tricuspid regurgitation, pulmonary hypertension, chronic obstructive pulmonary disease.	
Subacute and acute bacterial endocarditis	• *Chest pain:* present; also in abdomen, and in flanks (uncommon) • *Dyspnea:* present in approximately 50% of cases; depends on severity of disease or valve involved • *Fatigue:* present, usually as malaise • *Irregular heartbeat:* absent • *Peripheral changes:* weight loss, redness or swelling, heart failure symptoms	• Present or recent history includes acute infection, surgery or instrumentation, dental work, drug abuse, abortion, transurethral prostatectomy. • Past medical history includes rheumatic, congenital, or atherosclerotic heart disease.	

PHYSICAL EXAMINATION	DIAGNOSTIC STUDIES
• Usually low-grade fever, with sinus tachycardia disproportional to fever level • Inspection reveals erythema marginatum (ring- or crescent-shaped macular rash), subcutaneous nodules (uncommon except in children), swollen joints (arthritis), Sydenham's chorea. • Palpation reveals enlarged heart. • Auscultation reveals mitral or aortic diastolic murmurs, varying heart sound quality, and possibly gallop rhythm arrhythmias and ectopic beats.	• Erythrocyte sedimentation rate and WBC count elevated. • Throat cultures positive for beta-hemolytic streptococci. • Antistreptolysin titer elevated. • Chest X-ray may show cardiac enlargement. • EKG shows PR greater than 0.2 seconds; may further define arrhythmias.
• Inspection reveals lower sternal or left parasternal heave independent of apical impulse. • Palpation and percussion reveal enlarged, tender, pulsating liver, with tricuspid regurgitation; abdomen fluid wave and shifting dullness; hepatojugular reflux, indicating jugular vein distention; tachycardia. • Auscultation reveals right ventricular S_3 sound; murmur of tricuspid regurgitation.	• Central venous pressure readings are elevated.
• Daily fever • Inspection may reveal petechiae on conjunctivae and palate buccal mucosa; with longstanding endocarditis, clubbed fingers and toes; splinter hemorrhages beneath nails; tender red nodules on finger and toe pads (Osler nodes); pallor or yellow-brown tint to skin; oval, pale, retinal lesion around optic disk (seen with ophthalmoscope) • Palpation reveals splenomegaly. • Auscultation reveals sudden change in present heart murmur or development of new murmur and possibly signs of early heart failure or emboli.	• Blood cultures determine causative organism. • Echocardiography—particularly the two-dimensional (2-D) method—looks for vegetation.

(continued)

Guide to Cardiovascular Disorders *(continued)*

DISORDER	CHIEF COMPLAINT	HISTORY
Thrombophlebitis	• *Chest pain:* present with pulmonary embolism • *Peripheral changes:* pain and swelling of affected extremity; if leg veins affected, pain may increase with walking	• Childbirth 4 to 14 days before onset • History of present illness includes fracture, trauma, deep vein surgery, cardiac disease, cerebrovascular accident, prolonged bed rest. • Past medical history includes malignancy, shock, dehydration, anemia, obesity, chronic infection, use of oral contraceptives. • In superficial vein thrombophlebitis, recent history includes superficial vein I.V. therapy with irritating solutions.
Tricuspid regurgitation (incompetence)	• *Chest pain:* absent • *Dyspnea:* present • *Fatigue:* present; tires easily • *Irregular heartbeat:* atrial fibrillation; usually not noticed by patient • *Peripheral changes:* none	• Past medical history includes right ventricular failure, rheumatic fever, trauma, endocarditis, pulmonary hypertension.
Tricuspid stenosis	• *Chest pain:* usually absent • *Dyspnea:* present in varying degrees • *Fatigue:* present; often severe • *Irregular heartbeat:* usually absent • *Peripheral changes:* dependent peripheral edema	• Most common in women • Past medical history includes mitral valve disease.
Varicose veins	• *Chest pain:* absent • *Peripheral changes:* aching discomfort or pain in legs; pigmentation and ulceration of distal leg; possibly edema	• History of present illness includes leg cramps at night that may be relieved by leg elevation, itching in vein regions, leg fatigue caused by periods of standing. • Past medical history includes thrombophlebitis and family history of varicosities.

PHYSICAL EXAMINATION	DIAGNOSTIC STUDIES
• Slight fever • In deep vein involvement, inspection reveals, with severe venous obstruction, cyanotic skin in affected area; with reflex arterial spasm, pale and cool skin. • Palpation reveals warm affected leg, spasm and pain in calf muscles with dorsiflexion of foot (positive Homans' sign). • In superficial vein involvement, inspection reveals induration, redness, tenderness along course of vein; possibly no clinical manifestations.	• Ultrasound blood flow detector, thermography, and phlebography used to confirm diagnosis.
• Palpation reveals right ventricular pulsation, systolic liver pulsation, and possibly systolic thrill at lower left sternal edge. • Auscultation reveals blowing, coarse, or harsh systolic murmur heard along lower left sternal border; increases on inspiration.	• EKG usually shows atrial fibrillation.
• Inspection may reveal olive skin. • Palpation may reveal presystolic liver pulsation if in sinus rhythm; middiastolic thrill between lower left sternal border and apical impulse. • Auscultation reveals diastolic rumbling murmur heard along lower left sternal border; slow y descent in jugular pulse; normal blood pressure.	• EKG shows wide, tall, peaked P waves; normal axis. • Echocardiography may permit stenosis recognition. • X-ray shows enlarged right atrium. • Cardiac catheterization may reveal site of stenosis.
• Inspection reveals dilated tortuous vessels in legs, visible when patient stands; brown pigmentation and thinning of skin above ankles; ulceration of distal leg; positive Trendelenburg's test.	• None usually performed.

11

Gastrointestinal System

The gastrointestinal (GI) system fuels the body, through the processes of ingestion, digestion, and absorption, and removes body wastes, through the process of elimination.

This system often mirrors abnormal conditions in other systems and reveals a patient's need for preventive health teaching. Also, examination of the mouth lets you identify a patient's oral appliance, dentures, or bridges, so you can remove them before such procedures as intubation and suctioning—and prevent him from aspirating, choking on, or swallowing the appliance.

Comprehensive assessment of the gastrointestinal (GI) system requires that you perform oral, abdominal, and rectal examinations. Perhaps because oral examination is a simple assessment procedure, it's often overlooked as part of a gastrointestinal assessment. Yet, you may be the first to detect an oral lesion and refer the patient for early diagnosis and treatment. Abdominal assessment presents a real challenge because the abdomen contains most of the gastrointestinal system: the lower end of the esophagus, the entire stomach, and the small and large intestines. It also contains parts of other body systems—the urinary, reproductive, cardiovascular, nervous, and blood-forming and immune systems, for example. In fact, only the respiratory system lies completely outside the abdomen—yet a distended abdomen certainly affects breathing. The rectal examination helps detect hemorrhoids, furnishes clues to possible rectal cancer, and allows you to evaluate adjacent reproductive organs for abnormalities. It's usually performed last because it may be physically uncomfortable and emotionally distressing to the patient.

History data

Biographical data

Besides serving to identify your patient, biographical data—particularly age and sex—may indicate that your patient runs a greater risk of having certain gastrointestinal disorders. For example, more than 90% of oral cancer occurs in patients over age 45 (average age at onset is 60), and this disease affects twice as many men as women. Esophageal cancer occurs four times more frequently in men. Rectal cancer occurs most frequently in men between ages 50 and 60. Ulcerative colitis occurs primarily in young adult women. Diverticular disease is most prevalent in men over age 40.

History of present illness

The most common chief complaints associated with gastrointestinal disorders are *pain, dysphagia, nausea, vomiting, diarrhea,* and *constipation (see Guide to Gastrointestinal Disorders,* pages 236 to 245).

Here are some questions you may want to ask about these complaints to explore fully the history of your patient's present illness:
● **Pain.** *What does the pain feel like? What symptoms accompany the pain?* Fever, malaise, nausea, vomiting, warmth, redness, and swelling (such as in the mouth) may indicate viral infection or inflammation of the gastrointestinal (GI) tract. If the patient has painful mouth ulcerations, ask if he notices any relation between exacerbation of symptoms and stress, food, change of seasons, or other factors. Aphthous ulcers are sometimes associated with these factors.

Do you have heartburn or dyspepsia? These

conditions usually occur after eating certain spicy foods that produce excess acid in the stomach; dyspepsia may also occur with hiatal hernia or as a side effect of certain medications (such as salicylates), or it can reflect more serious GI disorders, such as cancer. If the patient has abdominal pain, ask about the relationship of the pain to meals. Peptic ulcer pain usually occurs about 2 hours after meals or whenever the stomach is empty; it may wake the patient at night. Arterial insufficiency to the bowel usually causes pain 15 to 30 minutes after meals and lasts up to 3 hours.

Have your bowel elimination patterns changed recently? When did you last have a bowel movement? Can you pass flatus? Does your abdomen feel distended? Your patient's answers may give clues to inflammatory or obstructive bowel disorders.

Do you have rectal discomfort? This type of pain can indicate local problems, such as pain from a large, hard stool that has torn the mucosa; inflammation from infections; and pain associated with hemorrhoids (see *Referred Pain*).

● **Dysphagia.** *When, during swallowing, do you feel discomfort? Does it occur between your mouth and esophagus? In the esophagus?* *Between the esophagus and stomach?* Asking the patient to point to the area of discomfort is important, because certain disorders affect specific points in the swallowing process. *Does the dysphagia result from ingesting solid food, or both solids and liquids? Did you have symptoms of reflux prior to the onset of dysphagia?* Dysphagia usually results from mechanical obstruction or loss of motor coordination. Because cancer is an important cause of mechanical obstruction, ask if the patient has experienced marked weight loss. Neurologic disease can cause loss of motor coordination, so ask about additional symptoms, such as dysarthria.

● **Nausea and vomiting.** *Do you feel nauseated before you vomit? Is the vomiting projectile?* Projectile vomiting often indicates central nervous system disorders. *Does the vomitus have an unusual odor?* A fecal odor, for example, usually indicates a small bowel obstruction. *Is the symptom related to a specific time period?* Pregnancy, metabolic disturbances, and excessive consumption of alcohol can cause early-morning vomiting. *Have you been emotionally upset recently? Have you vomited blood?* Hematemesis may reflect a GI disorder, such as severe esopha-

---

Referred Pain

Here's how referred pain occurs: Pain that's produced by an organ supplied with efferent nerves for pain from the same spinal cord segments supplying body walls and limbs is often felt on the surface. This pain may occur relatively near the affected organ or at some distance from it. Organ pain usually occurs more diffusely than surface pain. This chart identifies the areas to which organ pain is referred:

ORGAN	REFERRED PAIN AREA
Gallbladder	● Right upper quadrant ● Right posterior infrascapular area
Diaphragm	● Posterior neck ● Posterior shoulder area
Duodenum	● *Most commonly:* midline of the abdominal wall, just above the umbilicus
Appendix	● Umbilicus ● Parietal peritoneal involvement, right lower quadrant
Ureter	● Inguinal region ● Loin

gitis, or disorders outside the GI system, such as anticoagulant toxicity.

• *Diarrhea.* Ask about the frequency and consistency of the patient's bowel movements. *Have you been under emotional stress lately?* Psychogenic factors may affect bowel motility. *What particular foods did you eat before the diarrhea's onset?* Food poisoning (such as from custard-filled pastries and processed meats contaminated by staphylococci) may cause diarrhea, usually accompanied by abdominal cramping and vomiting. Fever, tenesmus, and cramping pain associated with diarrhea usually indicate an infection, most commonly viral. *Is the stool bloody?* This may be from an inflammation or a neoplasm involving the bowel wall. *Is the stool foul-smelling, bulky, and greasy?* This suggests a fat malabsorption problem. Passage of mucus suggests irritable colon. *Do periods of diarrhea alternate with periods of constipation?* This combination may be associated with irritable colon, diverticulitis, or colorectal cancer.

• *Constipation. How would you describe the size, character, and frequency of your bowel movements?* Many patients mistakenly claim to have constipation, so always ask this type of question to determine if constipation exists. *What is your typical daily diet like?* The absence of fiber in the diet (or inadequate fluid intake) may lead to constipation. Laxative abuse, decreased physical activity, and emotional stress may also produce this symptom. *Do you experience cramping abdominal pain and distention related to the constipation?* These symptoms suggest mechanical obstruction, such as from stricture or tumor. Find out if the problem is acute—in which case it's more likely to have an organic cause—or chronic, which is commonly caused by a functional problem.

Past history

Explore the following relevant areas when taking your patient's past history:

• *Gastrointestinal (GI) disorders.* Long-term GI conditions, such as chronic ulcerative colitis or GI polyposis, may predispose a patient to colorectal cancer.

• *Neurologic disorders.* Such conditions as cerebrovascular accident, myasthenia gravis, amyotrophic lateral sclerosis, and peripheral nerve damage may cause GI disorders. For example, these conditions can impair movement of the tongue, the uvula, the larynx, or the pharynx, which can lead to drooling, dysarthria, and difficulty chewing or swallowing.

• *Other major disorders.* Gastrointestinal signs and symptoms may also result from pathologic conditions in other body systems. A patient with chronic obstructive pulmonary disease may be constipated from weakness of the diaphragm and decreased strength to defecate. Endocrine disorders, such as hypothyroidism and diabetes mellitus with neuromuscular dysfunction, may also predispose a patient to constipation. Diabetes mellitus may predispose the patient to oral candidal infections.

• *Previous abdominal surgery or trauma.* Intestinal adhesions may result from trauma, inflammation, or previous abdominal surgery. These adhesions may produce pain or intestinal obstruction. Even such a relatively simple procedure as oral surgery may cause infection or bleeding. A fractured jaw may result in malocclusion.

• *Allergies.* Allergic reactions to certain foods and medications can produce a variety of GI complaints, such as pain, nausea, and diarrhea. Check especially to see if the patient is hypersensitive to penicillin, sulfonamides, or local anesthetics (such as procaine or tetracaine), which can lead to severe allergic symptoms affecting GI mucous membranes. Also ask the patient about hypersensitivity to lipsticks, toothpastes, or mouthwashes, which may cause symptoms on contact.

• *Chronic laxative use.* Laxatives, including mineral oil and stool softeners, affect intestinal motility. Habitual use of laxatives may cause constipation (from insensitive defecatory reflexes).

• *Medications.* Anti-infectives, cytotoxic drugs, and many other drugs can produce various GI side effects, such as oral ulceration, nausea, vomiting, diarrhea, or constipation.

Family history

Ask the patient if anyone in his family has ever had colorectal cancer or gastrointestinal (GI) polyposis. A family history of either disorder increases the patient's chances of developing colorectal cancer. GI symptoms may also result from diabetes mellitus, which can have a genetic basis.

Psychosocial history

To review your patient's psychosocial history, ask about his occupation. A sedentary occupation can contribute to constipation; a highly stressful job can lead to many gastrointestinal (GI) symptoms. An occupation that necessitates exposure to toxic substances can also cause GI disorders. For example, chronic lead or bismuth poisoning usually produces a blue-black or slate gray line next to the gingival crest.

Emotional problems can contribute significantly to GI symptoms—for example, pain, dyspepsia, nausea, anorexia, gluttony, or more idiosyncratic tendencies, such as cheek-biting.

Also pertinent in your patient's psychosocial history are financial problems, which may prevent him from seeking proper dental or medical care or from eating an adequate diet. In addition, financial worries contribute to stress-related GI symptoms. Odontophobia (an exaggerated fear of going to the dentist) may cause the patient to delay treatment for dental problems.

Activities of daily living

Explore the following aspects of your patient's daily life when investigating a gastrointestinal (GI) complaint:

● *Oral hygiene.* Ask your patient to describe his oral hygiene routine for a typical day. Note if he mentions using a toothbrush, dental floss, or gingival stimulants, but don't bias the patient's answers by naming these items in your questions. (Thus prompted, many patients who don't use these items will say they do.) If the patient wears a dental appliance, such as a bridge, note its type and location. Ask the patient with dentures if he wears them all the time. Ill-fitting dentures may cause gingival or palatal irritation. Ask the patient to describe how he cleans his dentures. Note how often he visits a dentist.

● *Eating habits.* Frequent between-meal snacking on sugar-rich foods may predispose a person to caries. Excessive consumption of very hot or very spicy foods may lead to stomatitis.

● *Smoking.* Remember, men between ages 45 and 64 who smoke cigarettes have a mortality ten times that of nonsmokers, and the effect of smoking on women's health is becoming increasingly significant. If your patient smokes cigarettes, note how much he smokes in *pack years* (number of packs of cigarettes smoked per day multiplied by the number of years the patient has been smoking at this rate). Cigarette smoking predisposes a person to oral cancer, and pipe smoking may cause stomatitis or lip cancer.

● *Alcohol and caffeine consumption.* Excessive alcohol consumption may be a factor in the development of oral cancer. A patient's stomach lining may be irritated by excess gastric secretions stimulated by the ingestion of large amounts of alcohol or caffeine.

Review of systems

Symptoms possibly related to gastrointestinal (GI) disorders may be revealed by assessment of your patient's other body systems.

● *General.* Ask your patient about recent *fever, weight loss, anorexia, fatigue,* or *weakness.*

● *Skin.* Generalized *jaundice* and *pruritus* may result from hepatocellular damage or biliary obstruction. *Pruritus in the anal region* may be caused by local infections and lesions or by specific dermatologic disorders, such as psoriasis.

● *Eye.* Ask about *eye pain* and *photophobia. Uveitis* may accompany ulcerative colitis or Crohn's disease.

● *Respiratory. Dyspnea* may result from limited respiratory excursion caused by ascites.

● *Urinary. Uremia* may cause GI bleeding. Abdominal pain may be a symptom of urinary disorders.

● *Musculoskeletal. Arthritis* may occur with ulcerative colitis or Crohn's disease.

● *Psychological. Anxiety, depression* and *other emotional disturbances* commonly accompany GI disorders.

● *Blood-forming and immune. Swelling* of cervical, supraclavicular, or inguinal lymphatics may signal GI cancer.

Physical examination

Preparations for a GI examination

Physical assessment of a patient's gastrointestinal system usually consists of oral, abdominal, and rectal examinations. You'll assess his mouth by inspection and palpation; his abdomen by inspection, auscultation, percussion, and palpation; and his rectum by inspection and palpation.

For mouth assessment, you'll need a direct light source (such as a head lamp or penlight), a tongue depressor, an angled mouth mirror, $2'' \times 2''$ gauze pads, and rubber gloves or finger cots. For abdominal assessment, you'll need a stethoscope, a ruler, a skin-marking pencil, and a tape measure; for rectal assessment, rubber gloves or finger cots and a lubricant.

Before the examination, explain the procedure to the patient to reduce his anxiety. Tell him you'll be looking at and touching his mouth, abdomen, and rectum, and that you'll be listening to abdominal sounds with a stethoscope. Assure the patient that the examination is routine, and that you'll proceed carefully to avoid causing him any discomfort. Warn him that he'll feel some pressure during abdominal palpation. If the patient is experiencing abdominal pain, tell him that you'll assess the painful area last or not at all, if it's contraindicated.

If the patient is hospitalized, tell him and his family that some of the procedures you'll perform—possibly all of them—may be repeated frequently to monitor changes in his condition.

Assessment of the mouth

Unless your patient has an urgent abdominal complaint, begin your assessment of his gastrointestinal system by examining his mouth. After assisting the patient to a sitting position, inspect for asymmetry or swelling around the lips and jaws. Then inspect the temporomandibular joint, and palpate it bilaterally—just anterior to the ears—while the patient slowly opens and closes his mouth. Observe carefully for limited mobility and for tenderness and crepitus.

Next, tell the patient to close his mouth and clench his teeth. Retract his lips and check his bite. The teeth should meet, with the upper incisors and canines slightly outside the lower ones. Note any malocclusion.

Lips. Be sure to ask a female patient wearing lipstick to remove it. Also ask the patient to remove any dental appliances, if necessary. Then, inspect your patient's lips for abnormal color or texture and for lesions. Next, put on

a rubber glove or a finger cot to palpate the outer lips. Invert the lips and, using your light source, inspect and palpate the inner lips with the patient's jaw closed. Note any lesions, nodules, vesicles, or fissures, especially at the junction of the upper and lower lips.

Teeth and gums. With your patient's mouth open, use your light source to inspect his teeth. Normally, an adult has 32 teeth, 8 on each side of each jaw. Note obvious caries and any teeth that are missing, broken, stained, or displaced. Carefully palpate the teeth and note if any are loose.

Next, inspect and palpate your patient's gums (gingivae). They should be pink, moist, and smooth. Carefully check the gingival crest for recession, which may cause tooth loss. Also, note any redness, pallor, hypertrophy, ulcers, bleeding, or tenderness on palpation.

Tongue. Ask your patient to stick out his tongue. Using your light source, inspect the tongue's superior surface. Normally, the lateral surfaces are pink and moist, with a slightly rough appearance because of the papillae. When the patient moves his tongue, note any deviation to one side, paralysis, or tremor. Also, note any abnormalities, such as redness, swelling, lesions, and any coating other than the tongue's normal thin white coating.

Next, grasp the tongue with a $2'' \times 2''$ gauze pad and palpate its superior surface and sides, paying special attention to its texture. Note any nodules or ulcerations. Ask the patient to touch the roof of his mouth with his tongue while you inspect and palpate the tongue's inferior surface and the floor of the mouth. Inspect carefully for ulcerations, which are especially prevalent in this area of the mouth and may be an early sign of oral cancer. Check, too, for leukoplakia (yellow-white leathery patches), which may be precancerous.

Buccal mucosa. With your patient's mouth open wide, your light source in position, and using your fingers as retractors, inspect and palpate the buccal mucosa on both sides. Record abnormalities, such as pallor, redness, excessive salivation or dryness, bleeding, swelling, ulcers or sores, and white patches or plaques. Be sure to move your fingers to various positions so you view the entire buccal mucosa area.

Hard and soft palates. Inspect and palpate the patient's hard and soft palates. Inspect the hard palate directly or, using a mouth mirror, indirectly. Normally, the hard palate is dome-shaped, pale, and transversed irregularly by rugae. The soft palate is normally pink and soft (as its name implies). Note any redness, lesions, patches, petechiae, or pallor.

Pharynx. To examine your patient's pharynx, tilt his head back and depress his tongue with a tongue depressor (not too far back or you'll trigger the gag reflex). Ask the patient to say "Ah." His uvula and soft palate should rise. Inspect the anterior and the posterior pillars, the tonsils, and the posterior pharynx, which is normally pink and may be slightly vascular. Note abnormalities, such as uvular deviation; the absence, hypertrophy, or induration of the tonsils; and swelling of the tonsils or the posterior pharynx. Observe also for lesions, plaques, exudate, or a gray membrane. Finally, note any unusual mouth odor and describe it in your notes—for example, *sweet and fruity* or *fetid and musty.*

Introduction to abdominal assessment

Before assessing your patient's abdomen, check for contraindications to palpation and percussion. Abdominal pain, for example, contraindicates repeated abdominal assessment. *Never* palpate the abdomen of a patient with suspected appendicitis or a dissecting abdominal aortic aneurysm, due to the possibility of rupture. Don't perform a physical examination on a patient with polycystic kidneys, because you might dislodge a cyst. The presence of transplanted kidneys or other organs in a patient also contraindicates percussion and palpation.

Assess your patient's abdomen according to the following sequence: inspection, auscultation, percussion, and palpation. Note that you'll perform auscultation—usually the last step in the assessment sequence—second. This is because percussing or palpating the abdomen *before* auscultating it can stimulate intestinal activity and produce misleading sounds.

When you auscultate your patient's abdomen, listen closely for bowel and vascular activity. Let the sounds you hear guide you in percussion, which helps outline major organs or masses. Your percussion findings then direct you in palpating for tenderness, size, mo-

bility, consistency, and the location of masses or enlarged organs.

For assessment purposes, the abdomen is divided into four sections, as formed by a vertical line down the patient's midline and a horizontal line across his umbilicus. These sections are called the *left upper quadrant, right upper quadrant, left lower quadrant,* and *right lower quadrant* (see *Abdominal Landmarks,* page 226).

Your patient's history should tell you in which quadrant his symptoms are located. Examine all four quadrants, not just the symptomatic one, and examine the three asymptomatic quadrants first. Otherwise, any pain you elicit in the symptomatic quadrant will cause the muscles in the other quadrants to tighten and make your examination more difficult. The sequence you use to examine the three asymptomatic quadrants isn't significant, but you should develop a routine for performing an abdominal examination and do it the same way every time. Perform all four techniques in the modified sequence—IAPP—in each quadrant, concentrating on the organs underlying that section.

Prepare your patient for examination. Instruct him to urinate. If he hasn't already removed all clothing from his abdomen, ask him to do so. Drape the pubic area for all patients—and the breasts, as well, for women. Position the patient comfortably on his back, with his knees bent and his arms at his sides, to prevent tensing of the abdominal muscles. Warm your hands and your stethoscope's diaphragm before beginning the examination.

Abdominal inspection

Begin your abdominal assessment by inspecting the patient's entire abdomen. Position him so he's lying on his back, and stoop at his side to view his abdominal contour. A normal abdomen has a convex profile, even with the patient supine. A flat abdomen may be normal in an athlete or a muscular person. A hollow or scaphoid abdomen may indicate malnutrition. A distended or protuberant abdomen, usually having an everted umbilicus, could indicate excess air or fluid in the peritoneal cavity. Inspect the umbilicus for abnormalities besides eversion. For example, an umbilicus with a blue tinge may indicate intraabdominal bleeding.

Abdominal Landmarks

Divide the patient's abdomen into quadrants, as shown in this illustration. Memorize the shape, size, and location of all abdominal structures within each quadrant. Refer to these landmarks when you're performing your assessment.

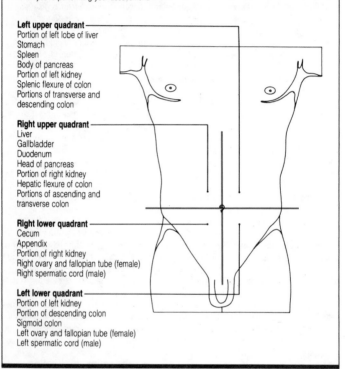

Left upper quadrant
Portion of left lobe of liver
Stomach
Spleen
Body of pancreas
Portion of left kidney
Splenic flexure of colon
Portions of transverse and
descending colon

Right upper quadrant
Liver
Gallbladder
Duodenum
Head of pancreas
Portion of right kidney
Hepatic flexure of colon
Portions of ascending and
transverse colon

Right lower quadrant
Cecum
Appendix
Portion of right kidney
Right ovary and fallopian tube (female)
Right spermatic cord (male)

Left lower quadrant
Portion of left kidney
Portion of descending colon
Sigmoid colon
Left ovary and fallopian tube (female)
Left spermatic cord (male)

Next, stand at the foot of the bed, and observe the patient's abdomen for symmetry of contour and for the presence of masses. An asymmetrical abdomen may result from previous abdominal trauma or surgery, an abnormal organ, or weak abdominal muscles.

Perform the rest of the examination from the patient's right side (if you're right-handed). Inspect the abdomen for movement from respiration, peristalsis, and arterial pulsations. Look for exaggerated abdominal movement during breathing that may indicate respiratory distress or severe anxiety. Normal peristaltic movement is rarely visible, even through a

thin abdominal wall. If you can see strong contractions (peristaltic waves) crossing the patient's abdomen, report this finding to the doctor, because it may indicate impending bowel or pyloric obstruction.

The only arterial pulsations you may see are those of the abdominal aorta, which may be visible in the epigastric area. In a thin patient, you may see femoral arterial pulsations.

Inspect the abdominal skin thoroughly. Tense, glistening skin may indicate ascites or abdominal wall edema. Note any scars, lesions, ecchymoses, striae, rashes, or dilated veins. Also inspect for an abdominal hernia, which may become apparent when you ask the patient to cough. Draw a diagram of the abdomen's quadrants, and record the location, size, and color of such abnormalities.

Many skin and vascular findings relate to pressure caused by engorgement within the abdomen from obstruction of the vena cava or the portal vein. Malfunctioning organs, such as the liver or the spleen, may cause skin changes. For example, if your inspection reveals jaundice, it may result from liver disease or splenic hemolysis. Chronic uremia may cause abdominal pallor or frost. Although vascular lesions in the skin may result from various causes, always consider the possibility that your patient has a gastrointestinal system disorder.

Abdominal auscultation

After inspecting your patient's abdomen, auscultate it. Use the diaphragm of the stethoscope first. Exerting only light pressure, listen for bowel sounds in all quadrants. Normally, air and fluid movement through the bowel create irregular bubbling or soft, gurgling noises about every 5 to 15 seconds. If you don't hear bowel sounds immediately, listen for at least 5 minutes to confirm the absence of bowel sounds, which may indicate paralytic ileus or peritonitis. Report this finding. Conversely, rapid, high-pitched, tinkling bowel sounds or loud, gurgling noises with visible peristaltic waves commonly accompany diarrhea or gastroenteritis and indicate a hyperactive bowel. These findings may also signal an early intestinal obstruction.

Next, use the bell of the stethoscope to listen to vascular sounds. Place the bell lightly over the midline to check for *bruits,* blowing sounds that seem to elongate the pulsation normally heard over a vessel. Check also for bruits over the renal vessels, the result of dilatation or constriction. If you note any bruits in the abdominal aorta, assess arterial perfusion in the patient's legs. Absence of pulses indicates decreased blood flow to the legs: notify the doctor promptly. Meanwhile, keep your patient quiet and *don't* palpate his abdomen, because these symptoms may reflect a dissecting aneurysm, which is a surgical emergency. The same symptoms may indicate arteriosclerosis obliterans, a chronic condition, but a doctor must make the diagnosis.

You can also use the bell of the stethoscope to detect other abnormal abdominal sounds. If you hear a *venous hum*—a hum of medium tone created by blood flow in a large, engorged, vascular organ such as the liver or spleen—check for other signs of fluid overload. A *friction rub,* which sounds like two pieces of sandpaper being rubbed together, may originate in an inflamed spleen or a neoplastic liver.

While auscultating the patient's abdomen, assess the abdominal surface for edema by watching the imprint left by the bell of the stethoscope. If the circular imprint of a *lightly* placed stethoscope remains visible on the skin, fluid has probably accumulated within the abdominal wall. This often results from a nutritional deficiency, such as low circulating protein levels.

Abdominal percussion

Percussion is used mainly to check the size of abdominal organs and to detect excessive amounts of fluid or air in the abdomen. Percussion notes in each abdominal quadrant depend on the underlying structure. Keeping the positions of these underlying organs in mind, follow a pattern when you percuss (see *Percussion Technique,* page 228). Abdominal percussion normally elicits tones ranging from dull or flat (over solids) to tympanic (over air). A sigmoid colon filled with stool produces dullness in the left lower quadrant. You'll usually hear high-pitched tympanic notes over a section of bowel filled with air (the degree of tympany reflects gaseous bowel distention). When ascites is present, you'll also detect dullness when you percuss the patient's flanks.

Another percussion technique you can use during abdominal assessment of a patient is fist percussion (see page 41). Because this technique detects tenderness instead of producing percussion notes, don't perform it until the end of the examination. Fist percussion usually produces discomfort in a patient with deep-seated tenderness, organomegaly, or inflammation. It can also elicit signs of liver or gallbladder involvement. To use fist percussion for this purpose, place one hand parallel to and below the right costal margin and strike it with the fist of the other hand. You can also use fist percussion to test for tenderness over

Percussion Technique

When percussing your patient's abdomen, move your hands clockwise, starting from the right upper quadrant unless your patient's experiencing pain. If he is, identify in which quadrant the pain's occurring and percuss that quadrant *last*. Remember, when tapping, to quickly move your right finger away so you don't damp vibrations.

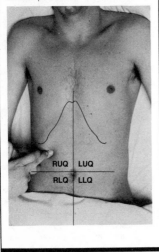

RUQ | LUQ
RLQ | LLQ

the kidneys. *Don't* perform fist percussion routinely when pain or discomfort results, especially in the splenic area (the left upper quadrant and left upper midclavicular area).

Light and deep abdominal palpation

Techniques for abdominal palpation range from bimanual maneuvers to ballottement. The most frequently used are light palpation and deep palpation (see page 37). To perform *light palpation*, use your fingertips to depress the abdominal wall a little more than ½″ (1.3 cm), examining each quadrant systematically. Using light palpation you can determine skin temperature, detect large masses and tender areas, and elicit guarding. You can also assess the patient's abdominal vasculature through light palpation. For example, you can usually palpate the femoral pulse in the groin area. To palpate the aortic pulse, press the patient's upper abdomen slightly to the left of the midline. (Deeper palpation may be necessary to locate this pulse.)

Light palpation may not allow you to feel normal-sized abdominal organs, especially in a patient with a significant adipose layer. But if you place your index finger parallel to and slightly beneath the right costal margin and ask the patient to take a deep breath, you may be able to feel the liver's lower edge. The deep breath pushes the liver's lower edge farther under the costal margin. Normally, this edge stops just below the margin. It feels like a firm, sharp, even ridge, with a smooth surface. If the patient grimaces during this maneuver or tells you it's painful for him, report the tenderness to the doctor immediately.

With the patient in the right lateral decubitus position, use light palpation under the left costal margin to assess for splenic tenderness. If you suspect an enlarged spleen, use very light pressure and watch the patient for signs of discomfort. *Never* use deep palpation on a tender spleen.

To perform *deep palpation,* press the fingers of one hand in about 3″ (7.5 cm) with the aid of the other hand. With deep palpation you can determine the position of organs and detect abdominal masses. Never use deep palpation on a patient who's just had a kidney transplant, on a patient whose organs are tender, or on a patient with polycystic kidneys. Defer deep palpation of a known abdominal mass because of the danger that tumor cells may spread. Deep palpation may also evoke rebound tenderness when you suddenly withdraw your fingertips, a possible sign of peritoneal inflammation. This technique is often used to assess a patient for appendicitis, but it should not be used repeatedly on such a patient. *Don't palpate the abdomen at all after a diagnosis of appendicitis.*

Deep palpation can also be used to assess the inferior liver border. Standing at the right of the recumbent patient and facing his feet, hook the fingers of both your hands over the costal margin and ask the patient to take a deep breath. You should be able to feel the border of the liver's right lobe. Assess it for contour, mobility, consistency, and tenderness.

Liver size and position

You can estimate the size and position of your patient's liver through percussion (see *Estimating Liver Size*). Beginning at the right iliac crest, percuss up the right midclavicular line (MCL). The percussion note becomes dull when you reach the liver's inferior border, usually at the costal margin, although it may be lower with liver disease. Mark this point, then percuss down from the right clavicle, again along the right MCL. Place your pleximeter between the patient's ribs as you tap, to avoid confusing the dull note of the liver's superior border (usually between the fifth to seventh intercostal spaces) with the dull note that results from percussing bone. Mark the superior border. The distance between the two marked points represents the approximate size of the liver's right lobe, normally from 2⅜″ to 4¾″ (6 to 12 cm). A liver size of more than 4¾″ in the MCL suggests hepatomegaly.

Assess the liver's left lobe similarly, percussing along the sternal midline. Again, mark the point where you hear dull percussion notes, and measure the size of the left lobe, normally 1¼″ to 3⅛″ (4 to 8 cm).

Several structures and conditions—the sternum, ribs, breast tissue, pleural effusions, or gas in the colon—can obscure the dull percussion notes you're listening for. This situation may require you to use palpation and auscultation, along with percussion, to determine the patient's liver size and position.

The *scratch test* can locate the liver's inferior border if you can't find it through percussion. To perform this test, lightly place the stethoscope's diaphragm over the approximate location of the inferior border. Then auscultate while stroking the patient's abdomen lightly with your right index finger in the pattern you used for locating the liver's inferior border through percussion. Start your stroke along the MCL at the right iliac crest and move upward. Because the liver transmits sound waves better than the air-filled ascending colon, the scratching noise you hear through your stethoscope becomes louder over the solid liver.

Abdominal masses

If you detect an abdominal mass through palpation, note its location and the patient's position. (A mass in the splenic area, for example, may be palpable only when the patient is in the right lateral decubitus position.) Determine the size and shape of the mass. Describe its contour as *smooth, rough, nodular,* or *irregular.* Its consistency may be *soft, doughy, semisolid,* or *hard.* Percuss the mass to determine whether it's tympanic (filled with air) or dull (filled with fluid). Also assess the mass for tenderness, and ask the patient about changes in its location or size.

Determine the relation of the mass to other abdominal organs. Note whether it's attached to the abdominal wall. Evaluate its mobility. Does it seem to float in surrounding tissues, or does it adhere to underlying structures? Lastly, assess the mass for pulsations that may be caused by a highly vascular tumor, an

Estimating Liver Size

To estimate the size of the liver, follow the percussion pattern shown here. First, percuss upward and then downward on the right midclavicular line. By noting in each sequence when dullness begins, you can approximate the lower and upper borders of the liver. Normally, the distance between these borders, or liver size, is 2⅜″ to 4¾″ (6 to 12 cm) at the midclavicular line.

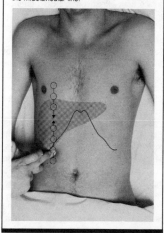

anomalous vessel, or a mass located over an artery.

Assessing ascites

You can assess your patient for ascites through three techniques: testing for shifting dullness, testing for fluid wave, and measuring the patient's girth. A dull percussion note may suggest fluid accumulation in the abdomen without visual signs of ascites. To confirm fluid accumulation, with the patient lying on his back, percuss his abdomen from the umbilicus toward each flank. On the patient's abdomen, draw a line between areas of dullness and tympany. Then, turn the patient to one side, causing ascitic fluid to shift, and repeat percussion from the umbilicus toward the flanks. Again draw a line between areas of dullness and tympany, and compare this line to the one you drew previously. The distance between these lines indicates the presence of fluid. Repeat the procedure with the patient lying on his other side.

The *shifting dullness* sign confirms ascites and also provides a baseline for daily comparison of the distance between the lines, which may indicate an increase or decrease in the accumulated fluid. However, the shifting dullness sign can produce a false finding, such as when an engorged loop of bowel—not free peritoneal or ascitic fluid—shifts and causes dull percussion tones. Adhesions from previous surgery or cancer may also prevent fluid from shifting freely in the patient's abdomen. Be sure to analyze all your findings carefully and consider possible false or misleading causes when performing this test.

Eliciting a *fluid wave* can help you distinguish between fluid retention and air retention in a patient with a slightly distended abdomen. You'll need someone to help you perform this technique—perhaps the patient himself, a family member, or a co-worker. Have the other person place the ulnar surface of his hand on the patient's abdominal midline and push down slightly, to dampen any movement of the abdominal wall. Then, place one of your palms on one of the patient's flanks and sharply tap the opposite flank. If a large amount of fluid is present, you'll feel a moving wave in the palm that's resting on the patient's flank.

You can also monitor abdominal distention

by measuring your patient's *girth* (probably the most reliable method). The patient must be lying down when you do this. Draw the tape firmly but not tightly around his abdomen, and then measure his girth during exhalation. Mark the patient's flanks to ensure the same area is measured each time.

Rectal inspection

Always examine the rectum last. Turn the patient on his left side, with his knees up and his buttocks close to the edge of the examining table. (If the patient is ambulatory, ask him to stand and bend over the examining table.) Spread his buttocks to expose the anus. Rectal skin is normally darker than the surrounding area. Inspect for inflammation, lesions, scars, outpouching, fissures, and external hemorrhoids. Check for hemorrhoids while the patient strains as though to defecate.

Rectal palpation

For this technique, which follows inspection of the rectum, use a disposable glove and a lubricant. While the patient strains as though to defecate, use your index finger to palpate any weak anal outpouchings, nodules, or tenderness on movement. Then, explain to the patient that you'll insert your gloved finger a short distance into his rectum and that this pressure may make him feel as though he needs to move his bowels. Wait for the anal sphincter to relax, then insert your finger gently and rotate it to palpate as much of the rectal wall as possible. Palpate for any nodules, irregularities, or tenderness, and for fecal impaction. As you palpate the anterior rectal wall of the male patient, remember to assess the prostate's lateral lobes and median sulcus. Test any fecal matter adhering to the glove for occult blood, using the correct guaiac or Hematest procedure.

Pediatric assessment

Pediatric history

To assess a child's gastrointestinal system properly, you'll need to obtain a thorough nutritional history. For example, if you note periods of decreased appetite in a young child, check to see if his growth and weight have been affected. Remember, decreased appetite may be normal for the child's age (for instance, for a toddler).

Because abdominal pain is a common childhood complaint, be sure to ask about it. Instead of asking the child directly about stomach pain, determine the pain's nature and severity through such indirect questions as *Did you eat your dinner last night? Did you sleep last night? What toys did you play with this morning?* Use indirect questions to obtain objective answers from anxious parents too.

Determine the characteristics of any nausea and vomiting (especially projectile vomiting) the child has experienced, as well as the frequency and consistency of his bowel movements. Does the child suffer from diarrhea or constipation? (When asking these questions, make sure the parents understand such terms as nausea, diarrhea, and constipation.) Remember, diarrhea can be serious in infants, because their extracellular fluid volume is proportionately larger than that of an older child or adult. Thus, diarrhea can quickly lead to dehydration, electrolyte imbalance, and possibly metabolic acidosis. Also determine if bowel symptoms occur during toilet training periods. (Ask at what age the child was toilet-trained.) Does the child ever eat dirt, grass, paint chips, or other nonfood materials?

Ask about any changes in life-style, such as a recent death in the family or a change in schools, that may be creating stress for the child.

Inquire if the child brushes his own teeth. Determine, too, if the parents leave a bottle of formula, milk, or juice in the crib with him at night, which may predispose the child to caries from nursing bottle syndrome. Ask about thumbsucking, which may cause malocclusion, especially if continued after age 4. Question the child's parents about family members who have malocclusion; this finding increases the child's risk of developing it.

Because abdominal symptoms may also indicate pathology outside the abdomen, ask if the child has other symptoms, such as a sore throat, a cough, or burning on urination.

Positioning the child

You'll usually assess a child's mouth while he's sitting. An uncooperative child will have to be restrained—an infant in the supine position and a toddler in the supine or sitting position, preferably in the parent's lap.

When examining a young child's abdomen, you may want to place your knees against the parent's knees to form an impromptu examining table. Or, if possible, have a parent hold the child. If this isn't possible, position the child so he can see his parent. Abdominal tenseness can impede your examination. To ease tenseness, flex an infant's knees and hips. Ask an older child to assume this position so you can examine him.

Mouth assessment

Usually you'll examine a child's mouth as you would an adult's, but the patient's age may require you to modify your methods.

A toddler or preschool-age child may cooperate more easily if you examine his parent's mouth first. He'll probably want *his* mouth examined, too. Let the child handle the tongue depressor before you examine him to allay any fears he may have. You can also let the child place the depressor on his tongue as you guide his hand.

Inspecting an uncooperative child's mouth isn't easy or pleasant. One technique for bypassing clenched teeth is to ease a depressor along the lips, toward the back of the mouth, and then insert it between the posterior teeth in a downward motion, which triggers the gag reflex when you depress the posterior tongue. You then have a brief period to examine the child's mouth.

Avoiding the gag reflex. To avoid making a child gag when examining his mouth, try these tips:
- Tell the child to stick out his tongue and pant like a puppy while you examine his mouth.
- Avoid touching the patient's posterior tongue when using a tongue depressor except when viewing the posterior pharynx (or examining an uncooperative child).
- Use the tongue depressor on each side of his tongue and examine one half of his throat at a time.

Teeth. If you can identify dental or mouth problems in a child, he may be able to receive treatment before costlier (or permanent) sequelae occur. First, observe the child for malocclusion. Don't ask him to *show* you his teeth, because reflex alignment may make his bite appear normal. Instead, ask him to bite down hard while his mouth is closed; then evert his lips and observe his bite.

Inspect the child's teeth carefully for dental caries and tooth eruption. Dental caries in primary teeth pose a special problem because of possible infection, loss of teeth, and loss of space for permanent tooth eruption. Also check for lack of tooth eruption by age 1 and for missing teeth in older children.

Gums. Inspect the child's gums carefully. Gingivitis, a common condition among children, usually results from a combination of such factors as:

• mouth breathing (often associated with nasal insufficiency from such problems as enlarged adenoids or allergies) in which constant passage of air dries out the gums and inflames the anterior labial gingiva

• tooth eruption (the presence of both primary and permanent teeth commonly causes abnormal gingival stimulation from chewing and from food impaction)

• puberty (hormonal stimulation, especially in girls, contributes to gingivitis).

Gingivitis may also result from a combination of poor hygiene, crooked teeth, retained primary roots, and poor diet. (*Note:* Gingivitis may also be the first clinical sign of leukemia.)

Tongue and buccal mucosa. When you inspect and palpate a child's tongue, check for abnormalities that are often seen in children. These include the strawberry (later raspberry) appearance that occurs during scarlet fever and the condition of being tongue-tied—unable to touch the tongue to the lips because of shortness of the frenulum.

In a child with a history of fever, chills, and coughing, be sure to check the buccal mucosa opposite the first and second molars for small white spots on erythematous bases (Koplik's spots), the prodromal hallmark of measles.

White, slightly raised patches on the buccal mucosa (or on the tongue and pharynx) that are indurated and tend to bleed when removed characterize *thrush,* an infection caused by *Candida albicans.* Thrush usually begins on the buccal mucosa or tongue and spreads to other areas of the mouth.

Inspect a young child's tongue for a dry, shriveled appearance, which may be a clue to

dehydration. Absence of tongue papillae suggests avitaminosis.

Palate and lips. Abnormalities of a child's palate that you may encounter during inspection and palpation include bruising, which may result from forced feeding, and cleft palate, a congenital abnormality. Cleft palate may be partial or complete. It may affect only the soft palate, or it may extend through the hard and soft palate to the incisive foramen. Cleft palate commonly occurs with cleft lip, another congenital defect, which may be unilateral or bilateral. Cleft lip usually affects the alveolar ridge and varies in severity from a notch in the border of the lip to a complete cleft involving the floor of the nose. The nasal cartilage may also be deformed or displaced.

Abdominal skin turgor

Tissue turgor is important in an infant, because dehydration—which may be fatal—proceeds so rapidly. Diarrhea accompanying gastroenteritis is a common cause of dehydration in infants. To test abdominal skin turgor, gently pull the child's skin and subcutaneous tissue up and then release it. Do the resulting creases disappear immediately after you let go of the skin? If not, consider the child dehydrated. If you suspect dehydration, assess the child's urinary output (see *Assessing Fluid Status,* page 248).

Abdominal inspection

The contour of a child's abdomen may be your first clue to a possible gastrointestinal disorder. In a child under age 4, you may see a mild potbelly (a normal finding) when the child stands or sits; from about age 4 to age 13, a mild potbelly is usually noticeable only when the child stands. An extreme potbelly may result from organomegaly, ascites, neoplasm, defects in the abdominal wall, or starvation; a depressed or concave abdomen may indicate a diaphragmatic hernia. Look for an area of localized swelling.

Note any scars or abdominal vascularity. Superficial veins are readily visible in a normal infant (to a degree considered pathologic in an adult).

In children, respiratory movements are primarily abdominal; costal respiratory movements may indicate peritonitis, obstruction, or accumulation of ascitic fluid. The transition from abdominal to costal respirations is rather gradual.

To inspect an infant's abdomen, stand at the foot of the table and direct a light across his abdomen from his right side. Observe for peristaltic waves. (These waves normally progress unseen across an infant's abdomen from left to right during feeding.) Because peristaltic waves aren't normally visible in a full-term infant, their appearance probably indicates obstruction. Reverse peristalsis generally indicates pyloric stenosis; other possible causes include bowel malrotation, duodenal ulcer, gastrointestinal allergy, or duodenal stenosis.

Also observe a young child for diastasis recti abdominis (separation of the two abdominal recti muscles, with a protrusion between them). This benign condition is common, especially in black infants. A normal variation, it usually disappears during the preschool years. Inspect for umbilical hernia. The best time to perform this inspection is when the child cries. Also inspect the umbilicus for cleanliness and scar tissue.

Abdominal auscultation

Auscultate a child's abdomen as you would an adult's. Significant findings (and their possible implications) include:

- *abdominal murmur:* coarctation of the aorta
- *high-pitched bowel sounds:* impending intestinal obstruction or gastroenteritis
- *venous hum:* portal hypertension
- *splenic or hepatic friction rubs:* inflammation
- *double sound,* or so-called *pistol shot,* in the femoral artery: aortic insufficiency
- *absence of bowel sounds:* paralytic ileus and peritonitis.

Abdominal percussion

Because a child swallows a lot of air when he eats and cries, you may hear louder tympanic tones when you percuss his abdomen, compared with those in an adult. Minimal tympany with abdominal distention may result from fluid accumulation or solid masses. To test for abdominal fluid, use the test for shifting dullness, instead of the test for a fluid wave.

In a neonate, ascites usually results from gastrointestinal or urinary perforation; in an

older child, the cause may be heart failure, cirrhosis, or nephrosis.

Abdominal palpation

Because of the child's underdeveloped abdominal wall, you should find palpation easier than in an adult. This part of an abdominal examination is very subjective; be sure to gain the child's cooperation so he'll report his symptoms truthfully. Because children tend to be more ticklish and tense than adults, you may need to distract a child while you're examining him—perhaps by starting a discussion or asking him to count or say the alphabet. Sometimes you can get a preschool child to cooperate by playing a game ("Let me feel what you had for breakfast.") and ensure his continued cooperation with amusing guesses ("A watermelon? A box of candy?"). To relax an infant's abdomen, have him suck a pacifier (not a bottle of milk, which may cause regurgitation).

Abdominal guarding is more common in children than in adults when pain is present. Remember to palpate the painful quadrant last. To minimize ticklishness and let the child feel he has some control over the situation, you can palpate with the child's hand under your own, which can identify localized pain. This procedure isn't sufficiently sensitive, of course, to detect most palpable findings. Other clues to a child's pain include facial grimacing, sudden protective movement with an arm or leg, and a change in the pitch of the child's cry. Palpation in a quadrant other than the painful quadrant should reveal a soft, nontender abdomen. If it doesn't, the child is still tense. Try to relax him before proceeding or you're certain to evaluate inaccurately. A slightly tender descending colon may be caused by stool. Tenderness in the right lower quadrant may indicate an inflamed appendix. If your palpation consistently reveals generalized tenderness and rigidity in the affected quadrant, peritoneal irritation is probably present.

Next, ask the child to cough. A reduced or withheld cough may confirm peritoneal irritation, contraindicating checking for rebound tenderness—a potentially painful procedure for the child.

Check the child for a hernia as you would an adult. (To get a child to perform the Valsalva's maneuver, have him puff out his cheeks or blow up a balloon.)

Umbilical hernias are commonly present at birth. They usually increase in size until age 1 month and then gradually decrease until about age 1 year. An umbilical hernia may not always be visible. Here's a test: Press down on the infant's umbilicus. If you can insert one fingertip, the infant has a small hernia. Treatment usually consists of letting the hernia close by itself without surgery. Any hernia larger than ¾″ (2 cm) or one that increases in size after age 1 month requires further assessment. (Black children have a higher incidence of all types of hernias.)

In most infants with pyloric stenosis, pyloric tumors are palpable. (Palpation is easiest immediately after the infant vomits.) Stand at the infant's left side and palpate with the middle finger flexed at a right angle. You'll find a tumor about the size and shape of an olive deep between the edges of the rectus muscle and the costal margin on the right side.

A child's potbelly with a plastic feel to the abdominal masses indicates megacolon.

Geriatric assessment

Assessment techniques
Assessing an elderly patient's GI system is similar to examining the younger adult, with these differences: Abdominal palpation is usually easier and the results more accurate, because the elderly patient's abdominal wall is thinner (from muscle wasting and loss of fibroconnective tissue), and his muscle tone is usually more relaxed. A rigid abdomen, which in a younger patient may be from peritoneal inflammation, is less common in the elderly. Abdominal distention is more common.

Gastrointestinal disorders
Mouth disorders. Inspect carefully for limited movement or pain of the temperomandibular joint. These symptoms may indicate degenerative arthritis.

Pay particular attention to the elderly patient's teeth. Often you'll find loose teeth (from bone resorption that occurs in periodontal disease) or missing or replaced teeth. Because many elderly patients don't replace lost teeth, common problems in this age-group include

keratosis of the ridge, irritation, fibromas, and malocclusion. Mouth pathology is more common among the elderly for several reasons. For one, they are predisposed to mouth disorders by the normal physiology of the aging process. Other contributing factors include:
• physical disability (such as arthritis) that inhibits proper oral hygiene
• inadequate diet, resulting in nutritional deficiencies, which in elderly persons may initially produce gastrointestinal symptoms
• chronic systemic illnesses, especially diabetes mellitus
• chronic irritation from smoking or alcohol
• inadequate dental care because of insufficient income.

Pathologic changes that are more common in the elderly include oral carcinoma, dysplasia, atrophic glossitis, xerostomia (dry mouth), and denture-related fibrous hyperplasia.

Esophageal disturbances. Esophageal peristalsis may decrease with age, leading to delayed emptying, irritation, and dilatation, and producing signs and symptoms of gastric reflux. Ask the elderly patient about any burning sensation after meals, because gastric reflux is the most common cause of heartburn. Chest pain, the other major symptom of gastric reflux, is usually substernal and varies from mild discomfort to a severe stabbing sensation. Pain is usually associated with food intake and may be accentuated when the patient stoops or lies down; antacids usually relieve it. The pain from gastric reflux is difficult to differentiate from cardiac or hiatal hernia pain, and necessitates medical consultation.

Because dysphagia is characteristic of esophageal cancer (and the incidence of this disease rises with age), refer any elderly patient with this symptom to a doctor.

In the elderly, hiatal hernia is the most common upper gastrointestinal tract problem, affecting about 70% of persons over age 70. This condition commonly results from weakened musculature around the diaphragmatic hiatus that allows herniation of the lower esophagus and cardiac sphincter into the thorax. Signs and symptoms, including substernal pain, usually appear after periods of intraabdominal pressure. Be sure to ask the patient if his problems seem to occur following bending or straining, or even vomiting or coughing. Also assess for ascites and obesity, which also can increase intraabdominal pressure. Ask the patient if changing his body position relieves the symptoms, because many of these hernias are sliding hernias, which move into the thoracic cavity when the patient lies down and return to the abdominal cavity when he sits or stands up. Ask the patient how many pillows he uses when he sleeps. Patients with hiatal hernia or gastric reflux often use two or three pillows.

Stomach disturbances. Atrophic gastritis, a common stomach disorder among the elderly, is chronic inflammation of the stomach. It causes gradual mucosal degeneration, diminishing the number of parietal and chief cells. As a result, the gastric acid content of the stomach also decreases (achlorhydria), which can lead to malabsorption of calcium and iron. Loss of parietal cells decreases production of the intrinsic factor necessary for the absorption of vitamin B_{12}; this can cause pernicious anemia.

About 15% of the U.S. population over age 60 suffers from peptic ulcers. The incidence of complications from peptic ulcers and of associated mortality is also higher in the elderly population. Testing the stool for occult blood is a good screening device.

Problems of the small intestine. Decreased enzyme secretion, which begins at about age 40, can cause problems in elderly persons because of decreased nutrient absorption (chiefly carbohydrates) and delayed fat absorption (causing interference with absorption of fat-soluble vitamins). Diminished gastrointestinal tract motility and impaired blood flow to the small intestine can also impair nutrient absorption. Remember, however, that an inadequate diet commonly causes vitamin and other nutritional deficiencies.

Problems of the large intestine. Assess for *dehydration* in an elderly patient with inadequate water intake, excessive salt intake, or a GI disorder that disturbs water absorption in the large intestine (such as inflammation, diarrhea, and vomiting).

Atherosclerosis narrows abdominal blood vessels, compromising circulation to the colon. Pathology can range from irritation and diminished absorption to complete vascular occlusion and bowel obstruction.

Diverticulosis, which occurs often in the elderly, is the asymptomatic presence of diverticula—pouches that bulge through the weakened intestinal wall because of persistent high intraluminal pressure. Diverticulosis may progress to a symptomatic form *(diverticulitis)*, in which inflamed diverticula produce pain (in the lower left or middle abdomen), changed bowel habits, flatulence, and possibly bowel obstruction.

The elderly have the highest incidence of *colorectal cancer.* Some signs and symptoms such as constipation, diarrhea, and changes in bowel habits are typically vague and may be minimized by the patient.

Rectal polyps can affect the elderly; normally, they're soft and difficult to palpate.

Constipation is a common GI problem among the elderly. It may result from several factors, so be sure to ask the patient about the following points:
- overdependence on laxatives
- anorectal lesions
- low dietary fiber
- habitual disregard of the urge to defecate
- emotional upset or stress
- lack of exercise
- insufficient fluid intake
- use of drugs (such as some tranquilizers, antacids, and iron preparations).

Ask the patient if he has difficulty passing stool. (Some patients think constipation means a decrease in elimination frequency to a degree they consider abnormal.) Refer the patient to a doctor if his constipation continues after correction of the apparent cause.

Fecal incontinence occurs in many elderly patients and results from such conditions as changes in intestinal motility, loss of internal sphincter muscle tone, or compromise of voluntary and involuntary brain centers controlling defecation. In your patient history, include questions about the patient's mobility (immobility may prevent him from reaching the bathroom in time). Also rule out fecal impaction and rectal anomalies, such as painful fissures, as causes of fecal incontinence.

Liver and biliary system. Always assess an elderly patient for jaundice, which may indicate such causes of obstruction of the common bile duct as cancer of the head of the pancreas or cholelithiasis. Patients with cholelithiasis (a condition that affects more than one third of all persons between ages 70 and 80) usually complain of midepigastric pain 3 to 6 hours after a heavy or fatty meal.

Guide to Gastrointestinal Disorders

DISORDER	CHIEF COMPLAINT	
Achalasia (second-degree abnormal peristalsis or obstructed esophagogastric junction)	• *Pain:* usually absent • *Nausea/vomiting:* possible regurgitation of food eaten hours before, without acid taste • *Dysphagia:* progressive difficulty with both solids and liquids	
Aphthous stomatitis	• *Pain:* may be severe • *Nausea/vomiting:* absent • *Dysphagia:* may be present	
Appendicitis	• *Pain:* sudden epigastric or periumbilical pain; later localizes in right lower quadrant at McBurney's point • *Nausea/vomiting:* both may be present following pain • *Constipation/diarrhea:* diarrhea or, later, constipation	
Cholecystitis	• *Pain:* severe, cramping pain in epigastrium or right upper quadrant; may be referred to back of right scapula; onset sudden, but subsides after about 1 hour; followed by dull ache • *Nausea/vomiting:* both present • *Constipation/diarrhea:* absent	
Cirrhosis	• *Pain:* mild right upper quadrant pain; increasing as disease progresses • *Nausea/vomiting:* both present • *Constipation/diarrhea:* both present	
Colorectal cancer	• *Pain:* abdominal cramping pain in later stages • *Nausea/vomiting:* absent • *Constipation/diarrhea:* blood-streaked stools occur as early sign; pencil-thin stools possible; constipation alternating with diarrhea	
Crohn's disease	• *Pain:* cramping lower right quadrant pain • *Nausea/vomiting:* nausea present, but vomiting usually absent • *Constipation/diarrhea:* mild, urgent diarrhea	

HISTORY	PHYSICAL EXAMINATION	DIAGNOSTIC STUDIES
• Weight loss, slowed eating, coughing, wheezing, and choking are related signs and symptoms, aggravated by emotional stress.	• Physical signs absent	• Barium swallow shows narrowed distal end of esophagus; proximal dilatation and fluid appear high in esophagus; biopsy and cytology done to exclude cancer.
• Stress, fatigue, anxiety, and menstruation are predisposing factors; common in young girls.	• Single or multiple shallow ulcers with white centers and red borders	• None pertinent
• Sudden onset of symptoms	• Mild fever, pain increases with right thigh extension, abdominal rigidity in right lower quadrant, rebound tenderness	• White blood cell count elevated; X-ray may show local distention.
• Fatty food intolerance, indigestion, flatulence, and belching are related signs and symptoms; most common in obese multiparous women over age 40	• Fever, abdominal tenderness in right upper quadrant, abdominal rigidity and guarding, palpable liver, palpable gallbladder, possibly jaundice, elevated pulse	• Cholecystography and ultrasound detect calculi; white blood cell count may be elevated; serum alkaline phosphatase and bilirubin levels may be elevated.
• Alcoholism, hepatitis, heart failure, and hemochromatosis are predisposing factors; malaise, fatigue, anorexia leading to weight loss, pruritus, dark urine, and bleeding tendencies are related symptoms.	• Palpable liver and possibly spleen, jaundice, spider angioma, peripheral edema; in progressive stages, ascites	• Liver biopsy provides definitive diagnosis; serum glutamic-oxaloacetic transaminase (SGOT), serum glutamic-pyruvic transaminase (SGPT), and lactate dehydrogenase (LDH) levels elevated; serum alkaline phosphatase and bilirubin levels elevated, reflecting liver damage; prothrombin time and partial thromboplastin times may be prolonged.
• Family history of cancer, polyposis, history of ulcerative colitis are predisposing factors; malaise and loss of appetite are related signs and symptoms.	• Weight loss; digital rectal examination may reveal palpable mass	• Sigmoidoscopy, colonoscopy, and barium enema visualize tumor; biopsy reveals cancer cells.
• Family history of disease and emotional stress are predisposing factors; flatulence, weight loss, weak-	• Low-grade fever; abdominal tenderness; possible mass in right lower quadrant	• Leukocytosis; sigmoidoscopy usually negative; barium enema shows string sign (segments of stricture *(continued)*

Guide to Gastrointestinal Disorders *(continued)*

DISORDER	CHIEF COMPLAINT	
Crohn's disease *(continued)*		
Diverticular disease (diverticulitis)	• *Pain:* occasional lower left quadrant pain • *Nausea/vomiting:* mild nausea present, but vomiting usually absent • *Constipation/diarrhea:* constipation more common than diarrhea; occurs with onset of pain	
Esophageal cancer	• *Pain:* may be present under sternum, or in back or neck; progresses with advancing disease • *Nausea/vomiting:* present in late stages • *Dysphagia:* difficulty with solids, progressive difficulty with liquids	
Esophagitis	• *Pain:* heartburn 1 hour after eating; aggravated by bending over, lying down, or straining; relieved by drinking or standing; pain may radiate to neck, arms, or jaws • *Nausea/vomiting:* possible nocturnal regurgitation into mouth • *Dysphagia:* intermittent	
Gastritis (acute and chronic)	• *Pain:* epigastric pain slightly left of midline; indigestion • *Nausea/vomiting:* if both present, hematemesis may occur • *Constipation/diarrhea:* melena; diarrhea may occur	
Gingivitis	• *Pain:* may be present • *Nausea/vomiting:* absent • *Dysphagia:* usually absent	
Glossitis	• *Pain:* usually present; may be severe • *Nausea/vomiting:* absent • *Dysphagia:* usually present	
Hemorrhoids	• *Pain:* occasional pain on defecation; sudden, severe pain, if thrombosed	

HISTORY	PHYSICAL EXAMINATION	DIAGNOSTIC STUDIES
ness, and malaise are related signs and symptoms		separated by normal bowel); biopsy confirms diagnosis.
• Long-term diet low in roughage and fiber is a predisposing factor.	• Low-grade fever; in severe disease, abdominal tenderness	• Leukocytosis; flat plate abdominal view shows free air with perforation; barium enema visualizes diverticula.
• Rapid weight loss and substernal burning after drinking hot fluids are related signs and symptoms.	• Cachexia, frequent coughing	• Cytology shows cancer cells; barium swallow outlines tumor obstruction with irregular lesion; esophagoscopy visualizes lesion.
• Hematemesis, melena, frequent eructation, increasing salivation, and nocturnal coughing are related signs and symptoms, aggravated by lying down.	• Physical signs usually absent	• Esophagoscopy shows eroded or ulcerated mucosa; cineroentgenography of esophagus with barium swallow shows weak peristalsis and failure of sphincter to relax.
• Drug or chemical irritation, ingestion of irritating foods, alcoholism, pernicious anemia, severe stress, burns, surgery, trauma, and sepsis are predisposing factors.	• Abdominal tenderness	• Fiberoptic endoscopy; mild leukocytosis; biopsy performed to diagnose chronic condition.
• Local irritation, blood dyscrasias, little or no gingival stimulation, mouth breathing, and pregnancy are predisposing factors; most common during puberty.	• Gingival swelling, redness, bleeding, change in normal contour	• None pertinent
• Irritation, injury, poorly fitting or improperly fitted dentures, alcoholism, tobacco smoking, diet of spicy foods, allergy to toothpastes and mouthwashes are predisposing factors; difficulty in speaking and chewing and changes in taste are related signs.	• Reddened, ulcerated, or swollen tongue; swelling may obstruct airway	• None pertinent
• Prolonged sitting and multiple pregnancies are pre-	• External hemorrhoids	• Proctoscopic examination visualizes internal hemorrhoids.

(continued) |

Guide to Gastrointestinal Disorders *(continued)*

DISORDER	CHIEF COMPLAINT	
Hemorrhoids *(continued)*	• *Nausea/vomiting:* absent • *Constipation/diarrhea:* absent	
Herpes simplex, primary (herpes simplex Type 1 virus)	• *Pain:* may be severe • *Nausea/vomiting:* absent • *Dysphagia:* may be present	
Hiatal hernia	• *Pain:* usually absent; occasional heartburn (gastroesophageal reflux); severe pain if incarcerated • *Nausea/vomiting:* nocturnal regurgitation, aggravated by lying down, relieved by standing • *Dysphagia:* if hernia produces esophagitis, esophageal ulceration or stricture	
Intestinal obstruction	• *Pain:* colicky abdominal pain in epigastric or periumbilical area; in distal colon obstruction, pain referred to lumbar spine area • *Nausea/vomiting:* in high obstruction, present; in large bowel obstruction, vomiting usually absent • *Constipation/diarrhea:* in complete obstruction: constipation; in partial obstruction (by tumor): pencil-thin stools; in obstruction caused by adhesions: diarrhea possible	
Necrotizing ulcerative gingivostomatitis (Vincent's disease, trench mouth)	• *Pain:* may be severe enough to interfere with eating • *Nausea/vomiting:* absent • *Dysphagia:* may be severe	
Oral cancer	• *Pain:* usually absent; presence depends on location, degree of invasion, and pressure on surrounding tissue • *Nausea/vomiting:* absent • *Dysphagia:* usually present only in advanced stages	
Pancreatitis (acute and chronic)	• *Pain:* constant epigastric pain; may radiate to back; pain worsened by lying down • *Nausea/vomiting:* both present with bilious vomiting • *Constipation/diarrhea:* absent	

HISTORY	PHYSICAL EXAMINATION	DIAGNOSTIC STUDIES
disposing factors.		
• Irritability, headache, and fever are related symptoms; most common in children.	• Multiple vesicles that ulcerate rapidly, forming yellow-white ulcers with red halos; lesions may appear on gingival, labial, or buccal mucosa	• Confirmation requires isolation of the virus from local lesions, histologic biopsy, and serologic tests.
• Increased intraabdominal pressure, caused by straining, obesity, ascites, or coughing, is a predisposing factor; most common in elderly women.	• Physical signs absent	• Barium swallow shows pouching in lower esophagus.
• Family history of cancer is a predisposing factor; weight loss and weakness are related signs and symptoms.	• Abdominal distention and tenderness; paralytic ileus with absent bowel sounds; low-grade fever; possible palpable mass	• Leukocytosis; X-ray shows distention; sigmoidoscopy and colonoscopy visualize obstruction; small intestine X-ray shows stepladder fluid and gas distribution.
• Poor oral hygiene, lowered resistance, agranulocytosis, and leukemia are possible predisposing factors; headache and malaise are related symptoms; most common in men ages 20 to 25.	• Ulcerative erosion of gingival papillae, gray pseudomembrane oval covering, low-grade fever, regional lymphadenitis	• Culture may reveal fusiform bacillus or spirochete.
• Smoking or chewing tobacco, overexposure to sunlight, and alcoholism are predisposing factors; most common in men over age	• Early lesions are white with varying texture, or red, soft, and smooth; ulcerating cancer has raised, firm, and fixed margins; may bleed	• Biopsy provides differential diagnosis.
• Alcoholism, previous cholelithiasis, peptic ulcer, and use of drugs, such as azathioprine, are predisposing factors; pain aggravated by food or alcohol ingestion and restlessness are related symptoms.	• Mild fever, tachycardia, hypotension, abdominal distention, decreased bowel sounds, abdominal tenderness, and, if severe, abdominal rigidity and rales at lung base	• Serum amylase level elevated; marked leukocytosis; serum calcium level decreased; hyperglycemia; X-rays show distortion or edema of duodenal loop or calcification of pancreas.

(continued)

Guide to Gastrointestinal Disorders *(continued)*

DISORDER	CHIEF COMPLAINT	
Peptic ulcer	• *Pain:* gnawing, burning pain more than 1 hour after eating; described as a feeling of nausea or hunger; relieved by eating; gastric ulcers may cause pain immediately after eating	
Periodontitis	• *Pain:* usually absent at first; later, slightly painful around teeth's supporting area; if abscess develops, severe local pain may occur • *Nausea/vomiting:* absent • *Dysphagia:* usually absent	
Peritonitis	• *Pain:* sudden, severe abdominal pain • *Nausea/vomiting:* both present • *Constipation/diarrhea:* inability to pass flatus or feces	
Ulcerative colitis	• *Pain:* cramping abdominal pain • *Nausea/vomiting:* both present • *Constipation/diarrhea:* profuse, episodic, bloody diarrhea with mucus possible	
Upper gastrointestinal (GI) bleeding (secondary)	• *Pain:* present; in ulcer disease, usually relieved by bleeding • *Nausea/vomiting:* vomiting present; bright red from acute bleeding; dark red suggests past bleeding • *Constipation/diarrhea:* bloody diarrhea with acute GI hemorrhage; melena with chronic upper GI bleeding	
Viral hepatitis, Type A and Type B	• *Pain:* mild, constant pain in right upper quadrant • *Nausea/vomiting:* nausea present; vomiting may be present • *Constipation/diarrhea:* clay-colored stool may be present	

HISTORY	PHYSICAL EXAMINATION	DIAGNOSTIC STUDIES
• Emotional stress and drugs irritating to gastrointestinal (GI) tract are possible predisposing factors; signs and symptoms occur in clusters, then subside and later recur.	• Abdominal tenderness	• Upper GI series: crater easily visualized; endoscopy performed to confirm diagnosis; biopsy performed to rule out cancer; serum gastrin level elevated.
• Uncontrolled diabetes, blood dyscrasias, pregnancy, traumatic irritation, and poor oral hygiene are predisposing factors; most common in pubescent females.	• Gingival recession; periodontal pocket containing food, bacteria, calculi; tenderness on percussion; teeth mobility in advanced stage	• Dental X-ray shows destruction of supporting osseous tissues; biopsy provides differential diagnosis.
• Abdominal distress, abdominal surgery, and traumatic abdominal injury are predisposing factors.	• Fever; abdominal rigidity; pallor; sweating; hypotension; thirst; tachycardia, shallow respirations; decreased bowel sounds; paralytic ileus causes resonance and tympany; rebound tenderness	• Leukocytosis; abdominal X-ray shows free gas and fluid in abdomen; paracentesis reveals cause.
• Family history of disease and emotional stress are predisposing factors; weight loss and anorexia are related signs.	• Low-grade fever; abdominal tenderness	• Leukocytosis; electrolyte imbalance; anemia; increased erythrocyte sedimentation rate; sigmoidoscopy shows increased friability and pus, mucus, and blood; barium enema shows extent of disease.
• Prior ulcer disease, alcoholism, and abuse of certain drugs, such as inflammatory agents, are predisposing factors.	• Weakness, fainting, orthostatic changes in blood pressure, tachycardia, diaphoresis	• Hemoglobin and hematocrit measured to evaluate extent and type (acute or chronic) of blood loss; prothrombin time measured to determine clotting problems.
• *Type A:* Contaminated food or water and contact with infected person are predisposing factors; *Type B:* usually transmitted parenterally but also through contact with infected secretions; headache, cough, coryza, loss of appetite, aversion to	• Fever, chills, abdominal tenderness in right upper quadrant; in second stage: hepatomegaly, jaundice, and possibly splenomegaly and cervical adenopathy	• Serum glutamic-oxaloacetic transaminase (SGOT) and serum glutamic-pyruvic transaminase (SGPT) levels elevated; bilirubin level elevated; prolonged prothrombin time indicates impending hepatic failure; serum alkaline phos-

(continued)

Guide to Gastrointestinal Disorders (continued)

DISORDER	CHIEF COMPLAINT	
Viral hepatitis, Type A and Type B (continued)		
Zenker's diverticulum (pulsion-type diverticulum)	● *Pain:* scratchy throat ● *Nausea/vomiting:* regurgitation of food partially digested or eaten the day before ● *Dysphagia:* intermittent; progresses with continued eating	

HISTORY	PHYSICAL EXAMINATION	DIAGNOSTIC STUDIES
smoking, fatigue, arthralgia, myalgia are related symptoms.		phatase level slightly elevated; serum albumin level low; serum globulin level elevated; antibody to hepatitis A virus (antiHAV) confirms hepatitis A; hepatitis B surface antigens (HB_sAg) and hepatitis B antibodies (antiHB) confirm hepatitis B.
• Nocturnal coughing, halitosis, and weight loss are related signs and symptoms.	• Protrusion on neck	• Barium swallow shows pouching in upper esophagus; esophagoscopy performed to rule out other problems.

12

Urinary System

The body's systems depend on the kidneys to maintain homeostasis. In turn, the kidneys depend on other body systems for the same critical purpose. The kidneys are coordinated with the *nervous system,* which helps regulate blood pressure and control urination; with the *endocrine system,* which maintains sodium and water balance by producing aldosterone and antidiuretic hormone; and with the *musculoskeletal system,* which relies on the kidneys for vitamin D synthesis.

These are just a few examples of the kidneys' importance to a person's overall health and ability to function. Remember, you may uncover clues to possible problems in *any body system* when you assess a patient's renal system. So remain alert to the kidneys' vital homeostatic role every time you assess a patient.

History data

Biographical data

When you collect biographical data, pay particular attention to age and race. Age is significant because the signs and symptoms of some renal diseases are more common in certain age-groups. For instance, polycystic kidney disease, which can remain dormant for years, usually manifests its first signs and symptoms in persons between ages 40 and 60. Race is also related to the incidence of some renal diseases; for example, malignant hypertension, which can lead to nephrosclerosis and renal failure, is most prevalent in blacks.

History of present illness

The most common chief complaints regarding urinary disorders are *output changes* (polyuria, oliguria, anuria), *voiding pattern changes* (frequency, urgency, nocturia), *urine color changes,* and *pain* (suprapubic pain, flank pain, dysuria). (See *Guide to Urinary Disorders,* pages 256 to 261.)

Here are some questions you may want to ask about these complaints to explore fully the history of your patient's present illness:

● **Output changes.** *Have you noticed a change in the amount of urine excreted? How often do you have this problem? Does it occur only if you drink a lot of fluids?* Always compare intake and output before considering a patient's output abnormal.

● **Voiding pattern changes.** *How many times a day do you usually urinate? Recently, how many times a day have you been urinating? Have you noticed a change in the size of your urine stream? Does your bladder still feel full after you've urinated? Do you urinate small amounts frequently? Do you wake up during the night to urinate? Are you unable to wait to urinate? Do you have a problem controlling your urine?* Most voiding pattern changes suggest bladder dysfunction or an infectious process. In an edematous patient on bed rest, nocturia may result from rapid fluid reabsorption.

● **Urine color changes.** *What color is your urine? How long has it been this color?* A dark amber color may indicate concentrated urine, usually associated with diminished volume. A clear, watery appearance may indicate dilute urine, associated with increased volume. Brown or bright-red urine may contain blood. Other color variations may result from taking certain medications.

● **Pain.** *Do you ever have pain when trying to urinate? Do you ever feel a burning sensation when urinating? How often?* Painful spasms during urination suggest calculi. Dysuria described as a burning sensation usually indicates a disorder of the lower urinary tract. *Do you have painful distention of your abdomen? Do you have pain over the pubic area or in your lower back? Is the pain dull or sharp? Does repositioning relieve suprapubic or flank pain?* Position changes don't relieve pain from renal colic, but lying down does reduce inflammatory pain.

Past history

Focus your past history questions on the following areas:

- **Kidney or bladder problems.** Kidney and bladder stones tend to recur.
- **Systemic diseases.** Signs and symptoms of diabetic nephropathy—hypertension, edema, and azotemia—may appear 10 to 15 years after onset of diabetes mellitus. Urinary symptoms of systemic lupus erythematosus (SLE), such as nephritis, may appear at onset or later. (SLE may also produce recurrent swelling that's characteristic of the nephrotic syndrome.) Tuberculosis may reach the urinary tract; disseminated intravascular coagulation can lead to severe renal perfusion problems; and hepatic disease can occur with renal failure.
- **Nerve damage.** In multiple sclerosis, demyelination can affect bladder musculature, causing urinary hesitancy and chronic urinary tract infections.
- **Sexually transmitted disease.** Gonorrhea causes urinary tract problems (discharge, dysuria, urgency, and frequency) that may be the first indications of the disease.
- **Streptococcal infection.** A recent episode of streptococcal infection increases a patient's risk of glomerulonephritis.
- **Allergies.** Some immune complex reactions (to foods, insects, drugs, or contrast media, for example) can cause tubular damage; severe anaphylactic reactions can produce temporary renal failure and permanent tubular necrosis.
- **Medications.** Many drugs can produce signs and symptoms of urinary disorders. So be sure to check a reliable source for possible urinary side effects of your patient's medications.
- **Urinary tract surgery.** Be sure to ask your patient whether he's ever had surgery for a urinary disorder. If so, ask how long ago it was performed.

Family and psychosocial history

Ask your patient if anyone in his family has ever had any of the following conditions:

- **Noninherited renal disorders.** Although they're not hereditary, such disorders as urinary tract infections, congenital anomalies, and urinary calculi recur in some families.
- **Hereditary renal diseases.** Polycystic kidney disease and all types of hereditary nephritis (such as Alport's syndrome) are genetically transmitted conditions that can progress to end-stage renal disease.
- **Inheritable systemic diseases.** Hypertension and diabetes mellitus can eventually cause nephropathies.

An occupation or activity may keep a person so busy he can't (or won't) take time to urinate when he feels the urge. This can predispose him to bladder or urinary tract infections.

Activities of daily living

When questioning your patient about his daily activities, concentrate on the following areas:

- **Diet.** Learning about your patient's diet may provide valuable information. As the patient describes his usual diet, determine if he takes in an adequate amount of fluid, salt, and protein. Ask if he's on a special diet and, if so, whether a doctor prescribed it. (Prolonged reducing diets involving liquid protein are associated with kidney dysfunction.) Special diets for renal patients include sodium, potassium, protein, and fluid restrictions.
- **Sleeping.** Disturbed sleep from nocturnal muscle cramps of the calves and thighs is common in early renal failure. A reversal in sleep patterns (awake at night, asleep during the day) is also a symptom of renal failure.

Review of systems

Your review of systems should include questions about the following signs and symptoms:

- **Skin.** Itchy skin may indicate calcium or uremic deposits.
- **Cardiovascular.** Hypertension may result from renal disease or predispose a person to it. Shortness of breath, paroxysmal nocturnal dyspnea, orthopnea, and edema may indicate kidney disease. Sudden weight change may result from an altered water balance.

Assessing Fluid Status

To assess your patient's fluid status, weigh him daily at the same time, using the same scale. He should wear the same type of clothing. If maintaining these constants isn't possible, document whatever's different about each weigh-in. Measure and compare intake and output daily, and report changes in output. Because of insensible loss from skin and lungs, output should equal only about two thirds of intake over 24 hours. The normal hourly output is 30 to 100 ml; normal 24-hour output, 720 to 2,400 ml. When measuring output, be sure to consider fluid loss from diarrhea, vomiting, fever, or wound drainage. Use daily intake-output records and weights to validate each other. One ml of water weighs 1 g, so if a patient's intake exceeds his output by 1,000 ml in 24 hours, his weight should increase by about 1 kg. If his output exceeds his intake, the negative fluid balance should produce weight loss.

• **Gastrointestinal.** A metallic taste or urinous breath odor (uremic fetor) may indicate diminished renal function. Anorexia, nausea, and vomiting may accompany any stage of renal dysfunction.
• **Musculoskeletal.** Weakness and lethargy may indicate neuropathy or anemia caused by renal insufficiency.
• **Neurologic.** Progressive renal failure can cause increased intracranial pressure, headaches, fasciculations, asterixis (flapping tremor), seizures, or coma.
• **Psychologic.** Extreme behavior changes, such as agitated depression, delusions, and psychosis, can occur in a patient with renal failure.

Physical examination

General physical status
Begin the examination by weighing the patient and comparing the result with a baseline figure, if available. Significant weight gain or loss within 24 to 48 hours indicates a change in fluid status, not body mass. Weight monitoring is especially valuable during hospitaliza-

tion of patients with urinary disorders (see *Assessing Fluid Status*).

Observe the patient's position and movements, noting any abnormalities. For example, a patient who can't lie flat in bed may be suffering from severe respiratory distress, as in acute pulmonary edema, which can coexist with primary renal failure. Such a patient may sit with his arms extended in front of him, perhaps resting them on his overbed table. The patient who keeps changing position, attempting to relieve severe stabbing flank pain, may have renal colic.

Monitor the patient's vital signs. Measure blood pressure in both arms for comparison. Also take blood pressure readings with the patient lying down and sitting up. If blood pressure drops severely when the patient sits up, he may have volume depletion. Fever may suggest an acute urinary tract infection. Tachycardia with systolic hypotension is a sign of shock and demands immediate intervention. Mild tachycardia and normal or slightly elevated blood pressure suggest fluid overload. Pulse irregularities, such as bradycardia or other arrhythmias, may indicate potassium imbalance. The rate and character of respiration also may be altered by severe electrolyte imbalance. For example, Kussmaul's respiration suggests severe acidosis or right heart failure secondary to renal insufficiency. Severe hypotension (systolic pressure less than 90 mmHg) and severe hypertension (diastolic pressure greater than 120 mmHg) are ominous signs. Sustained severe hypotension (systolic pressure less than 70 mmHg) results in diminished renal blood flow and may produce acute renal failure.

Hypertension can cause renal insufficiency and can also result from vascular damage caused by a primary renal disorder.

Mental status
Evaluate your patient's general appearance and behavior. Then check his motor activity; orientation to person, place, and time; and memory of the immediate past. Renal dysfunction may cause an inability to concentrate and loss of recent memory. Chronic, progressive renal failure can lead to toxin accumulation and electrolyte imbalance, producing neurologic signs and symptoms, such as lethargy, con-

fusion, disorientation, stupor, somnolence, coma, and convulsions.

Internal eye examination

Perform an internal eye examination, especially if your patient has malignant hypertension, because renal vascular changes parallel retinal arteriolar changes (see pages 121 to 123). Hypertension may result from kidney disease or cause urinary symptoms by compromising renal microcirculation. Thickened retinal arteriolar walls with small areas of infarction or hemorrhage indicate damage to the intimal layer of the retinal vessels. An internal eye examination may also reveal papilledema; cottonwool patches from edema; and dilated, tortuous veins. Reddened conjunctivae due to calcium deposits may result from chronic renal failure.

Skin, hair, and nails

Inspect your patient's skin color for anemic pallor and for the yellow-tan coloration that results from retained urochrome pigment. Pallor results from a normocytic, normochromic anemia that gradually worsens as the kidneys fail. End-stage renal failure results in reduced erythropoietin production that in turn causes decreased red blood cell production. Also, uremic toxins shorten the life span of red blood cells.

Inspect the patient's skin for large bruises and for purpura, both characteristic of clotting abnormalities and decreased platelet adhesion from chronic renal failure. Check also for uremic frost (white or yellow urate crystals on the skin), which indicates a late stage of renal failure. Then note his skin integrity and observe for possible secondary infection, because a patient with chronic renal disease is more susceptible to infections.

Assess your patient's hydration by inspecting the mucous membranes in his mouth. A dry mucosa indicates mild dehydration; parched, cracked lips with a very dry mucosa and sunken eyes suggest severe dehydration. Then inspect the patient's skin for dryness and scratches, because renal failure causes sweat and oil glands to atrophy and results in subcutaneous calcium deposits. In a patient with long-standing renal failure, the scratches from itching may be severe. Next, evaluate his skin turgor. If the skin doesn't return to its normal shape immediately—and your patient isn't old and hasn't recently lost weight—dehydration is advanced.

Inspect your patient's neck veins for distention. Dependent edema (ankle, sacral, and scrotal) or total body edema (periorbital, abdominal, and pulmonary), together with distended neck veins, indicate fluid overload (see *Peripheral Edema Test*, page 250).

Examine your patient's hair for dryness and hair loss and his nails for thinness and brittleness. Then check for anemia by pressing two or more of the patient's fingernails; the normal pink color should return immediately after blanching. If capillary refill is delayed and the patient's skin is cool and clammy, he may have circulatory insufficiency and peripheral vasoconstriction from dehydration.

Chest and abdominal assessment

When examining your patient's chest and abdomen for signs and symptoms of kidney disorders, use the same basic preparatory procedures used for cardiorespiratory and GI assessment.

Observe the patient's chest for symmetrical expansion and possible retractions. Auscultate all lung fields for rales and rhonchi, which suggest fluid overload. Then note the patient's cardiac rate and rhythm and the quality of his heart sounds. (Remember that fluid overload may obscure normal heart and breath sounds.) Changes in heart rate and rhythm without underlying cardiac disease may indicate that the patient has severe fluid or electrolyte imbalance (especially of calcium or potassium). A gallop rhythm suggests fluid overload; a systolic murmur may indicate anemia from renal failure.

Examine the patient's abdomen for indications of fluid retention—distention, tight and glistening skin, and umbilical protrusion. Note any striae—a sign of rapid skin stretching. Note and inquire about any surgical scars not mentioned in your patient's history. If you suspect ascites, perform the fluid wave test (see page 229). If the patient has an ileal loop diversion or ureterostomy, remove the collection bag and inspect the site. Usually, you'll see immediate urine production and a cherry-red stoma. Note any irritation or excoriation of the surrounding skin—usually an indica-

Peripheral Edema Test

Here's how to test for peripheral edema: Press a finger against the suspected edematous area for 5 seconds. Then, remove your finger quickly and completely. If edema's present, the skin won't rebound to its original contour right away. Instead, you'll notice a small depression, or pit, in the skin. Measure the pit with a scale approved by your hospital. Here's how to use one widely accepted system, the four-point scale: Record a barely perceptible pit, like the one shown on the left, as + 1. Record a deep pit like the one on the right, which takes over 30 seconds to rebound, as + 4.

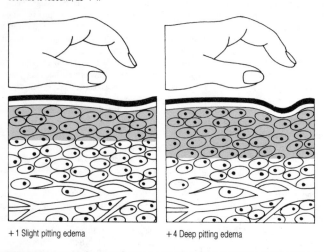

+ 1 Slight pitting edema   + 4 Deep pitting edema

tion of a poorly fitted appliance or inadequate care.

Kidney examination

Palpate the patient's kidneys for size and tenderness. The kidneys lie behind other organs, protected by muscle—so unless they're enlarged, they may not be palpable. If the patient is very thin, you may feel the lower pole of the right one and, rarely, the tip of the left. Remember that excessive pressure on a kidney can cause your patient intense pain.

To perform bimanual deep palpation of the right kidney, stand at the patient's right side and elevate his right flank with your left hand (see *Kidney Palpation and Percussion,* page 251). Then place your right hand below the costal margin, with your fingers facing left. Ask your patient to breathe in deeply, so you can palpate the abdominal tissues. When he

releases his breath, release the pressure and you may feel the right kidney's lower pole move back into place. To palpate the left kidney, reach across the patient's abdomen and repeat this technique, using your left hand to support the left flank and your right hand to palpate.

Next, use blunt percussion to evaluate kidney tenderness. Ask your patient to sit or—if he can't sit—to lie on his side. Then, place one palm over the costovertebral angle, between the spine and 12th rib, and strike lightly with your fist. The spleen's sound is dull; the kidney's is resonant.

Usually, you can help a patient localize mild or vague back pain by percussing bilaterally or pressing one finger into the soft tissue of the costovertebral angle. Be sure to ask if the pain radiates to the groin or labia (or scrotum). If percussion elicits tenderness, suspect

Kidney Palpation and Percussion

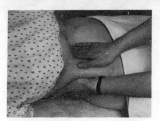 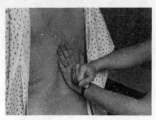

1 To bimanually palpate your patient's kidneys, follow the technique shown here. If palpable, note each kidney's contour and size. Also, check for lumps and masses.
2 To check for kidney tenderness, use fist percussion, as shown here. Alert your patient before you percuss. Otherwise, you may startle him, causing a reaction similar to that associated with acute tenderness.

kidney, liver, or gallbladder inflammation. Suprapubic or low back pain suggests simple cystitis.

Now, using the bell of your stethoscope, try to auscultate the renal arteries. This is especially important if the patient is hypertensive. Listen in the periumbilical region for bruits, which are characteristic of renal artery stenosis.

The bladder and genitalia

Inspect the contour of your patient's lower abdomen for bladder distention. Then palpate and percuss the area, starting at the umbilicus and proceeding toward the symphysis (see *Bladder Examination,* page 252). If the bladder is normal, you won't feel it. A slightly dull percussion note above the symphysis indicates mild distention. On palpation, a smooth, rounded, fluctuant suprapubic mass suggests severe distention; a fluctuant mass extending to the umbilicus indicates extreme distention. (Remember that palpation and percussion usually stimulate the micturition reflex.)

Check the patient's genitalia for swelling from localized edema. Also observe him for such signs and symptoms of obstruction as dribbling, frequency, or urgency. In an adult male patient, these problems indicate the need for examination for prostatic enlargement (see pages 267 and 268).

Assessing the extremities

Examine the patient's legs and ankles for edema by pressing your fingers against his lower tibia (see *Peripheral Edema Test*). Also check for arm and leg pain and limited range of motion, because chronic renal insufficiency can lead to osteodystrophy as a result of hyperparathyroidism and changes in calcium metabolism.

Laboratory tests

Laboratory tests and radiography are regularly used to confirm the cause of a patient's renal problems. The simplest (and perhaps most informative) laboratory test is routine urinalysis, which measures pH and specific gravity and also tests for protein, glucose, blood, and bacteria (see *Evaluating Urine Color,* page 253). The pH is a measure of the body's acid-base balance; when renal tubular absorption is impaired, pH is low (acidic). Specific gravity (or the solute-solvent ratio) indicates the kidneys' ability to dilute or concentrate urine.

Glycosuria, in the presence of normal serum glucose levels, indicates impaired proximal tubular reabsorption. This condition may appear with chronic renal insufficiency or primary tubular defect. Transient proteinuria may result from febrile illness or strenuous exercise, but persistent proteinuria suggests significant glomerular disease and indicates the need for quantitation of a 24-hour urine specimen. Uri-

Bladder Examination

 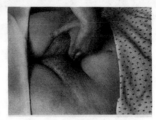

1 Percuss the area over the bladder, starting 2″ (5 cm) above the symphysis pubis. Continue percussion, moving downward. You'll hear a tympanic sound if the bladder is normal. If you hear a dull sound, the bladder may be retaining urine.
2 Palpate your patient's bladder bimanually, beginning midline about 1″ to 2″ (2.5 to 5 cm) above the symphysis pubis, as shown here. Continue palpating until you locate the edge of the bladder, which normally is not accessible when empty.

nalysis may also show gross or microscopic hematuria. Pyuria can appear with some non-bacterial inflammatory diseases, but a large number of white cells with bacteria probably indicates urinary tract infection (a culture is required for confirmation).

The most accurate and clinically practical laboratory measure of kidney function is the glomerular filtration rate, which represents the amount of blood filtered per minute (cc/minute). This test measures serum creatinine levels in a blood sample drawn during a timed urine collection (usually a period of 4 to 72 hours).

Additional laboratory tests include measurements of hemoglobin and hematocrit—which are usually low in chronic renal disease. Depending on the type and severity of the patient's disease, blood chemistries show changes in serum electrolytes (including potassium, sodium, chloride, and bicarbonate ions), blood urea nitrogen (BUN), creatinine, calcium, and phosphorus. BUN and creatinine are routinely measured to screen for kidney disease.

Pediatric assessment

Anatomy and physiology

A newborn infant's kidneys are anatomically and functionally immature. Their glomerular filtration rate and ability to concentrate urine and excrete acid, as well as their tubular reabsorption of sodium, are less than those of adult kidneys. Generally, a child's kidneys become functionally mature between ages 6 months and 1 year, although creatinine clearance (dependent on lean muscle mass), normal serum creatinine, and urinary output per kilogram of body weight (.50 to .75 cc/kg of body weight/hour) are lower than in an adult. Lack of perirenal fat increases the immature kidneys' vulnerability to traumatic injury. A normal child develops the physiologic ability to control urination between ages 2 and 3.

Pediatric history questions

Ask your patient's mother about problems during pregnancy and delivery that may be associated with urinary tract malformations. Inquire about congenital anomalies: low-set, malformed ears; chromosomal disorders, such as trisomy D and E; imperforate anus; or a single umbilical artery. A history of an imperforate anus associated with fistula development or spina bifida also makes a child more susceptible to infection because of impaired innervation.

Other history considerations include delayed growth and development, feeding problems, vomiting, unexplained fevers, colic

Evaluating Urine Color

APPEARANCE	POSSIBLE CAUSES
Colorless or straw-colored (diluted urine)	• Excessive fluid intake, chronic renal disease, diabetes insipidus, nervous conditions
Dark yellow or amber (concentrated urine)	• Low fluid intake, acute febrile disease, vomiting, diarrhea
Cloudy	• Infection, purulence, blood, epithelial cells, fat, colloidal particles, urates, vegetarian diet, parasitic disease
Yellow to amber, with pink sediment	• Hyperuricemia, gout
Orange-red to orange-brown	• Urobilinuria, such drugs as phenazopyridine (Pyridium), obstructive jaundice (tea-colored)
Red or red-brown	• Porphyria, hemoglobin, erythrocytes, hemorrhage, such drugs as pyrvinium pamoate (Povan)
Green-brown	• Bile duct obstruction, phenol poisoning
Dark brown or black	• Acute glomerulonephritis, chorea, typhus, methylene blue medication
Smoky	• Prostatic fluid, fat droplets, blood, chyle, spermatozoa

associated with voiding, and persistent enuresis after age 5. Bladder or urethral irritation or an emotional problem can cause bedwetting.

Also ask the parent about the child's urinary stream—its color, odor, frequency, and amount. If the child is very young, ask if his diaper is soaked or barely wet, or bloodstained, when the parent changes it. Also ask how many times a day the child's diaper must be changed.

Finally, determine if the child has had pharyngitis or a skin infection, such as impetigo, in the past 3 weeks. These conditions can cause acute poststreptococcal glomerulonephritis.

Examination techniques

Take the child's blood pressure using an appropriate-sized cuff. Inspect his skin for anemic pallor, which may indicate a congenital renal disorder, such as medullary cystic disease. Also inspect for anomalies associated with congenital urinary tract malformations: low-set or malformed ears, absence of abdominal musculature, undescended testes, and inguinal hernia.

Palpate the child's abdomen carefully for bladder distention and kidney enlargement. Remember, you'll probably be able to palpate and percuss an infant's bladder at the umbilical level. Bladder distention in an older child may indicate urethral dysfunction or a central nervous system defect. Unless a child has ascites, you'll be able to palpate his kidneys more easily than in an adult, so always try to feel the kidneys to detect enlargement. In a preschool-age child, a firm, smooth, and palpable mass adjacent to the vertebral column—but not crossing the midline—suggests Wilms' tumor. If you detect such a mass, avoid further deep palpation and refer the patient immediately for additional evaluation.

Next, inspect the patient's external genitalia closely for abnormalities associated with congenital anomalies of the urinary tract. A child may be bashful about allowing you to examine his or her genitalia, so take time to explain the procedures and their purpose. Be gentle but thorough, and complete your examination as quickly as possible. Note the location and size of a boy's urethral meatus, the size of his testes, and any local irritation, inflammation, or swelling. The meatus should be in the center of the shaft; you may note epispadias (urethral opening on the dorsum of the shaft) or hypospadias (urethral opening on the underside of the penis or on the perineum). Note the location of a girl's clitoris, urethral meatus, and vaginal orifice. So-called female epispadias, with the mons and clitoris divided along the midline, may indicate hermaphroditism. Also check for irritation, swelling, and abnormal discharge—possible signs of urethritis. Then palpate the meatus for urethral caruncles.

Childhood urinary disorders

After the respiratory tract, the urinary tract is the most commonly infected area in infants and children. In an infant, signs and symptoms of a urinary tract infection (UTI) may be nonspecific. Look for fever, irritability, feeding problems, vomiting, diarrhea, and jaundice. Usually the presenting sign is fever: When it occurs with such specific urinary tract signs as hematuria, odorous urine, and recurrent enuresis, obtain a urine culture of a clean-catch specimen.

In an infant or young child, a UTI (especially if recurrent) that's confirmed by urine culture suggests a congenital structural anomaly of the urinary tract, such as retrocaval ureter, ureterocele, bladder diverticulum, or vesicoureteral reflux. The underlying cause of any UTI must be found and treated to prevent acute pyelonephritis and renal damage.

Acute glomerulonephritis is the most common form of nephritis in children. A group A beta-hemolytic streptococcal infection usually precedes the disease 7 to 14 days before the sudden onset of symptoms. Symptoms include urinary abnormalities (hematuria, proteinuria, and decreased urinary output), edema, and hypertension. The child is lethargic, pale, and anorexic. If only the urinary abnormalities appear, diagnosis is more difficult. A bacterial urine count should be used to rule out a UTI.

If proteinuria persists for a week, postural proteinuria may be present.

Geriatric assessment

Anatomy and physiology

After age 40, a person's renal function may diminish; if he lives to age 90, it may have decreased by as much as 50%. This change is reflected in a decline in the glomerular filtration rate resulting from age-related changes in renal vasculature that disturb glomerular hemodynamics. Diminished renal blood flow from reduced cardiac output and from atherosclerotic changes also occurs with age. In addition, tubular reabsorption and renal concentrating ability decline in elderly persons, because the size and number of functioning nephrons decrease. As a person ages, his bladder muscles weaken; this may result in incomplete bladder emptying and chronic urine retention—predisposing the bladder to infection.

Age changes may predispose to, but do not cause, urinary incontinence. About 86% to 90% of community-living elderly and 55% to 60% of nursing home residents have no trouble with urinary control. Furthermore, many causes of urinary incontinence can be treated and some patients may even be able to regain urinary control.

Geriatric history concerns

An older patient who has had scarlet fever or other streptococcal infections, especially before the introduction of sulfonamides and penicillin, is at risk to develop renal damage secondary to glomerulonephritis. Prolonged hypertension predisposes the patient to arteriolar nephrosclerosis, which can impair renal function. Atherosclerosis can reduce renal circulation.

Tests: Values and hazards

For geriatric patients, normal values for some laboratory tests are different from those established for younger adults, because of decreased renal function. An elderly patient's blood urea nitrogen level, for example, is normally higher by 5 mg/100 ml. Because an older person's kidneys have diminished concentrating ability, some diagnostic tests are more hazardous to him than to a younger patient. For instance, dehydration induced in preparation for radiologic studies, or resulting from the osmotic diuresis produced by contrast agents, may predispose an elderly patient to intravascular volume contraction and further renal function deterioration.

Geriatric urinary disorders

Because of degenerative changes affecting body functions, elderly persons are more susceptible than younger adults to some renal disorders. Susceptibility to infection, for example, increases with age, and kidney infection from obstruction is a common cause of hospitalization among older patients. An immobilized elderly patient is especially vulnerable to infection from urinary stasis or poor personal hygiene.

An alteration in cardiac output (such as in congestive heart failure) lowers renal perfusion and may result in azotemia. The kidneys compensate by retaining sodium and increasing edema. Medications to improve a patient's myocardial contractility, and therapy with diuretics, may increase his renal function temporarily, but prerenal azotemia from depletion of intravascular volume often results.

Poor musculature from childbearing and from aging may predispose elderly women to cystocele. This condition can result in frequent urination, urgency, incontinence, urine retention, and infection. Obstruction in an elderly woman may result from uterine prolapse or pelvic cancer.

Prostatic enlargement, common among elderly men, may contribute to obstruction. Retrograde pressure from urine causes distention of the kidneys, pelvis, and calices, resulting in renal tissue damage. If untreated, prostatic enlargement may also result in hydronephrosis, infection, and uremia. Prostatic cancer, the most common type of cancer in men over age 50, may also lead to urinary tract obstruction.

The potential for cancer is higher in the elderly. Bladder cancer, common after age 50, is more prevalent in men than in women. Symptoms of bladder cancer include frequency, dysuria, and hematuria.

You may have difficulty identifying uremia as the cause of an elderly patient's confusion, because an altered level of consciousness in an elderly person can also arise from organic brain syndrome or environmental disorientation.

Guide to Urinary Disorders

DISORDER	CHIEF COMPLAINT	
Acute glomerulonephritis	• *Output changes:* oliguria, possibly progressing to anuria • *Voiding pattern changes:* none • *Urine color changes:* hematuria, smoky or coffee-colored • *Pain:* none	
Acute pyelonephritis	• *Output changes:* polyuria or none • *Voiding pattern changes:* frequency, urgency • *Urine color changes:* hematuria • *Pain:* tenderness over one or both kidneys	
Acute renal artery occlusion	• *Output changes:* oliguria possible • *Voiding pattern changes:* none • *Urine color changes:* none • *Pain:* sudden, sharp, constant pain over upper abdomen or flank	
Acute tubular necrosis	• *Output changes:* oliguria dominates in early stages; leads to renal failure • *Voiding pattern changes:* none • *Urine color changes:* dark and smoky or clear • *Pain:* none	
Bladder neck obstruction	• *Output changes:* anuria with complete obstruction • *Voiding pattern changes:* frequency, urgency • *Urine color changes:* none • *Pain:* dysuria	
Carcinoma of the bladder	• *Output changes:* oliguria possible, depending on mass size • *Voiding pattern changes:* frequency, urgency, nocturia • *Urine color changes:* hematuria, intermittent or constant • *Pain:* dysuria, flank pain	
Chronic glomerulonephritis	• *Output changes:* none • *Voiding pattern changes:* none • *Urine color changes:* none • *Pain:* none	
Chronic interstitial nephritis	• *Output changes:* polyuria • *Voiding pattern changes:* nocturia	

HISTORY	PHYSICAL EXAMINATION AND DIAGNOSTIC STUDIES
• Poststreptococcal infection of throat or skin • Systemic lupus erythematosus, Schönlein-Henoch purpura, pregnancy, vasculitis, or scleroderma	• Hypertension • Edema; starts in periorbital areas and progresses to dependent areas, ascites, and pleural effusion • Costovertebral tenderness • Urine analysis reveals proteinuria and RBC casts. • Further diagnostic studies include renal computerized tomography and biopsy.
• Sudden onset	• Fever and chills • Nausea and vomiting • Kidneys tender on palpation • Urine analysis reveals pyuria and bacteriuria.
• Emboli from endocarditis or atherosclerosis	• Severe hypertension present • Further diagnostic studies include renal arteriography.
• Crush injury or illness associated with shock, such as burns or trauma • Muscle necrosis • Use of a nephrotoxic agent, such as lead, or intravenous pyelography dye	• Anorexia • Vomiting • Pulmonary edema, heart failure • Urine analysis reveals low specific gravity, granular casts, and hematuria. • Blood analysis reveals elevated BUN and creatinine levels. • Further diagnostic studies include spot urine sodium and urine creatinine analyses.
• May be acquired or hereditary	• Incontinence • Nausea and vomiting • Distended bladder • Diagnostic studies include cystoscopy and cystography.
• Exposure to analine dyes • Chronic infestation of schistosomes • Heavy cigarette smoking	• Fever • Flank tenderness, muscle weakness • Blood analysis reveals elevated WBC count and anemia. • Positive urine cytology • Further diagnostic studies include cystography, cystoscopy, and biopsy.
• May be asymptomatic until advanced stages	• Renal failure • Hypertension • Urine analysis reveals proteinuria. • Blood analysis reveals anemia. • Further diagnostic studies include biopsy.
• Urinary abnormality, such as obstruction or reflux	• Hypertension • Blood analysis reveals elevated BUN. *(continued)*

Guide to Urinary Disorders *(continued)*

DISORDER	CHIEF COMPLAINT	
Chronic interstitial nephritis *(continued)*	• *Urine color changes:* light color due to poor concentration • *Pain:* none	
Chronic renal artery stenosis	• *Output changes:* none • *Voiding pattern changes:* none • *Urine color changes:* none • *Pain:* none	
Cystitis	• *Output changes:* none • *Voiding pattern changes:* frequency, urgency, nocturia • *Urine color changes:* cloudy hematuria • *Pain:* dysuria, low back pain or flank pain	
Hypernephroma	• *Output changes:* none • *Voiding pattern changes:* none • *Urine color changes:* hematuria, gross or microscopic • *Pain:* flank pain	
Nephrolithiasis	• *Output changes:* none • *Voiding pattern changes:* frequency, urgency • *Urine color changes:* hematuria • *Pain:* severe, radiating pain	
Polycystic kidney disease	• *Output changes:* polyuria • *Voiding pattern changes:* nocturia possible • *Urine color changes:* hematuria, possibly gross • *Pain:* flank pain	
Renal vein thrombosis	• *Output changes:* oliguria possible if thrombosis is bilateral • *Voiding pattern changes:* none • *Urine color changes:* hematuria • *Pain:* severe lumbar pain	
Urethral obstruction	• *Output changes:* polyuria • *Voiding pattern changes:* incontinence, hesitancy, urgency • *Urine color changes:* none • *Pain:* dysuria	

HISTORY	PHYSICAL EXAMINATION AND DIAGNOSTIC STUDIES
• Early stages may have no specific symptoms.	• Urine analysis reveals WBC casts. • Further diagnostic studies include intravenous pyelography and biopsy.
• Fibromuscular dysplasia or atherosclerosis	• Hypertension that's difficult to control • Renal arteriography
• Recurrent urinary tract infections • Recent chemotherapy, systemic antibiotic therapy • Recent vigorous sexual activity • Commonly affects women	• Suprapubic pain on palpation • Fever • Nausea and vomiting • Inflamed genital area • Urine analysis reveals bacteriuria (10^5/ml). • Urine culture and sensitivity tests repeated 2 weeks after therapy ends.
• Allergies • Use of nephrotoxic drugs	• Palpable mass • Fever, hypertension, weight loss • Fatigue and malaise • Blood analysis reveals anemia or polycythemia. • Further diagnostic studies include intravenous pyelography, ultrasonography, angiography, renal computerized tomography.
• Excessive dehydration and infection • Previous kidney stones • Hyperparathyroidism • Renal tubular acidosis	• Fever and chills • Nausea and vomiting • Blood analysis reveals leukocytosis. • Urine analysis reveals increased specific gravity, crystalluria, and leukocyturia. • Further diagnostic studies include retrograde intravenous pyelography.
• Family history of polycystic disease • Symptoms start after age 40	• Enlarged, palpable kidneys • Hypertension • Urine analysis reveals proteinuria, bacteriuria, and calculi. • Further diagnostic studies include urography, ultrasonography, radioisotopic renal scan, renal computerized tomography.
• Metastatic disease, nephrotic syndrome, thrombophlebitis, periarteritis, abdominal injury, unexplained leg edema, or recurrent emboli	• Enlargement of affected kidney • Blood analysis reveals leukocytosis. • Urine analysis reveals proteinuria and RBC casts. • Further diagnostic studies include inferior vena cavography.
• Injury, infection, carcinoma, or congenital anomalies • Past history of calculi	• Enlarged kidney (to compensate for obstructed kidney) • Renal failure • Distended bladder *(continued)*

Guide to Urinary Disorders *(continued)*

DISORDER	CHIEF COMPLAINT	
Urethral obstruction *(continued)*		
Urethritis	• *Output changes:* polyuria may result from forced fluids • *Voiding pattern changes:* frequency, urgency • *Urine color changes:* hematuria • *Pain:* dysuria possible; burning at start of urination; urethral pain	

HISTORY	PHYSICAL EXAMINATION AND DIAGNOSTIC STUDIES
	• Urine analysis reveals proteinuria. • Further diagnostic studies include cystoscopy.
• Infections • Exposure to chemicals or bubble bath • Recent vigorous sexual activity	• Fever • Edema and redness around urinary meatus and vulva • Urethral and/or vaginal discharge

13

Male Reproductive System

Many common disorders of the male reproductive system have serious consequences. And disorders in this system, along with possibly altering other body systems, can affect male sexuality as well as a male's attitude toward his sexuality. So if your assessment helps to uncover a male patient's potential sexual dysfunction, you'll have contributed not only to his health but also to the quality of his life.

Another important reason for this assessment is that many patients don't volunteer any information about their sexual dysfunction. They're either afraid or too uneasy to inquire about it—or they're unsure whether it can be treated (see *Discussing Sexual Problems,* page 263).

Remember, too, that all health-care professionals need to be attuned to the signs and symptoms of sexually transmitted diseases (formerly referred to as *venereal diseases*), the most common communicable diseases in the United States. Only early detection and prompt treatment can prevent the potentially devastating secondary complications of these diseases.

History data

Biographical data
Age is perhaps the primary consideration in assessing the male reproductive system. For example, gonorrhea is usually associated with young people and is most prevalent between ages 19 and 25. On the other hand, elderly men are more likely to develop prostate disorders, primarily benign prostatic hypertrophy and prostatic cancer. In fact, more than half of all men over age 50 have some degree

of prostatic enlargement, and prostatic cancer is one of the most common malignant neoplasms in men over age 50. When it occurs, testicular cancer usually develops in men between ages 15 and 40, with the highest incidence occurring at age 32; in the United States, it's also the most common type of solid tumor in males.

Race is another significant biographical factor. For example, the highest incidence of prostatic cancer occurs in blacks and the lowest incidence occurs in Orientals.

History of present illness
The most common chief complaints associated with the male reproductive system are *changes in voiding pattern, penile discharge, scrotal or inguinal mass, pain or tenderness, impotence,* and *infertility* (see *Guide to Male Reproductive System Disorders,* pages 272 to 277).

Here are some questions you may want to ask about these complaints to explore fully the history of your patient's present illness:
- **Changes in voiding pattern.** *Do you have to wait longer than a few seconds before urine flow begins? Do you strain to urinate? Do you have a feeling of urgency to urinate? Does the urinary stream seem smaller in caliber or less forceful than usual? Have you been urinating more frequently, or do you wake up in the middle of the night to urinate?* An obstructed or decreased urinary flow or an increase in urinary frequency (including nocturia) is commonly caused by an enlarged prostate gland. Also consider that the patient may have a urinary system disorder. (See *Guide to Urinary Disorders,* pages 256 to 261.)
- **Penile discharge.** *How much discharge is there? Is the discharge present only during*

Discussing Sexual Problems

Knowing how to discuss your patient's sexual problems or concerns is important for two reasons. First, it helps you identify areas that require active treatment. Second, it shows the patient that you view sexual function as an integral part of his life-style, and that you're willing and able to discuss the subject. Here are some guidelines to help you:

● To begin, tell the patient that you need some information about his sexual functioning so you can provide appropriate care. Explain which areas of questioning you'll explore—such as his relationship with his partner, his sexual experiences, and his sexual preferences. Assure him that his answers will remain confidential.

● In your discussion, move from less sensitive to more sensitive areas. For example, discuss the patient's urinary problems before you bring up the subject of his sexual functioning.

● Integrate your questions with those dealing with his activities of daily living. This way you'll help him feel that discussing sexual functioning is acceptable. To encourage discussion, ask open-ended questions. Instead of asking, "Did you just notice this problem recently?", ask, "When did you first notice this problem?"

● Because medical terminology may be confusing to him, try using the sexual terms your patient understands. But be sure you're both talking about the same thing. Misunderstandings can easily occur if your patient uses slang (or accepted terms) incorrectly. To avoid confusion, you might begin by using several different words that mean the same thing, to clarify your point and get an idea of the type of terminology he uses. For example, you might ask: "Do you have any pain in your penis—your sexual organ?" Use his response to guide your use of terminology as the discussion continues.

● Introduce common or slang terms into the conversation selectively and cautiously. You'll do this more often with younger patients, because they tend to use more slang in general conversation. First make sure you've established rapport, so the patient doesn't feel uncomfortable with the familiarity that slang implies.

● Don't react to your patient's comments in ways that discourage conversation. If he senses your disapproval, he'll be less willing to continue the discussion.

● Be sure to end your discussion by asking the patient if he has additional questions or concerns that he wants to discuss.

---

urination? What color is it? What consistency is it? Large quantities of thick, creamy, yellow-green discharge usually indicate gonorrhea. A thin, watery discharge may suggest a nonspecific urethritis or a prostate infection. A bloody discharge may indicate an infection or cancer in the urinary or reproductive tract.

● *Pain or tenderness. Is urination painful for you?* This may suggest a nonspecific urinary tract infection or a sexually transmitted disease. *Is the painful passage of urine accompanied by spasms (strangury)?* This may result from bladder or prostate infection. *Does dull, aching scrotal pain worsen when you strain?* This could indicate an inguinal hernia. On the other hand, extreme scrotal pain that begins suddenly suggests testicular torsion. Gradual onset of acute pain, accompanied by warmth, heat, and swelling, usually indicates an infection. Flank pain suggests renal calculi.

● *Scrotal or inguinal mass. Does the mass disappear when you lie flat on your back?* Nor-

mally, this indicates an inguinal hernia. *Have you recently received an injury to your genitals?* This may cause a hematocele. *How long has the mass been present? Are there any associated symptoms, such as pain?* Although benign conditions may be painless, testicular cancer must be considered.

● *Sexual impotence. Sexual impotence means different things to different people, so can you tell me what you mean by the term?* Clarifying the patient's understanding of impotence is important, because sexual terms are frequently misunderstood and misused. *What was your life-style like at the time the problem began? Did the problem begin suddenly or gradually?* Sudden impotence that occurs during a stressful time in the patient's life most likely originates psychogenically. (About 80% of all occurrences of sexual impotence are psychogenic.) *Do you have nocturnal or morning erections? Can you achieve an erection through fantasizing or mastur-*

Sources of Sexual Problems

If your patient complains of impotence, don't assume that's his primary problem. Impotence may be only a symptom of another condition. You'll want to find out the reason for his problem to help him deal with it. Consider these other possibilities:

● Loss of libido
● Lowered quality or quantity of sexual performance
● Ejaculatory incompetence
● Premature ejaculation
● Decreased volume or force of ejaculate
● Increased postcoital refractory period
● Disinterest in sexual partner
● Unwillingness or inability to meet sexual desires of actual or potential sexual partner
● Sexual exhaustion
● Normal aging changes
● Anxiety about penis size.

Reprinted from Walker/Hall/Hurst: *Clinical Methods*, 1st ed. (Woburn: Butterworths Publishing, Inc., 1976), with permission of the publisher.

bation? Patients with psychogenic impotence usually retain these capabilities (see *Sources of Sexual Problems*).

● **Infertility.** *How long have you and your sexual partner been trying to achieve pregnancy?* Suspect infertility only if the couple have engaged regularly in intercourse, without using birth control, for at least 1 year. *Do you have a low sex drive, premature ejaculation, or impotence? Was your sexual development normal? Have you had any infections or injuries to your testes?*

Past history

Focus on the following health problems when reviewing your patient's past history:

● **Metabolic and endocrine disorders.** *Diabetes mellitus* can cause irreversible, organic sexual impotence, probably from vascular impairment. (About half of all men with diabetes are impotent.) Diabetes mellitus can result in infertility, as can *panhypopituitarism* and, infrequently, *hypothyroidism* and *congenital adrenal hyperplasia.*

● **Nervous disorders.** Nerve damage occurring with *multiple sclerosis* may result in sexual impotence and infertility. *Spinal cord*

trauma also can cause sexual impotence.

● **Infections.** About 25% of all postpubertal males who acquire *mumps* (viral parotitis) develop orchitis, which can cause extreme pain and tenderness. If bilateral degeneration of the seminiferous tubular epithelium accompanies the infection, infertility may result. Sexually transmitted diseases and other *genital infections* can cause infertility.

● **Urinary disorders.** *Chronic renal failure* can result in sexual impotence and infertility. Previous surgical procedures—such as cystectomy, radical prostatectomy, and bilateral orchiectomy—can also cause impotence.

● **Drugs.** Many drugs, as well as alcohol, can impair the function of the male reproductive system.

Family and psychosocial history

Klinefelter's syndrome, a chromosomal pattern marked by the presence of two or more X chromosomes with at least one Y, is a relatively common condition resulting in primary hypogonadism. This condition is characterized by gynecomastia, underdeveloped testes, sparse facial hair, and azoospermia (semen that doesn't contain spermatozoa). Many of these patients are tall as a result of delayed epiphyseal closure.

When appropriate, ask your patient about his *sexual practices and attitudes*. For example, does he have guilt feelings, fears, or other negative emotions about women? Inquire about his sexual relationships, including possible exposure to sexually transmitted diseases.

Because *stress* can interfere with sexual performance, ask your patient if he has any emotional conflicts at work or at home. Don't forget to question him about his work environment. A job that exposes him to harmful chemicals or radiation may cause infertility.

Activities of daily living

Ask your patient if he takes hot baths, rides a bicycle frequently, or wears tight underwear or an athletic supporter. These circumstances elevate scrotal temperature and may interfere with spermatogenesis, possibly producing temporary oligospermia. If your patient participates in sports, ask him how he protects himself from possible genital injuries. Also ask if he performs testicular self-examinations routinely.

Review of systems

Ask your patient if he has any of the following symptoms:

• *Skin.* Pruritus may accompany many infectious diseases of the reproductive system that cause an exudate.

• *Gastrointestinal.* Severe pain, such as the pain associated with testicular torsion, may cause *nausea* and *vomiting.*

• *Psychological.* Typical reactions to anxiety, such as *insomnia* and *restlessness,* may also accompany possible psychogenic sexual dysfunction.

Physical examination

Preparation and equipment

Before you begin examining a patient, be sure you have adequate lighting and the following equipment on hand: disposable gloves, lubricant, a flashlight (for transilluminating the scrotum), cotton swabs, culture tubes, and an agar plate (in case you notice a penile discharge during the examination).

Explain to the patient the procedures you're about to perform, to allay any fears he may have. Then conduct the general survey. Determine whether the patient can stand or whether you'll have to position him supine on an examining table. If he has to lie on the examining table, drape him carefully, exposing only his genitalia and groin.

Penis inspection and palpation

Inspection and palpation are the two most important techniques used to examine the male genitalia. Begin by observing the amount and distribution of your patient's pubic hair. It should be thickest at the symphysis pubis and continue over the scrotum and inner thighs. Then, observe his penis. Inspect its anterior surface first; then lift it to inspect the posterior surface.

Normally, the penis appears pink and smooth. Note any swelling, erythema, nodules, or ulcers. Remember, the size of the penile shaft varies; evaluate it in terms of your patient's age and general development. Suspect an abnormality only if it appears extremely small and infantile.

Inspect the glans, noting whether the patient is circumcised. If he isn't, you'll have to retract the foreskin. You should be able to do this easily. (If you can't, the patient probably has *phimosis,* constriction of the foreskin over the glans, usually from a previous inflammation.) Normally, the glans is smooth. Note any lesions, erythema, discharge, or smegma. (A potential carcinogen, smegma may be responsible for the higher incidence of penile carcinoma in uncircumcised men.)

Next, inspect the urethral meatus. Note any abnormalities, such as hypospadias or epispadias. Also note any discharge (see *Penis Abnormalities,* page 266).

Finally, palpate the entire penile shaft between your thumb and first two fingers. In its nonerect state, the penis should feel soft. Note any indurations, nodules, or thickening.

Scrotum inspection and palpation

To inspect the scrotum, support the patient's penis against his symphysis pubis. The scrotal skin should appear wrinkled. The sac is normally asymmetrical, the left testis hanging about ½" (about 1 cm) lower in the relaxed scrotum than the right testis. If the patient's right testis hangs lower, make a note of it.

After inspecting the scrotum's anterior surface, be sure to lift it to inspect its posterior surface as well. Note any swelling. Scrotal enlargement may result from a hydrocele, which causes the skin to appear tight and shiny. Also inspect the scrotum for redness, ulcerations, cysts, or distended veins.

Next, gently palpate the scrotum. Begin by palpating each testis between your thumb and first two fingers. Note if the testis isn't present or isn't fully descended into the sac. Normally, testes are the same size. They should feel firm, smooth, and rubbery and move freely in the scrotal sac. Note any atrophy or softening, as well as any hard, irregular areas or lumps. If you find a mass, describe its location, size, consistency, and shape. Also note any tenderness and whether the mass transilluminates (see *Transillumination of Scrotal Masses,* page 267).

Now palpate each epididymis, usually located on the posterolateral surface of each testis. Note any tenderness, swelling, or in-

Penis Abnormalities

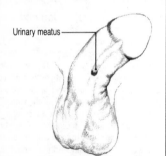

Foreskin or prepuce (may or may not be present)

Glans of the penis

Urinary meatus

Normal: foreskin retracts easily from the glans and readily returns to its original position

Urinary meatus

Hypospadias: urethral opening on posterior side of penis or on perineum

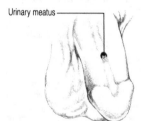

Urinary meatus

Epispadias: urethral opening on anterior side of penis

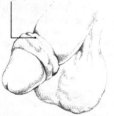

Foreskin (prepuce)

Paraphimosis: constricting foreskin behind glans, preventing its return to original position

Foreskin (prepuce)

Phimosis: constricting foreskin covering the glans, preventing foreskin retraction

duration. Finally, gently pinch each spermatic cord, which you can feel above the testis. You can readily identify the vas deferens within the cord; it feels noticeably different from the blood vessels and nerves. Using your thumb and forefinger, palpate the entire length of the cord, from the epididymis to the external inguinal ring. Normally, the 3-mm-wide cord feels smooth, round, and resilient. Note any nodular structures that feel like a bag of worms, which may indicate a varicocele—a mass of engorged dilated veins. (A varicocele will collapse slowly when you elevate a supine patient's scrotum.)

Examining inguinal and femoral areas

Begin this phase of your examination by inspecting the patient's inguinal and femoral areas, noting any bulges. Ask him to bear down, as though straining at stool. Note any tenderness or masses and whether a mass is reducible. Then, palpate each femoral pulse for possible clues to aortic problems.

Although you can't palpate the femoral canal, you can estimate its location to help you detect a femoral hernia. Place your right index finger (pointing toward the patient's head) on the patient's right femoral artery, keeping your other fingers close together. Your middle finger will then lie over the femoral vein and your ring finger will lie over the femoral canal. Use your left hand to check the patient's left side.

Next, palpate the lymph nodes in the inguinal and femoral areas. These freely movable masses usually feel firm. Normally, they're about 0.5 cm in size. Note any tenderness or enlargement. (Be careful not to mistake an enlarged lymph node for a femoral hernia.)

Continue to palpate the patient's entire inguinal area, noting any lumps or bulges. Ask him to bear down as you proceed. Also, as you proceed, ask the patient to cough. Look and palpate for the cough impulse. Then palpate the inguinal ring on each side (see *Palpating the Inguinal Area,* page 268). To do this, place your index finger on the neck of the patient's scrotum and gently push upward, unfolding the patient's loose scrotal skin. Use your right index finger for the patient's right side and your left index finger for his left side.

Follow the spermatic cord's course until you

Transillumination of Scrotal Masses

If a mass is present, use transillumination to evaluate it. Darken the room, then place a flashlight head flat against the posterior surface of the affected side of the scrotum. Switch on the flashlight, as shown, and observe the anterior surface. The testis will appear as an opaque shadow, as will any lumps, masses, or blood-filled areas. Transilluminate the opposite side to compare your findings.

reach the triangular opening of the external inguinal ring. (The ring should not be obstructed.) If possible, gently insert your finger into the inguinal canal and follow its course. (If you feel a mass protruding through the external inguinal opening, suspect an inguinal hernia.) With your finger in the inguinal canal, or just at the external ring, ask the patient to bear down and cough. Palpate for any herniating tissue. When assessing your patient for a hernia, remember to examine him in both supine and standing positions.

Prostate gland palpation

First instruct the patient to urinate. Then, lubricate the index finger of your gloved examining hand. Have your patient stand at the end of the examining table, with his elbows flexed and his upper body resting on the table. (If he can't stand, position him on the examining table in the left decubitus position, with his knees drawn up to his abdomen, or in the knee-chest position.)

Spread the patient's buttocks apart to expose his anus for examination. Note any lumps, inflammation, or skin tears. Ask him to bear down, to reduce sphincter tension. Gently in-

Palpating the Inguinal Area

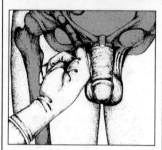

To locate the inguinal area, place your index finger on the distal aspect of the patient's scrotum and push upward. Follow the spermatic cord's course with your index finger until you reach the triangular opening of the external inguinal ring. If possible, gently insert your finger into the inguinal canal and follow its course. While maintaining this finger position, ask your patient to bear down or strain. Note any mass you feel with your finger.

sert your index finger into his anus. Palpate the anterior rectal wall and then find the prostate gland, located anterior to the wall's mucosa (see *Palpating the Prostate Gland,* page 269). Normally, the prostate doesn't protrude into the rectum; if it does, the gland is inflamed and enlarged.

The prostate should be nontender and feel smooth, firm (but not rocklike), and rubbery through the rectal wall. On palpation, the normal prostate gland feels like the mound that forms on the palm at the base of the thumb (thenar eminence) when you clench your fist. Locate the gland's right and left lateral lobes and the small, shallow groove that divides them. Estimate the prostate's diameter. A hypertrophied prostate gland is usually uniformly enlarged. Note any hard or irregular areas, which may indicate cancer; also note any tenderness or bogginess, which may reflect prostatic inflammation.

The seminal vesicles are slightly above the prostate gland on either side on the anterior rectal wall. Unless they're inflamed, you probably won't be able to palpate them. Finally, perform a complete rectal examination (see page 230).

Pediatric assessment

Growth and sexual development
A boy's penis, scrotum, and testes usually start growing between ages 10 and 13—this is typically the first sign of his sexual maturation. From ages 12 to 15, these structures grow rapidly; by age 17, growth is usually complete. A boy may experience his first ejaculation between ages 11 and 13, but normally, mature sperm aren't produced for another 3 years.

Pubic hair begins to grow, and the boy's voice deepens, between ages 12 and 14. Breast hypertrophy may also occur around this time but usually disappears between ages 14 and 17. Axillary hair may appear between ages 13 and 16; in later adolescence (between ages 15 and 17), chest hair and a beard may develop.

Penis and scrotum examination
If you observe an enlarged scrotum in a boy younger than age 2, suspect a scrotal extension of an inguinal hernia, a hydrocele, or both. (Hydroceles, often associated with inguinal hernias, are common among children in this age-group. To differentiate between the two, remember that hydroceles transilluminate and are neither tender nor reducible.)

When you assess an adolescent boy who is obese, his penis may appear abnormally small. When examining the patient, you may have to retract the fat over the symphysis pubis to properly assess penis size.

Before proceeding to palpate a boy's scrotum, explain what you'll be doing and why. Then make sure he's comfortably warm and as relaxed as possible. (Cold and anxiety may cause his testes to retract so that you can't palpate them.)

Hyperactive cremasteric reflexes commonly cause some patients' testes to retract into the inguinal canal during physical examination (see *The Cremasteric Reflex,* page 270). If this happens, locate the testes by milking the inguinal canal with your fingertips. This maneuver should promptly bring normal testes back down into the patient's scrotum. Or, in-

Palpating the Prostate Gland

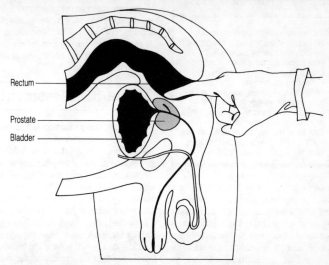

Rectum

Prostate

Bladder

To feel the prostate gland, palpate the patient's anterior rectal wall. It should feel smooth and elastic through the rectal wall mucosa.

The seminal vesicles, which are slightly above the prostate gland on the anterior rectal wall, are not normally palpable unless they're inflamed.

stead of milking the canal, you can have the child squat or sit cross-legged. This position counteracts the cremasteric reflex and increases intraabdominal pressure, which should bring normal testes back down into the scrotum. Examining the child while he is in a warm tub bath also usually brings the testes down (if they're normal). If these techniques are unsuccessful, your patient may have undescended testes.

Undescended testes

Undescended testes, or cryptorchidism, occurs when a testis or both testes fail to descend into the scrotum during fetal development. Instead, they remain in the abdomen or inguinal canal or at the external ring. If the testes are bilaterally undescended, the patient will need surgery before puberty, because a testis must be positioned properly in the scrotum for spermatogenesis to occur. Also, the patient

runs a greater risk of trauma and testicular cancer if he has an undescended testis.

If you suspect that a boy you're examining has undescended testes, check for an inguinal hernia, which occurs ipsilaterally in many patients. When examining a child for an inguinal hernia, don't rely entirely on his coughing to demonstrate a hernia; it may not increase his intraabdominal pressure sufficiently. Instead, ask him to try to lift a heavy object, such as a footstool, and observe whether this activity demonstrates the hernia. In young children, who can be difficult to examine, you may miss small hernias. A history of intermittent inguinal swelling can be diagnostically important. Remember, too, that many boys with undescended testes were born prematurely; check your patient's history.

Testicular torsion

This condition, in which the patient's testis

The Cremasteric Reflex

The cremaster muscle comprises muscle fiber bands that originate at the lower edge of the abdominal muscles and form muscular loops surrounding the spermatic cord and testis. If you stroke the patient's inner thigh with a sharp object, the corresponding cremaster muscle contracts reflexively, causing elevation of the testis on that side. This is called the *cremasteric reflex*. Presence of the reflex substantiates the integrity of the spinal cord. Because the reflex may be hyperactive in a boy, it should be suppressed before you examine him for undescended testes.

rotates spontaneously on its axis, occurs most often during sleep, in boys between ages 12 and 18. The left testis rotates counterclockwise, the right testis, clockwise. Concomitant rotation of the spermatic cord causes testicular strangulation; if untreated, unilateral strangulation leads to testicular infarction, and bilateral strangulation leads to infertility.

If your pediatric patient has testicular torsion, your examination will reveal a twisted or rotated spermatic cord and abnormally elevated testes that are usually warm and swollen. The patient will have severe pain and possibly an elevated temperature. The diagnosis may be confirmed by auscultating the patient's testes for pulses with a Doppler ultrasound stethoscope. In early presentation, if there is no pulsing in the testes because of diminished blood flow, testicular torsion is usually the cause. In later presentation, however, falsely increased pulses may be present because of secondary congestion and inflammation. Accurate assessment of testicular torsion is important, because manual and/or surgical detorsion should be performed as soon as possible.

Precocious puberty

A boy with true precocious puberty matures sexually before age 10. This condition may be idiopathic or caused by cerebral lesions. Your examination will reveal secondary sex characteristics and gonadal development.

In pseudoprecocious puberty, secondary sex characteristics become apparent, but gonadal development doesn't occur. Testicular tumor or adrenogenital syndrome can cause this condition. Laboratory tests can help you differentiate true precocious puberty from pseudoprecocious puberty by measuring serum hormone and plasma testosterone levels and by examining ejaculate for spermatozoa. A radiologist can evaluate skull and hand X-rays for bone age.

Geriatric assessment

Aging and the male reproductive system

The physiologic changes that occur in elderly men include decreased testosterone production that, in turn, may cause a decrease in sexual libido. Among other effects, decreased testosterone production causes the testes to atrophy and soften and decreases sperm production. Normally, the prostate gland enlarges with age and its secretions diminish. Seminal fluid also decreases in volume and becomes less viscous. During intercourse, elderly men experience slower and weaker physiologic reactions. These changes don't necessarily weaken a man's sex drive or lessen his sexual satisfaction (see *The Male Climacteric,* page 271).

Prostatic hypertrophy

Almost all men over age 50 have some degree of prostatic enlargement. In men with benign prostatic hypertrophy or advanced prostate cancer, however, the gland becomes large enough to compress the urethra and sometimes the bladder, obstructing urinary flow. The cause of benign prostatic hypertrophy is unknown, but evidence points to hormonal changes in elderly men. Possible precipitating factors include neoplastic, inflammatory, metabolic, arteriosclerotic, and nutritional disturbances.

If not treated, benign prostatic hypertrophy can impair renal function, causing such initial signs and symptoms as urinary hesitancy and intermittency, straining, and a reduction in the diameter and force of the urinary stream. As the gland continues to enlarge, urinary frequency increases and nocturia occurs, possibly with hematuria. All these signs and symptoms may also be caused by a urinary system disorder.

If your patient does have benign prostatic hypertrophy, you'll probably note nontender and enlarged lateral lobes. These lobes may feel like the thenar eminence of a clenched fist—whereas, in malignant prostatic hypertrophy, they feel more like a knuckle. You may not be able to detect an enlarged median lobe, because most of it rests anteriorly. Abdominal palpation and percussion may reveal a midline mass, representing a distended bladder.

The Male Climacteric

Here's a list of the physiologic changes that characterize the male climacteric:
● Erections require more time and stimulation to achieve.
● Erections are not as full or as hard.
● Testosterone production decreases.
● The prostate gland enlarges, and its secretions diminish.
● Seminal fluid decreases.
● Contractions in prostate gland and penile urethra during orgasm vary in length and quality.
● Refractory period following ejaculation may increase from minutes to days.
● Pleasure sensations become less genitally localized and more generalized.

Guide to Male Reproductive Disorders

DISORDER	CHIEF COMPLAINT	
Benign prostatic hypertrophy	• *Changes in voiding patterns:* urinary hesitancy, intermittency with dribbling; reduced urinary stream caliber and force; straining; possibly retention • *Penile discharge:* usually none • *Scrotal or inguinal mass:* none • *Pain or tenderness:* burning on urination with cystitis if accompanied by urinary tract infection • *Impotence:* possible if nerves innervating penis are damaged during open prostatectomy • *Infertility:* common following transurethral prostatectomy due to retrograde ejaculation	
Cancer of the penis	• *Changes in voiding patterns:* none usually present except in advanced stages • *Penile discharge:* usually not present; bleeding in later stage; purulent drainage with secondary infection possible • *Scrotal or inguinal mass:* enlarged inguinal lymph nodes may be caused by infection or metastasis • *Pain or tenderness:* painful, enlarged regional lymph nodes possible; penile pain in late stage • *Impotence:* usually none • *Infertility:* none	
Cancer of the prostate	• *Changes in voiding patterns:* in later stages, urinary hesitancy, dribbling, and possibly retention • *Penile discharge:* usually none • *Scrotal or inguinal mass:* none • *Pain or tenderness:* low back, hip, and leg pain common in advanced state, caused by metastases to the bones of the pelvis and spine • *Impotence:* follows radical resection of prostate • *Infertility:* follows radical resection of prostate	
Cancer of the testis	• *Changes in voiding patterns:* none in early stage • *Penile discharge:* none • *Scrotal or inguinal mass:* testicular mass present • *Pain or tenderness:* usually none until late stages, when accompanied by a feeling of heaviness or an aching or dragging sensation in groin • *Impotence:* psychogenic impotence possible • *Infertility:* none	
Epididymitis	• *Changes in voiding patterns:* usually none; frequency occurs if urinary tract infection is present • *Penile discharge:* usually none • *Scrotal or inguinal mass:* unilateral or bilateral scrotal swelling • *Pain or tenderness:* intense scrotal pain; may radiate to rectum, lower back, suprapubic region • *Impotence:* precipitated by pain • *Infertility:* possible with severe bilateral infection	

HISTORY	PHYSICAL EXAMINATION AND DIAGNOSTIC STUDIES
• Commonly occurs in men over age 50	• Rectal palpation reveals a firm, slightly elastic, enlarged, smooth prostate, with varying degrees of tenderness; rectal mucosa easily glides over hypertrophied gland. • Cystourethroscopy shows prostatic encroachment of the urethra and effects of enlargement on bladder.
• Poor personal hygiene may increase risk; usually occurs in uncircumcised men over age 50	• In early stage, dry, scaly lesion; later, ulceration and necrosis possible. • Biopsy confirms diagnosis. • Inguinal lymph nodes may be enlarged.
• More common in black men over age 50	• Rectal palpation reveals hard, irregular nodule on posterior prostate; becomes fixed as lesion progresses. • Biopsy confirms diagnosis; serum and phosphatase level elevated when tumor spreads beyond prostatic capsule.
• Common in men between ages 20 and 40	• Inspection and rectal palpation reveal firm, nontender testicular mass; doesn't transilluminate. • Biopsy confirms diagnosis. • Serum alpha-fetoprotein and beta human chorionic gonadotropin provide important information about tumor type and activity.
• Prior urinary tract infection may be present	• Fever • Inspection reveals enlarged epididymis, reddened, tender, and swollen scrotal skin. • Palpation reveals warm scrotal skin, painful epididymis. • Complete blood count reveals elevated WBC count; urinalysis may show pyuria.

(continued)

Guide to Male Reproductive Disorders *(continued)*

DISORDER	CHIEF COMPLAINT	
Genital herpes	• *Changes in voiding patterns:* none • *Penile discharge:* none • *Scrotal or inguinal mass:* tender, enlarged inguinal lymph nodes • *Pain or tenderness:* painful lesions during ulcerative stage; dysuria possible • *Impotence:* none • *Infertility:* usually none	
Gonorrhea	• *Changes in voiding patterns:* usually none, but frequency of urination possible • *Penile discharge:* present; thick and yellow-green but may start as milky white • *Scrotal or inguinal mass:* tender; lymph-adenopathy possible • *Pain or tenderness:* dysuria • *Impotence:* may be temporary, secondary to dysuria • *Infertility:* present only if untreated (in advanced stage secondary to scar tissue formation in epididymis)	
Hydrocele	• *Changes in voiding patterns:* usually none • *Penile discharge:* none • *Scrotal or inguinal mass:* present in scrotum • *Pain or tenderness:* usually none, except with very large mass • *Impotence:* none • *Infertility:* none	
Orchitis	• *Changes in voiding patterns:* usually none • *Penile discharge:* usually none • *Scrotal or inguinal mass:* unilateral or bilateral scrotal swelling • *Pain or tenderness:* varies from slight discomfort to extreme pain in one or both testes • *Impotence:* precipitated by pain • *Infertility:* possible with severe bilateral infection (mumps)	
Prostatitis	• *Changes in voiding patterns:* frequency, urgency; nocturia and and hesitancy possible • *Penile discharge:* if condition is acute, thin, watery, blood-streaked semen possible • *Scrotal or inguinal mass:* none • *Pain or tenderness:* dysuria common; possibly low back pain and/or perineal pressure; painful ejaculation possible • *Impotence:* decreased libido and potency possible • *Infertility:* possible	
Scrotal hernia	• *Changes in voiding patterns:* none • *Penile discharge:* none • *Scrotal or inguinal mass:* present in scrotum (extension of inguinal hernia) • *Pain or tenderness:* usually none, although mild, aching discomfort possible • *Impotence:* none • *Infertility:* none	

HISTORY	PHYSICAL EXAMINATION AND DIAGNOSTIC STUDIES
• Caused by sexual relations with infected partner	• Fluid-filled lesion usually on the glans penis, penile shaft, or foreskin. • Shallow ulcerative lesions, with local redness and swelling when ruptured. • Tissue culture may reveal herpes simplex Type 2 in vesical fluid. • Fever common
• Sexual exposure within preceding 2 weeks	• Edematous urethral meatus possible • Gram-negative intracellular diplococci on stained smear of urethral exudate • Positive culture on Thayer-Martin medium or equivalent
• Common in infants and adults; prior infection of testis, epididymitis possible	• Inspection reveals smooth, fluctuant mass in scrotum of pyriform or globular shape, with large end above; unable to reduce mass into abdomen; doesn't transmit cough impulse; transilluminates as a translucent mass.
• Prior infection, especially epididymitis or mumps	• Fever, possibly nausea and vomiting • Inspection reveals reddened scrotal skin, swollen testis. • Palpation reveals warm scrotal skin, tender testis. • Complete blood count reveals elevated WBC count.
• Chronic form commonly occurs in young men • Prior ascending urinary tract infection common	• Rectal palpation reveals, in acute form, firm, enlarged, tender, boggy prostate gland; in chronic form, enlarged prostate possible, as well as firmness due to prostatic calculi. • Fever and chills possible in acute form. • Third specimen of three- or four glass urine test contains many WBCs.
• Increased intra-abdominal pressure may be present on heavy lifting	• Inspection and palpation reveal inguinoscrotal mass that transmits cough impulse; doesn't transilluminate; possible to reduce mass into abdomen. • Auscultation may detect bowel sounds.

(continued)

Guide to Male Reproductive Disorders *(continued)*

DISORDER	CHIEF COMPLAINT	
Syphilitic chancre	• *Changes in voiding patterns:* none in early stage • *Penile discharge:* none • *Scrotal or inguinal mass:* enlarged inguinal lymph nodes possible • *Pain or tenderness:* none • *Impotence:* none • *Infertility:* usually none if detected and treated early	
Varicocele	• *Changes in voiding patterns:* none • *Penile discharge:* none • *Scrotal or inguinal mass:* present in scrotum, usually on left side • *Pain or tenderness:* no acute pain or tenderness; some discomfort caused by size of mass • *Impotence:* none • *Infertility:* none	

HISTORY	PHYSICAL EXAMINATION AND DIAGNOSTIC STUDIES
• Caused by sexual relations with infected partner	• Oval or round indurated ulcer, with raised edge • Dark-field microscopic examination of exudate confirms diagnosis.
• Common in males of high school or college age	• Inspection reveals lower-hanging testis on affected side, pendulous and irregular scrotum. • Palpation reveals soft, irregular mass; enlarged veins make scrotum feel like a bag of worms.

14

Female Reproductive System

A woman's reproductive system and child-bearing capabilities have physiologic, psychological, and social significance beyond her health concerns. Physiologically, the female reproductive system is complex and has wide-ranging effects on other body systems. Psychosocially, a woman's sexual or reproductive function can affect not only her self-concept but also how society views her.

The social aspects of reproduction can be overwhelming as well. Issues, such as contraception, artificial insemination, abortion, sexual preference, and unwanted children, are constantly before the public. And the incidence of sexually transmitted disease and teenage pregnancies continues to rise internationally. To sensitively assess a woman who has reproductive system concerns, be aware of these problems and of your patient's attitude, as well as your own, toward them.

History data

Biographical data
When you assess a woman's reproductive system, biographical data are always significant. A woman's race, personal circumstances, and the period of life she's in are related to various normal and abnormal reproductive system developments. Consider the following points when recording your patient's biographical data:

● *Age.* Menarche, the onset of menstruation, usually begins between ages 12 and 13. Girls who begin to menstruate at an earlier-than-normal age are at greater risk of developing breast cancer later in life.. Menopause—the period from when the ovaries' ability to produce eggs and estrogen declines until menstruation ultimately ceases—usually begins around age 50. If applicable, record your patient's age at the end of a 12-month period during which menstruation did not occur.

Women over age 35 are at greater risk of developing breast cancer than younger women. The risk of developing breast cancer (or endometrial cancer) is even greater after menopause. The risk of developing cervical cancer drops markedly after ovulation has stopped.

Sexually transmitted disease is more prevalent in women between ages 12 and 19 than in women who are 20 or older.

● *Race.* Whites are more likely to develop breast cancer than blacks. Blacks, however, are about three times more likely to develop benign uterine tumors than whites. Orientals have a low incidence of breast cancer.

History of present illness
The most common chief complaints expressed by women with reproductive system disorders are *pain, discharge, lumps and masses, abnormal uterine bleeding,* and *pruritus* (see *Guide to Female Reproductive Disorders,* pages 294 to 301).

Some patients may not have a chief complaint, but they may request a routine Pap smear or breast examination or may ask for information and instruction about contraception.

For all chief complaints concerning the female reproductive system or for requests for

information or evaluation, be sure to record the following information:
- the date your patient's last menstrual period began
- the date of the menstrual period before her last period
- the duration of her period, or the average number of tampons or sanitary napkins she uses during her period (to determine the amount of her flow)
- the date of her most recent Pap smear and pelvic examination
- the type of contraception she uses, if any
- the date of her most recent douching (because douching can alter Pap smear findings).

This information is vital for evaluating current and future reproductive system problems detected as a result of the history and the physical examination.

Here are some questions you may want to ask about these complaints to explore fully the history of your patient's present illness:
- **Pain.** *Where is the pain located?* Labial or groin pain is often referred from the kidneys; vulvar pain, commonly described as dysuria, usually results from an infectious process. (Because these sites may harbor lesions, consider the possibility of perineal or vulvar lumps.) Lower quadrant pain may be caused by an infectious, malignant, or functional process of supravaginal structures. *Did the pain occur suddenly or gradually?* Sudden pain that quickly reaches maximum intensity suggests a rupture or embolus, or sudden pain may be associated with dyspareunia (painful intercourse). Pain that increases over several days or weeks may be due to ovarian tumor, pelvic congestion, or endometriosis. *How long does the pain last? Is it constant or does it come and go?* Cyclic pain that occurs once a month suggests dysmenorrhea (pain during menstruation) or mittelschmerz (pain during ovulation). *What does the pain feel like?* The words the patient uses to describe the pain can be important in determining its cause. Remember to interpret her description according to her ability to express herself and to her understanding of the pain she's experiencing.
- **Discharge.** *When did it start?* Sudden onset may indicate an acute problem or the patient's ignorance of natural discharge, such as postcoital semen. Insidious onset usually indicates chronic inflammation from an infectious

or malignant process. *What does it look like? Is there an odor? How much discharge is there?* Vaginal discharge occurs in all women with adequate estrogen levels, so some staining is common throughout the menstrual cycle. Excessive staining can be a significant implication of pathology. A marked decrease in the usual amount of discharge may imply a low estrogen level or a vaginal or uterine obstruction. *Does a mucous discharge occur with ovulation?*

Are you using any form of contraception? Evaluate the patient's contraceptive method to distinguish between possible causes of irritation and infection. Oral contraceptives can cause amenorrhea and bleeding. Intrauterine devices can cause heavy menses and cramping and can increase the risk of pelvic inflammatory disease.

Has your sexual partner had an abnormal discharge recently? Both sexual partners usually require treatment for most sexually transmitted infections.

If the patient has a breast discharge, ask whether it's serous or bloody, which may reflect an inflammatory or neoplastic process in the breast. If the discharge is milky, ask the patient about recent pregnancy or abortion and whether she uses oral contraceptives or major tranquilizers. Be sure to question her about headaches or visual problems, because a pituitary neoplasm may be causing the discharge.

- **Breast lumps and masses.** *How long has the breast lump been present? Has it changed since you first noticed it? In what way?* Lumps of long duration with little or no recent change are usually benign, whereas new lumps that have undergone obvious changes can indicate cancer. *Is the lump tender?* A tender lump is probably due to an inflammatory or hormonal process. Remember, nipple discharge that concurs with the presence of a mass may indicate cancer (the incidence is at least 50% in women over age 50 when both a discharge and a mass are present). *Have you noticed any other breast lumps?* Women with multiple lumps (fibrocystic disease) are at an increased risk of developing a malignancy in one of the masses.

- **Perineal or vulvar lump.** *When did you first notice it?* Some lumps grow slowly and remain asymptomatic until they're quite large.

Others are noticed almost immediately because of presenting signs and symptoms, such as pruritus.

Can you feel the lump without touching it? The feeling that a mass is present is often associated with vaginal protuberances secondary to relaxation of pelvic support structures. The patient may liken the sensation of a perineal or vulvar lump to sitting on a ball. *Is it painful?* Discomfort can range from annoying to disabling. *Is it hard?* Hard, nontender lumps suggest malignancy; hard, tender lumps suggest an abscess. Clusters of soft, tender bumps, such as herpes genitalia, may be caused by a sexually transmitted disease.

● *Missed period.* Have you recently had unprotected intercourse? Did you experience an acute illness during the month before the missed period? Have you recently experienced emotional stress, or have you suddenly begun to exercise strenuously? Most women experience isolated anovulatory cycles during their reproductive years because of functional interference. Acute or chronic disease may also cause a woman to skip a period. Such periodic interruptions in the menstrual cycle are often referred to incorrectly as amenorrhea. Amenorrhea is correctly classified as primary or secondary. *Primary amenorrhea* is the absence of menarche by age 18. *Secondary amenorrhea* is the cessation of established menstruation for at least 3 consecutive months.

● *Increased menstrual flow.* Has the length of your period changed? How many additional tampons or sanitary napkins do you currently use? Has the flow increased gradually or suddenly? Are you passing clots? If so, what size are they? Determine whether the patient's complaint indicates *metrorrhagia* (sometimes prolonged flow, not occurring at the patient's customary cyclic intervals) or *menorrhagia* (excessive flow of usual duration, occurring at regular cyclic intervals). Remember that reproductive organ lesions cause most episodes of metrorrhagia or menorrhagia.

● *Spotting.* When does spotting usually occur in relation to your period? Spotting that commonly accompanies ovulation occurs during midcycle. Determine what the patient means by spotting. Does she mean an abnormally small amount of menstrual flow (*hypomenorrhea*)? Or does she mean vaginal bleeding that occurs between normal periods?

This condition is correctly termed *metrorrhagia*; it can range from stains to hemorrhages. *Are you using any medications that contain estrogen?* Medications that suppress ovulation can cause spotting and metrorrhagia. *Does the bleeding occur only after intercourse or the use of intravaginal objects?* Trauma or cervical erosion can cause temporary bleeding from the vulva, vagina, or cervical mucosa.

● *Pruritus.* Pruritus of the vulval or vaginal mucosa can follow any interruption in the normal production of acidic vaginal secretions. Its effects can range from annoying to debilitating. *Do you use a spray, powder, perfume, antiseptic soap, deodorant, or ointment in the genital area?* The chemicals used in these products can cause vaginal or perineal irritations. *Do you wear tight pants or nylon panties and panty hose?* Tight pants can trap moisture and cause chafing in the perineal area. Nylon panties and panty hose are poor conductors of moisture and air. Perspiration and secretions can accumulate in the perineal area, causing chafing and irritation.

What form of self-treatment have you attempted? Most douching solutions offer only temporary relief and carry the additional hazard of mechanical and chemical interference with vaginal acidity. *Have you used systemic antibiotics recently?* Broad-spectrum antibiotics allow superinfection of the vagina.

Past history

Obtain the following information when reviewing your patient's past history:

● *Pregnancies.* Note the patient's age at the time of her first pregnancy, the number of pregnancies (gravida #) and deliveries (para #), the weight of each baby, the length of each labor, the type of delivery, and the type of anesthetic used, if any. Describe any miscarriages or abortions, including any complications. Note any health problems that may have occurred during the patient's pregnancies, such as anemia, high blood pressure, mastitis, or toxemia.

Women who are infertile or nulliparous, those who have only one or two children, or those whose first pregnancy occurred after age 35 are at greater risk of developing breast cancer. Women who are nulliparous also have an increased risk of developing endometrial cancer.

• *Cystic breast disease.* This disorder increases the chance of developing breast cancer. Note whether the patient had a mammography or biopsy follow-up.

• *Breast cancer.* This is the most significant risk factor for future breast malignancies. Record the patient's treatment and follow-up.

• *Ovarian cysts, uterine tumors, or polyps.* These are common, usually benign, growths, but they may cause complications. Their presence normally contraindicates use of an intrauterine device.

• *Other gynecologic, medical, and surgical history.* Note why the patient sought treatment in the past for any other gynecologic problem. Describe any complications that may have resulted from treatment. If the patient has undergone surgery, note the specific organ or organs operated on or removed. A woman who has had a hysterectomy with a bilateral oophorectomy before age 40 has a reduced risk of developing breast cancer.

• *Diabetes mellitus.* This disorder can increase a patient's susceptibility to vaginal fungal infections. Diabetes also requires cautious use of birth control pills and may complicate pregnancy.

• *Other endocrine diseases.* Besides diabetes, ask the patient about adrenal, thyroid, and pituitary disorders, which can interfere with the menstrual cycle.

• *Sexually transmitted diseases.* Previously adequate treatment of sexually transmitted diseases may no longer be adequate to prevent complications or recurrences. This is because of the development of resistant strains of organisms. Moreover, no known cure exists for herpes genitalis. Remember that the most common complication of sexually transmitted diseases is pelvic inflammatory disease, which can cause sterility secondary to massive scarring or surgery. Also, when you question your patient about these diseases, be prepared to refer to them by their colloquial names when necessary.

• *Toxic shock syndrome.* This disorder, which usually affects women under age 30, tends to recur. It generally occurs in association with continuous use of tampons during the menstrual period. Typical symptoms include sudden onset of high fever, myalgia, vomiting, diarrhea, hypotension (which can lead to shock), and a macular erythematous rash, especially on the palms, fingers, and toes. A change in level of consciousness may also occur.

• *Trauma.* Breast or pelvic injuries resulting from rape, assault, or a motor vehicle accident may cause permanent physical and emotional dysfunction (see *Emergency Assessment: Caring for the Rape Victim,* page 282).

• *Musculoskeletal disorders.* Pelvic deformities from congenital anomalies or arthritis may cause mechanical dysfunction.

• *Psychiatric disorders.* Even if the patient has no past history of treatment for a psychiatric disorder, increased stress can cause menstrual irregularities and exacerbate menopausal symptoms.

• *Radiation exposure.* Cancer, of course, may develop in any organ exposed to excessive radiation. Ask the patient if she has been X-rayed many times, or if she has undergone any other diagnostic test or received therapy that involved X-rays. Also ask if she works at a job that exposes her to radiation.

Family history

Breast cancer on the maternal side of the patient's family doubles her risk of developing it. If the cancer was bilateral, the patient's risk is more than five times the average; if it was bilateral *and* premenopausal, the patient's risk is almost nine times greater than the average.

Diethylstilbestrol is an estrogenic compound used until recently to prevent miscarriages. If your patient's mother used this drug while pregnant with the patient, the risk exists that the patient will develop cervical lesions and vaginal cancer. This may possibly occur even before puberty.

Ask the patient if anyone in her family ever had sickle cell anemia, diabetes mellitus, or thyroid disease. These disorders directly affect the female reproductive system.

Psychosocial history

Sexually transmitted diseases occur in women of all socioeconomic levels. Because any woman you assess may have such a disease, inquire tactfully about every female patient's sexual activities. Ask about the gender and number of her partners and about such practices as oral and anal sex. Remember that the

Emergency Assessment: Caring for the Rape Victim

When dealing with a victim of rape, you can reduce both her trauma and her anxiety by following these guidelines:

• As a first consideration, your hospital should only entrust the rape victim to the care of a nurse and doctor of the same sex as the patient (who's usually female). Place the patient in a treatment area that's quiet, private, and secure. Introduce yourself. Show acceptance for her through eye contact, tone of voice, and (if appropriate) physical contact. Your hospital may have an arrangement with a local rape crisis center. If it does, ask your patient if she'd like to have a rape victim advocate with her during her hospital stay. If your hospital doesn't have such an arrangement, assure the patient that you'll be with her at all times throughout her emergency care.

• Set priorities according to your patient's needs. Physical injuries require immediate attention.

• Do not allow her to drink fluids or to wash her genital area. Explain that such activities would remove any existing semen, which is vital medicolegal evidence.

• After the patient is reasonably calm, explain that the doctor will ask her questions to identify the type of assault made on her. Be open to discussing her feelings and her fears. Demonstrate a nonjudgmental and supportive attitude. You'll find most rape victims have a need to talk.

• Introduce all hospital personnel entering the examination area to the patient.

• Tell the patient what treatment she'll receive: the doctor will perform a head-to-toe physical examination for signs of physical trauma and may order a Pap smear of her vagina, mouth, or rectum; saline suspensions to test for sperm presence; and an acid phosphatase test to determine how recently intercourse took place. The doctor will also order prophylactic antibiotics for sexually transmitted diseases. (When the patient is calm, discuss postcoital contraception, and possible pregnancy, with her.) The police will probably request the patient's articles of clothing as evidence (do not wash or discard them); they may ask you to try to find samples of the assailant's hair and skin tissue by combing the patient's pubic hair and examining her fingernails for deposits. Write down explanations of these procedures and the doctor's orders regarding such things as how often the patient should take antibiotics and when she should be reexamined. She can refer to these later.

• After your patient has been examined and treated, provide her with facilities to wash herself. Also provide mouthwash or a change of clothing, if needed. Before she leaves the hospital, be sure she understands the importance of getting retested for sexually transmitted disease in about 3 weeks, or sooner if symptoms occur. Some patients may require psychiatric referral. Give the rape victim written information about where to go for social, legal, or medical help, if needed.

---

incidence of cervical cancer rises with the number of sexual partners a woman has had. Also inquire about stress the woman may encounter at home or at work, which can alter her menstrual cycle.

Activities of daily living

As you review your patient's activities of daily living, ask about the following:

• **Self-assessment techniques.** Do you regularly examine your breasts? Have you ever examined your external genitalia for swelling or lumps? Do you watch for vaginal discharge, noting amount, color, odor, and persistence?

• **Self-care techniques.** Do you wash your hands before inserting a tampon? How long do you wear a tampon? Do you use feminine hygiene products, such as douches? Which products do you use, how frequently do you use them, and why do you use them? Using these products is often unnecessary and may injure the vaginal mucosa.

• **Exercise.** Bicycling, swimming, and other aerobic exercises—although generally healthy practices—are usually contraindicated during treatment of inflammatory disorders and pelvic support problems. If prolonged or strenuous, exercise can cause skipped periods and secondary amenorrhea.

• **Tobacco.** During pregnancy, smoking may increase the risk of fetal abnormalities. When combined with use of birth control pills, smoking increases the risk of myocardial infarction.

● *Alcohol.* Drinking during pregnancy may compound the risk of fetal abnormalities. It also reduces the effectiveness of treatment of some sexually transmitted diseases. Excessive alcohol consumption can cause amenorrhea.

● *Caffeine.* Coffee, tea, chocolate, and most cola drinks contain moderate to high amounts of caffeine, which may increase the incidence of breast lumps in some women.

Review of systems

Ask about the following symptoms as you proceed through a review of your patient's body systems:

● *General.* Have you noticed a recent weight change? Sudden weight loss or gain can cause menstrual irregularities. Have you had a fever? Fever may result from systemic infection secondary to an infection of a reproductive organ. Fever can also induce secondary amenorrhea.

● *Skin.* Acute acne, changes in hair texture or distribution, and skin lesions or rashes may result from altered gonadotropin function or systemic infection caused by a sexually transmitted disease or toxic shock syndrome. Hot flashes, sweating, and rapid changes in body temperature can result from withdrawal of estrogen medication or may be associated with menopause.

● *Nervous.* Headaches or dizziness may occur with reproductive system infection, estrogen withdrawal or intake, or the use of birth control pills.

● *Eyes.* Dry, scratchy eyes and vision changes may result from the use of birth control pills.

● *Mouth, throat, tongue.* Rashes, chancres, or sores in the mouth area can be caused by certain sexually transmitted diseases.

● *Gastrointestinal.* Anorexia, nausea, vomiting, severe abdominal cramps, and diarrhea or constipation can result from the use of birth control pills, menopause, or systemic infection. Difficulty with bowel movements usually accompanies and aggravates weakening pelvic support structures.

● *Respiratory.* Frequent coughing or sneezing can aggravate pelvic support defects.

● *Cardiovascular.* Menorrhagia may occur in a patient with congestive heart failure.

● *Urinary.* Difficult urination, stress incontinence, or frequent or urgent urination can result from vulvovaginal irritation or inadequate pelvic support.

● *Musculoskeletal.* Arthritic pains may accompany toxic shock syndrome and the secondary stages of some sexually transmitted diseases. Estrogen withdrawal decreases bone density, which predisposes women to stress fractures, especially of weight-bearing joints and vertebrae.

● *Psychological.* Menstrual and menopausal symptoms can be exacerbated by stress and by functional disorders.

Physical examination

Preliminary considerations

Because of the intimate and invasive nature of breast and pelvic examinations, approach these tasks with the utmost respect for your patient. Protecting her from emotional as well as physical discomfort throughout the examination should be a major concern.

Information you've gathered about your patient during history-taking should help you to understand her self-concept. For example, is she modest about or ashamed of her body? Is she comfortable with the basic language and terminology of the female reproductive system and its functioning? Observe secondary sex characteristics—voice pitch, hair distribution, body odor, musculoskeletal proportions, facial structure, breast development, and skin texture. These observations can provide important physiologic information on the adequacy of the patient's ovarian function.

Begin your preparations for the physical examination by checking state policy, as well as the policy of your facility, concerning chaperone attendance. Female examiners usually work without an attendant, but if the patient requests one—or if she's emotionally disturbed or handicapped in any way—obtain assistance from a staff member. Male examiners should always offer the patient the option of having a female attendant present throughout the examination.

During breast and pelvic examinations, try to keep your patient comfortable and relaxed. Warm hands, for example, increase not only the patient's tolerance of a particular maneuver but also the accuracy of your palpation. Whenever possible, observe your patient's face and hands for signs of discomfort, such as tense facial muscles or clenched fists.

Breast examination

Use inspection and palpation to examine your patient's breasts. You won't need any special equipment, but you'll need to determine the order in which to palpate the various sections of the breasts. The *spiral, quadrant,* and *spokes/radial* methods are three examples of breast examination patterns (see *Breast Examination Methods*). Each method includes inspection of the nipple, areola, body of the breast, and the tail of the upper outer quadrant of breast tissue, which extends into the axilla. Choose one approach and use it consistently for all breast examinations so that the procedure becomes routine. By doing so, you'll assure a thorough breast inspection for each patient you examine.

Begin the examination with the patient seated so that her breasts are at your eye level. Her arms should be at her sides and her hands should be resting in her lap. Drape only the patient's abdomen, because full anterior and lateral thoracic views are essential. Explain what you'll be doing; then inspect for nipple symmetry, color, contour, venous pattern, and skin integrity. Record all abnormal variations or conditions, such as a scar from a lumpectomy, nipple inversion and dimpling, enlarged

pores, and any nipple or areolar discharge. You can distinguish natural asymmetry of the breasts from unilateral edema by inspecting the pores. Edema accentuates or deepens sweat pores, causing the skin of the breast to look like an orange rind. This condition is known as *peau d'orange.*

To detect less obvious abnormalities before you palpate the breasts, have the patient raise her arms over her head and press her palms together. Then, ask her to press her palms into her hips. If the skin of the breasts is attached to the underlying tissues abnormally, you'll note a dimpling or retraction of the skin. For example, a malignant breast tumor can shorten suspensory ligaments, creating traction on the overlying skin. If the patient has unusually full or pendulous breasts, ask her to lean forward while you observe for flattening of the nipple area—another sign of unnatural attachment.

Palpation is usually performed with the patient in the supine position. However, if the patient has a breast mass as a chief complaint or in her past medical history, palpate the breasts when she's seated, as well. Follow this same procedure if the patient is at high risk of developing breast cancer or has pendulous breasts.

Begin breast palpation with the pads of your first and second fingers (some examiners add

Breast Examination Methods

SPIRAL

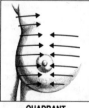
QUADRANT

SPOKES/RADIAL

When you examine your patient's breasts, use any of the palpation techniques illustrated here. Also, teach these methods to your patient so she can perform a breast self-examination at home. Encourage her to select one method and to use it routinely.

Obtain printed materials from such organizations as the American Cancer Society. Give them to your patient to reinforce your teaching.

a third), and move the patient's skin over underlying lymph nodes and tissue in a circular motion. Palpate first the axillary, the infraclavicular, and the supraclavicular areas, checking for enlarged or hard lymph nodes, tenderness, and accessory nipples. Because of the breast's abundant lymphatic drainage, a malignant breast tumor spreads first to lymph nodes in the axillae, above the clavicles, and to the mediastinal lymph nodes beneath the sternum. Enlarged axillary and supraclavicular lymph nodes can usually be detected during a physical examination, but enlarged mediastinal lymph nodes are too deeply embedded to be detected this way. You can differentiate an accessory nipple from a nevus by stimulating the accessory nipple's erectile tissue; a nevus will not become erect.

Apply more pressure as you palpate each area. Don't slide or stroke your fingers across the patient's skin—you could miss small nodules.

During palpation, keep normal breast variations in mind. The young breast has a firm elasticity; the middle-aged breast generally feels lobular; the older breast often has a stringy or granular feel. Other normal variations include premenstrual fullness, nodularity, and tenderness.

If the patient has large breasts, place a cushion under one scapula, to shift most of the ipsilateral breast tissue onto the anterior chest wall. This position allows you to feel significant masses more distinctly. You may note a firm transverse ridge of compressed tissue along the breast's lower edge. This is known as the *inframammary ridge*—don't confuse it with a tumor.

Palpate any suspicious areas you found on inspection. Firmly squeeze several inches around an area of altered contour and note the result. Describe any nodule in terms of its location even if you found the nodule in only one patient position: Note its consistency, mobility, size (in metric units), shape, delineation, and tenderness. Gently squeeze each areola and nipple clockwise, noting elasticity, enlarged pores, and discharge. If you detect a discharge, obtain a specimen and send it to the laboratory for cytology examination. Proceed to teach your patient breast self-examination.

Preparations for a pelvic examination

A pelvic examination should be conducted in a private area equipped with an examining table with stirrups. However, situations may arise in which an examining table is unavailable. For example, a visiting nurse may perform this examination in the patient's bedroom. Regardless of the situation, your caring attitude and careful explanation of each technique used during the examination will help the patient relax. Remember, too, that for you to inspect the uterus properly during a pelvic examination, the patient's bladder should be empty.

Assemble the following equipment within your reach:
● tight-fitting disposable gloves
● 1″ (2.5 cm) of water-soluble, sterile lubricating jelly on a paper towel (so you don't have to pick up the tube after the gloves are on)
● opened package of sterile swabs
● cervicovaginal spatula
● glass slides with frosted ends
● culture tubette
● cytologic fixative (hair spray works as well as ethyl-alcohol solutions or commercial sprays)
● several specula (usually medium-sized). If your patient is frightened, very young, or elderly, use a small speculum. If she's obese or multiparous, you may need a large one. Disposable plastic specula provide a more complete view of the vaginal wall coloring than metal specula, but they don't allow complete use of both hands. In addition, plastic specula aren't strong enough to expand the vaginal vault in tense or obese patients and may break; for these patients, the traditional metal speculum—even though follow-up sterilization is necessary—is superior.
● optional equipment, such as a specialized culture medium for gonorrhea (for example, Thayer-Martin medium), laboratory slips, specialized glass slides and coverslips, and a hand mirror for the patient to view her cervix.

Drape the patient's abdomen, pelvis, and breasts with a sheet. You may ask her to wear a hospital gown to cover her breasts. As the woman assumes the lithotomy position, help her by gently flexing her knees and hips and abducting her thighs. When she's properly positioned, place her heels in the stirrups—which should be level with and about 12" from the front edge of the examining table. Then ask the patient to lift and pull her pelvis, using her arms as leverage, to the front edge of the table. Touch her buttocks with your hand when she reaches the appropriate position.

Place a small pillow under her head. Then instruct her to rest her arms at her sides or on her thorax to give you full access to her relaxed abdomen. To minimize shadows from the patient's legs and your hands during inspection, position a gooseneck lamp nearby.

Examination of external genitalia

Put on the disposable gloves and either stand or sit at the foot of the examining table. Some examiners prefer to stand throughout a pelvic examination, but sitting is the most common approach. To help accustom the patient to the inspection, inform her that you will touch her inner thighs as you begin to inspect her vulva and perineum. Note odor, discharge, inflammation, hair type and distribution, any lice or lesions, and the presence of varicosities.

Palpate the labia majora, checking for subcutaneous lesions and tenderness. Then separate the labia majora, checking each specific vulval structure for signs of infection, breaks in tissue integrity, underdeveloped or overdeveloped clitoris, adhesions, neoplasms, and circulatory impairment.

Next, ask the patient to bear down as though she were straining during a bowel movement or during labor. Note any urinary incontinence or bulging of the vaginal vestibule that could indicate an overrelaxed pelvic support system. Note also an unusually tense fourchette, unbroken hymen, urethral abnormalities, or evidence of vaginal irritation or inflammation.

If you notice labial swelling or tenderness, insert your index finger into the posterior introitus and place your thumb along the lateral edge of the swollen or tender labium. Then check the Bartholin's gland by gently squeezing the labium; if discharge from the duct results, culture it.

If the patient's history suggests she may have an inflamed urethra, separate the labia with one hand and insert the water-moistened index finger of your other hand about 2½" (6.4

cm) into the anterior fornix. With the pad of your fingertip, gently press the anterior vaginal wall up into the urethra and pull outward, thus milking the urethra. Use Thayer-Martin medium for any resulting discharge; if Thayer-Martin medium is unavailable, obtain a specimen for Gram's staining.

Internal pelvic examination

Some examiners prefer to begin an internal pelvic examination using their fingers instead of a speculum. This allows quick discovery and removal of tampons or other foreign bodies without causing further trauma by an instrument. By using your fingers, you can also detect any deviation from the classic anterior position of the uterus and assess the vagina to determine the correct speculum size to use—thus preventing unnecessary contamination of equipment. A tense patient may relax more readily if you use your fingers to begin the examination.

For insertion, moisten your index and middle fingers with water rather than a lubricant, which would interfere with cytologic staining. Press your fingers into the posterior wall of the vagina as you insert them. Occasionally, the vagina may accommodate only one finger; in this case, keep your other fingers and thumb enclosed within your palm.

As your fingers enter the vagina, note how the vaginal walls softly engulf them. Record any tenderness or hardness you feel, except for the normally smooth firmness of the cervix on your fingertips when your fingers are almost fully inserted. Normally, the cervix measures about 1¼" (3 cm) in diameter and should move easily, without causing the patient discomfort. Note any variation in its position. (To continue the examination using palpation only, see *Palpation of Internal Structures.*)

Next, begin withdrawing your fingers, pressing the fingerpads posteriorly against the vagina. With your free hand, obtain the appropriate-sized speculum. Keep your fingers pressed at the posterior edge of the introitus, and ask the patient to bear down again, to relax her perineum. Slowly insert the closed speculum—long blade beneath the shorter one—diagonally into the vagina to avoid direct pressure on the sensitive urethra. (Try to avoid pulling the labial hair into the introitus.) Gently push the blades along the same slant

Palpation of Internal Structures

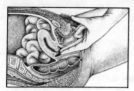

1 To palpate your patient's vagina, insert your fingers using the *palm up* position, as illustrated here. Note any tenderness, nodules, or deviations.

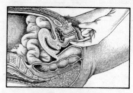

2 To palpate the urethra, sweep your fingers along the anterior vaginal wall, toward the vaginal opening. The urethra should be soft and tubular. Note any discharge or tenderness.

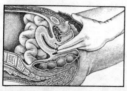

3 To palpate the cervix, sweep your fingers from side to side across the cervix and around the os. The cervix should feel moist, smooth, and firm but resilient and should protrude ½" to 1¼" (1.5 to 3 cm) into the vagina.

4 To palpate the fornix, place your fingers on the recessed area surrounding the cervix. Gently move the cervix; it should move ½" to ¾" (1.5 to 2 cm) in any direction.

that brought your fingers to the cervix. Then, gradually withdraw your fingers as you increase posterior pressure with the speculum.

When you can no longer advance the speculum, turn the blades horizontally so that the handles are vertical. To open the blades, press the handles together. Then, maneuver the blades until the cervix drops between them. (Locating the cervix is not always easy, but don't become discouraged or impatient.) As you maneuver the blades, note the vaginal rugae and the thick mucosa's multiple transverse ridges exposed between the length of the blades. In an elderly woman, the rugae may be atrophied to a shiny flat surface. Note also the type of discharge on the vaginal walls or on the bottom blade.

When the cervix is in full view, note its shape, color, and mucosal integrity. Examine the os for discharge, lesions, intrauterine device strings, or ectropion; its normal shape depends on whether the woman is nulliparous or multiparous. The cervix should be smooth, round, and rosy-pink, free of ulcerations and nodules. Ovulating discharge should be clear and watery. Slightly bloody discharge is normal just before menstruation. Any other colored discharge is abnormal and needs to be described and cultured.

If the patient's history suggests that she may have a sexually transmitted disease, particularly gonorrhea, first culture any discharge with Thayer-Martin medium. If you are using a metal speculum, lock the thumbscrew to keep the blades in place while you obtain a specimen for culture (see *Using a Vaginal Speculum,* page 288).

Obtaining a Pap smear

After examining the patient's cervix, obtain a Papanicolaou (Pap) smear, with the speculum still in place (see *Pap Smear Tests,* page 289).

Using a Vaginal Speculum

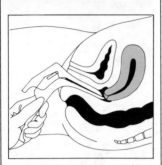

1 To properly insert the speculum into your patient's vagina, begin with the blades pointing down and the speculum handles at a 45° angle to the floor. Gently insert the speculum against the posterior vaginal wall. Move the speculum so the handle is vertical to the floor.

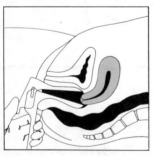

2 When the cervix is in view, open the blades as far as possible and lock them. If the speculum's correctly placed, you should be able to view the cervix.

When you've completed your examination, unlock the speculum blades and close them slowly, as you begin withdrawing the speculum. Before the blades reach the vaginal opening, close them completely. Then, withdraw the speculum from the vagina.

Usually, samples are taken from at least two areas. First, sample the squamous-columnar junction, where abnormalities that may indicate dysplasia or in situ carcinoma first appear.

This cellular sample is called an *endocervical specimen.* You can easily obtain it by inserting a cotton swab, through the speculum, ½″ (1 cm) beyond the external os, then rolling it several times between your thumb and index finger. (If you can't insert the swab beyond the external os, adhesions or neoplasms may be obstructing the canal's patency.) Clear cervical mucus should be present on the swab when you remove it. Gently wipe the swab on a glass slide marked *EC* (endocervical). Because cervical cells are fragile, fix the smear immediately with solution or a light, even spray. Then fan the solution dry.

To obtain the second sample, called the *cervical scrape,* press the longer, sculptured tip of the spatula into the external os and turn it clockwise a full revolution. Remove the spatula and gently smear the scraped cellular material on a clean glass slide marked *cerv* (cervical). If a patient has a history of cancer treated by hysterectomy, scrape the surgical stump and note the nature of the scrape on the laboratory slip and on the slide.

With the scrape completed, withdraw the speculum slowly. As the cervix relaxes, release the thumbscrew or allow the blades to close slightly. Again, observe the vaginal walls. Then press the blades posteriorly and diagonally as they close completely. After you've removed the speculum, examine the pool of mucus that will have collected in the bottom blade. If the mucus is colored or odorous, culture it. Inform the patient that she may experience some spotting after the specimens are obtained and that this is normal. If your patient is scheduled for a Pap smear but vaginitis is present, defer the Pap smear until a week after treatment is completed. (Acute inflammation from vaginitis can cause a cellular dysplasia that mimics early forms of cancer.)

Bimanual examination

You'll usually perform a bimanual (vaginoabdominal) examination of a patient while standing. To begin, generously lubricate your gloved index and third fingers. (Tell the patient she'll feel an initial cold sensation from the lubricating jelly.) Insert your fingers into the vagina and move them up to the cervix. Explore for tenderness or lesions. First, place your fingers in the anterior fornix (see *Bimanual Vaginal Examination,* page 290). Then,

Pap Smear Tests

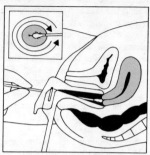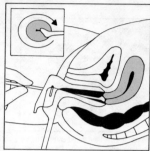

Before you take a Pap smear, review these instructions:

To obtain an endocervical specimen, use a cotton swab, as illustrated on the left. Rotate the swab clockwise and counterclockwise, as shown in the inset. Roll the swab on the properly labeled slide. Then, immediately immerse the slide in fixative.

To take a cervical scrape, use a spatula to obtain the cervical sample, as illustrated on the right. Follow the same guidelines as you would for the endocervical specimen, with these two exceptions: Rotate the spatula only *once* clockwise (as shown in the inset) *and smear* the sample on the properly labeled slide in a single circular motion.

Your institution may categorize laboratory results as follows:
- *Class I:* absence of atypical or abnormal cells
- *Class II:* atypical cytology but no evidence of malignancy (in many cases, the result of a temporary or chronic vaginitis)
- *Class III:* cytology suggestive of but not conclusive for malignancy
- *Class IV:* cytology strongly suggestive of malignancy
- *Class V:* cytology conclusive for malignancy.

If your patient's test result is Class II, Class III, or Class IV, reassure her that this does not necessarily mean she has cancer. Further testing is necessary. But because the Pap test is only an indicator, some doctors prefer to repeat the test. If your patient has vaginitis, defer repeating the test until several days after treatment is completed.

slip your other hand under the drape, place it on the patient's abdomen, halfway between the umbilicus and the symphysis pubis, and press down toward the cervix. Keep the hand in the patient's vagina aligned with the forearm of your external hand. If your patient is tense, let her press down on her abdomen with her own hand. As she relaxes, place her hand on top of yours as you proceed.

Use your fingers curled on the patient's perineum to press the fingers in the vagina inward and to locate the uterus. The fundus should be smooth, firm, mobile, nontender, and situated midline behind the symphysis pubis. If you can't feel the uterus in this position, direct your fingers into the posterior fornix and again try to palpate the uterus. If the uterus is en-

larged, suspect pregnancy or tumors (either necessitates additional laboratory work). If the patient's uterus is retroverted, you may be unable to palpate the fundus through the vagina.

Next, move your external hand to one of the lower abdominal quadrants and the hand in the vagina to the ipsilateral fornix. From this position, check one side of the patient's adnexa (ovaries, fallopian tubes, and supporting tissues). Normally, you can palpate the ovaries if the patient is sufficiently relaxed and not obese. The fallopian tubes and supporting tissue are usually not palpable, and if the woman is 3 to 5 years beyond menopause, her ovaries may not be palpable either. If you do feel an ovary in a postmenopausal woman, suspect an ovarian tumor.

Bimanual Vaginal Examination

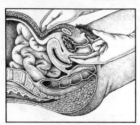

1 To palpate the uterus and anterior fornix, direct your index and middle fingers toward the patient's anterior fornix. In this position you should feel part of the anterior uterine wall. Place your other hand on the abdomen, just above the symphysis pubis, to palpate the posterior uterine wall.

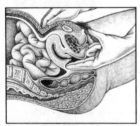

2 To palpate the posterior fornix, direct your index and middle fingers toward the patient's posterior fornix. Press upward and forward so that you can palpate the anterior uterine wall with your abdominally placed hand.

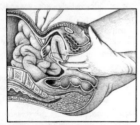

3 To palpate the adnexa, direct your index and middle fingers toward the patient's right lateral fornix and place your other hand on the patient's lower right quadrant. Palpate right and left sides.

Continue palpating. Note any uterine or adnexal masses, ovarian size, mobility, consistency, and shape. Then, palpate the other side.

Remove your hand from the patient's vagina. (If you suspect gonorrhea, replace your glove with a clean one, to prevent transferring infection from the vagina to the rectum, and lubricate it.) Insert your index finger into the patient's vagina and your third finger into the rectum. (Tell her beforehand that this may stimulate an urge to defecate.) Repeat the bimanual examination, using the rectal finger to palpate the rectovaginal septum, the cul-de-sac, the uterosacral ligaments, and possibly the fundus, if your patient has a retroverted or retroflexed uterus.

Proceed with a rectal examination (see page 230), using your index finger for palpation.

If your patient complains of leg cramps during the examination, slide the table tray forward and place her feet on it. Or, ask her to slide back on the table and rest her feet on its corners.

Pediatric assessment

Extent of the examination
The extent of a gynecologic examination for a pediatric patient depends on the child's age and her chief complaint. Inspection and palpation of the external genitalia usually suffice for a well-child examination. In some cases, you may also want to include inspection and palpation of her breasts and abdomen.

Bimanual palpation is never performed on a premenarchal child unless a serious gynecologic problem exists, such as anomalies of the external genitalia, vaginal bleeding (in a girl under age 8), or a possible foreign body in the vagina. It should be done only by a specially prepared examiner.

Perform a complete examination on a postmenarchal adolescent if you suspect a gynecologic problem, if the patient is sexually active, if she practices birth control, or if she requests information on contraception.

Positioning the pediatric patient
The way you position a child for an assessment of her external genitalia depends mainly on her age. You should also consider other individual factors, such as her size and the extent

of her sexual activity. Use the following guidelines:

• *Birth to age 3.* Position the child on the parent's lap, with her back reclining against the parent's chest at a 45° angle. To facilitate your examination, have the parent hold the child's knees against her chest.

• *Ages 3 to 5.* An examining table may be used for a child in this age-group. Position the table with the head at a 30° angle and rest the child against the incline. Have the parent hold the child's knees against her chest.

• *Ages 6 to 15.* The child should lie flat or at a slightly upward angle on an examining table, in a modified lithotomy position—legs flexed at the knees, heels close to the buttocks. Separate the knees so that the genitalia are visible. Have the mother, if present, stand at the head of the table and help the child keep her knees spread.

• *Over age 15.* Use the lithotomy position, as for an adult.

Examining the pediatric patient

When you examine the pediatric patient's breasts, remember that development doesn't actually begin until age 8 or 9. However, you may notice a firm, flat, buttonlike structure beneath the nipples, evidence of initial breast tissue growth.

After warming your hands, palpate the child's abdomen thoroughly. You'll feel the ovaries high in the pelvis. Because of the small pelvic cavity, if an ovarian tumor is present, it will be palpable toward midabdomen.

Before you begin the actual pelvic examination, tell the child to inform you immediately if she experiences any discomfort. First, make a general assessment of the external genitalia, noting any signs of poor perineal hygiene. If a dermatologic condition exists on the external genitalia, consider possible nutritional deficiencies, especially of the B complex vitamins. Begin your examination of the patient's genitalia by inspecting for the presence of pubic hair. Inspect and palpate the labia and clitoris for abnormal size for the child's age and for adhesions and signs of infection. Inspect the urethral meatus for redness, rashes, abnormal positioning (midline is normal), and discharge. Inspect the vaginal introitus for lesions, redness, swelling, rashes, and discharge. For maximum visualization of the introitus, ask the child to cough when you separate her labia. A foul-smelling, blood-streaked purulent discharge may indicate the presence of a foreign body. A domelike, outwardly bulging, purple-red membrane may indicate an imperforate hymen. (The membrane's appearance is caused by the collection of menstrual fluid behind it.) Finally, inspect and, if necessary, palpate the perineum for redness, rashes, and lesions.

If you must inspect the vagina with a speculum, remember that a premenarchal child's vagina is normally short and narrow, and the cervix is flat. Use a pediatric speculum (⅖″ to ⅗″ or 1 to 1.5 cm wide) for a child or sexually inactive adolescent and a small adult speculum for a sexually active adolescent.

Educational experience

Your assessment of the adolescent patient should be an educational experience for her. Begin by explaining the examination procedures to the patient and to her parent. (Usually her mother brings her for the examination.) If the patient prefers that her mother not be present during the examination, tactfully ask the mother to leave the room. Use visual aids to supplement your explanations. Most young women are receptive to the idea of viewing their genitalia in a mirror during the examination. You might use one, if appropriate, to teach the patient about female anatomy.

Pediatric gynecologic disorders

The following gynecologic disorders occur most commonly among children and adolescents:

• *Nonspecific vulvovaginitis.* This common disorder in premenarchal girls may be caused by a number of conditions, including poor perineal hygiene, respiratory tract infections (a child's hand may carry organisms from the upper respiratory tract to the vaginal area), skin infections and infected wounds, intestinal parasites, and foreign bodies. In most instances, the patient's mother notices the discharge or inflammation and seeks medical attention. The child may also complain of pruritus or dysuria. The vaginal discharge may be scanty or profuse, serous or purulent, but its appearance is not diagnostic.

Vaginitis is also a common complaint in the adolescent. *Candida albicans* is the most common causative organism. Other etiologic factors include birth control pills, deodorants, bactericidal soaps, antibiotics (for acne), and high-carbohydrate diets.

• *Genital injuries.* Most genital injuries are caused by falls, but they may also result from kicking, beating, or sexual assault. When confronted with such an injury in a young girl, inspect for injuries elsewhere on her body. Inspection may reveal vulval contusions and lacerations, vaginal wall lacerations (usually accompanied by vulval injuries), and vaginal hematomas. Depending on the injury, a doctor may order a general anesthetic in order to perform a pelvic examination, urethroscopy, or cystoscopy.

• *Genital tumors.* Although genital tumors in girls under age 14 are uncommon, almost every type of tumor found in women has been reported among girls in this age-group. About 50% of all genital tumors in children are malignant or premalignant. Signs and symptoms of genital tumors include chronic genital ulcer, nontraumatic swelling of the external genitalia, protruding vaginal tissue, bloody discharge, abdominal pain or gross enlargement before age 9, and premature sexual maturation.

• *Precocious puberty.* This condition is characterized by onset of sexual maturation before age 9. Breast development, pubic hair growth, and general acceleration of bodily growth usually precede uterine bleeding by several months. True precocious puberty must be differentiated from *pseudoprecocious puberty.* In true precocious puberty, the ovaries mature and pubertal changes proceed in an orderly manner. In pseudoprecocious puberty, genitalia mature and secondary sex characteristics appear with no corresponding ovarian maturation.

Approximately 85% of all cases of true precocious puberty are caused by early development and activation of the endocrine glands. Other causes include hypothyroidism and central nervous system disorders, such as encephalitis, intracranial neoplasms, McCune-Albright syndrome, and congenital anomalies.

• *Adolescent menstrual problems.* Establishing a regular menstrual cycle often preoccupies teenage girls, who associate it with being normal, feminine, and fertile. An adolescent who hasn't begun to menstruate may feel inadequate and anxious. Careful patient teaching on your part will help dispel her anxiety.

Irregular menstrual function may be accompanied by hemorrhage and resulting anemia. Ask a girl who has this problem how many sanitary napkins or tampons she uses daily and how often she changes them. A complete blood count may be necessary to evaluate blood loss.

An adolescent patient with primary dysmenorrhea usually complains of lower abdominal or back pain during the first 12 to 24 hours of menstruation. Refer such a patient to a doctor for a further evaluation of possible organic problems.

Geriatric assessment

History and physical examination

The history questions you'll ask an elderly patient and your physical examination of her reproductive system are basically the same as for a younger woman. However, you'll need to modify your approach to both aspects of the assessment process to deal effectively with the unique problems encountered by elderly women—especially those related to genital atrophy.

A complete gynecologic history of a geriatric patient should include her age at onset of menopause and specific conditions associated with menopause. Did menstrual flow diminish or increase with onset of menopause? Did she experience hot flashes? How long before onset of menopause was her menstrual cycle irregular? Did she notice any psychological changes, such as depression, moodiness, or irritability, as menopause approached?

Also note any bleeding that may have occurred since menopause started. Bleeding that occurs more than 12 months after a woman's last menstrual period must be investigated. If menopause has not yet begun, question your patient about the regularity of her periods. Has the flow recently become lighter or heavier?

Next, tactfully ask the patient about her sexual activity. If she is sexually active, inquire about pain on intercourse and use of lubricant, if any. Also ask if she has symptoms of pelvic relaxation. What are her elimination habits?

When you review an elderly woman's body

systems, keep in mind that diminishing estrogen levels can contribute to osteoporosis, a decrease in bone mass that afflicts about 25% of postmenopausal women and results in kyphosis, decreased height, and sometimes fractures.

When you begin the pelvic examination, remember that you may need to use a small speculum because of the decreased vaginal size in older women. To facilitate insertion, dampen the speculum with warm water; don't use a lubricant, because it may alter Pap smear results. Proceed slowly. Abrupt insertion of the speculum can damage sensitive degenerating tissue.

When you perform the bimanual examination, remember that the ovaries normally regress with age, and you may not be able to palpate them.

Gynecologic disorders in geriatric patients

The most common gynecologic disorders in postreproductive women are the following:

● *Vulval disorders.* External agents easily damage the vulva's atrophic skin and mucosa, resulting in irritation or abrasions. *Dyspareunia* results or increases when vulval shrinkage reduces the size of the vaginal introitus. Introital distention may cause lacerations (this condition is less common among women who have regular intercourse). Estrogenic cream applied locally may improve the condition. Intense *vulval itching* may result from sensitive vulval mucosa, senile vulvitis, senile vaginitis, urinary incontinence, or poor perineal hygiene. Underlying causes include infection, nutritional deficiency, allergy, trauma, and psychogenic factors.

● *Vaginal disorders.* Estrogen depletion can produce *atrophic* or *senile vaginitis.* Monilial infection may cause superficial vaginal ulcers that will bleed when touched. Monilial infection is often accompanied by diabetes mellitus. As the infection heals, adhesions may develop between the ulcerated areas. *Trichomonas* and *Hemophilus* infections are uncommon in elderly women.

● *Uterine disorders.* Superficial ulceration may develop on an atrophied endometrium, possibly accompanied by spotting or bleeding. (Postmenopausal bleeding may also originate from the cervix, the vagina, or the vulva.) Bleeding that occurs at least 1 year after menopause may indicate a malignant tumor in the uterus.

● *Reproductive cancers.* During the early stages, such cancers are usually asymptomatic. Breast cancer is the most common malignant neoplasm in women. Whereas cervical cancer occurs most often in women between ages 40 and 44, endometrial cancer is most common in women between ages 60 and 64. Ovarian cancer affects more women between ages 65 and 69 than in any other age-group, and the incidence remains high until about age 79.

Guide to Female Reproductive Disorders

DISORDER	CHIEF COMPLAINT	
Acute pelvic inflammatory disease (PID)	• *Discharge:* history of vaginal discharge of variable duration • *Pain:* sharp, bilateral, and cramping, usually in lower quadrants • *Abnormal uterine bleeding:* irregular bleeding and/or longer, heavier menstrual periods	
Atrophic vaginitis	• *Discharge:* follows intercourse or long walks; may go unnoticed by patient • *Pain:* vaginal burning and soreness; postcoital discomfort and dyspareunia possible • *Abnormal uterine bleeding:* spotting possible after douching or after intercourse • *Pruritus:* vaginal itching	
Bartholinitis (Bartholin adenitis)	• *Pain:* present in Bartholin's gland; reddened, tender overlying skin • *Lumps, masses, ulcerations:* large lump on one side of genitalia for several days	
Breast cancer	• *Discharge:* from nipple, usually bloody • *Pain:* absent; breast pain possible but infrequent • *Lumps, masses, ulcerations:* lump in breast	
Carcinoma of cervix in situ (preinvasive)	• *Pain:* absent • *Lumps, masses, ulcerations:* absent • *Abnormal uterine bleeding:* absent	
Chlamydia	• *Discharge:* purulent, rare • *Pain:* dysuria	
Condylomata acuminata (venereal warts)	• *Pain:* usually painless but pruritic unless warts become infected or irritated by friction; intercourse may be painful if condylomata	

HISTORY	PHYSICAL EXAMINATION AND DIAGNOSTIC STUDIES
• With PID: history of recent abortion, intra-uterine device use, sexually transmitted disease, dysuria, severe dysmenorrhea; with acute PID: nausea, vomiting, and elevated temperature, indicating peritoneal involvement or abscess involvement • Acute PID may become chronic, with accompanying complications of pelviperitoneal abscess, massive adhesions, and sterility. • PID may be confused with ruptured appendix, degenerating fibroids, ectopic pregnancy, or perforation of gastrointestinal pelvic abscesses caused by uterine perforations.	• Pelvic examination reveals tender cervix; bilateral adnexal enlargement, tenderness, immobility. • Laboratory analysis usually confirms diagnosis; cultured organism is usually *Streptococcus* or *Neisseria gonorrhoeae*.
• May have had bilateral oophorectomy and/or cessation of estrogen therapy. • Postmenopausal onset • If untreated, may lead to secondary infection, altered sexual self-esteem, and possibly marital discord and depressive reaction.	• Dry vulva, possibly vulvitis, friable mucosa, few or absent vaginal rugae, pale and shiny vaginal mucosa, and small and tender cervix
• Predisposing factors: Frequent sexual activity; use of feminine hygiene product. • Abscess or chronic infection possible	• Tender, hot, hard swelling without purulent drainage on posterior labium • Culture taken
• Most common in white women of middle or upper socioeconomic class and over age 35, and in those with a family history of breast cancer • History of long menstrual cycles; early menses or late menopause; first pregnancy after age 35; endometrial or ovarian cancer	• Possible enlarged, shrunken, or dimpled breast, nipple erosion, retraction, discharge; abnormality may not be obvious. • Palpation reveals lump, which is usually nontender, firm or hard, irregularly shaped and fixed to skin or fixed to underlying tissues; possible lymphadenopathy. • Laboratory tests include mammography, biopsy, and thermography.
• Predisposing factors include sexual activity before age 20, continued exposure to multiple sexual partners, infection, genital herpes. • Usually asymptomatic	• Lesion frequently overlooked; friable cervix and erosions of the ectocervix possible • Laboratory tests include Pap test, colposcopy, examination of biopsy specimen.
• Predisposing factors include frequent sexual activity and sex with partner who doesn't use condom. Usually asymptomatic. • Most common in the teens or 20s. • Complications: Trachoma; conjunctivitis; lymphogranuloma venereum; cervical cancer; salpingitis; newborn conjunctivitis and pneumonia; postpartum endometritis.	• Rough cervical patches; thickened cervix possible but not common • Culture taken; antibody titer urinalysis performed.
• May accompany trichomoniasis; resembles vulval cancer	• Inspection reveals soft, wartlike irregularly shaped growths on vulva and perineum and *(continued)*

Guide to Female Reproductive Disorders *(continued)*

DISORDER	CHIEF COMPLAINT	
Condylomata acuminata (venereal warts) *(continued)*	are large and/or extensive. • *Lumps, masses, ulcerations:* soft warts on perineal and perianal areas	
Cystocele (several degrees)	• *Pain:* dysuria, with infection, dragging back pain • *Lumps, masses, ulcerations:* fullness at vaginal opening	
Endometrial cancer	• *Pain:* present in later invasive stages of disease • *Abnormal uterine bleeding:* spotting for days to months; may go undetected	
Endometriosis	• *Pain:* menstrual; referred to the rectum and lower sacral or coccygeal regions; dyspareunia probable with uterosacral involvement or vaginal extension; pain on defecation with uterosacral involvement or vaginal extension; dysuria possible • *Abnormal uterine bleeding:* excessive, prolonged, or frequent, with no specific pattern	
Fibroadenoma of breast	• *Pain:* absent • *Lumps, masses, ulcerations:* well-defined mass or masses found in breast	
Fibrocystic breast disease breast (mammary dysplasia, cystic adenosis, cystic disease, cystic mastitis)	• *Discharge:* may be slight • *Pain:* cyst pain and tenderness possible, especially in premenstrual phase of cycle • *Lumps, masses, ulcerations:* thickened, nodular areas in breast (usually bilateral)	
Foreign-body vaginitis	• *Discharge:* purulent and fetid, lasting about 1 week • *Pain:* vaginal	
Functional ovarian cysts (follicle cysts, corpus luteum cysts)	• *Pain:* with large follicle cysts, mild pelvic discomfort, low back pain, or deep dyspareunia possible; with corpus luteum cysts, localized pain and tenderness possible • *Abnormal uterine bleeding:* with follicle cysts, occasional menstrual irregularities; with corpus luteum cysts, delayed menstruation, followed by persistent bleeding	

HISTORY	PHYSICAL EXAMINATION AND DIAGNOSTIC STUDIES
• Predisposing factors include frequent sexual activity, birth control pill use, prior pregnancy, massive immunosuppressive therapy, sex with partner who doesn't use condom.	in perianal, vaginal, and/or cervical areas; cauliflower or deep rose-colored lesions • Dark-field examination of cells from warts show vascularization of epidermal cells.
• Predisposing factors include multiparity, obesity, chronic ascites, prolonged labors, instrument deliveries, chronic cough, heavy-object lifting. May be asymptomatic • May result in withdrawal, depression	• Inspection reveals soft, reducible, mucosal mass bulging into anterior introitus; with Valsalva's maneuver, the mass increases and urine may squirt or dribble from meatus. • Laboratory tests include urinalysis.
• History of previous estrogen therapy, nulliparousness, obesity, and possibly diabetes, hypertension, or previous curettage, sterility, or poor fertility • Most common in menopausal or postmenopausal women	• Brown stain or red stain on crotch clothing; possibly cervical lesion. • Palpation may reveal uterus or adnexal mass, usually nontender. • Laboratory tests include tissue examination by D and C or by section biopsy.
• Most common in women ages 25 to 45 • History of menstrual disturbances • Commonly accompanied by constipation, pain with defecation during menstruation, infertility	• Multiple tender nodules palpable along the uterosacral ligaments or in the rectovaginal septum of the posterior fornix of the vagina. • Diagnosis can be confirmed only by visualization of the lesion: accomplished directly, with external lesions, or by laparotomy or endoscopy with internal lesions. • Uterus may be fixed in retroposition; severe pain if manipulated. • Endometrial cysts present as irregular enlargement of ovary.
• Most common in women in their teens or early 20s • Asymptomatic other than mass	• Round, firm, discrete, movable mass, ⅜" to 2" (1 to 5 cm) in diameter; usually solitary but may be multiple and bilateral. • Excision necessary for definitive diagnosis.
• Most common in women during productive years • May be exacerbated by caffeine intake	• Palpation of breast reveals single or multiple masses; usually bilateral, mobile, well-defined and tender. • Diagnosis established by aspiration of cysts or by biopsy.
• Predisposing factors include pessary, tampon, or diaphragm use; emotional or memory instability; inadequate sex education. Complications include vaginal fistula, cervical erosion, and adhesions.	• Obstructing mass in vagina that causes pain on removal • Possible laceration of cervix or vaginal mucosa • Culture taken
• Most common in women ages 20 to 40 • May be asymptomatic	• Bimanual palpation may reveal presence of cyst. • Laparoscopy or laporotomy may be performed to confirm diagnosis.

Guide to Female Reproductive Disorders *(continued)*

DISORDER	CHIEF COMPLAINT	
Genital herpes II	• *Discharge:* watery; accompanies appearance of lesions • *Pain:* blisters and/or sores for preceding 1 or 2 days; prodromal symptoms of burning or tingling in genital area possible; *may* be asymptomatic; severe vulval pain following appearance of lesions; severe dysuria or retention possible • *Lumps, masses, ulcerations:* blisters and ulcers covering extensive areas of the vulva and the perianal skin • *Pruritus:* mild itching in genital area preceding eruption of lesions	
Gonorrhea	• *Discharge:* slight to profuse, purulent • *Pain:* dysuria • *Pruritus:* may be present	
Hemophilus vaginalis	• *Discharge:* fishy odor; gray to yellow-white; soaks through clothing; may last for months • *Pain:* little or none	
Mammary duct ectasia	• *Discharge:* from nipple, accompanied by nipple retraction • *Pain:* in affected areas • *Lumps, masses, ulcerations:* rubbery lesions in breasts; inflammation	
Mastitis	• *Pain:* present, accompanied by tenderness in breast • *Lumps, masses, ulcerations:* hard, reddened breast	
***Monilia* (candidiasis)**	• *Discharge:* heavy, with yeasty, sweet odor for preceding 3 to 4 days • *Pain:* dysuria • *Pruritus:* present, with itching	

HISTORY	PHYSICAL EXAMINATION AND DIAGNOSTIC STUDIES
• Most common from late teens to early 30s • Predisposing factors include recent gynecologic or lower urinary tract examination, frequent sexual activity, sex with partner who doesn't use condom, recurrent infection. • If untreated, primary lesions persist for 3 to 6 weeks and heal spontaneously. • Symptoms of fever, malaise, or anorexia possible 3 to 7 days after exposure. • Complications include fever; enlarged, tender inguinal lymph nodes; urinary retention, leading to urinary tract infection, cervical cancer; spontaneous abortion or premature delivery; severely infected newborn if delivered vaginally; possibly viremia.	• Cervix may be covered with yellow-gray film; urethra, bladder, and vulva may be exquisitely tender. • Culture of vesicle or ulcer fluid; Tzanck test confirms diagnosis.
• Frequent sexual activity is a predisposing factor. Usually asymptomatic • Most common in the teens and 20s • Complications: urethritis; proctitis; salpingitis; pharyngitis; stomatitis; conjunctivitis. • If untreated, may lead to systemic infection, including PID, skin eruptions on trunk and legs, arthritis, and tendonitis.	• Urethral meatus may be erythematous and, when milked, may exude pus. • Cervix may be reddened and edematous. • Gram's stain smear for gram-negative diplococci; culture on Thayer-Martin media to confirm diagnosis
• Predisposing factors: Frequent sexual activity; birth control pill use; frequent douching; sex partner who doesn't use condom. • Episodes recur, leading to cervical erosion. • If untreated, may lead to contact dermatitis and secondary infection.	• Wet smear (clue cells) identifies organism.
• Most common in early stage menopausal and menopausal women.	• Inspection reveals nipple discharge and, possibly, nipple retraction. • Palpation reveals subareolar ducts as rubbery lesions filled with a pastelike material; enlarged regional lymph nodes possible.
• Usually occurs 3rd or 4th week postpartum; almost always preceded by history of cracked nipples • If untreated, may evolve into breast abscess, with palpable fluctuance and painful axillary lymphadenopathy	• Firm, tender, warm and reddened area apparent in affected breast • Culture usually yields offending organism: *Staphylococcus aureus*.
• Emotional stress, birth control pill use, prior pregnancy, diabetes mellitus, antibiotic or steroid therapy, severe illness. • Premenstrual onset. Episodes recur; may lead to chronic cervicitis and erosion. • May lead to excoriation/secondary infection.	• White curdlike profuse discharge on vulva, vagina, and cervix; erythema; pruritus; edema of vulvovaginal area • Culture; wet smear with 10% potassium hydroxide to confirm diagnosis

Guide to Female Reproductive Disorders *(continued)*

DISORDER	CHIEF COMPLAINT	
Ovarian carcinoma	• *Pain:* abdominal, in later stage of disease • *Lumps, masses, ulcerations:* mass in lower abdomen; may be first indication of disease; ascites possible • *Abnormal uterine bleeding:* irregular or postmenopausal bleeding possible but infrequent	
Primary syphilis	• *Discharge:* none • *Pain/Pruritis:* none • *Lumps, masses, ulcerations:* solitary, hard, oval ulcer (chancre) on vulva, perineum, labia, cervix, and possibly breasts, fingers, lips, oral mucosa, tongue for several days to weeks	
Prolapsed uterus (several degrees)	• *Pain:* heaviness in pelvis • *Lumps, masses, ulcerations:* feels as if patient's sitting on a ball • *Abnormal uterine bleeding:* menometrorrhagia	
Pubic lice	• *Pruritus:* severe itching of genital hair areas for several days	
Rectocele (several degrees)	• *Pain:* backaches possible • *Lumps, masses, ulcerations:* fullness at vaginal opening	
Toxic shock syndrome (TSS)	• *Pain:* abdominal; myalgia, arthralgia, headache	
Trichomoniasis	• *Discharge:* frothy, green-yellow, malodorous, profuse; lasts several days • *Pain:* possible vaginal soreness, burning, dyspareunia • *Pruritus:* vaginal itching	
Uterine leiomyomas (fibroids and myomas)	• *Pain:* in pelvic area; sensation of weight or dysmenorrhea • *Lumps, masses, ulcerations:* lump in lower abdomen possible; with large tumors, general enlargement of abdomen • *Abnormal uterine bleeding:* excessive menstrual flow and/or irregular bleeding	

HISTORY	PHYSICAL EXAMINATION AND DIAGNOSTIC STUDIES
• Possible urinary frequency/constipation • Most common in early stage menopausal or postmenopausal, nulliparous women • Usually asymptomatic in early stages • May be secondary site of cancer	• Lower genital tract usually normal, but displaced cervix possible. • Bimanual palpation usually delineates ovarian mass; malignant tumors are partly solid, bilateral.
• Frequent sexual activity is a predisposing factor. • May be asymptomatic between stages	• Enlarged inguinal lymph nodes possible • Fluorescent treponemal antibody absorption test and dark-field examination for syphilis
• Predisposing factors: Those for cystocele and rectocele, history of sacral nerve disorders, diabetic neuropathy, pelvic tumors. • Common with cystocele and rectocele • Commonly accompanied by urinary tract infection, constipation, and painful defecation but may be asymptomatic	• Cervix palpable, closer to introitus, and can be pushed in caudally; in advanced stage, mucosa of exposed mass outside introitus is ulcerated and friable.
• Predisposing factors include frequent sexual activity and household history of lice. • Lice transferred primarily by direct contact. • May infect any hairy part of body	• Oval, light-colored swellings near base of hair shafts; red, scratched, petechial and/or edematous skin under pubic hair; pubic hair feels bumpy and irregular due to lice ova.
• Predisposing factors: Multiparity; obesity; chronic ascites; prolonged labors; instrument deliveries; chronic cough; heavy lifting. • Chronic constipation, laxative/enema dependency, diarrhea may be present. • Most common in postmenopausal women	• Inspection reveals mass bulging into posterior introitus.
• Tampon use during active vaginal bleeding; previous episodes of TSS • Can occur also in males • May seem to be viral systemic illness	• Temperature over 102° F. (38.9° C.), nausea, vomiting, hypotension, photophobia, abdominal pain, myalgia, arthralgia, headache • Culture of *Staphylococcus aureus* from vaginal vault
• Predisposing factors: Prior pregnancy; sex with partner who doesn't use condom; close contact with infected person. • Premenstrual onset • Most common in childbearing years • Complications may include urinary tract infection, inflammation of Skene's and Bartholin's glands, increased cervical cancer risk.	• Erythema and edema of vulvovagina • Raised petechial lesions (strawberry epithelia) on vagina and cervix • Wet-mount smear of vaginal secretions made with physiologic saline (motile protozoa)
• History of involuntary infertility or repeat spontaneous abortion • Irritability, increased frequency of urination, possibly dysuria, constipation, and occasionally pain on defecation.	• Bimanual examination may reveal one or more nodular outgrowths on the uterine surface or within the uterine wall.

15

Nervous System

Evaluation of a patient's cerebral function, cranial nerves, sensory and motor functions, and reflexes can seem overwhelming. But the fact is that although tests for neurologic status are extensive, they're also basic and straightforward. They measure a patient's thought processes and coordination, as well as his ability to receive stimuli and respond accordingly. Your daily patient care may routinely include various parts of a neurologic examination.

The implications of neurologic assessment are far-reaching for the patient's nervous system and for his other body systems. The nervous system is related, directly or indirectly, to every other body system. Consequently, patients who suffer from diseases of other body systems can develop related neurologic impairment. Overall, your knowledge of nervous system functioning and appropriate assessment techniques will enhance your patient care and may save some patients from irreversible neurologic damage.

History data

Biographical data

Although a neurologic disorder can occur at any time in a person's life, some disorders occur most commonly within certain age-groups. For example, the incidence of muscular dystrophies, migraine headaches, and epilepsy is highest among children, adolescents, and young adults. Multiple sclerosis is most prevalent in young adults between ages 20 and 30. Parkinson's disease, Huntington's chorea, amyotrophic lateral sclerosis, and cerebrovascular accident most commonly affect persons over age 40.

History of present illness

The chief complaints most commonly associated with neurologic disorders are *headache/pain, motor disturbances* (including weakness, paresis, and paralysis), *seizures, sensory deviations,* and *altered states of consciousness* (see *Guide to Neurologic Disorders,* pages 322 to 337).

Here are some questions you may want to ask about these complaints to explore fully the history of your patient's present illness.

• **Headache/pain.** *Is the pain located across your forehead? On one side of your head? At the back of your head and neck?* Pain that emanates from specific areas of the head characterizes certain types of headaches. For example, tension headaches are often located in the occipital area, and migraine pain tends to be unilateral. *Is the pain tight (bandlike), boring, throbbing, steady, or dull?* Headaches can be identified by the quality of pain they produce. A dull, steady pain may indicate a tension (muscle) headache; severe or throbbing pain may indicate a vascular problem, such as a migraine headache. *Is the onset of pain sudden or gradual?* Migraine headaches may develop suddenly, with no warning, but are usually preceded by a prodromal disturbance. Headaches associated with hemorrhage characteristically occur suddenly and with increasing severity. *How long does the pain usually last? Is it continuous or recurrent?* Tension headaches may last from several hours to several days. Migraine headaches may also last this long. Cluster (histamine) headaches last about an hour.

Are the headaches occurring more frequently? A change in headache pattern may signal developing pathology. *Do the headaches occur in the evening? Do you wake up* with one during the night? Are the headaches worse when you wake up in the morning? Although tension headaches usually occur in the evening, a person may awaken in the morning with the headache. Patients who suffer from headaches caused by hypertension, inflammation, or tumors may awaken anytime with the pain. Cluster headaches often awaken the patient a few hours after he has fallen asleep.

Do you see flashing lights or shining spots or feel tingling, weakness, or numbness immediately before the headache occurs? These are common characteristics of the prodromal (premonitory) neurologic disturbance that frequently precedes a migraine headache.

Does the pain worsen when you cough, sneeze, or bend over? The Valsalva's maneuver may exacerbate a headache caused by an intracranial lesion, such as a subarachnoid hemorrhage.

Do you become nauseated or vomit during the headache? Such gastrointestinal distress may accompany a migraine headache or a brain tumor or hemorrhage. Have you recently been under a great deal of stress? Are you anxious or depressed? Headaches that occur daily for a prolonged period may be related to stress or depression.

What medication do you take for the headache? Is it effective? Aspirin is usually ineffective for migraine headaches. Do other approaches—lying down, applying heat, sleeping—relieve the headache? Some headaches respond to such techniques.

Would you describe the last headache you experienced as more severe than usual or possibly the worst you've ever had? How a particular headache differs from headaches a patient commonly experiences can give you valuable clues to the cause of his problem.

● **Motor disturbances.** How old were you when you first noticed the problem? Age is an important factor in identifying motor disturbances, such as epilepsy or parkinsonism. Did the problem occur suddenly? Sudden onset may indicate a vascular problem. Gradual onset usually indicates a dystrophy or a tumor. Is the problem constant or intermittent? A sign or symptom that is constant may indicate a muscle disorder or dystrophy; one that's intermittent may indicate impaired neuromuscular transmission. Does the problem occur

symmetrically or asymmetrically? A sign or symptom that presents symmetrically usually indicates a muscle disorder or a peripheral nerve disorder caused by a toxic substance. Asymmetrical presentations usually indicate central nervous system lesions, such as multiple sclerosis, or peripheral nerve disorders from systemic disease.

Do you have difficulty lifting objects, shaving, brushing your hair, walking, or climbing stairs? Such problems may indicate a myopathy in the proximal muscles of the affected arm or leg. Do you have difficulty turning doorknobs or picking up pins or similar objects? Do your feet or ankles turn easily, causing you to lose your balance or fall? Positive responses to these questions may indicate a peripheral nerve disorder (neuropathy). Does the problem occur after prolonged use of the affected arm or leg? Does it improve after rest? If so, your patient may have impaired neuromuscular transmission. Considering the symptoms you've described, would you say you've been more clumsy than weak? Clumsiness can indicate a problem related to the cerebellum (such as multiple sclerosis) or basal ganglia (such as Parkinson's disease); weakness can indicate a problem in the motor tracts.

Have you experienced tremors? How long? Do the tremors occur only in your hands or throughout your body? Tremors that occur only in the hands may be a sign of thyroid dysfunction, alcoholism, or Parkinson's disease. Tremors of the entire body are typical of anxiety or of delirium tremens, caused by alcoholism. Do the tremors worsen when you're resting or when you're trying to perform a task? Tremors that characterize disorders of the cerebellum begin after a voluntary movement and worsen as the movement continues. Tremors of Parkinson's disease characteristically occur when the patient is resting.

● **Seizures.** How old were you when you had your first seizure? When necessary, obtain information from a family member or friend. In children, seizures are commonly caused by birth injury, infection, epilepsy, or trauma. In adults, seizures can result from tumor, alcoholism, drugs, or trauma. In adults over age 60, vascular disease, tumor, and degenerative disease are possible causes of seizures. How often do the seizures occur? Frequency is an important factor in determining treatment.

How would you describe the seizures? Different types of seizures, such as focal motor seizures and petit mal seizures, produce characteristic movements, behavior, and sensory experiences. *Do flashing lights or sounds precipitate seizures?* Some seizures are induced by a certain type of sensory stimulus. *Do your seizures ever occur during times of stress or during alcohol consumption?* These conditions increase the possibility of a seizure. *Can you tell when a seizure is about to occur? Do you see, hear, smell, or feel anything unusual just prior to the seizure?* These characteristic preseizure symptoms or auras can help you identify the location of the disorder. *Do you regain full consciousness slowly or immediately?* Slow recovery can indicate a seizure disorder; immediate recovery, syncope. *What medication do you take for the seizures? Is it effective?* Inadequate therapy could remove the warning aura of seizures or cause undesirable side effects.

● *Sensory deviations.* Do you experience tingling, prickling, or numbness anywhere in your body? Ask the patient to indicate where on his body he feels the sensations. This will demonstrate the anatomic distribution of the lesion and will help identify the disorder. *Do you have difficulty perceiving pain, temperature changes, or touch?* Certain disorders produce a loss of sensation of any or all of the above.

● *Altered states of consciousness.* How long have you felt confused? Rapid onset of confusion can indicate metabolic encephalopathy or delirium; gradual onset usually indicates a degenerative disorder. *Does the confusion fluctuate?* This question can help you distinguish between an extracerebral disorder, such as metabolic encephalopathy, and a subdural hematoma caused by such intracerebral impairment as arteriosclerosis or senile dementia.

If the patient was found unconscious, where was he found? The answer will provide clues to the cause of the unconsciousness—for example, a toxic substance, drugs, or alcohol. Did the unconsciousness occur abruptly or gradually? Has the patient's level of consciousness fluctuated? Abrupt loss of consciousness may indicate a vascular accident. Gradual onset could result from metabolic, extracerebral,

toxic, or systemic causes. Fluctuating levels of consciousness can signal that systemic hypotension is affecting the brain. Did anything happen to the patient recently that could have exacerbated an existing condition, resulting in unconsciousness? An infection or a break in treatment of an existing condition can result in unconsciousness or coma.

Past history

Review the following significant health problems thoroughly when you take your patient's past history:

● *Head injury.* Head injury can lead to headache, seizures, or coma from increased pressure, fracture, or intracranial bleeding.

● *Birth trauma.* This is a common cause of seizures in children.

● *Recent infections.* Ear and sinus infections can cause headaches. Septicemia and pneumonia can cause confusion. Other infections can result in idiopathic polyneuritis.

● *Cardiovascular disorders.* In some patients, confusion may be a side effect of treatment with antihypertensives. Systemic hypotension causes reduced cerebral arterial perfusion, resulting in sensory and motor problems.

● *Respiratory disorders.* Any severe respiratory disorder can cause hypoxia, leading to confusion and coma.

● *Thyroid disorders.* Alterations in thyroid hormone secretions can change a patient's neurologic status. For example, patients suffering from hyperthyroidism commonly experience tremors and extreme overactivity— sometimes to the point of mania. Patients with hypothyroid conditions can experience weakness and coma. Thyroidectomy can result in myxedemic symptoms, including such mental status changes as lethargy and apathy.

● *Metabolic disorders.* In a patient with diabetes mellitus, hypoglycemia can result in confusion, seizures, and unconsciousness; hyperglycemia can cause lethargy and coma. Various neuropathies are classic complications of diabetes.

● *Urinary disorders.* Chronic renal failure can lead to uremic syndrome, characterized by confusion, convulsions, and coma.

● *Past neurologic testing.* The results of a patient's previous brain scan, computerized tomography scan, electroencephalography, skull X-ray, and lumbar puncture can usually provide pertinent information about his present problem.

● *Psychological disorders.* Chronic alcoholism and drug abuse can result in convulsions—especially during withdrawal—and produce such changes in a patient's neurologic status as neuropathy, delirium tremens, and confusion. Depression can cause confusion and should be clearly distinguished from organic changes, which sometimes also result in confusion.

● *Immunizations.* Inoculations can cause idiopathic polyneuritis.

● *Drugs.* Question the patient about his use of over-the-counter drugs for headaches, sleep disorders, and mental disturbances. Improper drug therapy can result in undesirable side effects and may exacerbate symptoms rather than improve them.

Family and psychosocial history

Some genetic diseases, such as Huntington's chorea, may be degenerative. Other genetic diseases, such as dystrophies, familial periodic paralysis, and Duchenne's disease, cause muscle weakness. The incidence of seizures is higher among patients whose family history shows idiopathic epilepsy. About 65% of persons suffering from migraine headaches show a family history of the disorder.

When you assess a patient with a neurologic disorder, consider that his home and work environment may be significant. Recent stress at home or at work and recent emotional disturbances or exposure to toxic substances (such as carbon monoxide, nitrates, or heavy metal fumes) can result in neurologic symptoms or can exacerbate an existing neurologic disorder.

Your review of the patient's activities of daily living should include questions about drug use. How much does the patient's condition interfere with his daily activities?

Review of systems

In your review of systems, ask the patient if he has experienced any of the following signs and symptoms:

● *Head.* When associated with fever, a headache and a stiff neck suggest infection or irritation of the meninges. Dizziness may be caused by influenza, high blood pressure, or impaired circulation to the brain.

● *Eyes.* Papilledema suggests increased intracranial pressure. Blindness may indicate tumors of the pituitary gland. Glaucoma can produce symptoms—such as headache—similar to those of neurologic disorders.

● *Respiratory.* A change in respiratory pattern (rate, depth, regularity) may indicate increasing intracranial pressure.

● *Musculoskeletal.* Muscle atrophy occurs in a variety of disorders of the motor cortex. Pain on movement of the spine may be caused by disease of the spinal disks, ligaments, or muscles. Certain signs indicate irritation or infection of the meninges. For example, Brudzinski's sign is positive when the patient's neck is flexed on his chest, causing flexion of both legs and thighs. Kernig's sign occurs when a patient (in the supine position) who has his hip flexed at a right angle cannot extend his leg.

● *Gastrointestinal.* Unexpected projectile vomiting may be an indication of increased intracranial pressure.

● *Reproductive.* Amenorrhea may be caused by a pituitary tumor.

Physical examination

Preparations

Ask your patient to remove his street clothes or pajamas and put on a hospital gown. (This allows you to inspect the patient's body for symmetry—an essential part of the physical examination—and allows the patient to move freely.) If he appears chilled or tense, drape him with a cloth or blanket, because his discomfort may otherwise interfere with the examination. Make sure you have the necessary examination equipment on hand (see *Examination Equipment,* page 306).

Plan your approach to a neurologic examination, keeping in mind that you can assess several areas at the same time. For example, you can combine assessment of your patient's mental status and speech with history-taking and your general survey, and assessment of several of the cranial nerves with examination of the head and neck. You can also combine inspection of your patient's arms and legs with evaluation of his peripheral vascular and musculoskeletal systems.

Examination Equipment

Before you begin the neurologic examination, gather this equipment:
- **Transparent millimeter ruler,** to measure pupil size and skin lesions
- **Tuning fork,** to test hearing and vibratory sensation
- **Stethoscope,** to auscultate for bruits
- **Penlight or flashlight,** to test pupillary reflexes
- **Tongue depressors,** to test gag reflex
- **Ophthalmoscope,** to assess eye grounds
- **Otoscope,** to examine ears
- **Toothpaste, tobacco, soap, cloves, or other familiar substances,** to assess sense of smell
- **Sugar, salt, and vinegar or lemon juice,** to assess sense of taste
- **Cotton wisp,** to assess light-touch perception
- **Coins or keys,** to test for tactile agnosia
- **Reflex hammer,** to test deep tendon reflexes
- **Safety pin,** to test pain and pressure perception
- **Test tubes of hot and cold water,** to test temperature perception
- **Snellen chart,** to test visual acuity

General survey and examination sequence

Begin a neurologic examination by performing a general survey of your patient, which may give you a clue to an underlying disease process. Check the patient's blood pressure and major arterial pulses bilaterally, because increased blood pressure and a decreased pulse rate may be signs of increased intracranial pressure.

Observe the size and shape of the patient's head and jaw. Inspect his nostrils and ear canals for patency (necessary to assess cranial nerves I and VIII, later in the examination). Observe his skin for rash, lesions, discoloration, or scars.

Palpate the patient's cranium for bony abnormalities, lumps, tenderness, and soft areas. Then palpate his carotid and temporal arteries for pulsations. Next, percuss his cranium firmly with your index and middle fingers, and then percuss his sinuses and mastoid processes for tenderness.

Moving to the patient's neck, auscultate bilaterally for bruits over the carotid artery: The presence of bruits indicates distortion of a blood vessel that could interfere with blood flow to the brain. Assess the patient's neck for suppleness by asking him to place his chin on his chest. He should be able to turn his head easily.

Finally, inspect the patient's spine for deformities, abnormal posture, and unusual hair growth. Palpate the vertebrae for structural abnormalities, pain, and tenderness.

Always examine a patient's nervous system in an orderly fashion, beginning with the highest levels of neurologic function and working down to the lowest. For this purpose, the complete examination is usually divided into tests for these five functions: *cerebral, cranial nerve, motor, sensory,* and *reflex.*

Cerebral function tests

To assess your patient's cerebral function, briefly evaluate his general appearance and behavior, level of consciousness and orientation, memory, general knowledge, arithmetic skill, and comprehension of abstract relationships and judgment. These tests, collectively known as the *mental status examination* (see pages 65 to 68), are designed to identify disturbing or abnormal mental processes. Be sure to take into account the patient's age and education. Inappropriate responses to your questions may be caused by these factors rather than by neurologic impairment.

You can perform part of the mental status examination—particularly the tests of orientation to time, person, and place and of memory—as you interview the patient. His subjective responses to your questions will allow you to make objective observations about his mental activity.

To determine a person's level of consciousness, note the flow of his speech, the quality of his voice, and the organization and clarity of his thoughts. Ask the patient to respond to such simple commands as "Close your eyes" and "Stick out your tongue." Note how promptly he responds. Also observe for apparent drowsiness or loss of contact.

To determine your patient's orientation to

person, place, and time, ask such questions as "What's your name? Where are you? What day is this?" If the patient was transferred several times because of surgery or diagnostic testing, accept a general response—for example, "the hospital"—to your questions about place. Don't expect him to remember his room number.

Assess your patient's ability to remember recent and past (remote) events—a function of the temporal lobe. Ask about past events with which he should be familiar. To test recent memory, show him two or three items and then ask him to recall them a few minutes later.

Speech results from the brain's ability to receive incoming verbal or written information (*receptive process*) and to communicate or send responses (*expressive process*). The brain's interpretation of the message occurs between the receptive and expressive processes.

By assessing the processes involved in speech, you can determine the general areas of dysfunction within the brain. For example, various types of aphasia relate directly to corresponding areas of brain dysfunction. Auditory-receptive aphasia results from temporal lobe dysfunction, whereas the visual-receptive form can be traced to disorders of the parieto-occipital area. Expressive aphasia in the form of an inability to write stems from a dysfunction of the posterior frontal lobe; the oral form of this type of aphasia suggests a problem in the inferoposterior frontal lobes.

To assess the receptive process involved in speech, which includes comprehension of both oral and written symbols, note your patient's response to simple commands when you test his level of consciousness. Then, ask the patient some questions that require an oral response of more than one word. Finally, ask him to read a paragraph from a newspaper and explain it to you in his own words.

Assessing the expressive process in speech also overlaps with testing for level of consciousness. Your patient's speech should be fluent, spontaneous, and clearly enunciated. Remember to judge it according to his native language, education, reading ability, and communication skills. If appropriate, make sure the patient wears his glasses or hearing aid during the examination, so you can record accurate responses (see *Abnormal Cranial Nerve Responses,* pages 308 to 311).

The cranial nerves

Cranial nerve I: Olfactory. After testing your patient's cerebral function with the mental status examination, begin your assessment of his cranial nerve function. Assess the olfactory nerve first, to determine any loss of smell or differences in the sense of smell between nostrils. Ask the patient to close both eyes and occlude one nostril. Then bring a nonirritating substance with a familiar odor, such as toothpaste or tobacco, near his open nostril and ask him if he smells anything. If he does, ask him to identify it. Then repeat the test on the other nostril. The test should be repeated several times, using a different-smelling substance each time. Because many odors are difficult to identify, consider the patient's olfactory nerve intact if he can perceive at least one odor.

Cranial nerve II: Optic. To assess the optic nerve, test your patient's visual acuity and visual fields and examine the fundus of each eye. Your findings should indicate the clarity of each eye's transparent media (cornea, anterior body, lens, and vitreous body), the adequacy of central vision, and the function of nerve fibers from the macula to the occipital cortex.

Before beginning your examination of the optic nerve, inspect the patient's eyes for foreign bodies, cataracts, corneal scarring or inflammation, and conjunctival redness. Then test his visual acuity with a pocket-sized Snellen chart (used for bedside testing) or a newspaper. Because refractive errors aren't particularly significant for neurologic assessment, the patient who wears glasses should be tested both with and without them. Ask the patient to cover one eye and read the smallest line he can on the Snellen chart, or one or two lines of a newspaper story set in small type. Then have the patient cover his other eye and repeat the test.

Normally, a person can read the bedside Snellen chart at 30″ (76 cm). Record the distance at which your patient can read the chart as a fraction of the normal distance. For example, if the patient can only read the chart at 15″ (38 cm), record his visual acuity for that eye as 15/30. To verify your examination, refer to the fractions printed on the eye chart

Abnormal Cranial Nerve Responses

NERVE	TEST
I Olfactory	• Have patient identify familiar odors applied to each nostril.
II Optic	• Shine light in affected eye.
	• Shine light in normal eye.
	• Approach patient's eye from side with your hand.
III Oculomotor	• Inspect eye.
	• Shine light in affected eye.
	• Shine light in normal eye.
IV Trochlear	• Have patient follow object without turning his head.
V Trigeminal	*Sensation* • Lightly touch cornea and skin above eye (1-ophthalmic division). • Lightly touch upper lip (2-maxillary division). • Lightly touch lower lip and chin (3-mandibular division).
	Motor • Have patient bite down or chew while you palpate masseter and temporal muscles.
VI Abducens	• Have patient look right and then left.
VII Facial	• Have patient raise and lower eyebrows; close eyes tightly while you attempt to pry eyes open; smile; puff cheeks.
	• Have patient identify tastes.
	• Have patient wrinkle forehead.
VIII Acoustic	• In children and uncooperative patients, clap hands close to patient's ear to elicit a startle reflex.
	• Place tuning fork on middle of patient's forehead (Weber test).

ABNORMAL FINDINGS	POSSIBLE CAUSES
• Anosmia, olfactory hallucinations	• Fracture of cribriform plate or ethmoid area • Olfactory bulb or tract tumor
• Absent direct and consensual pupillary constriction	• Direct trauma to orbit or globe • Fracture involving optic foramen • Pressure on geniculocalcarine tract
• Present direct and consensual pupillary constriction	• Laceration or intracerebral clot in temporal, parietal, or occipital lobe; rarely from subdural clot
• Absent blink reflex	
• Dilated pupil, ptosis, eye turns down and out	• Increased intracranial pressure causing herniating uncus (temporal lobe) on nerve just before it enters cavernous sinus • Fracture involving cavernous sinus
• Absent direct pupil reflex; present consensual reflex	
• Present direct pupil reflex; absent consensual reflex	
• Eye fails to move down and out	• Pressure on nerve around brain stem from tumor • Fracture of orbit
• Absent sensation of pain and touch; paresthesias	• Tic douloureux caused by sinus or dental problems • Irritation from tumor, aneurysm, meningitis, herpes zoster • Direct injury • Myasthenia gravis
• Palpated masseter and temporalis fail to contract	
• Affected eye fails to move laterally; diplopia on lateral gaze	• Tumor or trauma at base of brain • Fracture involving cavernous sinus or orbit
• No facial movement, eye remains open, or opens easily, angle of mouth droops, forehead fails to wrinkle	• Peripheral laceration or contusion in parotid region; Bell's palsy • Peripheral fracture of temporal bone • Supranuclear, intracerebral clot
• Above responses, loss of taste on anterior two thirds of tongue	
• No facial movement, forehead fails to wrinkle	
• No startle reflex	• Fractures of petrous bone • Ménière's syndrome • Acoustic neuroma
• Sound not heard by involved ear	*(continued)*

Abnormal Cranial Nerve Responses (continued)

NERVE	TEST
IX Glossopharyngeal	• Have patient identify taste at back of tongue.
	• Apply cotton to soft palate.
X Vagus	• Inspect soft palate and larynx with laryngoscope.
XI Spinal accessory	• Have patient push chin against your hand.
	• Have patient shrug shoulders.
	• Have patient stretch out hands toward you.
XII Hypoglossal	• Have patient stick out tongue.

for the smallest line the patient can read.

Visual field testing for a neurologic examination is the same as for an eye examination. A visual field abnormality may indicate a brain lesion anywhere along the visual pathway, causing damage to all or part of the nerve. You would also examine the fundus with a direct ophthalmoscope as for an eye examination.

Cranial nerves III, IV, and VI. Cranial nerves III, IV, and VI are usually tested together, because they control the closely coordinated functions of eye movement, pupil constriction, and eyelid elevation. The *oculomotor nerve* (CN III) is responsible for pupillary constriction, elevation of the upper lid, and most eye movements. The *trochlear nerve* (CN IV) makes downward and inward eye movements possible. The *abducens nerve* (CN VI) allows the eyes to move laterally. Your joint assessment of these three nerves should include inspection of the patient's eyes and eye-

lids and testing for accommodation, direct and consensual pupillary reflexes, and ocular movement.

Begin your assessment of the oculomotor nerve by inspecting the patient's eyes. Then, with the lights turned down, observe the size, shape, and equality of his pupils. They should be round and about equal in size. Use a small, bright light source to assess pupillary response by shining the light in one eye and observing for pupil constriction in this eye (direct response) as well as in the opposite eye (consensual response). Keep in mind that young people normally have larger, more responsive pupils than the elderly.

Assessing the ocular movement function of cranial nerve III allows you to simultaneously evaluate cranial nerves IV and VI. First, observe the patient's eyes at rest, for any obvious deviation. Then ask him to follow an object, such as a pen or pencil, without turning his head. Hold the object about 2′ (60 cm) from

ABNORMAL FINDINGS	POSSIBLE CAUSES
• Loss of taste posterior one third of tongue	• Tumor or injury to brain stem • Neck trauma
• Absent sensation on affected side of pal-ate	
• Sagging soft palate, deviation of uvula to normal side; gag reflex	• Tumor or injury to brain stem • Neck trauma
• Palpated sternocleidomastoid fails to contract	• Neck trauma • Radical neck surgery • Torticollis
• Palpated upper fibers of trapezius fail to contract	
• Affected arm seems longer; scapula not anchored	
• Tongue protrudes toward affected side; dysarthria	• Neck trauma, usually associated with major vessel damage

Reprinted with permission from *Clinical Symposia* by Cmdr. Frederick E. Jackson (Copyright © 1967, CIA-GEIGY Corporation).

the midline of the patient's face and move it to the right. Pause to observe if the patient's eyes are conjugately deviated—positioned in a uniform, parallel fashion—toward the object. Tell your patient to hold his gaze on the object, and ask him if he is experiencing double vision (diplopia). Observe for nystagmus—a rhythmic, bobbing movement of the eyes. Repeat this procedure through the six cardinal fields of gaze.

Cranial nerve V: Trigeminal. The trigeminal nerve is both a sensory and a motor nerve. It supplies sensation to the corneas, nasal and oral mucosa, and facial skin, and also supplies motor function for all muscles of mastication. The sensory division, which predominates, consists of three branches: ophthalmic, maxillary, and mandibular. To test the sensory division, ask the patient to close his eyes; then touch his jaw, cheek, and forehead bilaterally with a cotton wisp (light-touch sensation). Then touch each area with the point of a pin (pain sensation). Ask the patient to compare and describe the sensations on both sides. If you note any abnormality in pain sensation, test for temperature sensation by touching each area first with a test tube containing hot water, then with one containing cold water. Compare sensation on both sides.

Next, test the patient's corneal reflex with a cotton wisp. (If your patient wears contact lenses, ask him to remove them, because they can cause the corneal reflex to appear diminished or absent.) To prevent involuntary blinking, ask the patient to look away. Bring the wisp toward the eye from one side and touch the cornea—not just the sclera—with the point. The normal response is a bilateral blink. Then test the patient's light reflex.

To test the motor division of the trigeminal nerve, ask the patient to clench his teeth; then palpate the temporal and the masseter muscles bilaterally. Note the strength of the muscles. Next, ask the patient to clench and unclench his jaws several times. Observe for distorted movements or asymmetry. To assess muscle strength, ask the patient to clench his teeth again, while you try to pry his jaws apart against his resistance. Finally, ask the patient to press his jaw laterally against your hand, with his mouth slightly open, as a further test of muscle strength.

Cranial nerve VII: Facial. Like the trigeminal nerve, the facial nerve has both sensory and motor functions. Its predominant motor division innervates all facial muscles bilaterally. Some of the expressions controlled by the motor division of the facial nerve include wrinkling the nose, smiling, frowning, closing the eyes, and grimacing. The sensory division is responsible for taste perception on the anterior portion of the tongue.

Begin your assessment of the patient's facial nerve by observing the symmetry of his face. Then ask him to raise and lower his eyebrows. Again observe for symmetry. Next, ask him to close his eyes tightly while you attempt to raise the lids. Finally, ask him to smile, show his teeth, and puff out his cheeks, so you can assess facial muscle strength.

To test the sensory division of the facial nerve, first ask your patient to stick out his tongue. Then put some sugar on the anterior portion of one side of the tongue. Tell him to keep his tongue out until he's identified the taste. (If he pulls in his tongue prematurely, the test substance will spread to the opposite side, giving inaccurate results.) After he's identified the sugar, have him rinse his mouth. Repeat the procedure on the same side of the tongue, using salt, a sour substance like vinegar or lemon juice, and a bitter substance. Perform the same tests on the other side of the tongue.

For convenience, assess one function of the glossopharyngeal nerve (CN IX) at this time— perception of taste on the posterior third of the tongue. Test this nerve as you did the sensory division of the facial nerve, using a pipette or a swab to apply sweet, salty, sour, and bitter substances. Use a different swab for each substance, and instruct the patient to keep his tongue out during each test. Give the patient a card with the words *sweet, salty, sour,* and *bitter* printed on it, so he can answer your questions without pulling his tongue in to speak. After applying a particular substance,

ask him to point to the word that best describes its taste. Instruct the patient to take a sip of water after each test to avoid mixing tastes. Test each substance twice on each side of the patient's tongue.

Cranial nerve VIII: Acoustic. The acoustic nerve is a sensory nerve that consists of cochlear and vestibular divisions. The cochlear division is responsible for hearing; the vestibular division governs maintenance of equilibrium, body position, and orientation to space.

To make a gross assessment of the cochlear division, screen for hearing loss by first occluding one of your patient's ears. Then whisper, or rub your fingers together, near his other ear, and ask him if he hears the sound. For a more precise assessment of hearing acuity, use the Weber, Rinne, and Schwabach tests.

You wouldn't normally assess the vestibular division of the acoustic nerve as part of a neurologic examination unless your patient's history or physical examination reveals vertigo associated with nausea and vomiting or ataxia. When indicated, a doctor usually assesses this division, using cold water caloric testing.

Cranial nerves IX and X. You'll usually test cranial nerves IX and X together, because they're closely associated and similar in function. The motor aspect of the *glossopharyngeal nerve* (CN IX) innervates the stylopharyngeus muscle, used in swallowing; it also supplies sensation to the mucous membranes of the pharynx and is responsible for taste perception on the posterior one third of the tongue and for salivation. The *vagus nerve* (CN X) innervates thoracic and abdominal visceral organs; controls swallowing, phonation, and movement of the uvula and soft palate; and supplies sensation to the mucosa of the pharynx, soft palate, and tonsils. The 10th cranial nerve also carries sensory impulses from the gastrointestional tract, the heart, and the lungs. (You'll normally evaluate these functions during the general physical examination.) Begin your assessment of the glossopharyngeal and the vagus nerves by inspecting the patient's soft palate. It should appear symmetrical, with no deviation. When the patient says "Ah," the palate should rise promptly and symmetrically. Note any hoarseness.

To test the palatal reflex, touch the mucous

membrane of the soft palate with a swab. The palate should rise promptly on the side touched. Touch the posterior pharyngeal wall with a tongue depressor. The palate will elevate, and the pharyngeal muscles will contract. The patient may feel like he's gagging, a normal reaction known as the *gag reflex.*

Cranial nerve XI: Spinal accessory. A motor nerve, the spinal accessory nerve supplies the sternocleidomastoid muscles and the upper portion of the trapezius muscles. To evaluate your patient's spinal accessory nerve, test the strength and bulk of the sternocleidomastoid and the trapezius muscles bilaterally. To assess the sternocleidomastoid muscles, ask your patient to turn his head to the right and hold it in this position while you try to turn it toward the front. You should see the sternocleidomastoid muscles clearly. Inspect and palpate the muscles for fasciculations, weakness, and atrophy. Repeat the procedure with the patient's head turned to the left.

To evaluate the trapezius muscles, ask the patient to shrug his shoulders while you try to hold them down. Then ask him to raise his arms above his head. Inspect and palpate the muscles.

Cranial nerve XII: Hypoglossal. This motor nerve is responsible for normal tongue movements involved in swallowing and speech. Assess the hypoglossal nerve by first inspecting the patient's tongue in its normal resting position. Observe for asymmetry, deviation to one side, loss of bulk on one or both sides, and fasciculations. Next, ask the patient to stick out his tongue. It should protrude along the midline. As you hold a tongue depressor against one side of his tongue, ask him to push his tongue against the tongue depressor, to test tongue strength. Repeat against the opposite side of the tongue. Finally, ask him to move his tongue rapidly in and out and from side to side.

Tests for motor and cerebellar functions

To assess your patient's motor function, observe his gait and posture. Then test the tone and strength of his muscles and his balance and coordination. (For these techniques, see the physical examination section of Chapter 16, The Musculoskeletal System.)

To assess your patient's cerebellar functions of balance and coordination, test for Romberg's sign (see page 144). Then ask the patient to walk heel-to-toe in a straight line with his eyes open (tandem walking). Note any swaying to the right or left. The results of this part of the neurologic examination also reflect the adequacy of the patient's muscle innervation.

Coordination tests

These tests evaluate purposeful, fine movements and coordination of the arms and legs. Although the tests themselves aren't complicated, the instructions may be confusing, so show the patient what you expect him to do beforehand. Remember that the patient's nondominant arm or leg normally won't perform as well as the dominant one. Also, watch for patient fatigue, which may interfere with testing.

With the patient seated facing you, begin assessing his coordination by testing his arms. Ask him to touch each finger rapidly with his thumb, rhythmically pat his leg with his hand, and quickly turn his hand over and back. Have the patient perform each maneuver with each hand for about 30 seconds. Then, ask him to touch your index finger, then his nose, several times. Have him repeat this maneuver with his eyes closed.

To test his leg coordination, ask the patient to tap his foot on the floor or on your palm. Then ask him to place the heel of one foot on his opposite knee and slide the heel down his shin.

As the patient performs all these tests, observe for slowness, tremor, or awkwardness. Does he initiate the movement promptly, or does he hesitate? Does the arm or leg move smoothly and purposefully? Does the arm or leg return to its resting state directly, without extraneous movements?

Sensory function

To assess your patient's sensory function, you'll test these five areas of sensation: *pain, touch, vibration, position,* and *discrimination.* Your findings will help you locate the dermatomes where sensations may be absent, decreased, exaggerated, or delayed (see *Dermatome Chart,* page 315). Make sure your patient is relaxed before beginning the examination.

Have him close his eyes during each of the five tests, so he can't see what you're about to do. Because testing every square inch of the patient's body surface is impractical, try to test as many dermatomes as possible by distributing the stimuli over his body. Randomly apply each stimulus, so the patient doesn't anticipate it. Give him time to identify the stimulus and its location.

Note whether the patient perceives the stimulus appropriately and symmetrically. When testing pain and touch, compare distal and proximal parts of the patient's arms and legs. Test vibration and position distally. If you locate a dermatome in which sensation is absent or exaggerated, mark it. Then stimulate a nearby area of greater or lesser sensations, moving away from the suspect dermatome until the patient feels a change.

Pain and touch

Use a safety pin to test your patient's pain sensation. Starting at his shoulder, stimulate the skin of the arms, trunk, and legs along dermatomes with the sharp end of the pin. Next, use the blunt end to see if the patient can distinguish between sharp and dull sensations. If he responds normally to the pinpricks, you don't need to test his temperature sensation, because both of these sensations travel along related pathways.

To test the patient's sense of touch, lightly touch his skin along the dermatomes with a piece of cotton. Ask him to tell you where you're touching him each time. Once or twice, pretend you're touching him but don't actually do so—to see whether he can tell the difference. If an area of deficit is present, test from this area upward to a functioning area.

Vibration and position

Use a lightly vibrating tuning fork (128 cycles/second) to test your patient's response to vibration. Place it against a bony prominence on each arm and leg, such as the distal joint of a finger or the middle joint of the great toe. Make sure the patient understands he's trying to feel a vibration, not just pressure or touch. To demonstrate the sensation, place the vibrating tuning fork on one of the patient's joints. Then, while the fork is still vibrating on the joint, place your hand on it to stop it and ask the patient if he can feel the difference.

If the patient's sense of vibration seems impaired, test more proximal bony prominences, such as the wrists, the elbows, the medial malleoli, the patellas, the anterior superior iliac spine, or the spinous processes.

Next, test the position sense in each arm and leg. Holding one of the patient's fingertips between your thumb and index finger, slowly flex or extend the finger. Ask the patient to tell you when he feels the finger moving and in which direction he thinks it's moving. (Make sure the patient's eyes are closed.) Repeat the maneuver with each great toe. If your patient's position sense seems impaired at the distal joints, test proximal sites until he responds normally.

Discrimination

Discrimination testing assesses the ability of the brain's sensory cortex (in the parietal lobe) to interpret and integrate information. You'll perform these tests when the patient's other sensations seem normal, but you'll evaluate the posterior columns more closely. The following tests assess the parietal lobe's ability to interpret these sensations and the posterior column's ability to conduct them.

• *Stereognosis.* Place several small, familiar objects in the patient's hand—keys or coins will do. Ask the patient to identify them, one at a time.

• *Graphesthesia.* With the blunt end of a pen, trace several letters or numbers on each of the patient's palms and ask the patient to identify them.

• *Two-point stimulation.* Prick the patient's fingertip or another body area with two safety pins, held several millimeters apart. Ask the patient if he feels one or two pricks. Repeat the procedure several times, occasionally pricking him with only one pin to test the reliability of his responses. Find the minimal distance at which the patient can discriminate one prick from two, and compare it to normal findings:

—tongue: 1 mm
—fingertips: 2.8 mm
—toes: 3 to 8 mm
—palms: 8 to 12 mm
—chest, forearms: 40 mm
—back: 40 to 70 mm
—upper arms, thighs: 75 mm.

• *Extinction phenomenon.* Prick the patient's

Dermatome Chart

This dermatome chart illustrates the segmental distribution of spinal nerves that transmit sensations. Use it to document areas of sensory deficiency. For example, if your patient can't distinguish between sharp and dull sensations at the umbilical level, document a sensory loss in the T10 to T11 areas.

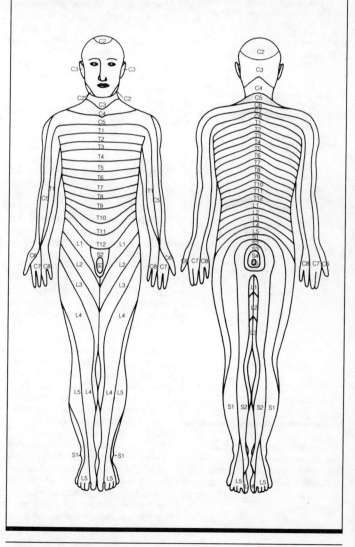

Grading Reflexes

Muscle stretch reflex grades
0   absent
1+ present but diminished
2+ normal
3+ increased but not necessarily pathologic
4+ hyperactive; clonus may also be present

Superficial reflex grades
0   absent
∓   equivocal or barely present
+   normally active

Record the patient's reflex scores by drawing a stick figure and entering the scores at the proper location. The figure shown here indicates normal muscle stretch reflex activity, as well as normal superficial reflex activity over the abdominal area. The *arrows* at the figure's feet indicate normal plantar reflex activity.

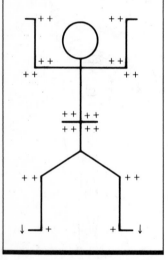

Testing reflexes

Reflexes are divided into two categories: deep tendon and superficial. You elicit deep tendon (or muscle stretch) reflexes when you apply a stimulus to a tendon, a bone, or a joint. You elicit superficial (or cutaneous) reflexes when you apply a stimulus to a skin surface or mucous membrane. Superficial reflexes respond more slowly to stimuli and fatigue more easily than do deep tendon reflexes.

Use a percussion hammer—preferably with a soft rubber end—to elicit deep tendon reflexes. To assess superficial reflexes, touch or scratch the patient's skin surface with an object that won't damage the skin, such as a tongue depressor.

For neurologic screening, evaluate only the most significant reflexes. Choose the deep tendon reflexes and the superficial reflexes that you think are most pertinent to your assessment. Test each reflex bilaterally before moving down the patient's body. Compare each reflex response symmetrically as you proceed, using a grading scale. In your notes, indicate the particular scale you used (see *Grading Reflexes*).

Deep tendon reflexes. The most commonly assessed deep tendon reflexes are as follows:

● *Biceps.* To elicit this reflex, have the patient relax his arm and pronate the forearm slightly, positioned somewhere between flexion and extension. (For best results, ask the patient to rest his elbow in your hand.) Then, percuss the biceps tendon with the reflex hammer. The biceps muscle should contract, followed by flexion of the forearm.

● *Brachioradialis.* Position the patient's forearm in semiflexion and semipronation, resting it either in your hand or on his knee. Tap the styloid process of the radius 1″ to 2″ (2.5 to 5 cm) above the wrist. You should see flexion at the elbow and a simultaneous pronation of the forearm, as well as flexion of the fingers and hand.

● *Triceps.* Position the patient's arm about midway between flexion and extension. If possible, have the patient rest his arm on his thigh or in your hand. Tap the tendon above the insertion on the ulna's olecranon process, 1″ to 2″ above the elbow. The stimulus should elicit muscle contraction of the triceps and elbow extension.

skin simultaneously on opposite sides of his body, and ask him if he feels one prick or two. Repeat the procedure several times in different symmetrical areas. Occasionally, apply only one stimulus to test the reliability of the patient's responses.

• *Patellar.* Have the patient sit on a table with his legs dangling freely, or have him cross his legs. Place one of your hands over the patient's quadriceps, and use your other hand to tap his tendon just below the patella. A firm tap should draw the patella down and stretch the muscle, causing an extension of the leg at the knee.

• *Achilles.* Have the patient sit on a table with his legs dangling. (If the patient can't sit without support, have him sit or lie in bed.) Flex his leg at the hip and knee, and rotate it externally. If the patient is prone, flex his knee and hip and rotate the leg externally so that it rests on the opposite shin. Then, place your hand under the patient's foot, dorsiflex the ankle, and tap the tendon just above its insertion on the posterior surface of the calcaneus. You should see a plantar flexion of the foot at the ankle.

Superficial reflexes. The most commonly assessed superficial reflexes are as follows:

• *Upper abdominal.* To test this reflex, have the patient lie down and relax. Move a tongue depressor downward and outward from the tip of his sternum. You can also stroke the area horizontally, moving medially toward the umbilicus. The abdominal muscles should contract, and the umbilicus should deviate toward the stimulus.

• *Lower abdominal.* With the patient lying down, stroke his skin in an upward and outward movement from the symphysis or horizontally in the lower quadrants. The umbilicus should deviate toward the stimulus, along with abdominal contraction.

• *Cremasteric* (males only). Lightly stroke the inner aspect of the upper thigh with a tongue depressor. The testis on the same side as the stimulus should rise.

• *Gluteal.* Stroke the skin over the patient's buttocks, and observe for tense muscles in this area.

• *Plantar.* Firmly stroke the lateral surface of the dorsum of the patient's foot with a test object (the end of a percussion hammer works well). A normal response is plantar flexion of the foot and toes.

• *Pathologic reflex.* Babinski's sign or reflex is the opposite of the normal plantar reflex. When you firmly stroke the lateral aspect of the patient's sole with a blunt object, the great toe extends as the other toes fan out.

Special considerations. Reflexes should be symmetrically equal. If you note a brisk response on one side of the patient's body and an equally brisk response on the other side, the response is probably normal for the patient. Don't be alarmed if you can't elicit a reflex. Approximately 3% to 10% of persons with no central nervous system disease fail to exhibit one or more reflexes.

Remember also that it may be difficult to elicit a particular reflex in an athletic person with firm, well-developed muscles or in a tense, apprehensive person who may be unconsciously bracing his muscles. In these situations, you may need to divert the patient's attention from your test to relax his muscles (*reinforcement*). For example, you might ask the patient to hook his fingers together, then attempt to pull them apart as you test the reflex. Or you could ask the patient to clench his fists, grasp the arm of his chair, look at the ceiling, or take a deep breath. Simply talking to the patient about nonclinical matters as you proceed through the tests can also divert his attention and help him to relax. If you use reinforcement to elicit a reflex response, be sure to document the fact that you have done this. Note it on the patient's grading scale.

Pediatric assessment

Neurologic health history

To obtain a thorough health history of a child who may have a neurologic disorder, talk with him (if he's old enough to understand) and his parents. If the child attends a day-care center or has a regular babysitter, talk to the day-care worker or babysitter, too, if possible. Their observations of the child can prove invaluable to your assessment. For an older child, a history of school performance, with reports from the teacher, may be helpful.

Ask questions about the child's health and development from prenatal history to the present. First, inquire about his early development. For instance, did his mother have any diseases or other problems during the pregnancy? Was there any birth trauma or difficulty with the delivery? Did the child have significant jaundice, requiring phototherapy? (See Chapter 20, THE NEONATE.) Did he arrive at developmental milestones, such as sitting up, walking, and talking, at normal ages?

Ask about childhood diseases and injuries. Has the child experienced any head or nerve injuries? Any headaches, tremors, convulsions, dizziness, fainting spells, or muscle weakness? Is he overly active? Has he ever seen spots before his eyes? At what age did these occur?

Inquire about possible emotional problems. Has the child exhibited any personality change? Has he been lethargic or had hallucinations, delusions, or any unusual cognitive or perceptual experiences? Has he ever experimented with drugs?

Finally, depending on the child's age, ask about school. To determine whether the child is well-adjusted socially, ask if he plays well with other children. Is he aggressive or shy? Does he earn good grades? Does he have any speech or coordination problems?

Neurologic physical examination

Although the equipment you'll use for a pediatric neurologic examination is essentially the same as for an adult examination, a few special props might be helpful with young children. For instance, you might use familiar objects—such as blocks, buttons, or bottle caps—to test for tactile agnosia. Try peanut butter or candy to test the child's sense of smell. To assess motor strength and coordination, give the child toys or other objects to play with or give him a pen or pencil and ask him to draw.

Head and neck. Because a very young child may be frightened when you try to assess his head and neck, you might want to delay percussion, palpation, and auscultation of his head and neck until later in the examination, when the child feels more comfortable with you. Meanwhile, watch him as he plays or interacts with his parents. Are his head and face symmetrical? Does he appear to have muscle weakness or paralysis? Watch how he cries, laughs, turns his head, and wrinkles his forehead.

To examine a child's cranial bones, gently run your fingers over his head, checking the sutures and fontanelles. Look for fullness, bulging, or swelling, which may indicate an intracranial mass or hydrocephalus. Note the shape and symmetry of his head. Abnormal shape accompanied by prominent bony ridges may indicate craniosynostosis (premature suture closure).

Until a child reaches age 2, measure his head size during every examination. Note any sudden increase in size or failure to grow at a normal rate. Head size changes proportionately throughout maturation.

If you feel a snapping sensation when you press the child's scalp firmly behind and above the ears (similar to the way a table-tennis ball feels when you press it in), this may indicate craniotabes, a thinning of the outer layer of the skull. Although this thinning is normal at the suture lines, premature infants are susceptible to craniotabes, and such thinning can also be a sign of rickets, syphilis, hypervitaminosis A, or hydrocephalus. A resonant, cracked-pot sound (Macewen's sign), heard when you percuss the parietal bone with your finger, is normal in an infant with open sutures. But if the sutures have closed, this can signal increased intracranial pressure.

If you suspect that a child has an intracranial lesion, hydrocephalus, or decreased brain tissue, transilluminate his skull, using a flashlight fitted with a special rubber ring at the lighted end. Darken the room, and place the light against the child's skull. A small ring of light around the edges of the flashlight is normal, but illumination of the entire cranium is not. If you detect any unusual transparency, refer the child to a doctor.

Next, assess the child's head and neck muscles. Neck mobility is an important indicator of such neurologic diseases as meningitis. With the child supine, test for nuchal rigidity by cradling his head in your hands. Supporting the weight of his head, move his neck in all directions to assess ease of movement.

Cerebral function. A child's cerebral function depends on his age, of course, so you'll need to have an understanding of normal growth and development. A standardized test, such as the Denver Developmental Screening Test, can be helpful for gross screening.

To assess *level of consciousness* in a young child, use motor rather than verbal clues. Is the child lethargic, drowsy, or stuporous? Or, at the opposite extreme, is he hyperactive? When you assess *orientation*, remember that young children are not oriented to time, so only assess their orientation to person or place.

To test a child's *attention span and concentration,* ask him to repeat a series of numbers after you. Generally, a 4-year-old can repeat three numbers; a 5-year-old, four numbers; and a 6-year-old, five numbers. Repeating familiar words, such as *cat* or *dog,* usually holds the interest of a child younger than age 4.

To test a child's *recent memory,* show him a familiar object and tell him that you'll ask him later what it was. Five minutes later, ask him to recall the object.

To test a child's *remote memory,* ask him something like, "What did you have for dinner last night?" Then verify the response with the child's parents.

Language development. To assess *receptive speech development,* ask the child to obey simple commands, such as "Sit down" or "Pick up the block." Be careful not to give the child nonverbal clues to your commands. The child's age is important when giving commands. For example, a 3-year-old may fully understand the command but not respond because of shyness or stubbornness.

You can determine a school-age child's ability to comprehend written symbols by asking him to read from a book. Of course, speech can't be tested in infants, but you can evaluate the quality and pitch of an infant's cry. It should be loud and angry-sounding, and it shouldn't be high-pitched.

Cranial nerves. Assessing the cranial nerves can be difficult in a child under age 2, but you *can* check his symmetry of muscle movement, gaze, sucking strength, and hearing by simple observation. In a child over age 2, assess the cranial nerves as you would an adult's, making the following alterations:

● *CN I* (olfactory). Ask the child to identify familiar odors, such as peanut butter and chocolate or peppermint candy. For a very young child who may not be able to identify a smell, try a same-different game to determine whether he can distinguish one smell from another.

● *CN II* (optic). You can test a child's visual acuity as you would for an adult, but using Allen cards for a very young child or preschooler. For visual field testing, also follow the procedure for an adult, with one variation: You might want to hold a bright object near the end of your nose to help the young child keep his eyes focused.

● *CN V* (trigeminal). Test the sensory division of this nerve as you would for an adult, but make a game out of it by telling the child that a gremlin's going to brush his cheeks, pinch his forehead, and so on. Test the motor division by having the child bite down hard on a tongue depressor as you try to pull it away. At the same time, palpate his jaw muscles for symmetry and contraction strength.

● *CN VII* (facial). Test the muscles controlled by this nerve as you would for an adult, but instead of asking the child to perform certain movements, have him mimic your facial expressions. Test the sensory division of the facial nerve with salt and sugar, as for an adult.

● *CN VIII* (acoustic). Test the cochlear division of the acoustic nerve in a child by checking his hearing acuity and sound conduction.

● *CN IX, X, XI,* and *XII* (glossopharyngeal, vagus, spinal accessory, hypoglossal). Test these nerves as you would for an adult, using games to facilitate the examination when necessary.

Motor function. Assess balance and coordination in a child by watching motor skills, such as dressing and undressing. You can also have him stack blocks, put a bead in a bottle, or draw a cross. Depending on his age, he should be able to draw a cross in two movements, without changing the pencil to his other hand.

A child age 4 should be able to stand on one foot for about 5 seconds, and a child age 6 should be able to do this for 5 seconds with his arms folded across his chest. By age 7, he should be able to do it for 5 seconds with his eyes closed. A child should demonstrate a preference for one-hand dominance before age 12 months.

To evaluate cerebellar function in an infant, observe his coordination during sucking, swallowing, reaching, kicking, and grasping.

Sensory function. Test the sensations of pain, touch, vibration, and temperature in an older child as you would for an adult. (Most of these tests aren't applicable to an infant or very young child. Younger children may respond to pain and touch, but their responses may be unreliable.) Consider the following variations from the adult tests when assessing a child's sense of direction and discrimination:

● *Position.* Children under age 5 usually have no concept of up and down. To test an older child's directional sense, play an up-down game. Ask the child to put out his hand, palm up, close his eyes, and then tell you whether his fingers are up or down as you bend or straighten them. Touch only the sides of the child's fingers, so the weight of your fingers doesn't give him clues.

• *Discrimination.* To test *stereognosis* in a child, ask him to close his eyes, and tell him you'll put one of three objects in his hand (for instance, a bottle cap, a coin, or a button). Then remove the object, and tell the child to open his eyes. Ask him which object it was.

When testing *graphesthesia,* remember that school-age children can usually identify numbers as well as adults. For younger children, use geometric figures or lines (parallel or crossing). Draw the same figure on the child's palms twice, or draw two different figures, and ask the child whether the figures are the same or different. (To make sure the child understands, play the game first with the child watching, then with his eyes closed.) Very young children will probably be difficult to test accurately, because they might not fully understand the concepts of *same* and *different.* Note if an older child consistently fails these tests or seems to do better with one hand.

To test *texture discrimination,* have the child close his eyes and tell you whether a piece of cloth is rough or smooth. Test *two-point discrimination* as you would for an adult, but make a game of it by asking the child to close his eyes and tell you if he feels one or two mosquitoes (pinpricks).

Test the *extinction phenomenon* as you would for an adult. For developmental reasons, this test isn't always accurate in children under age 6. If an older child feels only one sensation when you touch him in two places, he might have a parietal lobe defect.

Reflexes. Make a special effort to relax a child when assessing his reflexes. Many children (and some adults) will tighten their muscles, so that testing reflexes is almost impossible. Asking a child to relax usually doesn't work, but having him clench his fingers together and then pull on the count of three (while you tap the tendon) often distracts him, so the appropriate muscles relax. But because this also enhances the reflex, keep in mind that the reflex has been artificially magnified. A positive Babinski's sign may nor-

mally be present up to age 2.

Hydrocephalus

Children can develop many of the same pathologic conditions of the nervous system as adults: benign and malignant cerebral tumors, cerebral hematomas, spinal cord injuries, seizure disorders, and neurologic infections. With few exceptions, these problems occur in children the same way they do in adults.

Hydrocephalus merits special attention, because it's one of the most easily diagnosed neurologic disorders in both children and adults (although it's less common in adults). This condition results from an imbalance in the production and absorption of cerebrospinal fluid (CSF), which causes excess fluid to accumulate in the brain's ventricular system. CSF pressure is usually elevated, but occasionally it may be almost normal. Hydrocephalus can occur congenitally or result from a birth trauma, an acquired tumor, or a cerebral infection or injury. Acquired hydrocephalus can develop slowly or rapidly, depending on the cause. In severe congenital hydrocephalus, the infant's head may be enlarged at birth, causing a very difficult delivery. The hydrocephalic child may have some neurologic and motor impairment, depending on severity and on treatment. (The child treated with a shunt is prone to bacterial infection.)

Down's syndrome

Down's syndrome, a chromosomal disorder also known as trisomy 21, is characterized by specific neurologic deficits. Down's syndrome causes generalized muscular hypotonicity and facial and structural anomalies. (See *Guide to Neurologic Disorders,* pages 322 to 337.) These signs may be apparent in the neonatal phase of development. An infant with Down's syndrome is commonly described as a floppy baby, exhibiting poor muscle tone and posture and an inability to hold his head up. His sucking reflex is usually weak, and his reflexes are generally slow. Brushfield's spots may be found in the iris of the eye. The child develops slowly physically; later testing reveals mild-to-severe mental retardation. Physical examinations throughout childhood and adulthood reveal the same deficits present in the infant: hypotonicity; poor coordination, posture, and balance; and slowed reflexes. He seldom reaches a stature beyond that of a child age 10. Associated cardiac anomalies may be present. The child may have a greater potential to develop infections and acute leukemia. The child with Down's syndrome is usually extremely friendly and restless. He learns activities of daily living slowly.

Geriatric assessment

Examination findings

When you perform a neurologic examination of an elderly patient, you'll usually detect an alteration in one or more senses. The patient may also exhibit akinesia (a slowing of fine finger movements), which makes it difficult for him to perform such maneuvers as the finger-to-nose test. Deep tendon reflexes may be diminished or absent, position sense may be impaired, and vibration detection may be diminished. Gait disturbances are also common.

Neurologic diseases in the elderly

The neurologic disease processes common in elderly persons can result from primary neurologic degenerative changes or can occur secondary to changes in other body systems. *Alzheimer's disease,* which results from progressive brain atrophy, exaggerates the effects of the normal aging process. *Parkinsonism,* which results from degeneration of the basal ganglia, interferes with the extrapyramidal motor system. Decreased production of dopamine, a neurotransmitter, has been associated with this disease process, but the cause is unknown. Physical findings include pill-rolling tremor; slowed, shuffling gait; and posture disturbances (see *Guide to Neurologic Disorders,* pages 322 to 337).

Chronic brain syndrome, an organic and irreversible disorder, results in progressive degeneration of memory and intellect. *Acute brain syndrome,* which is usually reversible, may result from dehydration, anemia, or cerebrovascular accident. Unlike chronic brain syndrome, the patient's history usually shows a relatively recent onset.

Other disease processes are caused by alterations of other body systems (such as the cardiovascular system) that in turn impair neurologic functioning. *Senile tremor* is a tremor that affects the head and hands but doesn't cause rigidity or bradykinesia. A decreased blood supply to the brain, or cardiac arrhythmia, can lead to *senile epilepsy,* which causes convulsions or loss of consciousness. Interruption in blood supply to the brain stem can cause drop attacks, without loss of consciousness. Gait changes may occur from destruction of the spinal cord's lateral columns.

Guide to Neurologic Disorders

DISORDER	CHIEF COMPLAINT	
Alzheimer's disease (presenile dementia) and senile dementia	• *Motor disturbances:* expressive and receptive aphasia, echolalia, apraxia, spatial disorientation, repetitive movements, incontinence • *Seizures:* possible • *Altered level of consciousness:* personality changes; progressive dementia; loss of recent memory at first, and then remote memory; decreased attention span; faulty concentration; loss of abstract thinking; restlessness and overactivity	
Amyotrophic lateral sclerosis (Lou Gehrig's disease)	• *Headache/pain:* pain in arms and legs • *Motor disturbances:* muscle atrophy and weakness, especially in forearms and hands; impaired speech; difficulty chewing, swallowing, and breathing; choking; excessive drooling; urinary frequency, urgency, and difficulty initiating a stream • *Sensory deviations:* paresthesias • *Altered level of consciousness:* depression; crying spells and inappropriate laughter caused by bulbar palsy	
Arteriovenous malformation	• *Headache:* migraine on side of malformation; accompanied by vomiting • *Motor disturbances:* signs of increased intracranial pressure, depending on area of malformation; paresis and cerebrovascular accident from rupture • *Seizures:* general, focal, or jacksonian; may be first sign of rupture resulting from ischemia • *Sensory deviations:* visual disturbances; sensory loss depending on area involved; symptoms same as hemorrhage from cerebrovascular accident • *Altered level of consciousness:* dementia resulting from brief ischemia	
Botulism	• *Motor disturbances:* ptosis, paralysis of ocular muscles, weakness of trunk and jaw muscles, dysphagia, dysarthria, constipation, urinary retention • *Seizures:* convulsions at terminal stage • *Altered level of consciousness:* mental faculties preserved, but coma terminal	
Brain abscess	• *Headache:* present, with nausea and vomiting • *Motor disturbances:* hemiplegia, speech disturbances, cranial nerve palsies • *Seizures:* focal or generalized • *Sensory deviations:* visual field defect (hemianopia), depending on position of abscess • *Altered level of consciousness:* behavioral changes or loss of consciousness	
Carbon monoxide poisoning	• *Headache:* present • *Motor disturbances:* hemiplegia, aphasia, athetoid movements, all transient; may develop parkinsonism in later years • *Sensory deviations:* cortical blindness, multiple neuritis • *Altered level of consciousness:* amnesia after incident, fatigue, mental confusion, seizures, coma, respiratory failure resulting in death	

HISTORY	PHYSICAL EXAMINATION
• Most common in women over age 50	• Difficulty comprehending written and verbal speech; slow reflexes; shuffling gait; memory changes; hyperactivity; irritability
• Onset usually between ages 40 and 70 • Most common in white males • Precipitating factors include nutritional deficiency, vitamin E deficiency (damaging cell membranes), autoimmune disorder, interference with nucleic acid production, acute viral infections, and physical exhaustion.	• Deep tendon reflexes absent; muscle twitches
• Patient may complain of swishing sensation in head; sudden "stroke" in young patients	• Pulsating exophthalmos from ocular pressure; papilledema; retinal hemorrhage if carotid artery bleeds into cavernous sinus; hydrocephalus if membrane causes pressure on aqueduct of Sylvius; bruits over lesion, which disappear with pressure over ipsilateral carotid artery
• Symptoms apparent 12 to 48 hours after ingestion of contaminated food (bacterial toxins); may affect several members of same household	• Pupils dilated, no reaction to light; difficulty in convergence of eyes
• Predisposing factors include mastoid and nasal sinus disease; bacterial endocarditis; pulmonary, skin, and abdominal infections; head trauma.	• Normal or decreased temperature, papilledema, signs of increased intracranial pressure • Signs similar to those of meningitis, such as nuchal rigidity, positive Brudzinski's and Kernig's signs
• Inhalation of automobile exhaust fumes • Defective coal heater in home stove	• Cherry-red skin and mucous membranes • EKG changes • Gradual poisoning may show fever, excessive sweating, decreased exercise tolerance, dyspnea during exertion or rest, signs of increasing intracranial pressure. • Arterial blood gases reveal acidosis. *(continued)*

Guide to Neurologic Disorders (continued)

DISORDER	CHIEF COMPLAINT
Cerebral aneurysm and intracerebral or subarachnoid hemorrhage	• *Headache:* sudden, severe headache, with nausea and projectile vomiting • *Motor disturbances:* depends on site of aneurysm and degree of bleeding or ischemia; hemiparesis; aphasia; ataxia; vertigo; syncope; facial weakness • *Seizures:* focal or generalized, depending on area of hemorrhage • *Sensory deviations:* visual impairment with pressure on optic nerve or chiasm; double vision with third, fourth, and fifth cranial nerve compression • *Altered level of consciousness:* stupor to coma, irritability
Cerebral palsy (spastic, athetoid, and ataxic forms)	• *Motor disturbances:* In spastic form, hyperactive deep tendon reflexes, rapid alternating muscle contractions and relaxations; in athetoid form, grimacing, dystonia, wormlike movements, sharp and jerky movements before becoming more severe during stress and disappearing during sleep; in ataxic form, muscle weakness, loss of balance and coordination, especially in arms • *Seizures:* in spastic form, seizure disorders possible • *Sensory deviations:* in spastic form, visual and hearing deficits possible • *Altered level of consciousness:* in ataxic form, emotional disorders, mental retardation in about 40% of cases
Cerebrovascular accident	• *Headache/pain:* present, when affecting carotid artery • *Motor disturbances:* when affecting middle cerebral artery, aphasia, dysphasia, contralateral hemiparesis or hemiplegia; when affecting carotid artery, weakness, contralateral paralysis or paresis (especially leg or foot); when affecting vertebral and basilar arteries, contralateral weakness, diplopia, poor coordination, dysphagia, ataxia; when affecting anterior cerebral artery, weakness, loss of coordination, impaired motor function, incontinence; when affecting posterior cerebral artery, contralateral hemiplegia • *Sensory deviations:* when affecting middle cerebral artery, pain and tenderness in affected arm or leg, numbness, tingling; when affecting carotid artery, numbness and sensory changes on opposite side, visual disturbances on same side, transient blindness; when affecting vertebral and basilar arteries, visual field cut, numbness around lips and mouth, dizziness, blindness, deafness; when affecting anterior cerebral artery, numbness of lower leg or foot, impaired vision; when affecting posterior cerebral artery, visual field cut, pain and temperature impairment, cortical blindness • *Altered level of consciousness:* when affecting middle cerebral artery, altered level progressing to coma; when affecting carotid artery, altered level, mental confusion, poor memory; when affecting vertebral and basilar arteries, amnesia, confusion, loss of consciousness; when affecting anterior cerebral artery, confusion, personality changes; when affecting posterior cerebral artery, coma
Cluster headache	• *Headache/pain:* intense, stabbing eye pain; sudden onset • *Motor disturbances:* drooping eyelids

HISTORY	PHYSICAL EXAMINATION
• No symptoms until bleeding or rupture • Precipitating factors include hypertension, oral contraceptives, arteriovenous malformations, family history, recurrent headaches.	• Temperature may reach 102° F. (38.9° C.) or higher; irregular respirations, dilated and fixed pupils, papilledema, retinal hemorrhage, bilateral Babinski's reflex early after rupture, positive Brudzinski's and Kernig's signs, nuchal rigidity, signs of increased intracranial pressure, blood in cerebrospinal fluid
• Maternal infection, especially rubella • Prenatal radiation, anoxia • Birth difficulties, such as forceps delivery, breech presentation, placenta previa, premature birth • Infection or trauma during infancy, such as brain infection; head trauma; prolonged anoxia	• Underdeveloped affected limbs; hard-to-separate legs; leg crossing, rather than bicycling, when child's lifted from behind; scissors gait; muscle weakness; hyperactive reflexes; contractures; persistent favoring of one hand; nystagmus; dental abnormalities
• Precipitating factors include atrial fibrillation, subacute bacterial endocarditis, recent heart valve surgery, lung abscess, tuberculosis, air embolism during abortion, pulmonary trauma, surgery, thrombophlebitis, transient ischemic attack, diabetes mellitus, gout, arteriosclerosis, intracerebral tumors, trauma.	• Labored breathing; rapid pulse rate; fever; nuchal rigidity; evidence of emboli to arms, legs, and intestines and other organs, such as spleen, kidneys, or lungs • When affecting carotid artery, bruits over artery; retinal vessels blanch on pressure
• Mostly affects young males • Onset same time each day, usually during evening or one or two hours after falling asleep	• Tearing of affected eye; red, runny nose; sweating on affected side of face; Horner's syndrome *(continued)*

Guide to Neurologic Disorders *(continued)*

DISORDER	CHIEF COMPLAINT	
Cluster headache *(continued)*		
Down's syndrome	• *Motor disturbances:* generalized muscular hypotonicity; structural, facial abnormalities • *Altered level of consciousness:* impaired mental capacity	
Encephalitis	• *Headache:* present • *Motor disturbances:* residual parkinsonian paralysis with acute attack; paralysis; ataxia • *Seizures:* may occur during acute attack; residual seizures in about 60% of cases • *Altered level of consciousness:* lethargy or restlessness progressing to stupor and coma; may remain comatose several days, weeks, or longer after acute phase subsides; personality changes; mental deterioration in about 60% of cases	
Epidural (acute) and subdural (acute and chronic) hematomas	• *Motor disturbances:* hemiplegia or facial weakness on opposite or same side as hematoma; hemiparesis • *Seizures:* generalized • *Altered level of consciousness:* irritability, mental confusion, and progressively decreasing level of consciousness; with chronic form, severe impairment of intellectual faculties	
Extramedullary spinal tumor (neurinomas, meningiomas, sarcomas)	• *Headache/pain:* dull aching and soreness of muscles, mild pain along nerve root • *Motor disturbances:* spastic weakness of muscles below lesion; with severe compression, loss of bladder and bowel control; atrophy of muscles; paraplegia • *Sensory deviations:* paresthesias; impairment of proprioception and cutaneous sensation below lesion; with severe compression, loss of sensation below lesion	
Grand mal seizure (major motor, generalized, tonic clonic)	• *Headache:* present on awakening, possibly accompanied by nausea • *Motor disturbances:* generalized tonic and clonic movements; residual hemiparesis or monoparesis possible • *Seizures:* generalized • *Sensory deviations:* weakness, dizziness, numbness, peculiar sensation • *Altered level of consciousness:* loss of consciousness; mental	

HISTORY	PHYSICAL EXAMINATION
• Persists nightly from several weeks to several months • Triggered by alcohol • Use of vasodilators, such as nitroglycerin	
• Family history of Down's syndrome • Most common in infants born to mothers over age 35 or in firstborn of very young mothers • Growth and development slower than normal	• Gutteral cry; small, round head; flat, occipital, low-set ears; mongoloid slant to eyes; small mouth, with protruding tongue; increased fat pad at nape of neck; short, heavy hands; transverse palmar crease; incomplete Moro's reflex; Brushfield's spots (gray-white specks on iris)
• Predisposing factors include mosquito bite, measles, chicken pox, mumps, herpesvirus, polio vaccine or virus, syphilis (10 to 25 years after infection).	• Fever, nuchal rigidity, back pain, abnormal EEG, signs of increased intracranial pressure • With history of syphilis, tremors, dysarthria, generalized convulsions, increased deep tendon reflexes, bilateral Babinski's sign; with history of herpes simplex, progressive confusion, recent memory loss, temporal lobe seizures, increased antibody levels to herpes simplex virus; with history of measles virus, memory impairment, seizures, myoclonic jerks, ataxia
• Signs occur when hematoma has grown large enough to compromise circulation to the brain (increased intracranial pressure). • With acute form, complaints rapidly develop (within 48 hours). • With chronic form, complaints develop more slowly (within a few days to weeks). • Not all lesions cause signs of increased intracranial pressure (especially chronic).	• Positive Babinski's reflex • Signs of increased intracranial pressure • Epidural hematomas cause a rapid rise in intracranial pressure and should be treated as a surgical emergency.
• Most common in young and middle-aged adults • Predisposing factors include Hodgkin's disease and metastatic carcinoma. • Symptoms worsened by exertion	• Muscle atrophy and impairment of reflexes, depending on location and extent of injury and amount of time since injury occurred; sensory sparing in some cases; with half the cord compressed, Brown-Séquard syndrome
• Onset early in life with idiopathic disorder; can occur at any age with secondary disorders, but those associated with fever commonly occur in children. • Predisposing factors include, with idiopathic seizure disorders (epilepsy), familial history of seizures, genetic involvement; with secondary seizure disorders, cerebral palsy,	• Shrill cry, pupillary change, loss of consciousness, tonic and clonic movements, tongue-biting, abnormal respiratory pattern (absent during tonic phase), urinary or fecal incontinence, upward deviation of eyes, excessive salivation
	(continued)

Guide to Neurologic Disorders *(continued)*

DISORDER	CHIEF COMPLAINT	
Grand mal seizure (major motor, generalized, tonic clonic) *(continued)*	confusion after awakening, lasting several hours or days	
Head injury	• *Headache:* varies in intensity and duration; generalized, with nausea and vomiting • *Motor disturbances:* specific to area of injury; dysphagia; dysarthria; paralysis; ataxia • *Sensory deviation:* vertigo, tinnitus worsened by change in posture • *Altered level of consciousness:* unconsciousness varies in depth and duration, depending on severity and area of injury (the more severe the injury, the greater the depth and duration of unconsciousness); confusion after regaining consciousness (the greater the duration of unconsciousness, the greater the incidence of permanent brain damage)	
Hydrocephalus	• *Motor disturbances:* spastic movements of arms and legs (more severe in legs), increased tendon reflexes • *Altered level of consciousness:* apathy, lethargy, irritability	
Infantile spasm	• *Motor disturbances:* sudden dropping of the head and flexing of the arms; clonic movements of the arms and legs; developmental and mental retardation	
Intracranial tumors (medulloblastoma, meningioma, astrocytoma, acoustic neuroma, oligodendroma)	• *Headache/pain:* headache; worse in morning; may be accompanied by vomiting • *Motor disturbances:* motor deficits, depending on location of tumor • *Seizures:* generalized or focal, depending on site of tumor • *Sensory deviations:* dependent on pressure on cranial nerves • *Altered level of consciousness:* progressive deterioration of intellect; behavior changes possible; decreased level of consciousness with increased intracranial pressure	
Intramedullary spinal tumor (gliomas)	• *Headache/pain:* sharp, tearing, or boring pain, depending on location of tumor; increased by movement and relieved by change of posture • *Motor disturbances:* weakness in one or both legs, clumsiness, shuffling or spastic gait, incontinence • *Sensory deviations:* paresthesias occur after pain diminishes; complete sparing of sensation in legs possible	

HISTORY	PHYSICAL EXAMINATION
birth injury, infectious diseases, meningitis, encephalitis, cerebral trauma, metabolic disturbances, cerebral edema, carbon monoxide poisoning, insulin shock, anoxia, brain tumor, drug overdose, child abuse, noncompliance with medication regimen	
• Some type of fall or accident, such as a vehicular or industrial accident; blow to the head	• Signs of increased intracranial pressure, retrograde and posttraumatic amnesia, hyperthermia, shock, scalp bleeding, evidence of other injuries
• Normal head size at birth, increasingly more rapid growth than normal	• Head growth exceeds normal by ½″ (1.27 cm) per month; distended scalp veins; full, tense fontanelles; widened cranial sutures; asymmetric appearance of head; setting-sun sign (eyes pushed down in orbit); inability to hold head up; strabismus; cracked-pot sign on skull percussion; high-pitched cry • Skull transilluminates
• Usually lasts until age 4, then possibly changes to generalized seizures	• Brief myoclonic jerks involving entire body • EEG changes
• Medulloblastomas most common in young children • Meningioma most common in women over age 50 • History of present illness includes progressive deterioration of motor function, increasing frequency and duration of headaches, personality changes.	• Signs of increased intracranial pressure: widening pulse pressure and bounding pulse (Cushing's phenomenon), ipsilateral (same side as lesion) pupil dilation and contralateral (opposite side of lesion) muscle weakness (Weber's syndrome), decreasing level of consciousness, irregular respiratory patterns progressing to respiratory arrest, temperature fluctuation, papilledema, decorticate or decerebrate posturing • Motor and sensory deficits appropriate to affected area
• Possible limb heaviness or feeling as though walking on air • Symptoms worsened by exertion	• Overactive leg reflexes, leg weakness, sensory sparing (loss)

(continued)

Guide to Neurologic Disorders *(continued)*

DISORDER	CHIEF COMPLAINT	
Jacksonian seizure (partial motor and partial sensory)	• *Motor disturbances:* focal seizures, lesions of motor cortex or strip (jacksonian motor seizure) • *Seizures:* partial, with no loss of consciousness • *Sensory deviations:* numbness, tingling of one arm or leg or one half of body, auditory alterations (such as ringing noises), lesions of the sensory strip (jacksonian sensory seizure)	
Landry's or Guillain-Barré syndrome (acute idiopathic polyneuritis)	• *Motor disturbances:* muscle weakness in legs, extending to arms and face in 24 to 72 hours and progressing to total paralysis and respiratory failure; flaccid quadriplegia possible; cranial nerve paralysis; ocular paralysis in about 25% of cases • *Sensory deviations:* paresthesias vanishing before muscle weakness occurs	
Lead poisoning	• *Motor disturbances:* paralysis following seizure, cerebellar ataxia, hemiplegia, decerebrate rigidity, facial or oculomotor paralysis • *Seizures:* generalized or focal • *Sensory deviations:* polyneuritis • *Altered level of consciousness:* lethargy, coma, delirium	
Meningitis	• *Headache:* present, with nausea and vomiting • *Motor disturbances:* exaggerated, symmetrical deep tendon reflexes • *Seizures:* may occur; generalized • *Sensory deviations:* visual disturbances, such as photophobia • *Altered level of consciousness:* irritability, confusion, stupor, or coma	
Methyl alcohol ingestion	• *Headache/pain:* headache with nausea and vomiting; abdominal pain • *Motor disturbances:* blurred vision; dizziness • *Sensory deviations:* temporary or permanent blindness • *Altered level of consciousness:* drunkenness, drowsiness, delirium, central nervous system depression leading to coma, respiratory failure, and possible death	
Migraine (common, hemiplegic, ophthalmoplegic, basilar artery, temporal artery)	• *Headache/pain:* with common migraine, recurrent and severe incapacitating headache (unilateral or bilateral), aura with gastric pain; with hemiplegic or ophthalmoplegic migraine, severe unilateral headache; with basilar artery migraine, severe occipital throbbing headache with vomiting; with temporal artery migraine,	

HISTORY	PHYSICAL EXAMINATION
• Predisposing factors include birth injury, trauma, infection, and vascular lesions.	• Clonic twitching begins in one part of body, usually one side of the face or the fingers of one hand, and often progresses from face to hand, to arm, to trunk, to legs on the same side of the body (jacksonian march); if twitching begins in the foot, it may progress reversely through the body; rhythmic clonic movements may affect one area (face, arm, leg) without marching. • Speech loss possible • Sensory deviations may also progress or march through the body. • May progress to a secondary generalized seizure (grand mal)
• Onset at any age • Predisposing factors include recent viral or bacterial infection, surgery, influenza vaccination, Hodgkin's disease, lupus erythematosus, gastroenteritis • Rapid onset of muscular symptoms	• Retinal hemorrhage, sinus tachycardia or bradycardia, choked disk, hypertension, signs of increased intracranial pressure, elevated cerebrospinal fluid pressure, cranial nerve paralysis (VII), symmetrical loss of tendon reflexes, ascending peripheral nerve paralysis or weakness, impaired proprioception, loss of bowel and bladder control, muscle tenderness to pressure
• Most common in infants and children • Ingestion of lead paint from crib or wall or from water standing in lead pipe • Exposure to lead (metallic toxins) in the form of fumes from burning batteries, melting lead, or solder	• Symptoms of acute increased intracranial pressure; optic atrophy; anemia; wristdrop, footdrop
• Predisposing factors include otitis media, mastoiditis, ruptured brain abscess, sinus infection, hepatitis, tonsillitis, herpes zoster or herpes simplex, bone or skin infection, heart valve or lung infection, skull fracture, recent surgery to head or face, recent viral or bacterial infection, general malaise.	• High- or low-grade fever, rash, sinus arrhythmias, photophobia, nuchal rigidity, opisthotonos, back pain, shock, signs of increased intracranial pressure, positive Brudzinski's and Kernig's signs
• Ingestion of methyl alcohol (wood alcohol) used in solvent, antifreeze, paint remover, denatured alcohol, such as sterno • Symptoms usually appear 12 to 24 hours after ingestion.	• Visual field defect or loss of vision • Pupils dilated and nonreactive • Arterial blood gases reveal acidosis.
• Most common in females • Family history of *sick headache* • Onset usually around age 30 • Predisposing factors include emotional disturbance, fatigue, or anxiety; intense concen-	• With common migraine, tearing, pallor or flushing, perspiration, tachycardia during attack, transitory motor or sensory defects, tenderness and prominent blood vessels on head *(continued)*

Guide to Neurologic Disorders (continued)

DISORDER	CHIEF COMPLAINT	
Migraine (common, hemiplegic, ophthalmoplegic, basilar artery, temporal artery) (continued)	throbbing unilateral headache, generalized muscle pain • *Motor disturbances:* with hemiplegic and ophthalmoplegic migraine, extraocular muscle palsy, ptosis, possible permanent third nerve paralysis, hemiplegia; with basilar artery migraine, ataxia, dysarthria • *Sensory deviations:* with common migraine, aura may include visual flashing lights, hemianopsia, visual field defects, numbness, nausea, vomiting, vertigo, sensitivity to light and noise; with hemiplegic and ophthalmoplegic migraine, hemiparesis; with basilar artery migraine, partial vision loss, vertigo, tinnitus, tingling of fingers and toes; with temporal artery migraine, visual loss • *Altered level of consciousness:* with common migraine, aura includes fatigue, depression, anxiety, and euphoria; with temporal artery migraine, confusion, disorientation	
Multiple sclerosis (disseminated sclerosis)	• *Motor disturbances:* slurred speech, intention tremor, nystagmus (Charcot's triad), spastic paralysis, poor coordination, loss of proprioception, ataxia, transient muscle weakness, incontinence or retention • *Sensory deviations:* numbness and tingling, vision impairment • *Altered level of consciousness:* euphoria, emotionally unstable	
Myasthenia gravis	• *Motor disturbances:* progressive muscle weakness during activity; respiratory muscles affected during crisis; dysarthria; dysphagia • *Sensory deviations:* double vision, weak eye muscles	
Neurofibromatosis (von Recklinghausen's disease)	• *Headache:* pain along nerve distribution • *Motor disturbances:* rarely any weakness or atrophy • *Altered level of consciousness:* may occur with brain tumor	
Parkinson's disease	• *Motor disturbances:* tremor; characteristic rhythmic, unilateral pill-rolling movement involves thumb and forefinger; muscle rigidity; akinesia; inability to initiate and perform volitional motor activities; slow, shuffling Parkinson's gait—may be retropulsive or propulsive; fatigue • *Sensory deviations:* thermal paresthesia, hyperhidrosis, pain in one or both arms • *Altered level of consciousness:* minor intellectual deficit	

HISTORY	PHYSICAL EXAMINATION
tration or anxiety; oral contraceptives; menstruation; change in routine; hypothyroidism or hyperthyroidism; food additives; drinking wine or sleeping late. • Temporal artery migraine mostly affects females over age 60.	• With hemiplegic or ophthalmoplegic migraine, ptosis, third cranial nerve dysfunction, hemiplegia • With basilar artery migraine, ataxia • With temporal artery migraine, occasional fever; swollen and tender temporal arteries
• Most common in young white adults • Higher incidence in northern climate • Genetic tendencies • Initial attack and subsequent relapse may follow acute infections, trauma, vaccination, serum injections, pregnancy, stress.	• Pale optic disk on temporal side, increased deep tendon reflexes, joint contractures and deformities, scanning speech, cranial nerve involvement (vertigo, trigeminal neuralgia), decreased or diminished abdominal reflexes, unsteady gait
• Onset usually between ages 20 and 40 • Most common in females • Remissions and exacerbations common • Symptoms worsen with emotional stress, prolonged exposure to sunlight or cold	• Deep tendon reflexes present • Double vision, weak eye closure; ptosis; expressionless face; nasal vocal tones; nasal regurgitation of fluids; weak chewing muscles; weak respiratory muscles; weak neck muscles, can't support head; proximal limb weakness (may be asymmetrical)
• Onset may be anytime from childhood to age 50 • Family history of neurofibromatosis—congenital • May be accompanied by meningiomas, gliomas of the central nervous system	• Multiple tumors under the skin of the scalp, arms, legs, trunk, and cranial nerves; pigmentary lesions, café au lait spots; symptoms similar to brain or spinal tumor, depending on tumor's location; overgrowth of skin and of skull and neck tissue; hypertrophy of face, tongue, arms, and legs; skeletal anomalies; bone cysts • Cranial nerve abnormalities if affected
• Onset usually between ages 50 and 65 • Predisposing factors include family history of parkinsonism; past viral infections, such as influenza • Symptoms include increasing difficulty performing activities of daily living; slow eating and walking; inability to write in script—reversion to printing • Increased tremor during stress or anxiety; tremor decreases with purposeful movement and with sleep	• Resistance to passive movement; postural deformities of arms, legs, and trunk; small, festinating gait; arms fail to swing when walking; cogwheeling; eczema; micrographia; bradykinesia; hand tremor at rest; low, monotone speech pattern

(continued)

Guide to Neurologic Disorders *(continued)*

DISORDER	CHIEF COMPLAINT	
Petit mal (absence)	• *Motor disturbances:* myoclonus, automatisms, usually no loss of tone in muscles • *Seizures:* petit mal • *Altered level of consciousness:* brief loss of consciousness characterized by fixed gaze and blank expression; postictal period: immediately followed by alertness and continued activity	
Polyneuritis	• *Motor disturbances:* leg weakness or paralysis progressing to arms and trunk; weakness most severe in distal extremities and in extensors; footdrop; ataxia; absent leg reflexes; impairment of bowel and bladder function and sphincter control • *Sensory deviations:* paresthesias in hands or feet; anesthesia or hyperesthesia in distal parts of arms and legs; impaired vibratory and kinesthetic sensibilities; nerves sensitive to pressure	
Psychomotor seizure (focal)	• *Motor disturbances:* speech disturbance; destructive, aggressive behavior • *Seizures:* temporal lobe dysfunction (behavior disturbance) • *Sensory deviations:* olfactory hallucinations and other sensory manifestations depending on location of focus; feeling of déjà vu and déjà pensé • *Altered level of consciousness:* slower thought processes; altered consciousness; partial amnesia	
Reye's syndrome	• *Motor disturbances:* In stage I, none; in stage II, hyperactive reflexes; in stage III, decorticate rigidity; in stage IV, decerebrate rigidity, large and fixed pupils; in stage V, loss of deep tendon reflexes, flaccidity • *Seizures:* none, until stage V • *Altered level of consciousness:* in stage I, lethargy; in stage II, coma; in stage III, deepening coma; in stage IV, deep coma	
Spina bifida	• *Motor disturbances:* weakness, loss of tendon reflexes in legs due to atrophy of leg muscles, gait disturbances, incontinence • *Sensory deviations:* impaired cutaneous and proprioceptive senses in legs	
Spinal cord injury (contusion, compression, complete transection of cord)	• *Motor disturbances:* with contusion and compression, muscle weakness or paralysis; with complete transection, permanent motor paralysis below level of lesion; with upper motor neuron damage, spastic paralysis; with lower motor neuron damage, flaccid paralysis • *Sensory deviations:* related to size of injury and degree of cord shock; absence of perspiration on affected part; with contusion or compression, pain at level of lesion; with complete transection, total sensory loss	

HISTORY	PHYSICAL EXAMINATION
• Idiopathic seizure disorder diagnosed usually between ages 4 and 12; onset rare after age 20 • Predisposing factors include birth injury or developmental defect, acute febrile illness	• Petit mal triad: myoclonic jerks, automatisms, transient absences • May only be characterized by brief staring periods with occasional eye blinks
• Precipitating factors include alcohol abuse, inadequate diet and malnutrition, pregnancy, gastrointestinal disorders, vitamin B deficiency, weight loss. • Common in diabetics over age 50	• Dry, scaly skin on back of wrists and hands, hyperpigmentation of skin, plantar responses absent, abdominal skin reflexes decreased or absent, increased pulse rate possible; reduced or absent patellar and Achilles tendon reflex • Feet tender in diabetics
• Secondary to birth injury or congenital abnormalities in infants, lesions or trauma in children and adults, arteriosclerosis in adults	• Aura may occur in the form of a hallucination or perceptual illusion • May begin with aura • Characterized by automatisms (patterned behavior): lip-smacking, head-turning, dressing, undressing • Extreme psychotic behavior possible
• Acute viral infection 1 to 2 days before onset of symptoms • Prodromal symptoms include malaise, cough, earache, rhinorrhea, sore throat	• Vomiting; hyperventilation or respiratory arrest; hyperactive reflexes; absent deep tendon reflexes; decorticate or decerebrate rigidity; large, fixed pupils; rash • Serum ammonia level above 300 mg/100 ml, elevated BUN, elevated liver enzymes (SGOT and SGPT), increased intracranial pressure, prolonged prothrombin time, decreased carbon dioxide pressure (arterial blood gases)
• May be asymptomatic • Weakness in legs	• Palpable defect; scoliosis; valgus, varus, or caries deformities of feet, usually unilateral
• Auto and motorcycle accidents, athletic injuries (football, diving), falls, gunshot wounds, stab wounds • Cervical injuries most common	• Urinary retention, priapism, perspiration on one side; first 24 to 48 hours, flaccid paralysis, then exaggerated reflexes or spastic paralysis if lower motor neuron remains intact • Specific levels of injury intact and functional loss: with C1 to C2, quadriplegic, no respiratory ability; C3 to C4, quadriplegic, loss of phrenic innervation to diaphragm, absent respirations; C4 to C5, quadriplegic, no arm movements; C5 to C6, quadriplegic, gross arm movements only; C6 to C7, quadri- *(continued)*

Guide to Neurologic Disorders *(continued)*

DISORDER	CHIEF COMPLAINT	
Spinal cord injury (contusion, compression, complete transection of cord) *(continued)*		
Sydenham's chorea (St. Vitus' dance)	• *Motor disturbances:* sporadic movements of face, trunk, and extremity muscles; incoordination; muscle weakness; facial grimacing; arthritis; arthralgia (growing pains) • *Altered level of consciousness:* restless, emotional instability	
Syringomyelia	• *Headache/pain:* painful shoulder • *Motor disturbances:* weakness; hyporeflexia, hyperreflexia, or areflexia; wasting of muscles at level of spinal cord involvement (usually hands and arms); spasticity of lower levels; nystagmus; atrophy and fibrillation of the tongue • *Sensory deviations:* anesthesia in hands or face	
Tetanus (lock jaw)	• *Motor disturbances:* generalized spasms and muscle contractions, stiff neck and back muscles, rigid facial muscles, dysphagia, dysarthria, ptosis, diplopia • *Seizures:* generalized convulsions, paroxysmal tonic syndrome • *Altered level of consciousness:* irritability, restlessness	
Transient ischemic attack	• *Motor disturbances:* depends on location of ataxia; dizziness; falling; weakness • *Sensory deviations:* numbness, depending on location of affected artery; paresthesias; double vision; fleeting monocular blindness • *Altered level of consciousness:* drowsiness, giddiness, decreased level of consciousness	
Wernicke's encephalopathy	• *Motor disturbances:* ophthalmoplegia, ataxia, nystagmus, tremors • *Seizures:* may occur • *Sensory deviations:* paresthesias of hands and feet • *Altered level of consciousness:* drowsiness; impaired recent memory; unaffected remote, past memory; confabulation; time disorientation; apathy; mild lethargy; occasional frank delirium	

HISTORY	PHYSICAL EXAMINATION
	plegic, biceps movement, no triceps movement; C7 to C8, quadriplegic, triceps, no intrinsic muscles of hands; thoracic L1 to L2, arm function intact, loss of some intercostals, and loss of leg, bladder, bowel, sex function; lumbar below L2, motor and sensory loss, impairment of bladder, bowel, sex function according to nerve root damage; sacral, loss of bladder, bowel, sex function
• Onset usually between ages 5 and 15 • Symptoms include rheumatic fever, lack of sleep due to involuntary movements, nightmares; progress over 2 weeks	• Muscle weakness, facial grimacing, no muscle atrophy or contractures
• Onset usually between ages 30 and 50 • Symptoms include spontaneous fractures, painless injuries, ulcers from anesthesia; progress irregular (may be in remission for long period)	• Horner's syndrome, nystagmus, knee or shoulder joint deformities, clonus, spasticity, hyperreflexia • Loss of deep tendon reflex, gradual loss of pain and temperature sense
• Predisposing factors include puncture wounds, such as from blank cartridges, fireworks, nails, or splinters; compound fracture; septic abortion; parenteral injections, such as from heroin injections.	• Cyanosis, increased pulse arrhythmias, fluctuating hypotension and hypertension, increased respiratory rates, possible respiratory failure, trismus, rigid facial muscles (sardonic smile), stiff back muscles (opisthotonos); moderate-to-severe spasm, with pain, hyperactive deep tendon reflexes; inability to swallow; aspiration of secretions; fever and excessive perspiration
• Higher incidence in black men over age 50 • Symptoms include atherosclerosis, transient neurologic deficit lasting seconds to no more than 24 hours; hypertension.	• Normal neurologic examination between episodes
• Predisposing factors include inadequate diet, low thiamine intake, and alcohol addiction. • Pernicious vomiting possible during pregnancy	• Mental disturbance, retrograde or anterograde amnesia, paralysis of eye movements, ataxia, diplopia, nystagmus, broad-based stance

16

Musculoskeletal System

Because the musculoskeletal system is intricately related to virtually all other body systems and functions, it's seldom assessed alone. Problems usually are identified in the process of doing a complete physical assessment.

Primary musculoskeletal problems may result from congenital, developmental, neoplastic, infectious, traumatic, or degenerative disorders of the system itself. Disorders of other body systems also can cause musculoskeletal problems for your patient.

In nearly all our day-to-day activities, we rely on our ability to move about. When you're examining a patient in whom you've identified a musculoskeletal disorder, try to get a sense of how he perceives his problem and the effect it may have on his life. Remember that the problem may interfere with his social life, his ability to perform his job, or both. If prompt assessment and treatment can't relieve the problem, he faces the possibility of reduced ability to earn a living and to interact with his friends and family—he may even find that his role in the family will change. Remember, too, that bone disease or deformity, or muscle wasting, can change your patient's appearance and negatively affect his self-image.

History data

Biographical data

Your patient's age and sex may prove significant in assessment of a suspected musculoskeletal disorder. For example, osteoarthritis occurs in approximately 85% of people over age 70. Reiter's syndrome most commonly afflicts men between ages 20 and 40, whereas carpal tunnel syndrome and osteoporosis occur most often in postmenopausal women. Osteogenic sarcoma rarely occurs after age 40. Approximately 90% of patients with ankylosing spondylitis are men.

History of present illness

Common chief complaints associated with the musculoskeletal system are *pain, joint stiffness, redness and swelling, deformity and immobility,* and *sensory changes* (see *Guide to Musculoskeletal Disorders,* pages 354 to 363).

Here are some questions you may want to ask about these complaints to explore fully the history of your patient's present illness:

• *Pain. Can you point to its exact location?* Deep, poorly localized pain usually indicates damage to blood vessels, fascia, joints, or periosteum. *Would you describe the pain as an ache? A constant throbbing?* Bone pain is often described as throbbing; muscle and joint pain, as an ache.

Does the pain worsen with movement? With temperature changes? When you're carrying something heavy? Pain that increases with motion indicates a joint disorder. The pain of degenerative joint disease of the hip occurs with weight-bearing. Leg pain that worsens with standing, walking, or exercise and that persists for longer than 10 minutes after the patient stops the activity is probably caused by a degenerative hip or knee joint problem. Bending or lifting can elicit leg or back pain in a patient with a herniated lumbar disk. Pain associated with carpal tunnel syndrome worsens after extensive use of the hands. Cold and damp weather increases osteoarthritis pain.

Is the pain worse at any particular time of day? The pain caused by inflammation of the tendons and bursae may become intolerable at night. Joint discomfort from degenerative disease is often most intense at the end of the day. *Is the pain relieved by rest?* Pain from most forms of degenerative joint disease is relieved by rest. *Does aspirin relieve the pain?* Aspirin relieves joint pain caused by inflammation. *Have you recently fallen or been injured?* Trauma causes such injuries as fractures, torn ligaments, and back problems.

● *Joint stiffness. Which of your joints feel stiff? How many joints would you say are involved?* The patient's answers will help you identify the cause of his problem. *Does stiffness and pain in your joints stop for extended periods, maybe several weeks, and then recur?* Certain joint diseases, such as ankylosing spondylitis, are characterized by patterns of exacerbation and remission.

Is the stiffness severe when you wake up in the morning? How long after that does it last? In a patient with degenerative joint disease, inactivity during sleep causes stiffness that diminishes with joint use during the day. *Is the stiffness relieved or aggravated by temperature changes?* Heat relieves joint stiffness by alleviating muscle spasms. In a traumatic joint injury, however, heat applied immediately after the injury may aggravate stiffness by increasing bleeding into the joint. Generally, failure to use the joint and exposure to cold and dampness exacerbate joint stiffness.

Is the stiffness accompanied by locking of the joint? Can you feel or hear the bones rubbing together? Locking indicates poor bone alignment within the joint. Crepitus can occur in a fracture or from destruction of the joint's cushioning structures.

● *Redness and swelling. How long have you had the swelling? Did pain occur at the same time?* Edema and pain often occur simultaneously in traumatic injuries to muscles and bones. They are also present simultaneously in certain forms of bursitis, such as housemaid's knee. Swelling associated with degenerative joint disease can occur weeks or months after the pain, because of proliferative changes in cartilage and bone. *Does the swelling limit motion?* Swelling of soft tissue over a joint may act as a splint and immobilize it. Swelling within a joint also inhibits motion.

Does rest or elevation relieve the swelling? Elevation relieves swelling from a fresh injury because it facilitates blood return and prevents fluid from pooling in the extremity. *Has a cast* *or splint been removed from the affected part recently?* This may have caused the swelling, because the loss of muscle tone that normally occurs in a casted extremity impairs venous blood return. *Did the affected area ever appear red or feel warm?* Redness and warmth are signs of acute inflammation, infection, or recent trauma. These signs don't usually occur in degenerative joint disease.

● *Deformity and immobility. Did you notice the deformity recently, or has it been gradually increasing in size?* A slow-growing mass may be a tumor. Gradual bony enlargement of a joint causes deformity.

Does the deformity limit your movement? Is it always present, or is it more evident at certain times, such as after you've been active or when your body's in a particular position? In a patient with degenerative joint disease, movement limitation depends on the joints involved and the progression of the disease. A patient with contracture of the hand, for example, can't extend his fingers. *Does the deformity or limitations of movement interfere with your daily activities? In what specific ways have you had to alter your routine because of these restrictions?* How the patient carries out his daily activities determines how the deformity affects his ability to function.

Do you need, or prefer to use, any support equipment, such as crutches or elastic bandages? This information will give you a general idea of the severity of the patient's limitation of movement.

● *Sensory changes. Have you noticed any loss of feeling? Is it associated with pain?* Swelling can put pressure on a nerve, causing a loss of sensation in the area distal to the affected site. Compression of nerves or of blood vessels by a tumor or fracture also can cause a loss of feeling. Sensory changes sometimes accompany arm or hand pain.

Past history
Focus on the following relevant health problems when reviewing the past history:

● *Endocrine disorders. Diabetes mellitus* can predispose the patient to development of degenerative joint disease.

● *Blood dyscrasias. Hemophilia* and *sickle cell anemia* can cause bleeding into joints and muscles, leading to pain, swelling, tenderness, and possibly permanent deformity.

• **Skin or autoimmune disease.** *Psoriasis* may precede the onset of psoriatic arthritis. *Systemic lupus erythematosus* may cause joint deformities.

• **Previous injuries.** Repeated trauma resulting in damage to cartilage can cause degenerative changes in the joints.

• **Drugs.** Many drugs can affect the musculoskeletal system. For example, an anticoagulant overdose can cause hemarthrosis, and the use of corticosteroids can precipitate avascular necrosis of the head of the femur, predisposing the patient to septic arthritis. And discontinuing corticosteroid therapy too rapidly can cause arthralgia.

Family and psychosocial history

A number of musculoskeletal disorders, including ankylosing spondylitis, gout, and the development of Heberden's nodes in distal interphalangeal osteoarthritis, may be inherited. All forms of muscular dystrophy are inherited. Of patients with psoriatic arthritis, about 30% have a family history of psoriasis.

Find out if your patient's *occupation* requires any heavy lifting or strenuous activity, because this can lead to muscle strain, rotator cuff tears, and degenerative vertebral disk disorders. Occupations that involve long-distance driving or long hours of standing may also cause lower back pain.

Activities of daily living

Without realizing it, your patient may be damaging parts of his musculoskeletal system. For instance, poor alignment of the vertebrae caused by *poor posture* strains the spinal column. And *walking* in high-heeled shoes can cause contracture of the Achilles tendon. *Habitually carrying heavy objects,* such as a well-filled shoulder bag or attaché case, or photographic gear, can place uneven pressure on a person's spinal column.

Other important considerations to keep in mind when reviewing your patient's activities of daily living are *diet* and *exercise.* Poor calcium intake can lead to bone decalcification, and subsequent fractures and lack of exercise can cause both bone decalcification and muscle atrophy. Certainly a sedentary life-style results in poor muscle tone and an increased susceptibility to muscle strain. But sporadic exercise can be harmful, too, overworking

poorly toned muscles and causing sustained muscle contraction or spasm.

Contact sports, such as football and hockey, can lead to skeletal, joint, or soft tissue trauma; improper landing on the heels while jogging can damage the Achilles tendon. *Racquet sports,* such as tennis (or any other activity that requires a forceful grasp, wrist extension against resistance, or frequent rotation of the forearm), can cause joint pain.

Review of systems

Focus on the following signs and symptoms when reviewing your patient's body systems:

• **Skin.** Skin changes can be significant in helping identify musculoskeletal disease. For example, dry skin often occurs over the thumb and first two fingers of a patient with carpal tunnel syndrome. Skin lesions occur with Reiter's syndrome.

• **Eyes.** Conjunctivitis can be a symptom of Reiter's syndrome. Nongranulomatous uveitis may accompany ankylosing spondylitis.

• **Gastrointestinal.** Weight loss may occur in association with a neoplasm, and weight gain can aggravate degenerative joint disease. Chronic diarrhea may accompany arthritis associated with colitis and other gastrointestinal disorders.

• **Genitourinary.** Pain or burning with urination and urethral discharge are symptoms of Reiter's syndrome and gonococcal arthritis. A patient with a herniated lumbar disk sometimes has difficulty urinating.

• **Cardiovascular.** Tachycardia and hypertension may accompany gout. Carditis and aortic regurgitation may accompany Reiter's syndrome.

Physical examination

Preparations

During a musculoskeletal examination, at various times the patient will sit, stand, lie down, walk, and bend over. So the examination room should be large enough for him to move around. If possible, examine the patient under natural light (or lighting that simulates natural light). This lets you observe skin color changes and swelling without the distortion that artificial light causes.

Make sure the room temperature and the

examination table are comfortably warm, because temperature extremes can change the patient's skin color (and make him uncomfortable). Air-conditioning and tobacco smoke also can affect skin color. Finally, help your patient to relax for the examination.

The equipment you'll need for examining the patient's musculoskeletal system includes a metal or cloth tape measure, for measuring limb circumference and chest expansion, and a goniometer—a flexible protractor—for measuring range of motion in degrees. The patient should remove all clothing except underpants and wear a hospital gown.

Examination sequence and techniques

Begin your examination with general observation of the patient. Then proceed with a head-to-toe musculoskeletal assessment, systematically examining specific body parts. Check for gross abnormalities during the early stages of your assessment. For example, observe your patient's posture, build, and muscular development and bulk as he walks into the room. During the examination, observe the position of the different parts of his body at rest and when he moves.

Organize the examination so that it progresses smoothly, with minimal position changes for the patient. A good way to do this is to begin with the patient sitting on the edge of the examination table, so you can examine his head, neck, shoulders, and upper extremities. Then examine his chest, back, ilium, and gait with him standing and, later, walking. Finally, have the patient lie supine on the table while you examine his hips, knees, ankles, and feet.

Inspection and palpation are the principal techniques you'll use to examine a patient's musculoskeletal system. Inspect and palpate each body part; then test its range of motion and muscle strength. Examine each muscle and joint bilaterally, comparing both sides of the patient's body for equality of size, shape, color, and strength. (Remember that both sides of his body must be in the same position— for example, both arms extended—for you to compare them.)

You may auscultate to assess a vascular abnormality or bone crepitation; percussion may help you to assess fluid in a joint or to elicit tenderness.

Range of motion and muscle strength

After you've inspected and palpated each body part with the patient at rest, test its active and passive range of motion. During passive range-of-motion testing, assess the patient's muscle tone by feeling the muscles' movements under your hand. This adds to the information you obtained during your earlier palpation, when you felt the muscles at rest.

Next, test the strength of various muscle group functions, such as shoulder elevation and elbow flexion and extension. (Before you begin muscle strength tests, find out whether the patient is right- or left-handed, because the dominant arm is usually stronger.) To test the strength of each muscle group, ask the patient to perform active range of motion again as you apply resistance to his movements. Note the strength that the patient exerts against your resistance. If the muscle group is weak, you should lessen your resistance or provide no resistance to permit more accurate assessment. If necessary, position the patient's extremity so that he doesn't have to resist gravity, and repeat the test.

Record your findings according to the following five-point scale—developed to minimize subjective interpretations of test findings:
- **5/5:** Patient moves joint through full range of motion (ROM) against normal resistance and gravity
- **4/5:** Patient completes full ROM against moderate resistance and gravity
- **3/5:** Patient completes full ROM against gravity only
- **2/5:** Patient completes full ROM with gravity eliminated
- **1/5:** Patient's attempt at muscle contraction is palpable, but limb doesn't move
- **0/5:** Patient makes no visible or palpable muscle contraction; muscle is paralyzed.

Remember to test your patient's symmetrical muscles consecutively so that you can compare their strength.

Head and neck examination

First, inspect the patient's face for evidence of trauma and swelling and for symmetry. The mandible should be in the midline, not shifted to the right or left. Next, palpate the temporomandibular joint. Tenderness may indicate poor occlusion or trauma. If you note any tenderness over the temporomandibular joint, palpate the maxillary buccal mucosa posterior to the molars. This will cause pain if there is spasm of the pterygoid muscles caused by improper temporomandibular joint alignment.

To test range of motion, ask the patient to open his mouth so you can insert three fingers sideways. This distance should be 1″ to 2″ (2.5 to 5 cm). Observe this movement for smoothness, and check that the mandible maintains its midline position when it's opened. To test mandible muscle strength, place your hand under the patient's chin and ask him to open his mouth while you apply resistance.

Inspect the front, back, and sides of his neck, noting any abnormalities. Also look for symmetry of the neck muscles, and note any masses. Palpate the spinous processes of the cervical vertebrae and the supraclavicular fossae for any tenderness, swelling, or nodules.

Test the neck's range of motion by asking the patient to place his chin on his chest. Then hold the chin in the midline and raise the patient's head so that he's looking at the ceiling. Also ask the patient to touch his chin to each shoulder. Finally, ask him to try touching each ear to the ipsilateral shoulder. Test the patient's neck muscle strength by applying resistance with your hand as he tries to perform each motion a second time (see *Range of Motion of the Neck and Shoulders,* page 343).

The shoulders

Inspect and compare the shoulders, noting bony or muscular asymmetry, muscle atrophy, and deformities. Compare clavicles for symmetrical alignment. Inspect the deltoid muscle for atrophy, for prominence of the greater tuberosity of the humerus, and for the presence of hollows in the muscle (indicating displacement of the humerus).

Have the patient extend his arms and throw his shoulders back. Inspect the scapulae, checking for equal height and distance from the spinal column. Palpate the shoulders with the palmar surfaces of your fingers to locate bony landmarks; note any crepitus or tenderness. Using your entire hand, palpate the shoulder muscles for firmness and symmetry of size.

Range-of-motion testing of the patient's shoulders should include active and passive movement through forward flexion, backward extension, horizontal flexion and extension, abduction, and adduction. Test the rotator cuff muscles by passively abducting the extended arm to 90° and having the patient lower his arm slowly. If the patient has a rotator cuff tear, the arm will fall abruptly. A subluxated acromioclavicular joint may result from a sports injury, or it may occur in a patient with a paralyzed arm and shoulder that are poorly supported. If you note any tenderness during range-of-motion testing of this joint, test it by having the patient place his right hand on his left shoulder and lean forward. Then apply pressure to the distal end of the right clavicle. If the joint is subluxated, this maneuver will cause pain and abnormal movement of the clavicle. Repeat the procedure with the patient's other shoulder.

Test the trapezius muscle for strength by asking the patient to shrug his shoulders while you try to hold them down.

The elbows

For inspection, flex each of the patient's elbows to 90°. Compare the two elbows, noting any difference between the elbow joint angles when the patient holds his arms in passive extension. Check for redness, swelling, or a change in the contour of the joint or muscles. Palpate each elbow with the tips of your fingers, checking for subcutaneous nodules, bogginess, and enlargement of the supracondylar lymph nodes, which normally aren't palpable. (They are located just above the epicondyles; if you can palpate them, the patient may have an infection below the elbow.)

For range-of-motion testing, the patient should be able to demonstrate flexion, extension, supination, and pronation. Some people can hyperextend their elbows from 5° to 15°; this is usually a normal finding (see *Range of Motion of the Elbow and Wrist,* page 344).

The wrists

Inspect each of the patient's wrists for contour, and compare the two for symmetry. Also observe for thickening of the flexor tendon sheath of the median nerve, a sign of carpal tunnel syndrome. This may be seen on inspection of the palmar surface of the wrist. Then, using

Range of Motion of the Neck and Shoulders

This chart features some of the most common range-of-motion tests you'll perform passively and actively with your patient. Note that the ranges indicated are normals.

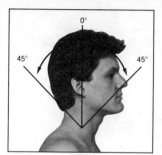

Neck: Flexion and extension

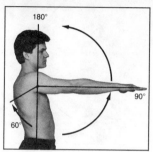

Shoulder: Forward flexion and backward extension

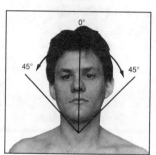

Lateral bending

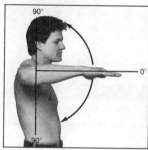

External and internal rotation

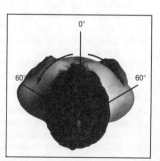

Rotation

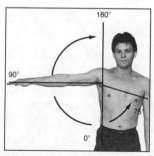

Abduction and adduction

Range of Motion of the Elbow and Wrist

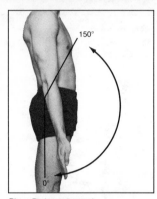

Elbow: Flexion and extension

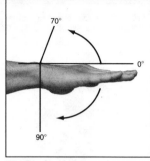

Wrist: Extension and flexion

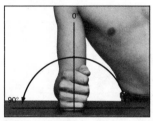

Supination and pronation

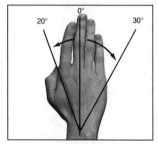

Radial and ulnar deviation

a circular motion, palpate the radial and ulnar styloid processes with the palmar surfaces of your fingers. Use two hands, with your thumbs on one side of the wrist and your fingers on the other. The styloid processes should be firm and nontender. Palpate the hollow on the radial side of each wrist, between the patient's thumb and index finger, by asking him to extend his thumb away from the fingers. He shouldn't feel any discomfort. For range-of-motion testing, remember that ulnar deviation is greatest with the wrist in supination.

Further testing for carpal tunnel syndrome is accomplished by holding the patient's wrist in flexion for 60 seconds. If he experiences Phalen's sign (numbness and paresthesia over the palmar surface of the hand, the first three fingers, and half of the fourth), the test is positive for carpal tunnel syndrome. A second test for carpal tunnel syndrome is positive if you can elicit Tinel's sign (a tingling sensation on the palmar aspect of the wrist). This may be done by tapping over the median nerve on the palmar surface of the patient's wrist.

Hands and fingers

Inspect your patient's hands, checking that they're about the same size. Inspect the thenar and hypothenar eminences for atrophy, which decreases the palmar depression. Thenar atrophy results from compression of the median nerve, as in a patient with carpal tunnel syndrome. Ulnar nerve disorders cause hypothenar atrophy.

Next, observe the contour of the metacarpophalangeal joints, and check the patient's hands and fingers for nodules, redness, swelling, deformities, and webbing between the fingers. Palpate the bony landmarks and the joints for tenderness, nodules, or bogginess. Soft hollows between the tendons indicate muscular atrophy. Now palpate the metacarpophalangeal joints. Normally, you'll feel depressions between them, but in some disorders (such as inflammatory or degenerative joint diseases) these depressions may disappear.

In range-of-motion testing, note any difficulty the patient has in flexing his thumb; de Quervain's disease can cause this finding. Perform Finkelstein's test by asking the patient to clench his fingers over his thumb. Then forcefully push the base of his thumb toward the ulna. If this maneuver causes pain on the radial side of his thumb, or toward the elbow on the radial side, the test is positive for chronic stenosing tenosynovitis. To assess muscle strength, apply resistance to the fingers as the patient tries to flex them, extend them, spread them, and bring them together. You can also assess general muscle strength by shaking hands with the patient (see *Range of Motion of the Thumb,* page 346, and *Range of Motion of the Finger,* page 347).

Back and chest

Ask the patient to stand with his back and buttocks exposed. Inspect the spinal column's curvature from both posterior and lateral views. In severe scoliosis, the chest becomes flattened on the side of the lateral deviation, and the opposite side, viewed posteriorly, becomes pronounced. Also, the scapulae become prominent, and the shoulders may not be level. Lordosis, an exaggerated lumbar curvature, occurs when the patient's abdomen protrudes or when the stomach muscles are weak, as in obesity or advanced pregnancy. Arthritis or muscle spasm may cause a loss of normal spinal curvature.

Ask the patient to bend over as far as he can. Muscular structures on both sides of the spine should be symmetrical in size, contour, and position. Postural kyphosis (accentuation of the convex thoracic curve) disappears when the patient bends over to touch his toes. The hump (razor back) deformity of scoliosis, caused by posterior protrusion of the ribs on the convex side of the spine, is also more apparent when the patient bends over.

Palpate the spinous processes and paravertebral muscles, noting tenderness or swelling. Palpate the paravertebral muscles, with the flat of your hand, to detect muscle hardening from spasm. To assess muscle strength, note any difficulty the patient has in performing range of motion for normal movements of the spinal column—including flexion, extension, hyperextension, lateral bending, and rotation. Measure chest expansion using the technique described on page 163. (See *Range of Motion of the Back,* page 349.)

Iliac crests

With the patient positioned so that your eyes are level with his pelvis, inspect the contour of his legs. Then observe his pelvis from the back. Place your fingers on the iliac crests and extend your thumbs in a straight line across the patient's back. Then draw an imaginary line from crest to crest. (The line should be straight.) Tilting may be from abnormal curvature of the spine, a muscle disorder, or unequal leg length. Observe the buttocks' muscles for symmetry. Asymmetry may be caused by congenital hip dislocation, scoliosis, muscle atrophy, or unequal leg length.

Gait and posture

Observe the patient as he sits, stands, and walks naturally. Gait varies from person to person, but normally you'll notice a certain rhythm. Ask the patient to walk about 20 steps and turn around. As he walks, observe his posture, his footing, his balance, the swing of his arms, his stride length, the rhythm to his walk, and any associated movements. A distance of 2" to 4" (5 to 10 cm) should separate his heels when he walks, and his stride length should be about 15", depending on his height. His arms should swing freely at his sides, he should be well balanced, and his posture should be erect. When he turns, his face and head should turn before the rest of his body.

Gait abnormalities suggest such problems as hip dislocation or ankylosis. The Trendelenburg gait—in which the patient's trunk lists to one side, producing a distinctive waddle with each step—is a sign of unilateral hip dislocation.

After observing his gait, ask the patient to walk in a straight line, heel to toe. If the patient can't do this, perform the Romberg test. (Stand

Range of Motion of the Thumb

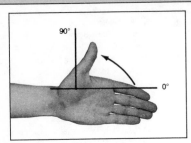

Thumb: Extension

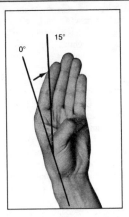

Carpometacarpal thumb joint: Flexion

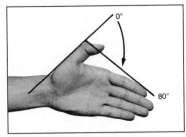

Interphalangeal thumb joint: Flexion

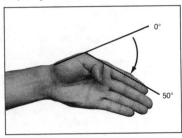

Metacarpophalangeal thumb joint: Flexion

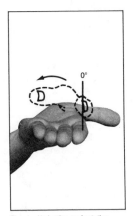

Thumb: Abduction and rotation

close to him to protect him if he loses his balance.) Have the patient stand unsupported with his arms at his sides, his feet together, and his eyes open. If he can do this, have him maintain this position but close his eyes. Normally, he should sway only slightly. If he's ataxic as a result of a cerebellar problem, he won't be able to maintain his balance with his eyes open or closed. If he maintains his balance with his eyes open but not when they're closed, he may have difficulty with his position sense—a positive Romberg's sign. If the patient is able to walk in a straight line and is reasonably healthy, ask him to hop in place on each foot. Successful completion of this task indicates normal motor function of the legs as well as normal cerebellar function and position sense.

Range of Motion of the Finger

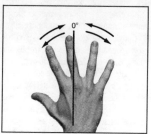

Fingers: Abduction and adduction

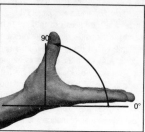

Fingers: Circumduction

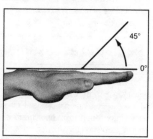

Metacarpophalangeal joint: Extension

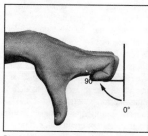

Distal interphalangeal joint: Flexion

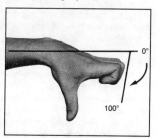

Proximal interphalangeal joint: Flexion

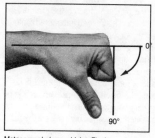

Metacarpophalangeal joint: Flexion

Hips and thighs

Have the patient climb onto the examination table and lie supine. Note any trouble he has in doing this. Then, with his legs aligned symmetrically, measure the length of each from the anterior superior iliac spine to the medial malleolus. The legs should be equal in length.

To check for a flexion deformity of the hips, perform the *Thomas test.* Flex one of the pa-

tient's hips by bending his knee toward his chest. Any hip flexion on the opposite side indicates a flexion deformity of that hip. If the patient experiences any pain, he may have a pelvic fracture (see *Range of Motion of the Hip and Knee,* page 351).

With the patient still on his back, perform the *straight-leg–raising test* to check for a herniated disk. Raise one leg from behind the heel until the patient complains of pain. Then dorsiflex the foot. Repeat the procedure with the other leg and compare the results. You should be able to raise both legs to 90° of hip flexion without causing pain (see *Range of Motion of the Hip and Knee,* page 351).

Pain behind the knees can indicate tight hamstrings; back pain can indicate pressure on the lumbosacral nerve roots from a herniated disk. Also while the patient is supine, test hip rotation by rocking each of his legs from side to side. Watch the patella and foot each time, to estimate range of motion. If this maneuver causes pain, carefully and gently carry out other range-of-motion and muscle-strength tests.

With the patient supine on the examination table, inspect his thighs for contour and symmetry. Measure their circumferences with a tape measure at the same level on each leg. The dominant leg may normally measure up to ⅜" (1 cm) larger. Palpate the thigh muscles with the palmar surfaces of your fingers, starting at the uppermost aspect of each thigh and moving lengthwise in a circular motion to cover the anterior, posterior, medial, and lateral aspects. The thigh muscles should be firm and continuous from origin to insertion.

Knees, ankles, and feet

With the patient supine on the examination table, inspect his knee alignment and contour. Note any deformities, such as knock-knees (genu valgum) or bowlegs (genu varum)—both most apparent with the patient standing. Observe the quadriceps muscle for atrophy, and look for absence of the normal hollows around the patella. Then palpate each knee by placing your thumb and forefinger over the suprapatellar pouch on both sides of the quadriceps. Note any thickening, bogginess, or tenderness of the synovial membrane. Also note any bony enlargement around the knee joint. With the other hand, palpate each side of the patella and the area over the tibiofemoral joint space, again noting any thickening, tenderness, fluid, or bogginess. Then palpate the popliteal space to check for swelling or cysts. Test each knee for full range of motion.

To test the muscle strength of the patient's hamstrings, have the patient alternately cross and uncross his legs. Then, you can test the quadriceps by trying to bend the patient's leg

at the knee while he tries to hold it stiff.

Inspect the patient's ankles and feet for swelling, redness, nodules, and other deformities. Check the arches, and look for any toe deformities. Note skin changes. Check the position of the ankles, noting whether the medial malleolus angles in or out abnormally. Also note any edema, calluses, bunions, corns, ingrown toenails, plantar warts, trophic ulcers, hair loss, or unusual pigmentation.

Palpate the bony and muscular structures of the patient's ankles and feet. Hold each foot behind the ankle with one hand and palpate with the fingertips of your other hand. Palpate the metatarsophalangeal joints and the metatarsal heads on the sole of each foot by compressing each joint. Test his ankles and toes for full range of motion (see *Range of Motion of the Ankles, Feet, and Toes,* page 352).

Pediatric assessment

History-taking considerations

When you're taking the past history of a child with a suspected musculoskeletal disorder, obtain information on his *immunizations* and on *past problems* he's experienced. A history of repeated fractures, muscle strains or sprains, painful joints, clumsiness, lack of coordination, abnormal gait, or restricted movements may indicate a musculoskeletal problem. A developmental history includes the ages when the child reached *major motor-development milestones;* this information will also help you determine if he has a musculoskeletal disorder. For an infant, some of these milestones include his age when he held up his head, rolled over, sat unassisted, and walked alone. Motor milestones for an older child include his age when he first ran, jumped, walked up stairs, and pedaled a tricycle.

During the family history, ask if any family member has experienced a musculoskeletal disease, such as arthritis or muscular dystrophy. Find out if the child's mother took any *medications* during the pregnancy. Certain drugs—such as streptomycin, tetracycline, meprobamate, and androgens and estrogens—can cause defects in fetal bone formation. Also ask if the mother has diabetes mellitus, which can predispose her child to hypoplasia of the femur.

Range of Motion of the Back

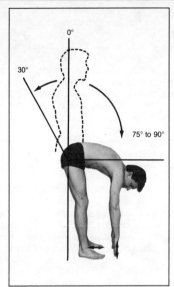

Extension and flexion

Lateral bending with pelvis stabilized

Rotation with pelvis stabilized

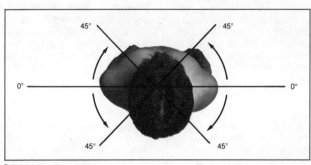

When reviewing activities of daily living, ask the parent about the child's usual daily *diet* and *recreational activities*. Calcium deficiencies can cause osteoporosis in children. Sports that involve throwing, such as baseball, may cause epiphyseal separation of the shoulder or wrist, especially at puberty.

Musculoskeletal examination

You can perform much of the testing of a child's range of motion, muscle strength, and gait while playing with him or watching him run, jump, sit, and climb. In infants and toddlers, you'll obviously assess only passive movements for range-of-motion testing. For children who are able to follow instructions and can do active range-of-motion movements, demonstrate what you want the child to do and ask him to mimic you. Observe the child's muscles for size, symmetry, strength, tone, and abnormal movements.

Test muscle strength in a preschool or school-age child as you would test it in an adult, by having the child push against your hands or your arms. To check muscle strength in a toddler or in an infant who is not yet able to understand directions, observe his sucking as well as his general motor activity.

Spine and gait: Check your patient's spine for scoliosis, kyphosis, and lordosis. If the child has scoliosis (most commonly seen in girls), differentiate between the functional and the structural type. Ask the child to bend over and touch her toes without bending her knees. (You'll get a better view of her spine if you squat to inspect it.) Functional scoliosis (also known as *postural scoliosis*) disappears with this maneuver, whereas structural scoliosis remains—and often becomes accentuated. Also, in structural scoliosis, one shoulder may appear higher than the other when the child bends over. Kyphosis and lordosis (which follows as a compensatory mechanism) most often result from poor posture.

To check a child's gait, balance, and stance, ask him to walk, run, and skip away from you and then return. If your patient's a toddler, remember that he won't want to walk *away* from his parents, but he will walk *toward* them. So to assess his gait, put the child down several yards away from his parents.

Keep developmental changes in a child's gait in mind, so you don't mistake them for abnormal conditions. For instance, a new walker (ages 12 to 18 months) normally has a wide-based gait with poor balance, whereas a preschooler usually has a narrow-based stance with enough balance to stand on one leg for a few seconds.

Hips and legs: Inspect the child's gluteal folds for asymmetry, which may indicate a dislocated hip. If hip dislocation is a possibility, test for Ortolani's sign (that is, a palpable and audible click when the affected leg is abducted).

Observe the child's legs for shape, length, symmetry, and alignment. *Genu varum* (bowlegs) is common in children between ages 1½

and 2½; *genu valgum* (knock-knees) is common in preschoolers. If these conditions do not improve over time or are excessive, evaluate the child for a tibial torsion (an internal or external rotation of the tibia). To test for bowlegs, have the child stand straight with his ankles touching. In this position, the knees shouldn't be more than 1″ (2.5 cm) apart. To test a child for knock-knees, have him stand straight with his knees touching. The ankles shouldn't be more than 1″ (2.5 cm) apart in this position. Also, look at the pattern of wear on the child's shoes: wear on the outside of the heel suggests bowlegs; on the inside, knock-knees.

Next, observe the child's feet for *club-foot* (talipes equinovarus); *outward-turned toes* (toeing out, or pes valgus), and *pigeon toes* (toeing in, or pes varus).

Finally, test the child for tibial torsion. One way to do this is to have him lie on his back with his knees flexed so that the feet are flat on the table, in a vertical line with his knees. Place your thumb and index fingers on the lateral and medial malleoli of both feet. In an infant, the four malleoli should be parallel to the table. In an older child, the external malleoli may normally rotate up to 20°.

Common childhood disorders

Because children's growing bones are somewhat flexible, *greenstick fractures* (incomplete fractures with angulation caused by disruption of the periosteum on one side of a bone) are common. Also known as an *infraperiosteal fracture,* this type of injury may be present whenever a child has bone pain accompanied by swelling and deformity.

Subluxation of the radius or shoulder sometimes results when an adult picks up or swings a child by the hands. In *subluxation of the radius,* the patient has elbow or wrist pain worsened by passive range of motion in all positions except supination. Shoulder pain accompanied by swelling and refusal to move the arm suggests *shoulder subluxation.*

Always be alert to the possibility that a child has been physically abused. Such a child usually will have multiple bone injuries, in different stages of repair, and may have other serious injuries, such as a subdural hematoma.

Necrosis of the head of the femur, known as *Perthes disease,* occurs in children (usually

Range of Motion of the Hip and Knee

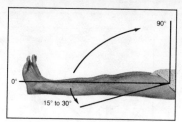

Hip: Flexion and extension with knee straight

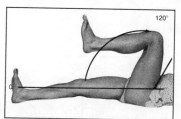

Hip: Flexion with knee flexed

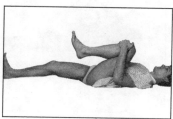

Thomas test for flexion contractures (Bend patient's knee toward chest to flex one hip.)

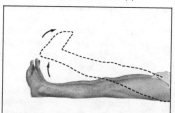

Straight-leg-raising test for herniated disk (Raise leg from behind the heel until he complains of pain, then dorsiflex the foot.)

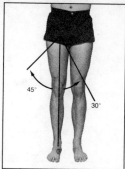

Hip: Abduction and adduction

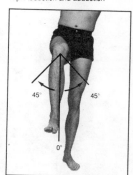

Hip: Internal and external rotation

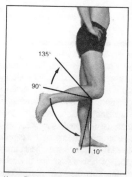

Knee: Flexion and extension

Range of Motion of the Ankles, Feet, and Toes

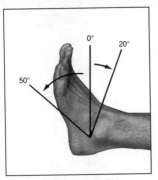

Ankle: Dorsiflexion and plantar flexion

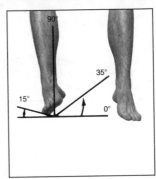

Foot: Inversion and eversion

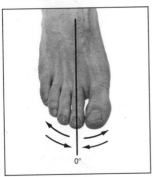

Toes: Abduction and adduction

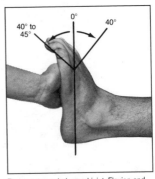

First metatarsophalangeal joint: Flexion and extension

boys) between ages 5 and 10. Clinically, the patient presents with a limp and with hip pain (often referred to the knee). Motion is restricted only on abduction and rotation.

Muscular dystrophy is an inherited disease characterized by progressive weakness from muscle atrophy. Skeletal muscle is primarily involved, but cardiac involvement can also occur. One of the first symptoms of Duchenne's form of muscular dystrophy, which occurs only in boys, is pelvic girdle weakness that causes toe-walking, falling, and waddling that begin

as soon as the child starts to walk. The disease progresses throughout childhood. By adolescence, the child is usually confined to a wheelchair. The Landouzy-Déjerine form of muscular dystrophy affects boys and girls, and usually first becomes apparent in adolescence. Most commonly, the first symptom is shoulder girdle weakness. Progression is slower than in Duchenne's form of the disease, with some children ultimately becoming disabled and others being scarcely aware of any symptoms throughout life.

Scoliosis, which is most common in girls, is an S-shaped lateral curvature of the spine that becomes apparent during periods of spinal growth, such as pubescence. In a child with scoliosis, one shoulder is elevated, one hip may be prominent, or the spinal curve itself may be noticeable. Of the two types of scoliosis, the most serious is *structural scoliosis,* caused by changes in the shape of the vertebrae or thorax. *Postural* or *functional* scoliosis is caused by poor posture.

Slipped femoral epiphysis is a disorder that occurs during epiphyseal closure, which marks the completion of skeletal growth. In this disorder, the femoral epiphysis gradually slips upward, often causing a slight limp on the affected side. Pain in the hip, sometimes referred to the knee, occurs as the disorder worsens, along with abduction and internal rotation of the affected limb.

Osteosarcoma (osteogenic sarcoma) is the most common primary malignant bone tumor of childhood. Although it may occur in other locations, osteosarcoma usually involves the end of a long bone—commonly the lower end of the femur or upper end of the tibia or humerus. Pain and swelling are the principal symptoms of this life-threatening disorder.

Geriatric assessment

Special history questions
Biographical data are significant for the elderly, because osteoporosis most commonly occurs after age 50.

If your patient's *chief complaint* is pain associated with a fall, determine if the pain preceded the fall. Pain present before a fall may indicate a pathologic fracture. Also, ask if your patient has noticed any vision or coordination changes that may make him more susceptible to falling.

When recording the patient's *past history,* determine if he's had asthma (treatment with steroids can lead to osteoporosis), arthritis (which produces joint instability), or pernicious anemia (inadequate absorption of vitamin B_{12} in pernicious anemia leads to loss of vibratory sensation and proprioception, resulting in falls). Cancer of the breast, prostate, thyroid, kidney, or bladder may metastasize to bone. Hyperparathyroidism leads to bone decalcification and osteoporosis. Hormone imbalance can result in postmenopausal osteoporosis.

During the *activities of daily living* portion of the history, ask your patient if he's decreased his activities recently. *Inactivity* increases the risk of osteoporosis. Also ask your patient to describe his usual *diet.* Elderly persons often have an inadequate calcium intake, which can cause osteoporosis and muscle weakness.

Physical examination findings
Your examination of an elderly patient with a suspected musculoskeletal disorder is the same as for a younger adult. But older patients may need more time or assistance with such tests as range of motion or gait assessment, because of muscle weakness and decreased coordination. Disorders of motor and sensory function—manifested by muscle weakness, spasticity, tremors, rigidity, and various types of sensory disturbances—are common in the elderly. Damaging falls may result from difficulty in maintaining equilibrium and from uncertain gait. Be sure to differentiate gait changes caused by joint disability, pain, or stiffness from those caused by neurologic impairment or another disorder. Bone softening from demineralization (senile osteoporosis) causes abnormal susceptibility to major fractures. Most patients over age 60 have some degree of degenerative joint disease, which causes joint pain and limits spinal motion.

Guide to Musculoskeletal Disorders

DISORDER	CHIEF COMPLAINT
Adhesive capsulitis (frozen shoulder)	• *Pain:* localized tenderness over biceps; worsens at night because of pressure while sleeping; aggravated by extremes in shoulder movement • *Joint stiffness:* shoulder stiffness • *Swelling and redness:* inflammation of capsule of scapulohumeral joint • *Deformity and immobility:* limited mobility
Ankylosing spondylitis (Marie-Strümpell disease)	• *Pain:* begins as lower back ache that radiates down thighs • *Joint stiffness:* decreased joint mobility and muscle stiffness • *Swelling and redness:* present, resembling rheumatoid arthritis, synovitis • *Deformity and immobility:* progressively limited back movement and chest expansion; in severe cases, fusion of entire spine
Bursitis	• *Pain:* severe on movement; in chronic form, nagging, intermittent pain possible • *Joint stiffness:* inflammation of bursae and calcific deposits in subdeltoid, olecranon (miners' elbow), trochanteric, or prepatellar (housemaid's knee) bursae • *Swelling and redness:* over affected joint
Carpal tunnel syndrome	• *Pain:* worsens after manual activity or at night; radiates up arm; may be intermittent or constant • *Swelling and redness:* soft tissue swelling possible • *Deformity and immobility:* inability to oppose thumb and little finger • *Sensory changes:* numbness, burning, or tingling on palmar surface (may be initial symptom)
Cervical disk herniation	• *Pain:* present in neck, shoulder, or arm; exact distribution depends on which nerve route is compressed; increases with neck flexion and rotation; paroxysmal • *Deformity and immobility:* limited neck range of motion; muscle (biceps) weakness • *Sensory changes:* paresthesia and sensory loss over neck, shoulder, arm, and/or hand, depending on specific nerve root involvement
Contractures	• *Pain:* absent • *Joint stiffness:* immobility caused by shortening of surrounding structures • *Deformity and immobility:* decreased mobility and function of affected part; deformity may result
Dislocation of the shoulder	• *Pain:* local, around involved joint • *Joint stiffness:* present; torn ligaments

HISTORY	PHYSICAL EXAMINATION AND DIAGNOSTIC STUDIES
• Predisposing factors include recent trauma to distal part of arm requiring shoulder immobilization; hemiplegia; cardiac disease; mastectomy.	• Decreased shoulder range of motion; shoulder tenderness on palpation • Diagnostic studies include X-rays.
• Most common in male children and young male adults ages 10 to 30 • Familial disorder; genetic predisposition	• Decreased spinal range of motion; abnormal vertebrae alignment; flattened lumbar curve; exaggerated thoracic curvature; decreased chest expansion; cardiac complication with long-standing disease; atrophy of trunk muscles; fever; fatigue; weight loss • Diagnostic studies include X-rays and HLA antigen studies.
• Predisposing factors include recent trauma to joint, occupational stress to joint, rheumatoid arthritis, gout, infection.	• Decreased range of motion in affected joint
• Predisposing factors include trauma or injury to wrist, rheumatoid arthritis, gout, myxedema, diabetes mellitus, leukemia, acromegaly, edema associated with pregnancy. • Most common in postmenopausal women and in women in advanced pregnancy	• Atrophy of thenar eminences; positive Tinel's sign (tingling present with wrist percussion); positive Phalen's sign (tingling with sustained wrist flexion); muscle weakness; dryness of skin over thumb and first two fingers • Diagnostic studies may include electromyography.
• Recent neck trauma or forceful hyperextension	• Cough, sneeze, or strain (downward pressure on head) in hyperextended position causes pain; diminished biceps or triceps jerk • Diagnostic studies include X-rays, myelography, computerized tomography scan.
• Trauma, infection, nerve lesions, result of immobilization	• Shortening of skin, muscle, or ligaments; flexion of joint
• Traumatic injury • Predisposing factors include congenital	• Decreased range of motion; altered joint configuration; changed extremity length *(continued)*

Guide to Musculoskeletal Disorders *(continued)*

DISORDER	CHIEF COMPLAINT
Dislocation of the shoulder *(continued)*	• *Swelling and redness:* soft tissue swelling • *Deformity and immobility:* displaced bones at joint; muscle atrophy
Fracture	• *Pain:* intensity increases until fragments are set • *Joint stiffness:* may be present with fracture near joint; crepitation • *Swelling and redness:* varying degrees of swelling and bleeding into tissues • *Deformity and immobility:* bone deformity; bone may project through skin; lost function of fractured part • *Sensory changes:* if nerves severed, bleeding and swelling cause pressure on nerves; if large vessel severed, blood loss to fractured part
Ganglion	• *Pain:* continuous aching aggravated by joint motion • *Joint stiffness:* present • *Swelling and redness:* gradual swelling over joint increased with extensive use of affected extremity; tense or fluctuant, rounded, nontender • *Deformity and immobility:* nodule over joint; weak fingers and joints next to ganglion, if connected to tendon sheath
Gout	• *Pain:* present, severe; worse after high purine food ingestion; frequently nocturnal; onset usually sudden • *Joint stiffness:* joint immobility caused by pain and swelling • *Swelling and redness:* red, or cyanotic tense, hot skin over affected swollen joint; in acute form, usually monoarticular • *Deformity and immobility:* painless tophi (urate deposits) in external ears, hands, elbows, and knees; can't bear weight on affected limb
Herniated lumbosacral disk (lower back pain)	• *Pain:* present with coughing, sneezing, straining, bending, or lifting; increases with sitting; occurs over dermatome for that specific disk; accompanied by mild or severe low back, buttock, or leg pain; may be associated with spasms • *Joint stiffness:* inflexible spine • *Deformity and immobility:* muscle atrophy of affected extremities • *Sensory changes:* decreased sensation, paresthesias; absent reflexes over dermatomes; voiding or defecating difficulties, particularly urinary retention
Kyphosis	• *Pain:* present in back; radiates to legs • *Joint stiffness:* stiff back • *Deformity and immobility:* round back in thoracic region; lordotic curve; hamstring tightness • *Sensory changes:* decreased sensation in lower legs
Ligamental tear	• *Pain:* tenderness on palpation • *Joint stiffness:* sensation of slight catching

HISTORY	PHYSICAL EXAMINATION AND DIAGNOSTIC STUDIES
changes in skeletal contour, weakness of musculature, past history of dislocation. • May reduce itself, or recur • Most common in young adults, athletes	
• Direct trauma • Indirect trauma above or below fracture • Predisposing factors include repeated stress, osteogenic sarcoma, osteoporosis, Paget's disease, hematopoietic diseases, nutritional deficiencies.	• Bone contour defect, abnormal bone motion, possibly shock • Diagnostic studies include X-rays.
• May occur after trauma, weight gain, compression • Disappears and recurs • Onset between adolescence and age 50 • Most common in women	• Limited range of motion of affected joint; palpable nodule more prominent on flexion, less prominent on extension
• Predisposing factors include renal disease, family history of gout, disorders that cause alterations in purine metabolism or decreased renal clearance of uric acid.	• Altered bone contour; elevated blood pressure; tachycardia; fever; nephrolithiasis; renal failure; thickened, wrinkled, desquamated skin • Diagnostic studies include uric acid levels; complete blood count; synovial fluid analysis; arthroscopy.
• Predisposing factors include recent spinal trauma, heavy lifting, or occupational stress on back; lack of exercise; weight gain; degenerative changes.	• Decreased spinal range of motion; unequal limb circumferences; abnormal posture; scoliosis; abnormal leg reflexes; diminished ankle or knee jerk; positive straight-leg–raising test (limited ability to straight-raise leg) • Diagnostic studies include X-rays and myelography.
• Compression fracture of thoracic vertebrae is a predisposing factor. • Recent spinal trauma, osteoporosis, chronic arthritis, tuberculosis	• Limited spinal range of motion; decreased pulmonary function • Diagnostic studies include X-rays.
• Popping sound heard when injury occurred; trauma to knee	• Unstable knee joint; abnormal knee range of motion; point tenderness; changed knee

(continued)

Guide to Musculoskeletal Disorders *(continued)*

DISORDER	CHIEF COMPLAINT	
Ligamental tear *(continued)*	• *Swelling and redness:* fluid around knee, swelling, ecchymosis • *Deformity and immobility:* excessive tibia motion at anterior and posterior femur • *Sensory changes:* weakness, instability	
Limb-girdle dystrophy (Erb)	• *Deformity and immobility:* mild kyphoscoliosis possible; severe disability late in disease	
Lower back strain	• *Pain:* acute and severe, or chronic, less severe, and aching; localized pain; may radiate • *Joint stiffness:* may be present • *Swelling and redness:* swelling caused by hemorrhage into tissues	
Meniscal tear	• *Pain:* acute pain or localized tenderness • *Swelling and redness:* local swelling • *Deformity and immobility:* muscle atrophy of quadriceps muscle above knee; inability to straighten knee	
Morton's neuroma	• *Pain:* severe, between third and fourth toes • *Swelling and redness:* swelling between third and fourth toes • *Sensory changes:* burning, numbness, and paresthesias between toes	
Muscle cramp	• *Pain:* present; cause unknown • *Deformity and immobility:* immobility during cramp; deformity also present	
Osteoarthritis	• *Pain:* during inclement weather; worse after exposure to cold, exercise, or weight-bearing; relieved by rest • *Joint stiffness:* transient stiffness worse in morning or after inactivity; affects weight-bearing joints • *Swelling and redness:* joints swollen and tender but not red or hot • *Deformity and immobility:* Heberden's nodes in distal joints; Bouchard's nodes in proximal joints; flexion contracture possible	
Osteogenic sarcoma	• *Pain:* persistent and progressive; local at first, then diffuse; bone tenderness • *Joint stiffness:* if tumor is located in joint • *Swelling and redness:* present in area of tumor; appears gradually as tumor grows; variable swelling; local heat • *Deformity and immobility:* pathological fractures; limited movement of affected part	

HISTORY	PHYSICAL EXAMINATION AND DIAGNOSTIC STUDIES
• Most common in athletes	joint contour
• Most common in adults ages 20 to 30 • Inherited • Rate of progression and severity are variable	• Primarily involves shoulder and pelvic girdle muscles; peculiar gait; muscle weakness; muscle contractions; muscle fasciculations; occasionally pseudohypertrophy of other muscles; may lead to respiratory and cardiac muscle involvement • Diagnostic studies include muscle biopsy, serum enzymes, electromyography.
• Muscle suddenly forced beyond capacity; trauma; degenerative disk disease; continued mechanical strain; pregnancy	• Tenderness with firm pressure; bruise; muscle spasm; inflammation; decreased range of motion
• Predisposing factors include twisting injury or direct blow to knee, repeated squatting or kneeling. • Most common in athletes	• Unequal knee contour; positive McMurray sign; blood in joint space
• Difficulty walking long distances; foot requires frequent massage • Use of high-heeled shoes • Most common in women	• None
• Common during pregnancy and in athletes • Usually occurs at night after strenuous activity	• Muscle is visibly and palpably tight; fasciculations; excessive sweating • Diagnostic studies include electromyography.
• Onset usually after age 55 • Moderate to severe disease more common in postmenopausal women • Predisposing factors include joint damage from trauma, infection, or stress; dietary calcium deficiency; history of arthritis in one or both parents; occupation.	• Decreased range of motion; altered bone contour; bony enlargement; malaligned joints; no systemic manifestations; crepitation on motion • Diagnostic studies include X-rays of affected joints.
• Peak incidence at age 20 • More common in males • Accompanying factors include weight loss. • Predisposing factors include history of Paget's disease, exposure to radiation, trauma.	• Decreased range of motion; unequal limb circumferences; venous engorgement; anemia • Diagnostic studies include biopsy and X-rays.

(continued)

Guide to Musculoskeletal Disorders *(continued)*

DISORDER	CHIEF COMPLAINT	
Osteomyelitis	• *Pain:* present in affected joint with movement • *Joint stiffness:* restricted movement caused by pain • *Swelling and redness:* onset of swelling in 1 to 2 days; inflammation; increased fluid in joint • *Deformity and immobility:* joint may be immobilized by pain	
Osteoporosis	• *Pain:* possible; symptom of fracture or vertebral collapse; aggravated by movement • *Deformity and immobility:* fractures of involved bones; collapse of vertebrae; increasing kyphosis or dowager's hump possible	
Paget's disease	• *Pain:* present in deep bone • *Joint stiffness:* present, as in rheumatoid arthritis • *Swelling and redness:* increased heat in affected area from increased vascularity • *Deformity and immobility:* bowing of long bones; kyphosis; frequent fractures with slight trauma • *Sensory changes:* headaches, deafness, vertigo, tinnitus, or other sensory changes possible; caused by bony growth that compresses nerves	
Poliomyelitis	• *Pain:* headache; muscle stiffness; aching and pain; sore throat • *Joint stiffness:* stiff neck • *Deformity and immobility:* progressive motor paralysis • *Sensory changes:* occasional sensory changes	
Reiter's syndrome	• *Pain:* present • *Joint stiffness:* present, usually in sacroiliac joint and sometimes in foot, knee, or ankle joints; weight-bearing joint involvement usually asymmetrical • *Swelling and redness:* signs of acute inflammation • *Deformity and immobility:* presence depends on extent of arthritis that is part of Reiter's syndrome	
Scoliosis	• *Pain:* present; radiates from back to extremities • *Joint stiffness:* hip or knee flexion contractures • *Deformity and immobility:* rib cage deformity; hamstring tightness; the higher the location of the scoliosis, the more severe the deformity • *Sensory changes:* decreased sensation to lower extremities	

HISTORY	PHYSICAL EXAMINATION AND DIAGNOSTIC STUDIES
• Predisposing factors include recent infection, surgery, fracture, puncture wound, bites, prolonged drug addiction. • Sudden onset	• Limited range of motion; unequal limb circumferences; local necrosis or lesion on skin surface; fever; chills; malaise • Diagnostic studies include blood cultures and X-rays.
• Predisposing factors include endocrine disorders, excessive cigarette smoking, chronic low dietary calcium intake, malabsorption, prolonged immobility. • Most common in postmenopausal women	• Evidence of healed fracture; loss of height; wedging of dorsal vertebrae or anterior vertebrae • Diagnostic studies include X-rays and bone densitometry measurements.
• Predisposing factors include recent deafness, family history of Paget's disease, cardiovascular and pulmonary disease. • Most common in men	• Altered bone contour; waddling gait; increased head size • Diagnostic studies include blood tests for increased calcium and alkaline phosphatase; bone scan; X-rays.
• Most common in infants, children, and young adults • Usually occurs in midsummer or fall	• Low-grade fever; nausea, vomiting, diarrhea, constipation; muscles tender on palpation; diminished or absent deep tendon reflexes • Diagnostic studies include examination of spinal fluid.
• More common in young men • Recent sexual activity • Cause unknown	• Limited range of motion • Lesions of mucous membranes, oral and genital skin, and nails; resembles psoriasis; lesions with yellow vesicles on soles and palms; low-grade fever; conjunctivitis; urethritis • Diagnostic studies include synovial fluid analysis.
• Predisposing factors include genetic history of scoliosis, poliomyelitis, congenital abnormalities.	• Limited spinal range of motion; fatigued or tired back; hair patches, dimples, and pigmentation on back; decreased chest expansion; impaired pulmonary or cardiac function (hypoxia, cyanosis, chronic obstructive pulmonary disease); one scapula, breast, or flank more prominent than other; shoulders and hips not level • Diagnostic studies include X-rays.

(continued)

Guide to Musculoskeletal Disorders *(continued)*

DISORDER	CHIEF COMPLAINT
Slipped femoral epiphysis (epiphyseal coxa vara)	● *Pain:* groin discomfort; subsides with rest; hip or knee aches; becomes intense in chronic phase ● *Joint stiffness:* stiff hip joint ● *Deformity and immobility:* limp; increases with fatigue; affected limb eventually becomes shorter
Spasmodic torticollis	● *Pain:* present with neck movement in trapezius, sternocleidomastoid, and other neck muscles; sudden or gradual onset; worsens under stress ● *Joint stiffness:* stiff neck caused by muscle spasm ● *Deformity and immobility:* muscle spasms cause head rotation to opposite side and flexion to same side
Sprain	● *Pain:* varying degrees over involved joint ● *Joint stiffness:* present ● *Swelling and redness:* soft tissue swelling; superficial bruise ● *Deformity and immobility:* limited range of motion ● *Sensory changes:* can be seen in cervical sprain
Temporomandibular joint syndrome	● *Pain:* facial, localized in ear or jaw; may extend to neck and shoulders; present on yawning or chewing, or with headache ● *Joint stiffness:* limited jaw movement, especially in morning ● *Swelling and redness:* swelling over joint ● *Deformity and immobility:* can lead to malocclusion
Tenosynovitis	● *Pain:* insidious or precipitated by strenuous activity; may radiate ● *Joint stiffness:* joint locking possible; inflammation common ● *Swelling and redness:* local swelling

HISTORY	PHYSICAL EXAMINATION AND DIAGNOSTIC STUDIES
• Predisposing factors include hip trauma, obesity. • Most common in boys ages 10 to 17 • Insidious onset • Occurs during rapid skeletal growth	• Muscle spasms; limited hip abduction, with internal rotation and flexion; abnormal waddling gait • Diagnostic studies include X-rays.
• Difficult birth is a predisposing factor. • Accompanying disorders include eye imbalance or defects, psychogenic problems, spinal or muscular defects. • Most common in adults ages 30 to 60	• Possible neck muscle spasms, which pull head forcibly to one side • Asymmetry of head and neck
• Sudden twisting injury	• Edema and discoloration around joint; no X-ray changes except soft tissue swelling; tenderness over joint
• Trauma, causing dislocation of joint • Osteoarthritis	• Joint clicks when mouth opens; limited range of motion
• Predisposing factors include injury or surgery of involved joint. • Most common in women in early 40s	• Decreased range of motion; pain on palpation

17

Blood-Forming and Immune Systems

Most systems of the body are composed of groups of organs. In contrast, the blood-forming system is made up of bone marrow and blood cells. The immune system is made up primarily of billions of cells that circulate throughout the cardiovascular system, as well as other structures—such as lymph nodes—distributed throughout the body. This means that the blood-forming and immune systems can directly affect—and are affected by—every organ system. Although some blood-forming and immune disorders cause hallmark signs and symptoms (such as the butterfly rash of systemic lupus erythematosus), detecting other problems in these systems can provide you with a real challenge. So besides performing a thorough physical examination, you'll want to be especially careful when taking your patient's history, because nonspecific symptoms from blood-forming and immune disorders can appear in any body system.

History data

Biographical data
Biographical information—particularly *age, sex, race,* and *ethnic background*—will assist you in your assessment, because some blood-forming and immune conditions occur more frequently in certain groups of people than in others. For instance, certain autoimmune diseases appear more often in women—especially young women—than in men. Sickle cell anemia occurs primarily in blacks and less frequently in Mediterranean, Middle Eastern,

and Asian peoples. Pernicious anemia occurs most frequently in Northern Europeans.

History of present illness
The most common chief complaints regarding blood-forming and immune disorders are *abnormal bleeding, lymphadenopathy, fatigue and weakness, fever,* and *joint pain* (see *Guide to Blood-Forming and Immune Disorders,* pages 376 to 383).

Here are some questions you may want to ask about these complaints to explore fully the history of your patient's present illness:
• ***Abnormal bleeding.*** Have you experienced any unusual blood loss? For instance, have you passed black stool, bloody urine, or unusually heavy menses? Excessive blood loss may result in anemia. Do you have frequent nosebleeds? Do you frequently notice bruises on your skin but can't recall their cause? A platelet or clotting mechanism deficiency can result in bruises from minimal pressure or slight bumps. Do you bleed for a long time when you cut your finger or have your teeth cleaned? Such excessive bleeding suggests a defective clotting mechanism. Do you start bleeding for no apparent reason? Does bleeding after injury start slowly and last a long time? All these signs and symptoms are indicative of vascular, platelet, or coagulation disorders (see *Tests for Blood Composition, Production, and Function,* page 366).
• ***Lymphadenopathy.*** Do you have swelling in your neck, armpit, or groin? Are the swollen areas sore, hard, or red? When did you first notice the swelling? Is it on one side, or both? Enlarged lymph nodes may indicate an in-

flammatory process, an infection, or the elevated lymphocyte production characteristic of certain leukemias. Enlargement from a primary lymphatic tumor usually isn't painful. Hodgkin's disease, however, may be accompanied by red, tender, enlarged lymph nodes. A large mass may indicate a lymphoma. Ask if a biopsy has ever been done on one of these lymph nodes. This may indicate a previously diagnosed malignancy.

• *Fatigue and weakness. Do you feel tired all the time, or only during exertion? Do you nap during the day? How many hours do you sleep at night? Are you experiencing weakness? Is the weakness more noticeable on one side than on the other? Is it adjacent to joints? Did it develop gradually? Is the weakness persistent? Were you ever told you were anemic?* Fatigue and weakness on exertion can suggest moderate anemia; extreme or constant fatigue and weakness can occur in a patient with severe anemia or with neuropathy from an autoimmune disease (see *Understanding Immunity,* page 368, and *Types of Immune Disorders,* page 369).

• *Fever. How long have you had a fever? Does your temperature drop to normal at all during the day?* Intermittent fevers occur with lymphomas. *Do you have periods of fever alternating with periods of normal temperature?* (Recurrent fever may be symptomatic of Hodgkin's disease.) *Do you have frequent fevers?* Fever from frequent infections may suggest a poorly functioning immune system. It may also suggest rapid cell proliferation. *Do you perspire excessively with the fever? When you look in the mirror, does your face appear flushed?* These symptoms usually accompany an infection.

• *Joint pain. Do you have joint pain? Which joints are affected? Did the joint pain occur in several joints at the same time? Did it affect additional joints? Did swelling, redness, or warmth appear with the pain? Are the joints painful when you're resting? Do you have early-morning stiffness?* Pain in the knees, wrists, or hands may indicate an autoimmune process or hemarthrosis from a blood disorder. *Do your bones ache?* Aching bones may result from the pressure of expanding bone marrow. *How do you relieve the pain?* Heat application or salicylates relieve pain from an inflammatory process.

Past history

Focus on the following relevant medical conditions when reviewing your patient's past history:

• *Surgery. Gastric surgery* decreases the level of instrinsic factor needed for vitamin B_{12} absorption. *Bilateral nephrectomy* may produce a diminished erythropoietin level. *Hepatic surgery* may reduce the formation of coagulation factors.

• *Sore throats.* Frequent sore throats may indicate poor resistance to infection.

• *Blood donation refusals.* A patient rejected as a blood donor may have long-standing anemia or a history of hepatitis or of jaundice with an undetermined cause.

• *Blood transfusions.* A history of blood transfusions may give you a clue to anemia. Try to determine the reason for the transfusions, how many units were given, and the patient's reaction, if any.

• *Autoimmune diseases.* The presence of one autoimmune disease can predispose a person to others.

• *Immunizations.* A history of the patient's immunizations is essential.

• *Allergies.* Ask the patient about known allergies to such substances as foods, drugs, insects, or environmental pollutants. Multiple allergies are common.

• *Asthma.* A history of asthma may indicate immunopathology.

• *Radiation therapy.* Radiation therapy can cause decreased blood cell production.

• *Medications.* A history of taking prescribed medications may indicate previous immune and blood-forming disorders. Also, note that certain drugs can produce side effects in the blood-forming and immune systems.

• *Gastrointestinal.* A patient's past history of peptic ulcer with excessive bleeding may be a clue to the presence of anemia.

Family and psychosocial history

Some blood-forming and immune disorders demonstrate familial tendencies. Others are hereditary. So always determine if your patient's family has a history of anemias, cancers in the system, abnormal bleeding problems (particularly in male relatives), or immune disorders, including allergies.

Increased *stress* may reduce a patient's resistance to infection and can trigger an au-

Tests for Blood Composition, Production, and Function

Overall composition
- *Peripheral blood smear* shows maturity and morphologic characteristics of blood elements and determines qualitative abnormalities.
- *Complete blood count (CBC)* determines the actual number of blood elements in relation to volume and quantifies abnormalities.
- *Bone marrow aspiration* or *biopsy* allows evaluation of hematopoiesis by showing blood elements and precursors, and abnormal or malignant cells.

RBC function
- *Hematocrit (HCT)* (packed cell volume) measures the percentage of RBCs per fluid volume of whole blood.
- *Hemoglobin (Hgb)* measures the amount (grams) of hemoglobin per 100 ml of blood, to determine oxygen-carrying capacity.
- *Reticulocyte count* allows assessment of RBC production by determining concentration of this early erythrocyte precursor.
- *Schilling test* determines absorption of vitamin B_{12} (necessary for erythropoiesis) by measuring excretion of radioactive B_{12} in the urine.
- *Mean corpuscular volume (MCV)* describes the red cell in terms of size.
- *Mean corpuscular hemoglobin (MCH)* determines average amount of hemoglobin per RBC.
- *Mean corpuscular hemoglobin concentration (MCHC)* establishes average hemoglobin concentration in 100 ml of packed RBCs.
- *Serum bilirubin* measures liver function and extravascular RBC hemolysis.
- *Sugar-water test* assesses the susceptibility of RBCs to hemolyze with complement.
- *Direct Coombs' test* demonstrates the presence of IgG antibodies (such as antibodies to Rh factor) and/or complement on circulating RBCs.
- *Indirect Coombs' test*, a two-step test, detects the presence of IgG antibodies on RBCs in the serum.
- *Sideroblast test* detects stainable iron (available for hemoglobin synthesis) in normoblastic RBCs.

Hemostasis
- *Platelet count* determines number of platelets.
- *Prothrombin time (Quick's test, pro time, PT)* aids evaluation of thrombin generation (extrinsic clotting mechanism).
- *Partial thromboplastin time (PTT)* aids evaluation of the adequacy of plasma-clotting factors (intrinsic clotting mechanism).
- *Thrombin time* detects abnormalities in thrombin fibrinogen reaction.
- *Activated partial thromboplastin time (APTT)* aids assessment of plasma-clotting factors (except factors VII and XIII) in the intrinsic clotting mechanism.

WBC function
- *WBC count, differential* establishes quantity and maturity of WBC elements (neutrophils [called polymorphonuclear granulocytes or bands], basophils, eosinophils, lymphocytes, monocytes).

Plasma
- *Erythrocyte sedimentation rate (ESR)* measures rate of RBCs settling from plasma and may reflect infection.
- *Electrophoresis of serum proteins* determines amount of various serum proteins (classified by mobility in response to an electrical field).
- *Immunoelectrophoresis of serum proteins* separates and classifies serum antibodies (immunoglobulins) through specific antiserums.
- *Fibrinogen (Factor I)* measures this coagulation factor in plasma.

toimmune disease. *Exposure to chemicals*—such as industrial cleaning fluids, glues used in some hobbies, or insecticides used in gardening or farming—may cause blood dyscrasias.

Activities of daily living

When recording your patient's activities of daily living, focus on his *diet*. Specifically, determine his typical daily diet and inquire about idiosyncratic, religious, or cultural dietary restrictions. Also, ask about recent significant dietary changes and weight loss.

Poor nutrition can greatly affect a person's immune system. For example, a severely protein-deficient diet can result in lymphoid tissue atrophy, diminished antibody response, fewer circulating T cells, and impaired cellular immunity. Although infection increases the need for nutrients and caloric intake, it may paradoxically cause anorexia. Also ask about the patient's alcohol consumption. If it's excessive, he may have nutritional deficits. Ask, too, about exercise and rest patterns. Problems associated with these daily activities may give you a clue to a blood-forming or immune disorder.

Review of systems

• *General. Frequent illness* suggests immunologic problems.

• *Skin.* An anemic patient may have pale, sallow, or clammy skin. Anemia can also cause nail changes (brittleness, ridges, flattening). Subcutaneous nodules may indicate an autoimmune disorder. Characteristic skin rashes, such as the butterfly rash of systemic lupus erythematosus, accompany some autoimmune disorders.

• *Eyes. Keratitis* and *retinal hemorrhages* may be present in patients with clotting and autoimmune disorders.

• *Mouth. A sore throat, a sore and burning tongue, dysarthria,* or *dysphagia* suggests (among other things) infection or inflammation. Mouth ulcers may indicate anemia or an immune disorder.

• *Cardiovascular. Tachycardia* may result from the blood's reduced ability to carry oxygen.

• *Respiratory. Wheezing* or *rhinitis* can indicate an allergic response. *Dyspnea* or *or-thopnea* may suggest anemia or connective tissue disease.

• *Genitourinary.* Hematuria can occur in some anemias and in advanced autoimmune disease. Pernicious anemia can cause *incontinence* and *impotence.*

• *Gastrointestinal. Nausea* or *appetite loss* may result from infection, an inflammatory process, or advanced autoimmune disease.

• *Neurologic.* If the patient has difficulty walking or experiences a *pins-and-needles* sensation, he may have a vitamin B_{12} deficiency, resulting in pernicious anemia. Central nervous system complications of systemic lupus erythematosus may cause emotional instability, headaches, irritability, and depression.

Physical examination

Preparations

During the physical examination, your patient will alternate between sitting and lying down, so adjust the examining table to an appropriate height for both positions. Ensure proper lighting for skin inspection—a key part of blood-forming and immune assessment. Remember, if lighting produces a glare, you may not be able to detect subtle color changes. Before starting the examination, give your patient the opportunity to urinate, because you'll be doing deep abdominal palpation.

Be sure to explain the purpose of the examination to the patient, and tell him what you'll be doing before starting each procedure. Have the necessary equipment ready—stethoscope, sphygmomanometer, ophthalmoscope, scale, and measuring tape.

General physical and mental status

Because signs and symptoms of blood-forming and immune disorders are often nonspecific, a thorough observation of your patient's general physical status is essential. Inspect his general appearance and note if he looks acutely ill. Observe his face for flushing, profuse perspiration, or grimacing (as if he's in pain). Then observe for indications of chronic illness, including dehydration, pallor, emaciation, and listlessness.

Does your patient look his stated age?

Understanding Immunity

Immunity, innate or acquired, is the body's capacity to prevent tissue and organ damage by resisting invading organisms and toxins. *Innate immunity* includes phagocytosis of bacteria by leukocytes and reticuloendothelial cells, skin resistance to invading organisms, and the destruction of organisms by acids secreted in the stomach and by chemicals in the blood.

Antibodies with the ability to bind antigens are known as *immunoglobulins.* These are divided into five classes, based on their individual structures and functions. The symbol for immunoglobulins is *Ig,* and each class is designated by a letter—IgA, IgD, IgE, IgG, and IgM.

Acquired immunity can be humoral or cellular. In *humoral immunity,* the antibodies are specific to an antigen. The stem cells develop into the lymphocytes (immature B cells). These migrate to the lymph nodes, liver, and spleen. They bind with an antigen, and their antibodies become specific for that antigen. Activated B cells form clones with two cell lines. Some become plasma cells and are secreted into the blood to fight the antigen through the release of their surface antibodies. Some (memory cells) are stored in the lymph nodes for future use. When the same antigen is again encountered, the memory cells activate.

Cellular immunity refers to the production and release of T lymphocytes sensitized to a specific foreign substance or antigen. In cellular immunity, stem cells from the embryonic yolk sac seed the thymus and develop into T cells. T cells migrate to the lymph nodes, where they may come in contact with an antigen that they can bind with, thus becoming sensitized T cells. Some T cells kill the invading cell directly by releasing a lymphotoxin (a poison) against the cell. Other T cells attract macrophages into the area and promote the phagocytosis of the invading cell.

When antibodies bind with a specific antigen, they form the *antigen-antibody complex.* This complex renders the antigen harmless. This may occur in any of several different ways:
● If the antigen is a toxin, the antigen-antibody complex neutralizes it.
● The antigen-antibody complex can cause agglutination of invader cells.
● The antigen-antibody complex can change the shape of the antibody slightly to expose complement-binding sites. These initiate activity that releases enzymes, which destroy the invading cells.

Acquired immunity can be broken down into types that include:
● *active immunity*—antibody production by the body in response to vaccination or the contraction of a disease
● *passive immunity*—injection of an antibody into the body from another person or animal, for example, a tetanus toxoid
● *passive-active immunity*—antibody and antigen injection that triggers antibody production
● *active-passive immunity*—antibody injection during antigen exposure to reduce severity (for instance, a gamma globulin injection).

Chronic disease and nutritional deficiencies associated with blood-forming and immune problems may make a patient look older than he is.

Next, weigh the patient and measure his height. Compare his weight to the ideal for his height, bone structure, and build. Weight loss may result from anorexia and gastrointestinal problems associated with blood-forming or immune conditions. If your patient appears undernourished or cachectic, assess him for chronic disease.

Next, inspect your patient for abnormal body posture, movements, or gait; these can indicate joint, spinal, or neurologic changes.

Finally, record your patient's vital signs. Changes in blood pressure, pulse, and temperature may indicate infection, inflammation, elevated metabolic rate, or fluid and electrolyte disturbances—all possibly indicative of blood-forming or immune disorders.

Observe your patient's behavior to assess his mood. Of course, a chronically ill patient, regardless of the nature of his disorder, may be depressed or angry. But irritability, confusion, hallucinations, or other symptoms of

Types of Immune Disorders

TYPE	DESCRIPTION	EXAMPLE
Immunodeficiency	Deficiency in phagocytosis, immunoglobulin production, cellular functioning, or a combination of these	• *Primary:* DiGeorge's syndrome • *Secondary:* Immunosuppression caused by radiation or chemotherapy; AIDS
Gammopathy	Abnormal production of high levels of dysfunctional gamma globulins	• Multiple myeloma, macroglobulinemia
Hypersensitivity (allergy)	Exaggerated or inappropriate response to sensitizing antigens, classified as follows:	
	Type I (anaphylactic): Humoral mediation (IgE binds to mast cells); immediate onset	• Hay fever, allergic asthma, anaphylactic shock caused by allergies to, for example, penicillin or contrast medium
	Type II (cytotoxic): Humoral mediation (IgG or IgM binds to cell surface antigen); immediate onset	• Transfusion reactions
	Type III (immune complex): Humoral mediation (IgG or IgM forms complex with soluble antigen); immediate onset	• Serum sickness, acute glomerulonephritis
	Type IV (cell-mediated): Cellular mediation (T cells and macrophages cause tissue destruction); delayed onset	• Graft rejection, reaction to tubercle bacillus
Autoimmunity	Altered discrimination between self and nonself, causing immunologic attack on self antigens	• Pernicious anemia, systemic lupus erythematosus, rheumatoid arthritis, myasthenia gravis

psychosis (such as paranoid thinking) may occur with immune disorders, particularly systemic lupus erythematosus. Forgetfulness and sleeplessness may occur with anemia. Slowed responses or a poor attention span can result from either blood-forming or immune disorders.

Skin, hair, and nails

Inspect your patient's skin color, noting any pallor, cyanosis, or jaundice. Pallor can result from decreased hemoglobin content. Cyanosis suggests excessive deoxygenated hemoglobin in cutaneous blood vessels caused by hypoxia, which appears in some anemias. Cyanosis or pallor in a patient's fingers or toes may result from Raynaud's phenomenon, seen in some autoimmune diseases.

Examine the patient's face, conjunctivae, hands, and feet for ruddy cyanosis or plethora (red, florid complexion), which appear in polycythemia. Then, inspect for erythema, a possible sign of local inflammation or fever.

Look for jaundice in the patient's sclerae, mucous membranes, and skin. For dark-skinned patients, also inspect the buccal mu-

Palpating Neck Nodes

 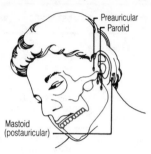

To palpate the preauricular nodes, position your fingers as shown here.

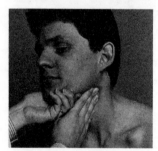 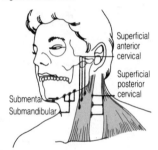

To palpate the submandibular, submental, and cervical nodes, position your fingers as shown here. Palpate over the mandibular surface and continue moving up and down the entire neck. You can flex the head forward or to the side being examined to relax the tissues and make enlarged nodes more palpable.

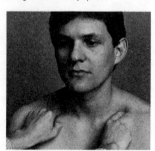 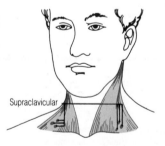

To palpate the supraclavicular nodes, first encourage your patient to relax, so his clavicles drop. Flex his head slightly forward with your free hand, to relax the soft tissues of his anterior neck. Then, hook your left index finger over the clavicle lateral to the sternocleidomastoid muscle. Rotate your finger deeply into this area to feel these nodes.

Palpating Axillary Nodes

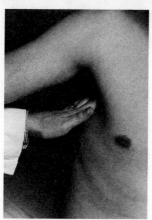
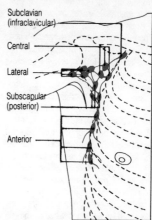

Subclavian (infraclavicular)

Central

Lateral

Subscapular (posterior)

Anterior

To palpate the axillary nodes, gently press the soft tissues against the chest wall and the muscles surrounding the axilla (the pectoral muscles, latissimus dorsi, subscapularis, and serratus anterior muscles).

cosa, palms of the hands, and soles of the feet. For an edematous patient, examine the inner forearm for jaundice. An elevated bilirubin level may be secondary to increased erythrocyte hemolysis—a problem that may be hereditary or acquired. (Remember, excessive intake of carrots or yellow vegetables may cause yellow skin but will not cause color change in the sclerae or mucous membranes.)

If you suspect a clotting abnormality, inspect the patient's skin for purpuric lesions, which result most commonly from thrombocytopenia. These lesions can vary in size. For dark-skinned patients, assess the oral mucosa or conjunctivae for petechiae or ecchymoses. As blood is reabsorbed, skin color changes from yellow to yellow green. (These two skin changes are difficult to detect in dark-skinned patients.) Also, inspect for such abnormalities as telangiectasias, and note their location.

Assess skin integrity, noting if the patient has any signs of infection, such as abnormal temperature, wound drainage, poor wound healing, or ulceration. Check for rashes; among many possible causes, a rash can in-

dicate autoimmune disease. Certain autoimmune diseases have uniquely characteristic rashes—the butterfly rash of systemic lupus erythematosus, the heliotrope rash of dermatomyositis. So be sure to note the rash's distribution.

Inspect your patient's hair growth patterns, noting any alopecia on the arms, legs, or head. Remember, alopecia patches may occur in systemic lupus erythematosus.

Inspect the patient's nails and note any abnormalities. Specifically, note any longitudinal striation, which is associated with anemia, or koilonychia (also called *spoon nail*), which is characteristic of iron deficiency anemia. Look for platyonychia (abnormally broad or flat nails), which may precede development of koilonychia, and for onycholysis or loosening of the nails. Inspect for clubbing, indicative of chronic hypoxia—which can result from a blood-forming or immune disorder. (See *Nail Abnormalities*, pages 104 to 105.)

Lymph nodes

Normally, you'll inspect and palpate the patient's neck, axillary, epitrochlear, and inguinal lymph nodes as you examine the areas of the body (see *Palpating Neck Nodes*, page 370 and *Palpating Axillary Nodes*, page 371). First inspect the skin over the nodes, noting any color abnormalities or obvious enlargements. Then palpate the nodes, using your finger pads to move skin over the area. (When you're palpating the nodes in the patient's neck, he should be sitting.) To palpate axillary nodes, the patient should remain sitting or be supine, with his right arm relaxed. Use your nondominant hand to support his right arm and put your other hand as high in his right axilla as possible. Palpate against the chest wall for the lateral, anterior, posterior, central, and subclavian nodes. Use the same procedure for the patient's left axilla. For the epitrochlear nodes, palpate the medial area of his elbow. For the inguinal nodes, palpate below the inguinal ligament and along the upper saphenous vein. As you palpate all nodes, note their size, consistency (hard or soft), and whether they're fixed or movable, tender or painless.

Red streaks in the skin, palpable nodes, and lymphedema may indicate a lymphatic disorder. Enlarged (palpable) nodes suggest current or previous inflammation. Nodes covered by red-streaked skin suggest acute lymphadenitis (you'll usually see an obvious infection site). Hard nodes may suggest a tumor. General lymphadenopathy can indicate an inflammatory or neoplastic process.

Inspecting the eyes and the mouth

Inspect your patient's eyelids for signs of infection or inflammation—such as edema, redness, or lesions. Note the eyes' position and alignment, and check the conjunctivae for engorged or enlarged vessels. (Keratoconjunctivitis, as well as iritis and scleritis, may accompany rheumatoid arthritis.) Then use the ophthalmoscope to examine the patient's retinas (see pages 121 to 123). Vessel tortuosity may result from sickle cell anemia; hemorrhage or infiltration can suggest, among other possibilities, hemorrhagic leukemia, vasculitis, or thrombocytopenia.

Inspect your patient's buccal mucosa, lips, gums, teeth, tongue, and palate. Red mucous membranes may result from polycythemia; an enlarged tongue from multiple myeloma (among other possible disorders); absence of papillae from pernicious anemia; and purpuras and telangiectasias from bleeding disorders. Tonsillar hypertrophy appears in lymphomas; gingival hypertrophy that makes teeth look sunken may result from myelogenous leukemia. (*Note:* These changes occur in chronic, not acute, neoplastic diseases.) Oral nasopharyngeal ulcers may accompany systemic lupus erythematosus.

Cardiovascular/respiratory assessment

Auscultate the patient's precordium for heart murmurs (see pages 195 to 200). Ventricular enlargement and apical systolic murmurs may result from severe anemia. Mitral, aortic, and pulmonic murmurs can occur in sickle cell anemia. Tachycardia may also occur in some anemias. Congestive heart failure or pericardial effusions may develop in a patient with systemic lupus erythematosus or rheumatoid arthritis.

Next, inspect your patient's peripheral circulation. Raynaud's phenomenon may occur in some patients with autoimmune diseases.

Assess the patient's chest carefully (see Chapter 9, RESPIRATORY SYSTEM). First, note any signs of respiratory distress, particularly dyspnea, coughing, or cyanosis. These can be associated with a blood-forming or immune disorder. Auscultation may detect wheezing—a possible sign of allergy or asthma. Percussion and auscultation may reveal a pleural effusion; a patient with rheumatoid arthritis or systemic lupus erythematosus may develop this condition.

Abdominal examination

Place your patient in the supine position, with a pillow under his head. Then percuss and palpate his liver (see page 229). Next, percuss the left upper quadrant to examine his spleen. Normally, percussion in this area will produce a dull note between the sixth and tenth ribs just posterior to the mid-axillary line. (Always place your percussion finger—pleximeter—between the ribs to avoid eliciting a dull note from the bone.) The gastric bubble, which creates a tympanic note, is near the spleen, so isolating the dull splenic note requires careful comparison (see *Spleen Palpation and Percussion*).

Spleen Palpation and Percussion

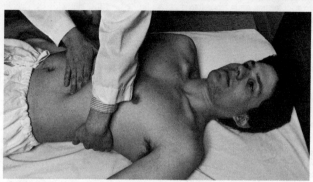

To palpate your patient's spleen properly, place him in the supine position. Approach him from his right side and reach over him, as shown here. With your left hand, support his lower left rib cage and move it forward. Place your right hand below the left costal margin and press inward.

Tell your patient to take a deep breath. You may be able to feel the edge of the spleen as the patient slowly exhales. Note: Usually you cannot palpate the spleen unless the person is very thin. If you can feel your patient's spleen on inspiration and expiration, it's probably enlarged. In such a patient, the spleen may extend into the left lower quadrant and even across the midline.

When you percuss your patient's spleen, you should hear normal dullness between the 6th and 10th ribs, posterior to the midaxillary line. If splenic dullness can be heard over a larger area than normal, suspect splenic enlargement. In such a patient, you should percuss the spleen in the lowest interspace in the anterior axillary line.

Normally, a patient's spleen cannot be palpated unless it's enlarged. An enlarged spleen is usually tender (this finding is most common in acute disorders), so when percussion is difficult, use light palpation to detect tenderness. Hepatomegaly and splenomegaly may result from congestion caused by cell overproduction (as in polycythemia or leukemia) or from excessive demand for defective cell destruction (as in hemolytic anemias).

Neuromuscular assessment

Test your patient's range of motion, particularly the joints of his hands, wrists, and knees (see Chapter 16, Musculoskeletal System). Systemic lupus erythematosus, rheumatoid arthritis, or hemarthrosis can limit a patient's range of motion and cause joint enlargement. Note any joints that are inflamed, erythematous, swollen, or asymmetrical.

Also test your patient's equilibrium and observe for Romberg's sign. Hemorrhage, cellular infiltration, or metabolic abnormalities from blood-forming disorders can affect the central and peripheral nervous systems.

Be sure to assess the patient for neuropathies, which may occur with systemic lupus erythematosus and rheumatoid arthritis. The patient's history or your other assessment findings may indicate the need for a more extensive neurologic examination.

Pediatric assessment

Immunity and blood production

The neonate's immune system depends on passive immunity acquired from the mother transplacentally. This means that the infant is susceptible to infectious diseases the mother hasn't had. And as his passive immunity diminishes, the infant may experience repeated infections until his own immune system matures. Development of his own immunity begins during the first few months after birth, when bone marrow and the reticuloendothelial system mature.

Immunity may also be acquired in other ways. Breast-feeding, for instance, introduces special immunoglobulins into the gastrointestinal tract. And immunizations also fortify the body's immune system.

Because an infant can't conjugate bilirubin and excrete it into bile as rapidly as occurs in an older child, his elevated bilirubin level may produce physiologic jaundice.

The health history

When recording the health history of a child with a suspected blood-forming disorder, check for anemia by asking the parents if the child has had the common signs and symptoms—pallor, fatigue, failure to gain weight, malaise, and lethargy. If you suspect a clotting disorder, determine if the family has a history of abnormal bleeding tendencies. Make sure you ask the patient's mother about obstetric bleeding complications, and note any history of Rh incompatibility.

When recording past history, determine if the child has any known congenital abnormalities. Ask about a history of past infections. Continual severe infections may suggest thymic deficiency or bone marrow dysfunction. Thoroughly document any history of allergic conditions. Remember, a child is more susceptible to allergies than an adult. Also, record a complete immunization history.

Ask about a family history of infections and allergic or autoimmune disorders, because these may suggest a pattern of immune deficiencies. If you're assessing a bottle-fed baby, ask the mother if she uses an iron-fortified formula.

Pediatric examination considerations

The physical examination for a child with a suspected blood-forming or immune disorder is the same as for an adult, but normal findings are different. In a child under age 12, normal lymph nodes are often palpable. You may feel normal cervical and inguinal nodes ranging in size from about 3 mm across to as much as 1 cm across. Moderate numbers of nodes that are cool, firm, movable, and painless indicate past infection. Palpable cervical nodes

of this description, for example, can suggest a past respiratory infection.

You may be able to palpate a normal liver and spleen in a child. Usually you'll feel the liver edge 1 to 2 cm below the right costal margin. (If it extends further than 3 cm, the liver may be enlarged; this finding calls for further investigation.) In some normal children, the liver doesn't extend below the costal margin and so won't be palpable. If you are able to palpate a child's spleen, normally you should just feel the tip—anything more than that is abnormal. Use percussion to determine liver size. The child's liver and spleen should not be tender.

The normal range for laboratory values is wider in children than in adults (see APPENDIX).

Common disorders in children

Immune problems affecting children fall into three categories: immune deficiencies, autoimmune diseases, and allergies (see *Guide to Blood-Forming and Immune Disorders*, pages 376 to 383). A child's—and his family's—history of infections may indicate a pattern suggesting an immunodeficiency. About 5 to 6 viral infections a year is normal for an infant; about 8 to 12 is average for school-age children. However, two serious bacterial infections in a 2-year period, especially beginning in infancy, can indicate an immune dysfunction.

Certain autoimmune disorders that affect both adults and children have signs and symptoms, severity, and incidence that differ for the two age-groups. For instance, childhood systemic lupus erythematosus is usually more acute and severe than the form that occurs in adults. Schönlein-Henoch purpura is the most prevalent type of vasculitis in children. Juvenile rheumatoid arthritis—unlike adult rheumatoid arthritis—doesn't usually cause permanent joint damage. When it does cause permanent joint damage, the damage occurs much later in the disease process.

The most common problems in children are allergies, especially such respiratory allergies as rhinitis and asthma. In fact, asthma remains the leading cause of chronic illness in children, particularly of school age.

Many hematologic problems—including the anemias, leukemias, and clotting disorders—

begin during childhood. Hereditary anemias usually diagnosed during childhood include sickle cell anemia and thalassemia. The most common hematologic problem in children, as well as the most common form of anemia, is iron deficiency anemia.

Acute leukemias are the most common types of cancer in children. Clotting disorders, including hemophilia and von Willebrand's disease, affect both children and adults but are usually detected early in life.

Geriatric assessment

Physiologic changes

Immune system function starts declining at sexual maturity and continues to decline with age. As an elderly person's immune system begins losing its ability to differentiate between self and non-self, the incidence of autoimmune disease increases. The immune system also begins losing its ability to recognize and destroy mutant cells; this inability presumably accounts for the increased incidence of cancer among older persons. Decreased antibody response in the elderly makes them more susceptible to infection. Tonsillar atrophy and lymphadenopathy commonly occur in older persons.

Total and differential leukocyte counts don't change significantly with age. However, some persons over age 65 may exhibit a slight decrease in the range of a normal leukocyte count. When this happens, the number of B cells and total lymphocytes decreases, and T cells decrease in number and become less effective.

As a person ages, fatty bone marrow replaces some active blood-forming marrow—first in the long bones and later in the flat bones. The altered bone marrow can't increase erythrocyte production as readily as before in response to such stimuli as hormones, anoxia, hemorrhage, and hemolysis. With age, vitamin B_{12} absorption may also diminish, resulting in reduced erythrocyte mass and decreased hemoglobin and hematocrit.

History and examination

Older patients have virtually the same signs and symptoms of blood-forming and immune disorders as younger adults, although cerebral and cardiac effects may be more pronounced. Ask if your elderly patient experiences joint pain, weakness, or fatigue. Does he take walks? If so, for how long? Does he have any difficulty using his hands? Ask about current medications, and note which ones produce side effects similar to signs and symptoms of blood-forming and immune disorders. For instance, digitalis may cause anorexia, nausea, and vomiting, and aspirin can produce mucosal irritation and gastrointestinal bleeding.

Determine your patient's typical daily diet. Also ask if he lives alone and cooks for himself. Because of limited income, limited resources, and decreased mobility, older patients may have diets deficient in protein, calcium, and iron—nutrients essential to the blood-forming process. Even with an adequate diet, nutrients may not be absorbed because of excessive laxative use or may not be metabolized because of fewer enzymes. (About 40% of people over age 60 have iron deficiency anemia.)

Physical assessment of the geriatric patient is the same as for the younger adult. However, when evaluating vital signs, remember that the elderly patient has a reduced febrile response to infection.

Guide to Blood-Forming and Immune Disorders

DISORDER	CHIEF COMPLAINT	
Acquired Immune Deficiency Syndrome (AIDS)	Varies greatly, may include: • fever • loss of appetite and weight • diarrhea • fatigue • lymphadenopathy • nonproductive cough	
Allergic rhinitis (hay fever)	• Sneezing, coughing, wheezing, dyspnea • Edema of mucous membranes • Red, weepy conjunctiva • Itchy eyes, nose, ears, and palate; rhinorrhea	
Aplastic anemia	• *Abnormal bleeding:* mild bleeding from nose, gums, vagina, or gastrointestinal tract • *Fatigue and weakness:* mild and progressive • *Fever:* may be present	
Asthma	• Tight, nonproductive coughing and wheezing • Tachypnea and dyspnea (with accessory muscle use), barrel chest possible • Abdominal pain • Profuse perspiration	
Hemolytic anemias	• *Fatigue and weakness:* present, variable	
Hemophilia	• Abnormal bleeding that may be mild, moderate, or severe and can include hemarthrosis, leading to ankylosis of involved joints • Hemorrhage into soft tissue or viscera • Muscle atrophy	
Hodgkin's disease	• *Lymphadenopathy:* asymmetrical enlargement usually involves cervical nodes, but occasionally involves axillary or inguinal or femoral nodes • *Fever:* may be present	

HISTORY	PHYSICAL EXAMINATION AND DIAGNOSTIC STUDIES
• Major risk factors include sexually active homosexual and bisexual men with multiple sex partners; abusers of intravenous drugs; Haitian entrants into the United States; hemophiliacs • Slow insidious onset	• Lymphadenopathy, manifestations of opportunistic diseases such as reddish purple lesions of Kappi's sarcoma; whitish mucoid exudate of candidiasis; tachypnea, possibly rales, rhonchi, cyanosis associated with pneumoceptis carinii pneumonia • Diagnostic studies include complete blood count, T cell count, T cell ratio, serum immunoglobulins; blood test to identify antibodies to AIDS virus (HTLV-III) newly developed.
• Strong family history • Seasonal • Usually not seen before age 4.	• Skin tests for allergies
• Predisposing factors include use of medication, such as chloramphenicol or benzene derivatives, that suppresses bone marrow; therapeutic X-rays; infectious hepatitis. • Insidious onset	• Pallor, ecchymoses, petechiae • Diagnostic studies include complete blood count, measurement of serum iron level, total iron-binding capacity, bone marrow biopsy.
• Family history of allergies or asthma • Noticeable before age 5.	• Complete blood count • Chest X-ray • Pulmonary function tests
• Predisposing factors include chronic immune-related illness, such as systemic lupus erythematosus; neoplastic disease; recent cardiac trauma; use of such drugs as amphotericin; toxin or poison ingestion; blood transfusion incompatibility; positive family history.	• Mild jaundice, pallor • Orthostatic hypotension, tachycardia, some cardiac murmurs • Splenomegaly possible • Diagnostic studies include complete blood count, bone marrow biopsy, Coombs' test, urine test for urobilinogen.
• Cyclic disorder; symptom-free periods alternate with repeated hemorrhages; noticeable during infancy • Family history of disorder in maternal male relatives • Occurs almost exclusively in males.	• Partial thromboplastin time • Factor assay
• Signs and symptoms include generalized and severe pruritus; anorexia and weight loss in advanced stage. • 50% of cases occur in persons aged 20 to 40.	• Enlarged, rubbery, painless nodes; splenomegaly; anemia • Symptoms depend on nodes affected and disease stage. • Diagnostic studies include lymphangiography; lymph node, bone marrow, liver, and spleen biopsies; blood tests (Coombs', complete blood count, erythrocyte sedimentation *(continued)*

Guide to Blood-Forming and Immune Disorders
(continued)

DISORDER	CHIEF COMPLAINT	
Hodgkin's disease		
Iron deficiency anemia	• *Fatigue and weakness:* present; increases with anemia's severity	
Juvenile rheumatoid arthritis	• Fever, occasional chills, malaise • Red macular rash on face, trunk, extremities • Arthralgia, joint stiffness, swelling and mild warmth with some limitation of movement of involved joints • Hepatosplenomegaly, abdominal pain • Lymphadenopathy • Pleurisy, dyspnea • Pericarditis, tachycardia • Growth disturbances possible	
Leukemia, acute	• *Abnormal bleeding:* nose and gum bleeding, easy bruising, prolonged menses • *Lymphadenopathy:* present; may be generalized or primarily involve cervical nodes • *Fatigue and weakness:* present; severity depends on extent of illness • *Fever:* may be high or low grade	
Leukemia, chronic	• *Abnormal bleeding:* rare • *Lymphadenopathy:* may be present • *Fatigue and weakness:* may be present; characterized by vague feeling of malaise and fatigue • *Fever:* low grade and unexplained in lymphocytic leukemia	
Multiple myeloma	• *Abnormal bleeding:* may be present • *Fatigue and weakness:* present; possibly severe • *Fever:* present	

HISTORY	PHYSICAL EXAMINATION AND DIAGNOSTIC STUDIES
	rate, alkaline phosphatase); chest X-ray; staging laparotomy, gallium scan, ultrasound of abdomen.
• Predisposing factors include poor nutrition; chronic blood loss from ulcers, gastritis, or excessive menstruation. • Signs and symptoms include headache, shortness of breath, pica (craving odd things to eat, such as starch or clay). • Most common in children, female adolescents, and women in their reproductive years	• Tachycardia, functional systolic murmur, slight cardiac and liver enlargement, spoon-shaped nails, poor skin turgor, stomatitis, pallor, ankle edema, menstrual disturbances • Diagnostic studies include complete blood count, measurement of serum iron level, possibly bone marrow biopsy; guaiac test performed to detect presence of occult blood in stool.
• Most common in children aged 2 to 5 and 9 to 12.	• Antinuclear antibody test • Erythrocyte sedimentation rate
• Exposure to radiation or benzene derivatives is a predisposing factor. • Signs and symptoms include headache, tinnitus, shortness of breath, chills, recurrent infections, abdominal or bone pain.	• Petechiae, ecchymoses, purpura, pallor, edema, splenomegaly, retinal hemorrhages on ophthalmoscopic examination • Diagnostic studies include complete blood count with differential and bone marrow aspiration and biopsy.
• Predisposing factors include exposure to therapeutic or accidental radiation or to such chemicals as benzene or alkalyzing agents. • Signs and symptoms include anorexia, weight loss, bone tenderness.	• Splenomegaly, hepatomegaly, edema, anemia; in lymphocytic leukemia, papular or vesicular skin lesions, herpes zoster, collapsed vertebrae • Increased white blood cell count with proliferation of one type of white cell (depends on type of leukemia) • Further diagnostic studies include complete blood count with differential count and bone marrow aspiration or biopsy.
• Signs and symptoms: mild, transient skeletal pain progressing to severe back, rib, or extremity pain; decreased urinary output; anorexia and weight loss; repeated bacterial infections • Most common in middle-aged and elderly men.	• Bone deformities from demineralization and pathologic fractures may occur as disease progresses. • Anemia, possible hepatosplenomegaly, renal insufficiency, peripheral neuropathy • Diagnostic studies include complete blood count, bone marrow aspiration, urine tests for protein and calcium, serum electrophoresis for protein, skeletal survey, intravenous pyelography. *(continued)*

Guide to Blood-Forming and Immune Disorders
(continued)

DISORDER	CHIEF COMPLAINT	
Pernicious anemia	• *Fatigue and weakness:* present, accompanied by light-headedness	
Polymyositis/ dermatomyositis	• *Fatigue and weakness:* insidious onset in proximal muscles of hips and neck • *Fever:* possibly low grade, intermittent, appearing after development of muscle weakness • *Joint pain:* arthralgia	
Primary polycythemia (polycythemia vera)	• *Abnormal bleeding:* nosebleeds, spontaneous bruising, bleeding ulcers • *Fatigue and weakness:* present • *Joint pain:* may be present	
Rheumatoid arthritis	• *Abnormal bleeding:* easy bruising in long-standing disease • *Lymphadenopathy:* generalized, or present only in the nodes proximal to the involved peripheral joints • *Fatigue and weakness:* generalized • *Fever:* may rise to 100.4° F. (38° C.) • *Joint pain:* joint stiffness and swelling; in advanced stages, deformities; vague arthralgias and myalgias; limited ROM	
Schönlein-Henoch purpura	• Erythematous maculopapular lesions on face, arms, trunk, and legs that become petechial and purpuric; may be accompanied by pruritus and paresthesia • Arthralgia with mild arthritis • Abdominal pain, constipation, vomiting, and gastrointestinal bleeding • Hematuria, azotemia • Headache • Hypertension • Fever, malaise	

HISTORY	PHYSICAL EXAMINATION AND DIAGNOSTIC STUDIES
• Predisposing factors include immune disorders, positive family history. • Signs and symptoms: gastrointestinal system—digestion disturbances, nausea, vomiting, diarrhea, constipation, anorexia; central nervous system—neuritis, peripheral numbness and paresthesias, impaired coordination and movement, light-headedness, altered vision; cardiovascular system—palpitations, dyspnea, orthopnea • Insidious onset; progresses slowly	• Pallor, slightly icteric skin and eyes, rapid pulse rate, cardiomegaly and possibly systolic murmur, slight hepatosplenomegaly, positive Romberg and Babinski reflexes, altered mental status • Diagnostic studies include gastric analysis for decreased acid and pepsin secretion, bone marrow aspiration, complete blood count, assay for serum vitamin B_{12}, Schilling test.
• Predisposing factors include respiratory or obscure systemic illnesses, neoplastic lesions, other connective tissue diseases. However, first symptoms may develop during excellent health. • Signs and symptoms include myalgias, dysphagia, anorexia, weight loss, dyspnea, photosensitivity. • Most common in females aged 5 to 15 and 45 to 60.	• Raynaud's phenomenon: dusky erythema over face, shoulders, and arms; heliotrope rash over eyelids; scaling maculopapular lesions over bony prominences; contractures • Diagnostic studies include erythrocyte sedimentation rate, complete blood count, serum enzymes, rheumatoid factor, electromyography, muscle biopsy.
• Signs and symptoms include headaches; dizziness, tinnitus, and vertigo; blurred vision; pruritus; chest pain; dyspnea; gastrointestinal distress; intermittent claudication. • May be asymptomatic in early stages • Most common in Jewish males from middle to old age	• Plethora or ruddy cyanosis of face, hands, and mucous membranes; ecchymoses; engorged conjunctival and retinal veins on ophthalmoscopic examination; enlarged, firm, and nontender spleen; hypertension, thrombosis, or emboli • Diagnostic studies include complete blood count, bone marrow biopsy, and analysis of arterial blood gases.
• Insidious or acute onset • Most common in women aged 40 to 50	• Keratoconjunctivitis sicca; increased warmth, tenderness and swelling of involved joints; rheumatoid nodules possible; skin ulcers; muscle atrophy; pleural effusion possible. • Diagnostic studies include erythrocyte sedimentation rate, latex agglutination test for rheumatoid factor, antinuclear antibody test, synovial fluid analysis, joint X-rays.
• Predisposing factors include respiratory tract infections and food and drug allergies. • Most common in children aged 2 to 8 and in males.	• Bleeding time, tourniquet test • Erythrocyte sedimentation rate • Complete blood count

(continued)

Guide to Blood-Forming and Immune Disorders
(continued)

DISORDER	CHIEF COMPLAINT	
Sickle cell anemia	• *Fatigue and weakness:* may be present • *Fever:* present • *Joint pain:* may be severe and involve multiple joints	
Systemic lupus erythematosus	• *Abnormal bleeding:* heavy menses possible • *Lymphadenopathy:* enlargement without tenderness • *Fatigue and weakness:* present • *Fever:* present • *Joint pain:* arthralgia common in fingers, hands, wrists, ankles, and knees; deformities possible	
Systemic sclerosis (scleroderma)	• *Abnormal bleeding:* present, in gastrointestinal tract • *Fatigue and weakness:* vague fatigue and weakness • *Fever:* rare, may reflect concurrent problem • *Joint pain:* diffuse aching and stiffness, polyarticular arthritis; deformities and immobility caused by skin encasement	
Thalassemia (Cooley's anemia)	• Severe anemia, pallor • Jaundice • Hepatosplenomegaly • Mongoloid facies, prominent upper teeth • Retarded growth and sexual maturity • Irritability	

HISTORY	PHYSICAL EXAMINATION AND DIAGNOSTIC STUDIES
• Recurrent infections caused by increased susceptibility • Inherited genes from both parents • Signs and symptoms include dyspnea, aching bones, chest pain. • Infection, stress, dehydration, and conditions that provoke hypoxia may provoke periodic crisis. • Most common in blacks of African descent	• Asthenic habitus with disproportionately long arms and legs in adulthood; retarded growth; delayed sexual maturity; tachycardia, cardiomegaly, and systolic murmurs; pulmonary infarctions; hepatomegaly leading to cirrhosis; jaundice, pallor; joint swelling; ischemic leg ulcers • Diagnostic studies include hemoglobin electrophoresis, liver biopsy, stained blood smear showing sickle cells, complete blood count.
• Predisposing factors include genetic disorder, viral infections. • Signs and symptoms include weight loss, anorexia, malaise, muscle pain, cough. • Most common in females aged 10 to 35	• Butterfly rash with blush and swelling or scaly maculopapular rash on cheeks and bridge of nose; pigmentation changes; patchy alopecia; pleural effusion; pericarditis; myocarditis; nephritis; Raynaud's phenomenon; hepatomegaly; convulsive disorders; mental status changes • Diagnostic studies include antinuclear antibody test, Coombs' test, rheumatoid factor LE-cell test, skin and renal biopsy.
• History of Raynaud's phenomenon may occur shortly before skin changes or may precede them by many years. • Signs and symptoms include weight loss (may be profound) and exertional dyspnea, dysphagia, heartburn. • Most common in women aged 20 to 50 • Family history rare	• Raynaud's phenomenon; thickened edematous skin that becomes waxy, taut, and atrophic; pigmentation changes; telangiectasias; pulmonary interstitial fibrosis; progressive cardiac involvement; progressive renal failure • Diagnostic studies include erythrocyte sedimentation rate, rheumatoid factor, antinuclear antibody test, skin biopsy, gastrointestinal X-rays, hand X-rays.
• Poor eating habits noticeable at ages 6 to 12 months • Most common in persons of Mediterranean ancestry. • Family history of disorder	• X-rays • Hemoglobin electrophoresis • Hematocrit

18

Endocrine System

The endocrine system functions primarily as the regulatory system for the entire body. It consists of eight glands that produce hormones—powerful chemicals that profoundly affect our lives. Hormones influence a person's growth and development, physical appearance, body functions, and emotional status. A disorder or imbalance of the endocrine system, therefore, affects not only a person's body functions but also his physical and emotional well-being (see *Guide to Endocrine Function*, pages 385 and 386).

Some endocrine disorders, such as pituitary dwarfism, can severely limit the affected person's ability to live a normal life. Other endocrine disorders are less physically obvious but have serious health implications. The sooner a patient's endocrine disorder is detected and treated, the better chance he will have to live a normal life. If you know how to assess the endocrine system properly, you may be able to identify subtle abnormalities that signal early stage endocrine problems.

History data

Biographical data

Knowing your patient's *age* and *race* helps you determine if variations in growth, pubertal development, or hair distribution are within normal limits.

History of present illness

The most common chief complaints regarding endocrine disorders are *fatigue and weakness, weight changes, abnormalities of sexual maturity or function, mental status changes,* and *polyuria and polydipsia.* Remember that these chief complaints may be related to an endocrine disturbance or they may be psychogenic. Careful questioning helps you differentiate between the two (see *Guide to Endocrine Disorders,* pages 398 to 405).

Here are some questions you may want to ask about these complaints to explore fully the history of your patient's present illness:

• **Fatigue and weakness.** *Is your fatigue constant or intermittent? If it's intermittent, when does it occur—when you wake up in the morning or at the end of the day? Do you feel more tired after strenuous exercise? What makes you feel better—rest?* Fatigue is a non-specific complaint that occurs in both organic and psychological illnesses. Fatigue from organic causes is intermittent—worse at the end of the day and after exercise, better in the morning and after rest. *Is your feeling of weakness generalized or localized?* In many cases, generalized weakness indicates systemic illness, such as an endocrine disorder; localized weakness may suggest a neurologic disorder. *Do you feel numbness or tingling in your arms or legs?* These sensations may indicate peripheral neuropathy, which occurs in some endocrine disorders.

• **Weight changes.** *How much do you usually weigh? What's the most you've ever weighed? The least?* Use these figures as baselines. *How long were you gaining (or losing) weight? Are you still gaining (or losing) weight? Has your weight gain (or loss) been intentional?* Answers to these questions should help you determine if the patient's weight changes are from an organic disorder or from overeating (or strict dieting). *What is your daily food intake, including alcoholic beverages?. Has your appetite increased or decreased? If it has decreased, is the decrease constant or are you intermittently hungry?* Persistent loss

Guide to Endocrine Function

GLAND	HORMONE SECRETED	TARGET STRUCTURE	PRIMARY FUNCTION
Anterior pituitary	Growth hormone	Bones, muscles, organs	Promotes growth and retention of nitrogen for protein metabolism
	Thyroid-stimulating hormone	Thyroid	Promotes growth and function of thyroid; controls release of thyroxine
	Adrenocorticotropic hormone	Adrenal cortex	Promotes growth and function of adrenal cortex
	Follicle-stimulating hormone	Ovaries and seminiferous tubules	Promotes development of ovaries, secretion of estrogen, and sperm maturation
	Luteinizing hormone	Ovaries	Promotes maturation of ovaries, ovulation, and secretion of progesterone
	Interstitial cell–stimulating hormone	Testes	Promotes secretion of testosterone
	Prolactin	Breasts and corpus luteum	Maintains corpus luteum; promotes secretion of progesterone and milk
Posterior pituitary	Antidiuretic hormone	Renal tubules	Promotes reabsorption of water
	Oxytocin	Uterus	Contracts pregnant uterus
Thyroid	Thyroxine	All tissues	Regulates metabolic rate
	Calcitonin	Bone, renal tubules	Maintains serum calcium levels, bone remodeling
Parathyroids	Parathyroid hormone	Gastrointestinal tract, bone, renal proximal tubules	Activates bone calcification; maintains serum calcium levels
Adrenal cortex	Glucocorticoids (cortisol)	All tissues	Metabolizes carbohydrates, fats, and proteins; acts as an anti-inflammatory
	Mineralocorticoids (aldosterone)	Primarily renal distal tubules	Balances sodium, potassium, and water concentrations

(continued)

Guide to Endocrine Function (continued)

GLAND	HORMONE SECRETED	TARGET STRUCTURE	PRIMARY FUNCTION
Adrenal medulla	Epinephrine, norepinephrine	Adrenergic receptors	Controls vasoconstriction
Pancreas	Insulin	Throughout body	Increases anabolism of carbohydrates; lowers blood glucose
	Glucagon	Throughout body	Elevates blood glucose

of appetite suggests an organic cause; intermittent loss of appetite may indicate a psychogenic problem, such as depression. *Are you eating more but losing weight?* This condition may result from an endocrine disorder.

• *Abnormalities of sexual maturity or function.* If your patient is a woman, ask the following types of questions: *At what age did you begin to menstruate? Describe the volume of your normal flow; for instance, is it heavy? How many days does your period usually last? When did you have your last normal period? How many periods have you missed? Could you be pregnant? Are you under a great deal of stress?* Severe stress can cause amenorrhea. *Did your periods resume normally after childbirth?* Unless the patient is breast-feeding her child, nonresumption of menstruation may indicate an endocrine disorder.

Ask both male and female patients: *Has your sexual desire increased or decreased? When did this change occur? How often do you normally experience sexual desire? Has your breast size changed?* Endocrine disorders can cause breast enlargement, especially in men. Make sure such enlargement isn't from weight gain. *Have your breasts been secreting milk?* Lactation from an endocrine disorder can occur in both men and women.

• *Mental status changes.* Do you have difficulty coping with your problems? Are you nervous? All the time? Do you have difficulty sitting still? Are these feelings triggered by specific events?* Endocrine disorders can cause nervous behavior or emotional lability. *Have you been feeling confused recently? How long have you felt this way? Was the onset quick or gradual? Is the feeling constant or intermittent? Have you had similar episodes before?* Confusion caused by endocrine disorders has a quick onset and is usually intermittent. *Do you have difficulty sleeping? For instance, do you have trouble falling asleep or staying asleep? How long have you been having difficulty sleeping? How many hours do you sleep? How is this different from your usual pattern? Do you feel you have to sleep during the day? Are you sleepy all day? How long have you felt this way? Do you wake up refreshed?* Changes in sleep patterns may result from endocrine disorders. Certain endocrine disorders may produce hallucinations and delusions, so note any reference to thought disorders during your conversation with the patient.

• *Polyuria and polydipsia.* How long have you been passing large quantities of urine? Was the onset sudden or gradual? How many times a day do you urinate? Do you pass large quantities of urine every time you urinate or only sometimes?* Varying amounts suggest dysuria, not polyuria. *Do you wake up at night to urinate?* This may suggest a urinary tract disorder instead of an endocrine disorder.

Is your thirst insatiable? Is it constant or variable? Do you prefer ice-cold fluids? A preference for ice-cold fluids may suggest an endocrine disorder; no preference may indicate psychogenic polydipsia. *How much fluid do you now drink? How much did you formerly drink? If you're deprived of fluid, do you urinate less frequently?* Answers to these questions help you distinguish the compulsive drinker from a patient with polydipsia caused by an endocrine condition.

Past history

When recording your patient's past history for assessment of a suspected endocrine condition, focus on these key areas:

• **Trauma.** Repeated fractures may indicate adrenal or parathyroid problems; fracture at the base of the skull may cause midbrain injury, resulting in pituitary and hypothalamus dysfunction. *Fright, stress,* or *trauma* may precipitate diabetes insipidus.

• **Surgical procedures.** *Bilateral oophorectomy* results in decreased estrogen and progesterone production, leading to signs and symptoms of the climacteric, such as amenorrhea. *Neck surgery* may cause thyroid function abnormalities. *Partial or total adrenalectomy* may result in adrenal crisis. *Hypophysectomy* impairs regulation of fluid volume by antidiuretic hormone. Also, the stress from any surgery can precipitate endocrine disorders, such as pheochromocytoma.

• **Obstetric history.** *Gestational diabetes mellitus* may indicate impending diabetes mellitus, as may giving birth to an infant weighing more than 10 lb (4.5 kg).

• **Drugs.** *Prescribed and over-the-counter medications for sleep problems, diet, or anxiety* may mask or simulate symptoms of endocrine disorders.

• **General.** *Unexplained neuromuscular disorders* and such nonspecific symptoms as nervousness, fatigue, and weakness may indicate underlying hyperthyroidism. Thyroid test results may reveal previous thyroid problems. *Long-standing obesity* contributes to the development of diabetes mellitus. *Irradiation* can cause glandular atrophy. *Meningitis* or *encephalitis* can cause hypothalamic disturbances.

Family and psychosocial history

Because certain endocrine disorders are inherited and others have strong familial tendencies, a thorough *family history* is essential. Ask your patient if anyone in his family is (or was) obese, or has had *diabetes mellitus, thyroid disease,* or *hypertension.* Diabetes mellitus (particularly Type II, or the non–insulin-dependent form) has an especially strong familial tendency. Thyroid conditions, such as goiter, also show familial tendencies. *Pheochromocytoma* may result from an autosomal dominant trait. *Delayed puberty* recurs in certain families; in women, this condition causes primary amenorrhea.

The most important aspect of your patient's psychosocial history is *environment,* because iodine deficiency in local water and food may cause thyroid enlargement.

Activities of daily living

When recording your patient's activities of daily living for endocrine assessment, be sure to ask about his *diet.* Specifically, determine whether he has any unusual eating habits. For instance, does your patient routinely follow a strict, limited, or fad-food diet? Adolescent girls often diet unnecessarily and may develop severe nutritional deficiencies and extreme weight loss, which can cause amenorrhea.

Also, determine whether your patient takes *drugs* or drinks *alcohol* regularly. If he does, ask how much and how often. Intoxication or withdrawal from drugs or alcohol can produce signs and symptoms that mimic endocrine disorders.

Review of systems

When recording the review of systems, ask your patient about the following symptoms:

• **General.** Frequent infections can occur in a patient with diabetes mellitus, because sugar-rich body fluids make infection control difficult (see *Guide to Life-Threatening Diabetic Complications,* pages 388 and 389). Also, protein depletion decreases resistance.

• **Skin.** Hirsutism occurs with ovarian and adrenocortical disorders that result in increased androgen production. *Excessive hair loss* may be an autoimmune response. *Loss of axillary and pubic hair* may result from a pituitary disorder. Episodes of *flushing* and *diaphoresis* may occur in association with *abnormal heat intolerance,* a classic complaint of patients with hyperthyroidism. *Abnormal cold intolerance* may indicate hypothyroidism.

• **Eyes.** Exophthalmos is present in endocrine disorders involving the thyroid. *Partial loss of vision* may indicate a pituitary tumor.

• **Mouth and throat.** Hoarseness can indicate laryngeal nerve compression from a tumor or, in women, excessive androgen

Guide to Life-Threatening Diabetic Complications

COMPLICATIONS	SYMPTOMS
Diabetic ketoacidosis (DKA)	● Anorexia, nausea, vomiting, polyuria, weakness, malaise, Kussmaul's respirations, abdominal pain, hyperglycemia (blood sugar from 400 to 800 mg/100 ml); if untreated, may lead to drowsiness, stupor, coma
Hyperglycemic hyperosmolar nonketotic coma (HHNK)	● Vomiting, diarrhea, tachycardia, rapid breathing, volume depletion, focal motor seizures, transient hemiplegia, severe hyperglycemia (blood sugar about 1,000 mg/100 ml), possibly leading to stupor and coma
Insulin shock (hypoglycemia)	● Sweating; tremors; increased blood pressure, pulse rate, respirations; headache; confusion; incoordination; blood sugar 50 mg/100 ml or less; can lead to convulsions, coma

production. *Difficulty swallowing* may be the result of compression or displacement of the esophagus by an enlarged thyroid gland.
● *Cardiovascular. Orthostatic hypotension* occurs in adrenal disorders. *Palpitations* with sweating and flushing may result from the hormonal imbalances of an endocrine disorder, such as hyperthyroidism, or possibly from an adrenal tumor that increases epinephrine production. *Leg swelling* from congestive heart failure or myxedema occurs in patients with thyroid disorders.
● *Nervous. Tremors* during periods of sustained posture (for instance, when a patient holds his arm out in front of his body for a period of time) may occur in patients with thyroid disorders. *Paresthesia* may result from peripheral neuropathies associated with certain endocrine disorders.
● *Musculoskeletal. Arthralgia, bone pain,* and *extremity enlargement* may result from disorders of the growth process.
● *Respiratory. Stridor* or *dyspnea* may occur in the patient with an enlarged thyroid gland that compresses his trachea.
● *Gastrointestinal. Frequent loose bowel movements* may accompany hyperthyroidism;

constipation may accompany hypothyroidism.

Physical examination

Considerations and techniques
Remember that because of the endocrine system's interrelationship with all other body systems, physical assessment of a patient's endocrine function consists of a complete evaluation of his body. Make sure the lighting in the examining room is adequate, because your assessment depends primarily on inspection. (To examine the patient's thyroid gland, you'll also use palpation and auscultation.)

General health status
Begin your assessment of the endocrine system by focusing on the patient's general physical appearance and emotional status. Often, during the initial moments of patient contact, an astute nurse can recognize the effects of major endocrine disorders, such as hyperthyroidism, hypothyroidism, myxedema, dwarfism, and acromegaly.

Observe the patient's apparent state of

CAUSE	INSULIN LEVELS	MORTALITY
• Cessation of insulin, or physical or emotional stress • Occurs predominantly in Type I diabetes (insulin-dependent)	• Zero	• In known diabetics, approximately 5% (most commonly due to late treatment)
• Stress, burns, steroids, diuretics • Severe dehydration from sustained hyperglycemic diuresis in which patient cannot sustain adequate fluid levels • Occurs predominantly in Type II diabetes (non–insulin-dependent)	• Low (some residual ability to secrete insulin)	• About 50%; treatment may be complicated by patient's age and debilitated state
• Too much insulin, too little food, excessive physical activity	• High	• Prognosis satisfactory when treated immediately; prolonged hypoglycemia can lead to permanent central nervous system damage

health, and note any signs of distress. Assess general body development—height and weight, body build and posture, and proportion of body parts. Note the distribution of body fat, too. In men, fat tissue should be distributed evenly over the entire body. In women, fat tissue normally concentrates in the shoulders, breasts, buttocks, inner thighs, and pubic symphysis. (In men and women who are obese, excessive fat accumulates in these same areas.) In endocrine assessment, you must distinguish between the fat distribution of obesity and that of Cushing's syndrome: In a patient with Cushing's syndrome, fat is concentrated on the face, neck, interscapular area, trunk, and pelvic girdle.

While you talk with your patient, assess his activity level. Does he move briskly or are his movements extremely slow? The former may indicate hyperthyroidism; the latter, hypothyroidism. Note his speech—its coherence, quality, and speed. The patient with hyperthyroidism can't get his words out fast enough; the patient with myxedema sounds hoarse and slurs his words.

Next, assess your patient's *vital signs.* Take his blood pressure in both arms. Hyperten-sion occurs in many endocrine disorders, particularly pheochromocytoma and Cushing's syndrome. Hyperthyroidism causes systolic blood pressure elevations. Arrhythmias may accompany metabolic disturbances. When taking a patient's apical pulse, note its quality and character. In an adult, a heart rate below 60 or above 100 beats/minute may suggest thyroid disease. Deep, rapid respirations (Kussmaul's respirations) may indicate diabetic ketoacidosis.

Skin color and condition

Focus first on skin color. Observe for hyperpigmentation, both generalized and localized, on the patient's exposed areas and at pressure points. Remember, hyperpigmentation can range from tan to brown. When assessing pigmentation, consider racial and ethnic variations. For example, hyperpigmented gums are normal in blacks but may indicate Addison's disease in whites. Also, observe the patient for areas of hypopigmentation (vitiligo), which may be associated with Addison's disease, thyroid disorders, or diabetes mellitus. You can distinguish yellow pigmentation caused by myxedema from jaundice by inspecting the patient's sclerae. Jaundice causes yellowing of the sclerae; myxedema doesn't.

Next, examine the patient's skin for hydration and texture. Dry, rough skin may be a sign of hypothyroidism or dehydration; smooth, flushed skin can accompany hyperthyroidism. Observe for areas of lipoatrophy and wasting, which may appear at injection sites in patients with diabetes mellitus. Easy bruising may be associated with the tissue breakdown of Cushing's syndrome. Skin lesions and ulcerations commonly appear in patients with diabetes mellitus. Also look for poor wound healing, which is associated with the peripheral circulation problems characteristic of some endocrine disorders, such as diabetes mellitus.

Nails and hair

Observe your patient's nails, noting color, shape, and quality. Thick, brittle nails may suggest hypothyroidism; thin, brittle nails may result from hyperthyroidism. Separation of the nail from the bed, beginning at the nail edge, may suggest a thyroid disorder. Increased nail pigmentation occurs in Addison's disease.

Inspect the patient's hair for abnormalities. Note the amount of scalp and body hair. Check for abnormal patterns of hair loss or hair growth; if your patient is a woman, note any excessive facial, chest, or abdominal hair (hirsutism). Remember to consider racial and ethnic variations in texture and distribution of hair.

Note the texture of the patient's hair by inspecting and touching it. Fine, soft, silky hair is characteristic of hyperthyroidism, in contrast to the coarse, dry, brittle hair you'll find in patients with hypothyroidism.

Observe for hair thinning or loss on the outer eyebrows, axillae, and genitalia in both men and women.

Face and neck

Carefully inspect your patient's face. First, study his expression. Does he stare and look alarmed? Or, is his expression dull and apathetic? Note any coarsening of facial features, such as his nose, lips, and ears, and check for a prominent forehead and protruding lower jaw. These are possible signs of a growth abnormality. *Moon face* is a sign of Cushing's syndrome. Also observe for facial edema, especially around the patient's eyes. With your index finger, apply firm pressure to this area and watch for pitting. Nonpitting facial edema, especially if accompanied by periorbital edema, may indicate hypothyroidism.

After observing your patient's entire face, carefully inspect his eyes. Observe their position and alignment. Be especially alert for abnormal protrusion of the eyeball with obvious lid retraction (exophthalmos), which may indicate increased thyroid function.

Test extraocular movements through the six cardinal fields of gaze (see pages 117 and 118). Note any evidence of extraocular muscle paralysis or reduced function, which can develop secondary to diabetic neuropathy or thyroid dysfunction. Test for eye convergence, which is usually poor in a patient with hypothyroidism. Inspect the relation of the upper eyelids to the eyeballs as the patient moves his eyes to gaze upward and then down. Lid lag—a margin of white sclera between the upper lid and the iris as the patient's gaze moves down—may indicate hyperthyroidism.

Use the Snellen chart to test your patient's visual acuity. Then test his visual fields. Some endocrine disorders, such as pituitary tumors, may cause visual field defects and reduced visual acuity.

Using an oblique light source, inspect for opacities in the cornea and the lens of your patient's eye. Premature cataracts may appear in a patient with diabetes or hypoparathyroidism. When performing a funduscopic examination, be alert for microaneurysms (tiny red spots), hemorrhages (large, slightly irregular red spots), and exudates (yellow spots), which are characteristic of diabetic retinopathy. Watch for arteriolar narrowing, which may be present in a patient with longterm hypertension associated with pheochromocytoma and Cushing's syndrome.

Next, examine the patient's mouth. Inspect the buccal mucosa for color and condition. Look for patchy, brown pigmentation of the gums, a possible sign of Addison's disease. Inspect the tongue for color, size, and tremors. (An enlarged tongue is associated with myxedema.) Note the patient's breath odor; if it smells fruity, like acetone, he may be in diabetic ketoacidosis.

Carefully inspect the patient's neck. First, move any hair and clothing away from his neck to check contour and symmetry. Then, observe his slightly extended neck for visible signs of thyroid enlargement or asymmetry. Note how the thyroid gland moves when the patient swallows. Ask him if he has difficulty swallowing, and if he has any hoarseness or neck pain.

Palpation of the thyroid gland

To examine the thyroid, stand facing the patient or behind him, and ask him to lower his chin. (This relaxes the neck muscles and makes the examination easier.)

Palpate the thyroid gland for size, shape, symmetry, tenderness, and nodules. When palpating from the front, use your index and middle fingers to feel for the thyroid isthmus, below the cricoid cartilage, as the patient swallows. (Swallowing raises the larynx, the trachea, and the thyroid gland—but not the lymph nodes and other structures.) To palpate one lobe at a time, ask the patient to flex his neck slightly to the side you're examining. To palpate the right lobe, use your right hand to move the thyroid cartilage slightly to the right. Then, grasp the sternocleidomastoid muscle with your left hand (tips of index and middle fingers behind the muscle, thumb in front), and try to palpate for the right lobe of the thyroid between your fingers. To palpate the left lobe, use your left hand to move the thyroid cartilage and your right hand to palpate.

To palpate the thyroid from behind the patient, gently place the fingers of both hands on either side of the trachea, just below the thyroid cartilage. Try to feel the thyroid isthmus as your patient swallows. While you're palpating one lobe at a time, ask the patient to flex his neck to the side being examined. To feel for the right lobe, use your left hand to move the thyroid cartilage to the right. Grasp the sternocleidomastoid muscle with your right hand, while placing your middle fingers deep into and in front of the muscle. For the left lobe, use your right hand to move the cartilage to the left and your left hand to palpate. (See *Thyroid Gland Palpation: Two Approaches*, page 392.)

In most patients, you won't feel the thyroid gland, but you may feel the isthmus. (You may see or feel a normal thyroid in a patient with a thin neck.) When you do palpate a large mass, don't confuse thick neck musculature

with an enlarged thyroid or goiter. An enlarged thyroid may feel finely lobulated, like a well-defined organ. Thyroid nodules feel like a knot, protuberance, or swelling. A firm, fixed nodule may be a tumor.

When you detect an enlarged thyroid, perform Kocher's test to determine if it's compressing the patient's trachea. Ask your patient to inspire deeply as you apply slight pressure on the gland's lateral lobes. If the enlarged gland is causing tracheal compression, the pressure you apply will produce stridor on deep inspiration. When you elicit a positive response to Kocher's test, observe your patient for dyspnea.

Thyroid gland auscultation

If you palpate an enlarged thyroid, auscultate the gland for systolic bruits. Place the stethoscope's diaphragm over one of the thyroid's lateral lobes. Then listen carefully for a bruit—a low, soft, rushing sound. This occurs in hyperthyroidism because accelerated blood flow through the thyroid arteries produces vibrations. (You may have to ask the patient to hold his breath and not swallow, so tracheal sounds don't interfere with your auscultation.) To distinguish a bruit from a venous hum, listen for the rushing sound, then gently occlude the jugular vein with your fingers on the side you're auscultating and listen again. A venous hum disappears during venous compression.

Breast, abdomen, and genitalia examination

Inspect your patient's breasts for areas of hyperpigmentation, especially the nipples and skin creases. Note the presence of purple-red striae, which may occur in a patient with Cushing's syndrome. If you suspect an endocrine disorder characterized by galactorrhea (such as a pituitary dysfunction), milk the breasts and note the character of the drainage. (You may ask your patient to do this, for the sake of comfort.)

Inspect the patient's abdomen for abnormalities associated with endocrine disorders. Observe the abdominal contour and the distribution of fat, and look carefully at the skin, noting any purple-red striae. If your patient is a woman, observe for abdominal hair distribution.

Next, inspect the patient's external genitalia

Thyroid Gland Palpation: Two Approaches

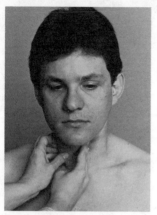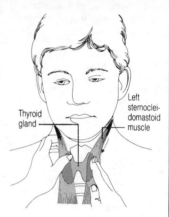

1 When palpating from the front, here's how to position your hands. The examiner in this photograph is palpating the right thyroid lobe.

Thyroid gland

Left sternocleidomastoid muscle

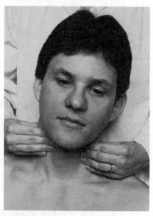

2 When palpating from the rear, position your hands this way. The examiner shown here is palpating the left thyroid lobe.

for sexual maturation, particularly the size of the testes or clitoris. Small testes may indicate hypogonadism; an enlarged clitoris suggests virilization. Also note the amount and distribution of pubic hair.

Musculoskeletal assessment

Inspect the size and proportions of your patient's body. Extremely short stature suggests dwarfism; disproportionate body parts, such as enlarged hands or feet, may be caused by excessive amounts of growth hormone, as in acromegaly.

Next, inspect the patient's vertebral column for such deformities as an enlarged disk or kyphosis, which may appear in acromegaly and hyperparathyroidism. Observe the joints for enlargement and deformity, and use range-of-motion tests to check for stiffness and pain (see Chapter 16, Musculoskeletal System). All these signs and symptoms can result from hypothyroidism. Inspect the patient's muscles for atrophy and tremors. Atrophy occurs in Cushing's syndrome and hyperthyroidism, and tremors may also indicate hyperthyroidism.

Neurologic examination

Assess your patient's sensitivity to pain, touch, and vibration, and his position sense. Sensory loss may occur in diabetic neuropathy; paresthesias can result from hypothyroidism, diabetes, and acromegaly. Note any loss of motor function. Wristdrop or ankledrop may signal extreme diabetic neuropathy.

Assess deep tendon reflexes in your patient, noting any evidence of hyperreflexia with delayed relaxation—associated with hyperthyroidism and hypoparathyroidism. Hyporeflexia, especially with ankle jerk, may occur in a patient with hypothyroidism or diabetic neuropathy.

Keep in mind that alterations in consciousness, including coma, may result from uncontrolled diabetes or myxedema.

Hypocalcemic tetany

You can determine if your patient has hypocalcemic tetany (a rapid drop in serum calcium levels from hypoparathyroidism or parathyroid gland removal) by testing for Trousseau's sign and Chvostek's sign. To check for Trousseau's sign, apply a blood pressure cuff to the patient's arm just above the antecubital area. Inflate the cuff until you've occluded the blood supply to his arm. If this procedure precipitates carpal spasm (finger contractions and inability to open the hand), Trousseau's sign is positive. Test for Chvostek's sign by tapping one finger in front of the patient's ear at the angle of the jaw, over the facial nerve. If contracture of the lateral facial muscles results, Chvostek's sign is positive.

Further diagnostic tests

Your initial impressions should serve primarily as indications for further investigation. Diagnostic tests provide you with important additional information. They're especially significant in differentiating endocrine disorders from disorders affecting other body systems—which may cause many of the same signs and symptoms. These tests include blood and urine analyses, scanning, and tissue biopsy. Laboratory tests that measure blood and urine levels of various hormones can determine if a gland or a feedback mechanism is functioning properly in your patient (see *Laboratory Tests for Endocrine Function*, pages 394 and 395). Tests can be performed for each endocrine gland and hormone.

Pediatric assessment

Special history-taking considerations

When you assess a child's endocrine function, your findings may be critical in the early detection of abnormalities or disorders. (Remember, endocrine dysfunction can occur even at birth and cause permanent physical and mental damage.) Although many endocrine disorders present the same signs and symptoms in children as in adults, some have manifestations unique to children. Perhaps the most common signs and symptoms of endocrine abnormalities in children are growth and developmental disturbances. However, these disturbances are often so subtle that only a thorough physical examination will reveal them. Parents may want their child examined because he's restless or doing poorly in school.

Common signs and symptoms for a neonate or infant include feeding problems, constipation, jaundice, hypothermia, or somnolence. With an older child, ask the parent or child to describe the child's activities on a typical day; this will help you distinguish a so-called quiet child from a child who's always tired and inactive and who may have decreased endocrine function. A quiet child will sit quietly and read; in the same circumstances, a child with endocrine problems will usually lie down and sleep. Review of daily activities can also help distinguish active children from hyperactive children: An active child

Laboratory Tests for Endocrine Function

ORGAN	LABORATORY TEST	PURPOSE
Thyroid	Serum triiodothyronine (T_3)	• Measures T_3 levels in the blood • Detects hyperthyroidism
	Serum thyroxine (T_4)	• Measures T_4 levels in the blood • Detects hyperthyroidism
	Serum thyroid-stimulating hormone (TSH)	• Measures TSH levels in the blood • Detects hypothyroidism
	Antithyroglobulin antibodies and antithyroid microsomal antibodies	• Detects antibody titers indicative of thyroid inflammation (Hashimoto's disease)
	Radioactive iodine (^{123}I) uptake	• Detects thyroid hypofunction and hyperfunction
	T_3 resin uptake	• Evaluates thyroxine binding to plasma proteins
	Thyroid scan	• Evaluates functional capacity of thyroid nodules • Detects thyroid nodules or tumors
	Thyroid ultrasonography	• Evaluates anatomic characteristics of thyroid nodules • Detects solid or cystic masses in the thyroid
Parathyroid glands	Parathyroid function tests: parathyroid hormone and calcium levels	• Measures parathyroid hormone and calcium levels in the blood • Detects hyperparathyroidism
Adrenal glands	Plasma cortisol	• Determines the release of cortisol from the adrenals • Detects abnormalities in cortisol secretion—hyperfunction (Cushing's syndrome) or hypofunction (Addison's disease)
	17-hydroxycorticosteroids	• Measures steroid levels in urine • Detects hyperadrenocorticism
	17-ketosteroids	• Measures steroid levels in urine • Detects hyperadrenocorticism
	Dexamethasone suppression test	• Measures suppression of adrenocorticotropic hormone production in conjunction with serum cortisone levels or 17-hydroxycorticosteroids • Detects Cushing's syndrome
	Plasma catecholamines (epinephrine and norepinephrine)	• Evaluates adrenal medullary function • Detects pheochromocytoma

(continued)

Laboratory Tests for Endocrine Function (continued)

ORGAN	LABORATORY TEST	PURPOSE
Adrenal glands *(continued)*	Urine vanillylmandelic acid	• Detects pheochromocytoma • Measures catecholamines
	Urine metanephrine	• Detects pheochromocytoma
Pituitary	Serum growth hormone	• Detects hyperpituitarism (gigantism and acromegaly)
	Prolactin levels	• Measures prolactin secretion • Detects pituitary tumors causing galactorrhea
	Insulin tolerance test or insulin stress test	• Measures growth hormone, which should increase as blood glucose decreases • Detects hypopituitarism
	Metyrapone test	• Measures adrenocorticotropic hormone production
Pancreas	Fasting blood sugar	• Measures blood glucose levels
	Glucose tolerance test	• Measures blood glucose levels • Detects decreased tolerance to glucose, as seen in diabetes mellitus and Cushing's syndrome • Detects increased tolerance to glucose, as seen in hypothyroidism, Addison's disease, and hypopituitarism

watch television, whereas a hyperactive child cannot do this.

When you evaluate a child, obtain a thorough family history from one or both parents, because many endocrine disorders are hereditary—such as diabetes mellitus and thyroid problems—or show a familial tendency—such as delayed or precocious puberty. Remember that an older child or adolescent can probably give you a more accurate history of his physical growth and sexual development than his parents can, so interview the child, too, when this is possible.

Growth and development
Childhood endocrine problems usually cause growth and developmental abnormalities that may acutely embarrass an older child or adolescent. For this reason, try to examine a child who's in this age range without his parents present.

Measure the child's height and weight. Height (in relation to age) and weight (in relation to stature and age) provide important indices of growth. Poor weight gain with little or no increase in height may indicate a lack of growth hormone. Hyperthyroidism can cause weight loss.

Some endocrine disorders selectively affect trunk or extremity growth. Check segmental measurements against those considered normal for the child's age and sex.

Also, test the child for age-related skills. If he's very young, for example, observe for such behavior as holding his head up, sitting, or walking. If your patient hasn't reached developmental milestones for his age, suspect physical or mental retardation, possibly of endocrine origin.

In your physical examination, always inspect the child's face to determine if his facial appearance correlates with his age. In cretinism, for example, a child retains his infantile facial appearance. When inspecting his mouth, check if the number of teeth corresponds with normal expectations for the child's age. Delayed eruption of teeth occurs in hypothyroidism and hypopituitarism. Normally, you'll examine a young child's thyroid gland by placing him in the supine position. Throughout the physical examination—and especially when you're examining the child's breasts, abdomen, and genitalia—inspect for the developmental signs of precocious puberty. Suspect delayed puberty if a child who's reached mid-adolescence has none of the physical changes associated with puberty. Endocrine dysfunction can cause both precocious and delayed puberty. Further diagnostic tests to confirm endocrine dysfunction are just as essential in a child as in an adult.

Growth hormone abnormalities

Growth hormone secretion fluctuates from day to day (it increases during exercise, for example) and over long periods. Accelerations of growth hormone production seem to result in the growth spurts noted on standard growth charts for children. Growth hormone deficiency can lead to dwarfism; excessive growth hormone production can result in gigantism in a prepubescent child or acromegaly in one who is older.

Signs and symptoms of thyroid dysfunction

In newborns, hypothermia, persistent neonatal jaundice, high birth weight from postmaturity, or posterior fontanelle enlargement suggest congenital hypothyroidism or cretinism. If the diagnosis of cretinism is not made at birth, the infant will gradually develop other signs and symptoms. These include failure to thrive, feeding problems, constipation, hoarse cry, somnolence, dry skin, poor abdominal tone, umbilical hernia, a puffy face, and an enlarged tongue. Hypothyroidism that begins in childhood can delay growth as well as mental and sexual development. Consider that an older child may have juvenile hypothyroidism if he's slightly overweight (but not obese), has retained the naso-orbital configuration of a

young child, has experienced delayed eruption of permanent teeth, or performs intellectual tasks poorly.

Childhood hyperthyroidism (most commonly occurring in school-age girls) can cause serious and even fatal acceleration in body metabolism. Signs and symptoms of this disorder during childhood include restlessness, hyperactivity, and a short attention span, as well as the classic adult symptoms. Children with this condition often fall into the upper percentile for height and the lower percentile for weight in comparison with standard growth charts.

Insulin disorders in children

Insulin is essential to a child's growth and development because it regulates blood glucose levels and plays a vital role in carbohydrate, fat, and protein metabolism, thus promoting the effects of other hormones that stimulate growth. *Type I diabetes mellitus* (caused by lack of insulin secretion from the islets of Langerhans in the pancreas) usually occurs in older children and adolescents. Children commonly experience an abrupt onset precipitated by some form of stress, such as infection or emotional upset. The earliest sign of this disease in children may be weight loss or growth retardation. Other signs and symptoms are similar to those of Type II diabetes mellitus.

Cushing's syndrome

Suspect Cushing's syndrome in children with exogenous obesity, especially if they show glucose intolerance and striae. Certain types of drug therapy (for example, synthetic corticosteroids, such as prednisone) may also result in high cortisol levels and produce the same signs and symptoms as those of Cushing's syndrome if the drug is used for a long time.

Typical assessment findings in a child with Cushing's syndrome (usually caused by a malignant tumor of the adrenal cortex) include an increased cortisol level, which causes obesity and hypertension; obesity, with accumulations of fat on the cheeks and chin and little fat on the extremities; red face, especially cheeks; signs of abnormal masculinization or feminization, from overproduction of androgen or estrogen; and purple striae appearing on hips, abdomen, and thighs.

Disturbances of sexual maturation

A child's precocious sexual maturation or delayed sexual maturation can indicate abnormal function of his hypothalamus, pituitary, adrenals, or gonads. Hypopituitarism, pituitary tumors, and adrenal and gonadal tumors can affect the onset of puberty. In addition, such endocrine problems as hypothyroidism can prevent sexual maturation by slowing the entire growth process.

Precocious puberty is usually defined as the appearance of secondary sex characteristics in a girl before age 8 and in a boy before age 9.

Puberty is considered to be delayed if secondary sex characteristics are not apparent before age 13 in girls and age 14 in boys, or if more than 5 years have elapsed between the first physical signs of puberty and onset of menarche in girls or completion of genital growth in boys.

Geriatric assessment

Endocrine signs and symptoms

Many endocrine disorders cause signs and symptoms in the elderly that are similar to changes that normally occur with aging. For this reason, these disorders are easily overlooked during assessment. In an adult patient with hypothyroidism, for example, mental status changes and physical deterioration—including weight loss, dry skin, and hair loss—occur. Yet these same signs and symptoms characterize the normal aging process.

Other endocrine abnormalities may complicate your assessment because their signs and symptoms are different in the elderly than in other age-groups. Hyperthyroidism, for ex-

ample, usually causes nervousness and anxiety, but a few geriatric patients may instead experience depression or apathy (a condition known as *apathetic hyperthyroidism of the elderly*). And an elderly patient with Graves' disease may initially have signs and symptoms of congestive heart failure or atrial fibrillation rather than the classic manifestations associated with this disorder.

Normal variations in endocrine function

A very common and important endocrine change in the elderly is a decreased ability to tolerate stress. The most obvious and serious indication of this diminished stress response occurs in glucose metabolism. Normally, fasting blood sugar levels aren't significantly different in young and old adults. But when stress stimulates an older person's pancreas, the blood sugar concentration increase is greater and lasts longer than in a younger adult. This decreased glucose tolerance occurs as a normal part of aging, so keep it in mind when you're evaluating an elderly patient for possible diabetes.

During menopause, a normal part of the aging process in women, ovarian senescence causes permanent cessation of menstrual activity. Changes in endocrine function during menopause vary from woman to woman, but normally estrogen levels diminish and follicle-stimulating hormone production increases. This estrogen deficiency may result in either or both of two key metabolic effects: coronary thrombosis and osteoporosis. Remember, too, that some symptoms characteristic of menopause (such as depression, insomnia, headaches, fatigue, palpitations, and irritability) may also be associated with endocrine disorders. In men, the climacteric stage causes a decrease in testosterone levels and in seminal fluid production.

Guide to Endocrine Disorders

DISORDER	CHIEF COMPLAINT	
Acromegaly	• *Fatigue/weakness:* weakness, lethargy • *Weight changes:* weight gain • *Mental status changes:* confusion, possibly progressing to convulsions and coma	
Addison's disease (primary adrenal insufficiency)	• *Fatigue/weakness:* slow, progressing fatigue and weakness • *Weight changes:* weight loss caused by poor appetite, food idiosyncrasies, nausea, vomiting, diarrhea • *Abnormalities of sexual maturity or function:* loss of secondary sex characteristics and libido in females • *Mental status changes:* depression, irritability, restlessness	
Adrenal virilizing syndromes	• *Abnormalities of sexual maturity or function:* reversal of primary and secondary sex characteristics, scanty menstrual periods, amenorrhea, increased sexual drive	
Cushing's syndrome	• *Fatigue/weakness:* present, loss of muscle mass • *Weight changes:* weight gain; distribution of fat increases on neck, face, abdomen, girdle • *Abnormalities of sexual maturity or function:* hirsutism; clitoral hypertrophy; amenorrhea; gynecomastia in males • *Mental status changes:* irritability, emotional lability, depression, psychosis • *Polyuria/polydipsia:* may be present with other symptoms of diabetes mellitus	
Diabetes insipidus	• *Fatigue/weakness:* may be present • *Weight changes:* weight loss may be profound because of water loss; anorexia • *Mental status changes:* irritability; apathy • *Polyuria/polydipsia:* present, may be severe; nocturia; preference for cold drinks	
Diabetes mellitus	• *Fatigue/weakness:* fatigue possible; loss of strength • *Weight changes:* weight loss; in chronic illness, bloating, fullness • *Abnormalities of sexual maturity or function:* impotency in males • *Polyuria/polydipsia:* present; classic symptoms of diabetes mellitus	

HISTORY	PHYSICAL EXAMINATION AND DIAGNOSTIC STUDIES
• Predisposing factors include cancer (most commonly bronchogenic), head injury, meningitis, encephalitis, brain abscess, cerebrovascular accident, neurosurgery to midbrain, tuberculosis.	• Retention of fluids • Diagnostic studies include BUN, serum creatinine, urine sodium, serum osmolality, serum antidiuretic hormone.
• Onset is insidious. • Predisposing factors include history of tuberculosis, treatment with exogenous steroids, and family history of adrenal insufficiency.	• Fasting hypoglycemia; hypotension and syncope; poor coordination; blue-gray hyperpigmentation on exposed areas of body and mucous membranes, occasionally with vitiligo; abdominal pain; salt craving from hyponatremia • Diagnostic studies include plasma cortisol and urine 17-ketogenic steroids.
• May be congenital or acquired • Most common in women • Difficult to detect in postpubertal males • Congenital syndromes are believed to be caused by mutant autosomal recessive genes.	• Hirsutism of face, body, and extremities; thinning of hair, temporal baldness; deepening of voice, Adam's apple enlargement; acne, increased sebum production; development of male habitus, increased muscle mass, and increased strength; breast and uterus atrophy, enlargement of clitoris • Diagnostic studies include 17-ketosteroids and 17-hydroxycorticosteroids in urine; dexamethasone suppression test; testosterone levels; adrenal tomography and adrenal angiography.
• Predisposing factors include steroid treatment and adrenal tumors. • Most common in women	• Hypertension; osteoporosis, spontaneous fractures, height reduction, backache; purple striae on arms, breasts, abdomen, and thighs; petechial hemorrhage, excessive bruising; decreased healing ability • Diagnostic studies include serum electrolytes, plasma cortisol, and urine 17-hydroxycorticosteroids.
• Onset may be insidious or sudden. • Predisposing factors include fright and head injury or tumors.	• Dry skin, poor turgor, headache • Diagnostic studies include plasma osmolality and dehydration tests.
• Predisposing factors include long-standing obesity, pancreatic disease, history in females of delivering large infants, and family history of diabetes. • In Type II, mild symptoms may be long-standing.	• Dry skin and mucous membranes, polyphagia, blurred vision, light-headedness, pruritus • In chronic illness, intermittent claudication, especially of feet; pain; paresthesia; hyperpigmentation; xanthomas; poor healing; microaneurysms and exudates in eyes; decreased sensation to pain and temperature; lipodystrophy (from repeated insulin injections); gastrointestinal hyperactivity; decreased perspiration; decreased reflexes *(continued)*

Guide to Endocrine Disorders *(continued)*

DISORDER	CHIEF COMPLAINT	
Diabetes mellitus *(continued)*		
Fasting hypoglycemia	• *Fatigue/weakness:* lethargy, weakness, paralysis • *Weight changes:* weight gain • *Mental status changes:* inability to concentrate; changes in sensorium; irritability; inappropriate affect	
Hyperparathyroidism	• *Fatigue/weakness:* weakness, fatigability • *Weight changes:* weight loss, anorexia • *Mental status changes:* difficulty concentrating; disorientation; delirium; psychosis; confusion; stupor; coma • *Polyuria/polydipsia:* polyuria may cause polydipsia	
Hyperthyroidism (thyrotoxicosis)	• May present with none of the usual chief complaints of thyrotoxicosis or of endocrine disorders	
Hypoparathyroidism	• *Fatigue/weakness:* lethargy • *Mental status changes:* irritability, emotional lability, impaired memory, confusion, depression, changes in level of consciousness	
Hypopituitarism	• *Fatigue/weakness:* lethargy; easy fatigability • *Weight changes:* may occur (usually loss) • *Abnormalities of sexual maturity or function:* general loss of secondary sex characteristics; amenorrhea • *Mental status changes:* somnolence, coma	
Hypothyroidism	• *Fatigue/weakness:* present, accompanied by lethargy; need for increased amount of sleep • *Weight changes:* weight gain • *Abnormalities of sexual maturity or function:* diminished sexual functioning; menorrhagia; impotence	

HISTORY	PHYSICAL EXAMINATION AND DIAGNOSTIC STUDIES
	• Diagnostic studies include fasting blood sugar and glucose tolerance tests.
• Predisposing factors include liver disease, family history of diabetes mellitus, and use of alcohol, propranolol, and salicylate. • Most common between ages 40 and 60	• Tachycardia, trembling, blurred vision, pallor, paresthesias, palpitations, diaphoresis, decreased coordination, nausea, vomiting, headache • May lead to convulsions • Diagnostic studies include glucose tolerance and fasting blood sugar tests.
• May vary in degree from asymptomatic, insidious onset to rapid onset with severe symptoms • Chronic renal disease • Rickets • Osteomalacia may lead to compensatory hyperparathyroidism.	• Cardiac irregularities; anemia; enlarged head; pathologic fractures; hypotonia of muscles; altered reflexes; decreased hearing; ataxic gait; renal symptoms, such as urinary tract infections, pyelonephritis, renal colic; severe headache; bone pain; epigastric pain; nausea; vomiting; pancreatitis; hoarseness; paresthesias for vibration • Diagnostic studies include serum electrolytes and radioimmunoassay for parathyroid hormone.
• Predisposing factors include radiation for thymic enlargement and congenital metabolic defects.	• Hoarseness; pain in neck area, difficulty swallowing; enlarged cervical lymph nodes • In thyrotoxicosis, tachycardia, heart failure, vascular collapse, hyperthermia • Diagnostic studies include ^{123}I scan, biopsy, serum thyroxine, and serum triiodothyronine.
• Predisposing factors include injury to or removal of thyroid (parathyroids taken with thyroid).	• Tetany (numbness; tingling in fingers, toes, and around lips), cyanosis; Chvostek's sign, laryngeal stridor, dyspnea; papilledema (sometimes associated with increased intracranial pressure); malformed, pitted nails; thinning hair, alopecia; coarse, dry skin; dysplasia of tooth enamel; diplopia, cataracts, eyes sensitive to light; convulsions, abdominal pain, nausea, vomiting; EKG changes • Diagnostic studies include serum electrolytes, primarily calcium.
• Predisposing factors include congenital abnormalities, acute infections, vascular problems, and pituitary tumor.	• Skin changes, such as discoloration (yellow), wrinkling, thinning, drying; slow pulse rate; hypotension; decreased growth; genital atrophy; loss of teeth; brittle nails; anorexia; constipation • Diagnostic studies include complete blood count, serum thyroxine, serum triiodothyronine, and urine 17-ketogenic steroids. Test results show decrease in one of pituitary hormones (rarely more than one).
• Predisposing factors include surgery or use of radioiodine to treat hyperthyroidism. • Onset usually insidious.	• Sparse (especially at eyebrows), brittle, coarse hair; muscle stiffness; diminished hearing; sensitivity to cold; constipation; hoarseness • Diagnostic studies include serum thyroxine, serum triiodothyronine, and basal metabolic rates.

(continued)

Guide to Endocrine Disorders *(continued)*

DISORDER	CHIEF COMPLAINT	
Hypothyroidism *(continued)*	• *Mental status changes:* abnormal tranquillity possible; answers to questions may be inappropriate; slowing of cognitive ability; depression	
Multinodal goiter	• Usual chief complaints of endocrine disorders not present	
Myxedema (severe)	• *Fatigue/weakness:* present, accompanied by lethargy; need for increased amount of sleep • *Weight changes:* weight gain, decreased appetite • *Abnormalities of sexual maturity or function:* diminished sexual functioning; menorrhagia; impotence • *Mental status changes:* in extreme cases, coma, overt psychosis possible	
Pheochromocytomas (tumors of adrenal medulla)	• *Fatigue/weakness:* malaise • *Weight changes:* weight loss • *Mental status changes:* nervousness; apprehension; feelings of impending doom (prodrome of attack)	
Pituitary tumor	• *Abnormalities of sexual maturity or function:* decreased libido; amenorrhea; impotence; changes in amount of sexual hair (such as beard and pubic) • *Mental status changes:* in advanced stages, drowsiness, stupor, convulsions, mental aberrations	
Primary aldosteronism	• *Fatigue/weakness:* muscle weakness; fatigue • *Polyuria/polydipsia:* polyuria present; polydipsia possible	
Syndrome of inappropriate hypersecretion of antidiuretic hormone	• *Fatigue/weakness:* progressive weakness • *Abnormalities of sexual maturity or function:* in early stages, increased libido, hypertrophy of genitalia; in later stages, decreased libido, galactorrhea, amenorrhea, impotence, deepening voice • *Mental status changes:* emotional instability • *Polyuria/polydipsia:* polydipsia present	
Thyroiditis (chronic form: Hashimoto's thyroiditis)	• *Fatigue/weakness:* fatigue possible; malaise	

HISTORY	PHYSICAL EXAMINATION AND DIAGNOSTIC STUDIES
● Most common in women ● Patient may be asymptomatic for years. ● Predisposing factors include iodine deficiency, familial history of disorder.	● Tenderness and visible enlargement of neck; respiratory difficulty, stridor, sensation of choking, hoarseness ● Diagnostic studies include serum thyroxine and [123]I.
● Predisposing factors include long-standing hypothyroidism, exposure to cold, use of respiratory depressants, such as anesthetics.	● Hypothyroidism symptoms continue. ● Dry, scaling, cool, yellow-orange, thickened skin; dull, expressionless face; hypothermia; heart enlarged; rate lowered; edema, especially periorbital; thickened tongue; decreased deep tendon reflexes ● Diagnostic studies include serum thyroxine, serum triiodothyronine, and basal metabolic rates.
● Familial incidence most common between ages 40 and 60 ● Sudden emotion or physical changes may precipitate attack.	● Hypertension, dyspnea, paresthesias, tetany, blurred vision, severe and throbbing headache, palpitations (possibly intense), profuse sweating, nausea, vomiting, anorexia, abdominal pain, pallor
● Neurologic symptoms	● Visual field and visual acuity defects, skin changes, headache, intolerance to cold, increased intracranial pressure ● Diagnostic studies include skull X-rays, computerized tomography, and carotid angiography.
● Most common in women between ages 30 and 50 ● Predisposing factors include use of oral contraceptives.	● Hypertension, headache, ventricular enlargement, cardiac arrhythmias, hypokalemia ● Diagnostic studies include serum electrolytes and urine 17-hydroxycorticosteroids.
● Insidious onset in third decade of life ● Continued increase in hat, glove, shoe size after puberty ● Rapid growth spurt or growth in adult life	● Face broadened; overgrowth of lips, nose, tongue, jaw, forehead; pain and stiffness in fingers and toes; increased pigmentation of skin; deep, thick skin creases; excessive sweating; increased facial hair; edema; hypertension; enlarged internal organs: heart, liver, spleen, glands (especially pancreas); polyphagia; headache, visual disturbances, paresthesia ● Diagnostic studies include X-rays and glucose tolerance test for growth hormone.
● Predisposing factors include family history of thyroiditis, Graves' disease, myxedema. ● Onset is insidious. ● Patient may be asymptomatic except for palpable gland and high titer; believed to be autoimmune disorder.	● Symptoms of hypothyroidism possible ● Enlarged thyroid (two to five times normal size; typically feels rubbery; lobular pyramidal lobe usually prominent); may experience choking feeling, swallowing difficulty, and sensation of local pressure. ● Diagnostic studies include antithyroglobulin antibody test and/or microsomal antigens.

(continued)

Guide to Endocrine Disorders *(continued)*

DISORDER	CHIEF COMPLAINT
Thyroid tumors	• *Fatigue/weakness:* weakness present and prominent, increased fatigue; muscle atrophy • *Weight changes:* decreased subcutaneous fat; weight loss despite increase in appetite • *Abnormalities of sexual maturity or function:* short and scanty menstrual periods; decreased fertility; possibly temporal recession of hairline in females • *Mental status changes:* anxiety; nervousness; difficulty concentrating; agitation; paranoid tendencies • *Polyuria/polydipsia:* polyuria possible, with increased thirst

HISTORY	PHYSICAL EXAMINATION AND DIAGNOSTIC STUDIES
• Predisposing factors include recent emotional crisis, infection, physical stress, family history of Graves' disease. • Relatively common disorder; symptoms depend on severity of disorder.	• Fine, moist palmar erythema; thin and brittle hair and nails; palpable thyroid; systolic bruit over thyroid; possibly tender supraclavicular lymph nodes; palpitations, tachycardia, paroxysmal atrial tachycardia; increased heat production, with excessive perspiration and decreased tolerance to heat; exophthalmos and lid lag characteristic of Graves' disease; pretibial edema; insomnia; fine tremors, exaggerated reflexes • Diagnostic studies include serum thyroxine and serum triiodothyronine.

19

The Pregnant Patient

Pregnancy affects a woman's entire body, so make your assessment of her health comprehensive. Begin with the common complaints of pregnancy and a complete assessment of each body system. Evaluate the patient's emotional stability, including her acceptance of the pregnancy, her preparation for parenthood, and the pregnancy's impact on the family.

Always assess a pregnant patient within the context of the *maternal-fetal unit*. Although mother and child have separate and distinct needs, their interdependent relationship means that factors influencing the mother's health may affect the health of the fetus, and alterations in fetal well-being may influence the mother's physical and emotional health. Remember that your assessment may indicate some practices in such areas as diet, rest, exercise, alcohol intake, and smoking that the patient should evaluate and change because they may be harmful to her or her baby.

History data

Biographical data
Biographical data are especially pertinent to your assessment of a pregnant patient. Before recording this information, assure your patient that it will be kept confidential. Here are some guidelines and points to follow in this part of your patient's health history:
● *Name.* During the initial interview, address the patient as *Ms. _____.* Never assume—even if the patient has given pregnancy as the reason for her visit—that she is married.
● *Age.* Your patient's exact age is important in determining the possibility of a high-risk pregnancy. Reproductive risks are greater

among adolescents under age 15 and women over age 35. The adolescent patient runs a whole gamut of serious risks: increased incidence of low–birth-weight and premature infants, preeclampsia, anemia, prolonged labor, and cephalopelvic disproportion. Expectant mothers over age 35 are at risk for placenta previa, abruptio placentae, hydatidiform mole, and vascular, neoplastic, and degenerative diseases, as well as for having fraternal twins or infants with genetic abnormalities, especially Down's syndrome (trisomy 21).
● *Race.* Black pregnant women should be screened for sickle cell trait; Jewish women of Eastern European ancestry, for Tay-Sachs disease.
● *Religion.* A woman's religious affiliation may affect her health practices during pregnancy and could predispose her to complications. For example, an Amish woman may not be immunized against rubella. Seventh-Day Adventists traditionally exclude dairy products from their diets.
● *Marital status.* Your patient's marital status may help you identify her family support systems, sexual practices, and possible stress factors.
● *Occupation.* If your patient is working in a high-risk environment (one that exposes her to such hazards as chemicals, inhalants, or radiation), inform her of the risks and consequences for her pregnancy and discuss the possibility of a transfer.
● *Education.* Your patient's educational experiences—both formal and informal—may influence her attitude toward pregnancy, the adequacy of her prenatal care and nutritional status, her knowledge of infant care, and the psychosocial changes that accompany childbirth and the parenting years.

History of presenting symptoms

If the patient hasn't specified pregnancy as the reason for her visit, you may want to be cautious about suggesting pregnancy as the reason—unless you've obtained a positive pregnancy test or other supportive data (see *Signs of Pregnancy*). To obtain the most helpful information, allow the patient to explain the reason for her visit in her own words. (Her explanation for seeking obstetric evaluation may also suggest her degree of acceptance of a possible pregnancy.) She may have specific complaints, such as *bleeding changes* (including amenorrhea and vaginal bleeding disorders), *nausea* (with or without vomiting), *urinary disturbances*, or *fluid retention*. You'll investigate these complaints to determine if she's pregnant and to identify pregnancy-related disorders (see *Guide to Pregnancy Disorders*, pages 420 to 423).

Here are some questions you may want to ask about these complaints to explore fully the history of your patient's presenting symptoms:

● **Bleeding changes (amenorrhea).** When was your last menstrual period? If the patient has difficulty recalling, refer to a calendar and try to prompt her memory with landmark dates, such as holidays. Consider the possibility of pregnancy when a woman who has regular menses abruptly misses a period. Consider it likely if the woman has missed two consecutive periods. *Was your last period "normal"? How long did the period last? Was the flow lighter than usual?* Although amenorrhea is the usual condition in a well-established pregnancy, a few women may report periodic bleeding for several months. Usually this bleeding is lighter and lasts for a shorter time than a normal menstrual flow. *Have you recently experienced an illness or unusual stress?* Recent illness, rapid or excessive weight loss, or change in daily routine may contribute to amenorrhea.

● **Bleeding changes (vaginal bleeding disorders).** What specific events preceded the bleeding? Sexual intercourse or a vaginal examination may traumatize the cervix. Exposure to infection or disease may precipitate a spontaneous abortion. Trauma can cause abruptio placentae. *When in your pregnancy did the bleeding begin?* Spontaneous abortion is a major cause of bleeding during the first 20 weeks of pregnancy. Bleeding that occurs

Signs of Pregnancy

Your pregnancy diagnosis depends on *presumptive* signs and symptoms (those which you or your patient recognize), *probable* signs and symptoms (evidence of pregnancy that you find during the physical examination), and *positive* signs (confirming diagnostic indications usually not apparent until the 4th month of pregnancy).

PRESUMPTIVE SIGNS	PROBABLE SIGNS	POSITIVE SIGNS
● Amenorrhea ● Nausea, with or without vomiting ● Frequent urination ● Breast changes ● Discoloration of vaginal mucosa ● Increased skin pigmentation and abdominal striae ● Fatigue ● Quickening	● Uterine enlargement ● Softening of the uterine isthmus (Hegar's sign) ● Changes in the shape of the uterus ● Softening of the cervix (Goodell's sign) ● Purplish or bluish color of upper vagina and cervix (Chadwick's sign) ● Braxton Hicks contractions ● Palpation of fetal parts ● Positive pregnancy test results for human chorionic gonadotropin in urine or serum	● Identification of fetal heart sounds ● Palpation of active fetal movements ● Identification of the fetal skeleton by radiology or sonography

later in the pregnancy can indicate such disorders as placenta previa or abruptio placentae. The bleeding may also be the *bloody show* that signifies the onset of labor. *Is the bleeding accompanied by pain and/or cramping?* Pain usually accompanies ectopic pregnancy, abruptio placentae, and spontaneous abortion. Hydatidiform mole, placenta previa, and spontaneous abortion caused by cervical incompetence are usually painless.

● *Nausea (with or without vomiting).* When did the nausea begin? Nausea and/or vomiting associated with pregnancy usually begins about 6 weeks after the woman's last menstrual period, when hormone levels are high. *When does the nausea and/or vomiting occur?* Nausea associated with pregnancy often occurs in the morning hours when the stomach is empty. However, it may persist throughout the day or evening. *What relieves the nausea?* Women generally report that nausea is relieved by eating dry crackers or toast in the morning and frequent small meals throughout the day (for example, six small meals instead of three large ones). However, the symptoms usually disappear through the normal course of pregnancy after 12 to 16 weeks. *Are you able to tolerate any food at all?* Severe nausea and vomiting, with little or no tolerance of food, may indicate hyperemesis gravidarum. *Have medical problems or stressful situations preceded the nausea?* You know that nausea is a universal symptom that can indicate many underlying problems, such as stress or physiologic disorders.

● *Urinary disturbances.* Have your bladder habits changed recently? When did the urinary disturbances begin? Pregnant women commonly experience urinary frequency with urgency, particularly during the first and third trimesters of pregnancy.

Have you noticed other urinary changes? Painful urination, foul-smelling or cloudy urine, color changes, and bladder tenderness may indicate a urinary tract infection.

● *Fluid retention.* Have you noticed any swelling? Do your rings fit more tightly? Are your eyelids puffy? Edema of the hands and face may indicate preeclampsia. Dependent edema of the feet and ankles, especially in late pregnancy, is common. *Is this your first pregnancy?* Preeclampsia occurs most often with first pregnancies, but its symptoms may

occur in later pregnancies if predisposing factors exist, such as diabetes mellitus, multiple gestation, fetal hydrops, hydatidiform mole, or underlying chronic vascular disease. *What decreases the swelling?* A woman may get relief by lying on her side, commonly the left. Decreasing or eliminating intake of salty foods may also help physiologic edema. *What other changes have you noticed?* Visual disturbances, headache, and epigastric and right upper quadrant pain may indicate progressive preeclampsia; refer the patient promptly.

Past gynecologic history

Explore your patient's gynecologic history with the following types of questions:

● *Menstrual history.* When did your last menstrual period begin? How many days passed between your last two periods? What is the usual amount and duration of menstrual flow? Based on this information, you can calculate your patient's estimated date of confinement, using Nägele's rule: *first day of last normal menstrual period, minus three months, plus seven days.* Because Nägele's rule is based on a 28-day cycle, you may need to vary the calculation for a woman whose menstrual cycle is irregular, prolonged, or shortened.

Age of menarche is important when determining pregnancy risks in adolescents. Pregnancy that occurs within 3 years of menarche indicates an increased risk of mortality, morbidity, and a newborn who's small for his gestational age. Keep in mind that pregnancy can also occur before regular menses are established. (For information on how to take a complete menstrual history, see Chapter 14, *Female Reproductive System.*)

● *Contraceptive history.* What form of contraception do you use? How long have you used it? Are you satisfied with the method? Pregnancy that results from contraceptive failure needs special consideration to ensure the patient's medical and emotional well-being. For example, birth control pills taken in the first trimester can be teratogenic. If your patient has used an intrauterine device, refer her to her obstetrician to have it removed promptly upon verification of pregnancy. This will avoid the risk of spontaneous abortion in the second trimester.

● *Sexual history.* When did you begin your sexual activity? How frequently do you engage in sexual activity? Are you experiencing any difficulties? Knowledge of the patient's sexual activity will inform you about her sexual knowledge and guide your patient teaching during her pregnancy. Don't assume that every pregnant woman is well-informed about sex.

Your patient's sexual desire may decrease during the first trimester, a common occurrence that may be attributed to the increased fatigue; nausea, and vomiting that most women experience then. During the second trimester, however, sexual desire often returns because of feelings of well-being and resolution of the first trimester's signs and symptoms. Alterations in comfort and additional psychophysiologic changes may decrease sexual desire again during the third trimester.

Past obstetric history

If your patient is a multigravida, you'll want to know about any complications that affected her previous pregnancies. A woman who has delivered one or more very large infants (more than 9 lb, or 4 kg), or who has a history of recurrent *Monilia* infections or unexplained unsuccessful pregnancies, should be screened for diabetes. A history of recurrent second-trimester abortions may indicate an incompetent cervix. A woman with a history of urinary tract infections in previous pregnancies will usually have this problem with every pregnancy. Be especially careful when you evaluate a woman whose pregnancies have been complicated by hypertension.

Always record your patient's obstetric history chronologically. Use a single-digit gravida number (G) to reflect the number of times the woman's been pregnant, followed by a four-digit para number (P), which tells you about the outcomes of the pregnancies. The para digits represent the number of full-term births (greater than 37 weeks' gestation), premature births (less than 37 weeks' gestation), abortions before 20 weeks, and living children. (The first letter of each word in *Florida Power And Light* may help you remember the order of the para digits.) For example, "G-2/P-1-0-1-1" represents a patient who's been pregnant twice, has had one full-term birth, no premature births, one abortion (before 20 weeks), and one living child.

An abbreviated but less informative version reflects only the gravida and para numbers

Obstetric History Data

When taking your pregnant patient's obstetric history, ask her about the following:
- History of infertility
- Genital tract anomalies
- Full-term pregnancies
- Preterm pregnancies
- Abortions
- Birthplace, weight, and condition of infants
- Type of delivery
- Medications used during pregnancy
- Complications during previous pregnancies and labors
- Duration of labor
- Rh of previous babies
- Postpartum problems the mother experienced after previous pregnancies
- Problems with previous infants during first several days after birth

and the number of abortions. For example, "G-3, P-2, Ab-1" represents a patient who's been pregnant three times, has had two deliveries after 20 weeks' gestation, and one abortion. (For other types of information that you should include in a complete obstetric history, see *Obstetric History Data*).

Past medical and family history

In this part of the history, ask the patient about previous medical problems that may be exacerbated by her pregnancy. For example, displacement of the stomach by the gravid uterus, along with relaxation of the cardiac sphincter and decreased gastric motility caused by increased progesterone, may augment symptoms of peptic ulcer disease, such as gastric reflux.

Find out whether the woman is taking any medications, including over-the-counter drugs. Most drugs cross the placenta and reach the fetus. The patient's doctor must carefully evaluate her medications, weighing the benefits of each drug against its risk to the fetus.

Also inquire about medical problems that may jeopardize the pregnancy. Maternal hypertension increases the risk of abruptio placentae. Preeclampsia occurs more often in women with essential hypertension, renal disease, or diabetes. In addition, diabetes can worsen during pregnancy and harm both mother and fetus.

Rubella infection during the first trimester may have teratogenic effects on the developing fetus. A pregnant woman with a history of genital herpes should be watched closely for any signs of active disease, because she may transmit the disease to her infant if she doesn't deliver by cesarean section.

Other problems that you should ask your pregnant patient about are: cardiac disorders, chronic obstructive pulmonary disease, tuberculosis, sexually transmitted disease, phlebitis, epilepsy, urinary tract infections, gallbladder disease, malignancies, alcoholism, smoking, drug addiction, and psychiatric problems.

A family history of varicose veins is important; some people have an inherited weakness in blood vessel walls that may become evident during pregnancy. Preeclampsia and eclampsia also have familial tendencies. Also ask about a family history of multiple births and congenital diseases or deformities. Sex-linked disorders may be attributed to the father. Some fetal congenital anomalies have been traced to paternal exposure to environmental hazards.

Activities of daily living

Talk with your patient about the following aspects of her daily life, which may affect the course of her pregnancy:

● *Nutrition.* Pregnancy places additional nutritional demands on a woman's body. Remember, a woman's health during pregnancy is influenced by her nutritional status prior to pregnancy as well as her nutrition during pregnancy. Carefully assess your patient's food preferences, any ethnic dietary practices, allergies, food intolerances, and present diet. (See Chapter 5, *Nutritional Assessment.*)

● *Exercise.* Exercise does not need to be limited in an uncomplicated pregnancy. If your patient exercised regularly before she became pregnant, she probably can continue. Don't advise a pregnant patient to start a new exercise program, such as jogging, however. Make sure the patient understands that she must get adequate rest whether she exercises or not.

● *Travel.* Travel during an uncomplicated pregnancy isn't harmful. If the patient must take lengthy trips, instruct her to exercise intermittently while traveling—for example, by walking every two hours. Advise her not to travel extensively during the final weeks of her pregnancy; she should stay close to her doctor and a hospital in case complications develop.

● *Personal hygiene.* Good personal hygiene habits can help prevent complications, such as infections, and help the woman feel more comfortable during her pregnancy. She should be careful, during bathing, to avoid falling. This is a greater hazard than usual in the final weeks of pregnancy, when the woman's enlarged uterus shifts her body's center of gravity. Douching, especially with a hand-held syringe, is contraindicated. Increased pressure from the syringe may dislodge her mucous plug.

● *Sexual activity.* Usually, a pregnant woman may have sexual intercourse without harming the fetus if she has no vaginal bleeding or pain and shows no signs of a ruptured membrane.

● *Smoking.* Small infants are more frequently born to mothers who smoke, and strong evidence exists that a mother who smokes is more likely to have an unsuccessful pregnancy.

● *Alcohol.* Excessive intake of alcoholic beverages during pregnancy may produce fetal alcohol syndrome in the newborn. Children of alcoholic mothers may also experience growth retardation and other related problems. No safe level of alcohol intake during pregnancy has been identified, so avoiding alcoholic beverages during pregnancy is the best precaution.

● *Drugs.* Chronic use of such drugs as amphetamines, barbiturates, and opium derivatives is harmful to the fetus. Low birth weight, intrauterine fetal distress, and withdrawal symptoms after birth are some of the common problems seen in infants of mothers who use these drugs.

● *Pets.* A pregnant woman shouldn't empty a cat's litter box, because the litter can harbor toxoplasmosis.

Review of systems

Conduct a complete review of systems to determine if your patient has any health disorders coexisting with her pregnancy. Also, ask her if she has any of the following signs and symptoms that may result from the physiologic changes of pregnancy (see *Danger Signs During Pregnancy*):

● *Metabolic. Weight changes* and *easy fatigability* are common during the early stages of pregnancy, possibly because of a fall in metabolic rate.

● *Skin. Pruritus* is the most common skin complaint during pregnancy. It may be localized to the abdomen or vulva or may spread over the body. The cause is unknown.

● *Ears.* Pregnancy may cause *impaired hearing*. The patient may complain that her ears feel as if they're stuffed with cotton. Occasionally, a pregnant woman's impaired hearing is caused by blocked eustachian tubes.

● *Nose. Altered sense of smell* and *nasal stuffiness* may occur. These signs and symptoms may be vasomotor in origin or may be associated with the mucosal hyperemia that occurs during pregnancy.

● *Mouth.* A pregnant woman may experience *increased gingival bleeding* when she brushes her teeth, secondary to increased estrogen levels.

● *Cardiovascular.* Uterine pressure during pregnancy may inhibit venous return and reduce cardiac output, causing *faintness* and *dizziness* when the woman's in the supine position. Pregnant women often complain of *headaches* in early pregnancy. Severe headache, especially after the 20th week of gestation, may be a sign of preeclampsia.

● *Respiratory.* Hyperventilation may result from increased progesterone levels.

Danger Signs During Pregnancy

If your patient reports any of the following, notify the doctor immediately. These signs and symptoms *may* pose a threat to the course of the pregnancy and to the mother's health.

SIGN OR SYMPTOM	POSSIBLE INDICATION
Dyspnea	● Impending cardiac decompensation, premature separation of the placenta, excessive amniotic fluid accumulation, or pulmonary embolus
Persistent or recurring headache	● Pregnancy-induced hypertension
Persistent nausea and vomiting	● Hyperemesis gravidarum or systemic infection
Vision changes (flashing lights, dots before eyes, dimming or blurring of vision)	● Pregnancy-induced hypertension
Dizziness when not supine	● Hypoglycemia, anemia, or cardiac arrhythmias
Abdominal pain	● Ectopic pregnancy, abruptio placentae, or uterine rupture
Edema of the face and hands	● Pregnancy-induced hypertension
Cessation of fetal movement	● Fetal death
Vaginal bleeding	● Placenta previa, abruptio placentae, or spontaneous abortion
Sudden escape of fluid from the vagina	● Premature ruptured membranes

• *Gastrointestinal.* During early pregnancy, increased progesterone levels relax smooth muscles throughout the gastrointestinal system, often causing *nausea* and *vomiting.* Heartburn may result from abnormal gastroesophageal sphincter activity, which permits reflux of gastric fluids. Flatulence, constipation, and hemorrhoids are also common complaints.

• *Reproductive.* Hormonal stimulation during pregnancy typically causes *breast tenderness, sensitivity, tingling,* and *engorgement. Vaginal discharge (leukorrhea)* and *itching* may occur during pregnancy. This often begins during the first trimester, when hormonal influences cause hyperplasia of the vaginal mucosa and increased secretion of mucus by the endocervical glands. These symptoms may also signal vaginitis, especially from *Monilia;* this type occurs more commonly in pregnancy. *Dyspareunia* may result from pelvic congestion, uterine pressure, vulval varicosities, or psychogenic causes, such as fear of hurting the baby.

• *Musculoskeletal. Backache* is a common complaint of pregnancy. It may be due to kyphosis and slouching caused by enlarging breasts and/or lumbar lordosis, which occurs as the uterus enlarges.

• *Psychological. Mood changes, sleeplessness,* and *irritability* may result from the physical signs and symptoms of the first trimester—such as fatigue, nausea, and vomiting. Emotional stress associated with pregnancy may also cause these signs and symptoms.

Physical examination

Scheduling antepartal care

The antepartal period in pregnancy ranges from the first day of the woman's last menstrual period to the start of true labor. The period of time is usually divided into trimesters: weeks 1 to 12 constituting the first trimester; weeks 13 to 27, the second trimester; and weeks 28 to 40, the third trimester. Antepartal-care visits are usually scheduled every 4 weeks for the first 32 weeks of pregnancy; every 2 weeks until week 36 of pregnancy; then weekly until delivery, which usually occurs between weeks 38 and 42.

An early first visit followed by regular visits will help assure a successful pregnancy. Women with known risk factors or who develop complications during the course of pregnancy require more frequent visits.

First visit

On the patient's first visit, perform a complete physical examination, noting the normal changes of pregnancy. Then continue with the first visit examination, as described below.

Breast examination. As you inspect and palpate the woman's breasts (see page 284), you'll note some normal variations, including increased size and nodularity during the first 20 weeks. This marked and rapid breast hypertrophy may cause *striae* (stretch marks) to appear. The woman may complain of a tingling sensation or breast heaviness during the first and third trimesters. Nipples and areolae usually darken, and superficial veins may dilate. The tubercles of Montgomery usually enlarge; colostrum may appear after the 12th week. Around the 20th week of pregnancy, you'll note the secondary areola—a series of pale spots that surround the primary areola. In multiparas, the breasts are usually less firm.

Abdominal examination. Other than routine examination of the abdomen, initial abdominal examination of the pregnant woman includes inspection for such normal changes of pregnancy as linea nigra—darkened skin in the abdominal midline. If the pregnancy is sufficiently advanced (usually by the 12th week), palpate for fetal height and position, and auscultate for fetal heart tones (see *Fundal Height Measurement,* page 413).

In early pregnancy, the umbilicus is usually deeply indented, but it becomes more shallow as the pregnancy progresses. At term, the umbilicus is usually level with or protruding from the surface of the abdomen. You may also hear uterine souffle—a soft, blowing sound caused by blood pulsating through the placenta. It occurs at the same rate as the maternal pulse. If the woman's pregnancy is sufficiently advanced, check fetal heartbeats with an ultrasonic stethoscope (at 10 to 12 weeks' gestation) or fetoscope (at 16 weeks' gestation). Fetal heartbeats should range between 120 and 160 beats/minute.

Pelvic examination. Begin pelvic examination of the pregnant patient by inspecting her external and internal genitalia. Keep in

Fundal Height Measurement

By estimating your patient's uterine size, you can evaluate the fetus' gestational age. How? By measuring fundal height. Between the 18th and 32nd weeks of pregnancy, the fundal height in centimeters equals the fetus' gestational age in weeks. Say your patient's at 24 weeks' gestation; her fundal height should be about 24 cm. Remember, though, that fundal height measurements taken late in pregnancy may not be accurate, because fetal weight variations can distort your reading.

To measure fundal height, follow these steps. With your patient lying flat, place the end of a tape measure at the level of her symphysis pubis. Stretch the tape to the top of the uterine fundus. Record this measurement. Another method of determining fundal height involves using three landmarks: the symphysis pubis, the umbilicus, and the xiphoid process. At 16 weeks, the fundus can be found halfway between the symphysis pubis and the umbilicus. At 20 to 22 weeks, the fundus is at the umbilicus. At 36 weeks, the fundus is at the xiphoid process.

Choose one method of determining fundal height, and use it consistently throughout the patient's pregnancy. Depending on your clinical setting, you may measure with calipers. Remember: Such factors in your patient as a full bladder, amniotic fluid volume, obesity, or tension may affect fundal height measurement.

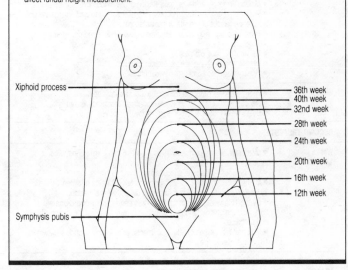

Xiphoid process — 36th week / 40th week / 32nd week / 28th week / 24th week / 20th week / 16th week / 12th week

Symphysis pubis —

---

mind several normal deviations that occur during pregnancy. The labia majora are usually loose and pigmented; the vagina, which appears pink or dark pink at the start of pregnancy, turns purple-blue by the 8th to 12th week.

During the first 4 weeks of gestation, the cervix becomes enlarged in the anteroposterior diameter. At 4 to 6 weeks, softening of the uterine isthmus occurs (Hegar's sign). By the 8th week, the cervix is uniformly softened (Goodell's sign), and Ladin's sign, a soft area

of the uterus near the junction of the uterine body and the cervix, occurs as well. The cervix appears blue. (See *Guide to Pregnancy Assessment,* pages 414 and 415.)

The pear-shaped uterus, which normally is mobile within the pelvis and has a smooth surface, is located at the upper end of the vagina during early pregnancy. By the 8th week of pregnancy, it becomes globular and is often anteflexed against the bladder.

After completing your examination of the patient's pelvic organs, estimate the capacity

Guide to Pregnancy Assessment

GESTATIONAL AGE	NORMAL CHANGES OF PREGNANCY
FIRST TRIMESTER	
Weeks 1 to 4	• Amenorrhea occurs • Breast changes begin • Immunologic pregnancy tests become positive: radioimmunoassay test is positive a few days after implantation; urine hCG test is positive 10 to 14 days after occurrence of amenorrhea • Nausea and vomiting begin, between the 4th and 6th week
Weeks 5 to 8	• Goodell's sign occurs (softening of cervix) • Ladin's sign occurs (softening of uterine isthmus) • Hegar's sign occurs (softening of lower uterine segment) • Chadwick's sign appears (purple-blue vagina and cervix) • McDonald's sign appears (easy flexion of the fundus over the cervix) • Braun von Fernwald's sign occurs (irregular softening and enlargement of the uterine fundus at the site of implantation) • Piskacek's sign may occur (asymmetrical softening and enlargement of the uterus) • Cervical mucous plug forms • Uterine shape changes from pear to globular • Urinary frequency and urgency occurs
Weeks 9 to 12	• Fetal heartbeat detected using ultrasonic stethoscope • Nausea, vomiting, and urinary frequency and urgency lessen • By 12 weeks, uterus palpable just above symphysis pubis
SECOND TRIMESTER	
Weeks 13 to 17	• Mother gains approximately 10 to 12 lb (4.5 to 5.4 kg) during second trimester • Uterine souffle heard on auscultation • Mother's heartbeat increases approximately 10 beats between 14 and 30 weeks' gestation. Rate is maintained until 40 weeks' gestation. • By the 16th week, mother's thyroid gland enlarges by approximately 25%, and the uterine fundus is palpable halfway between the symphysis and umbilicus • Maternal recognition of fetal movements, or quickening, occurs between 16 and 20 weeks' gestation
Weeks 18 to 22	• Uterine fundus palpable just below umbilicus • Fetal heartbeats heard with fetoscope at 20 weeks' gestation • Fetal rebound or ballottement possible
Weeks 23 to 27	• Umbilicus appears level with abdominal skin • Striae gravidarum usually apparent • Uterine fundus palpable at umbilicus • Shape of uterus changes from globular to ovoid • Braxton Hicks contractions start
THIRD TRIMESTER	
Weeks 28 to 31	• Mother gains approximately 8 to 10 lb (3.6 to 4.5 kg) in third trimester • Uterine wall feels soft and yielding

Guide to Pregnancy Assessment (continued)

GESTATIONAL AGE	NORMAL CHANGES OF PREGNANCY
THIRD TRIMESTER (continued)	
Weeks 28 to 31 cont'd.	• Uterine fundus is halfway between umbilicus and xiphoid process • Fetal outline palpable • Fetus very mobile and may be found in any position
Weeks 32 to 35	• Mother may experience heartburn • Striae gravidarum becomes more evident • Fundal height no longer accurate indication of gestational age • Uterine fundus palpable just below the xiphoid process • Braxton Hicks contractions increase in frequency and intensity • Mother may experience shortness of breath
Weeks 36 to 40	• Umbilicus protrudes • Varicosities, if present, become very pronounced • Ankle edema evident • Urinary frequency recurs • Engagement, or lightening, occurs • Mucous plug expelled • Cervix effacement and dilatation begin

of her pelvis by taking several pelvic measurements, both internal and external, as discussed in *Pelvimetry Measurements*, page 416. You can take these measurements when you first examine the pregnant woman's pelvis. Remember, however, that the pelvic ligaments are more relaxed in the late stages of pregnancy. If you wait until then to take your patient's pelvic measurements, she'll be more comfortable during the procedure, and she'll tolerate it better.

Laboratory tests for pregnancy. The first laboratory tests performed for a pregnant patient are the pregnancy test, the test for blood type and Rh factor, a complete blood count, an antibody screen, and a Pap test. Other tests (with normal findings) include:
• hemoglobin/hematocrit—12 to 16 g;/dl blood/42% ± 5
• serologic test for syphilis (STS)—nonreactive
• gonorrhea culture (GC)—negative
• urinalysis—negative protein; small amount of glucose; pale yellow in color; negative RBC, WBC, casts; specific gravity of 1.015 to 1.025; and pH of 4.6 to 8.0
• rubella titer, most commonly the

hemagglutination-inhibition test—a ratio greater than 1:6 indicates immunity.

Chest X-rays are usually not required for a pregnant patient. But if you suspect tuberculosis, administer the tuberculin skin test. Other tests that may be necessary, depending on the patient's race and symptomatology, are sickle cell trait testing, vaginal cultures, and postprandial blood sugar testing.

Return visits

During each of your patient's return visits, always take an interval history of symptomatology. This should include questions concerning any abdominal pain, vaginal bleeding, headache, or urinary tract pain. Record the patient's weight and blood pressure; check her urine for glucose and protein; and examine her for edema, especially of the face and hands, which may indicate preeclampsia. Also be sure to document the first occurrence of quickening (fetal movement) as indicated by the patient, usually around the 16th to 20th weeks. At each visit thereafter, check with the patient to be sure the fetus is still active.

If your patient fails to gain weight, this may result in an unfavorable outcome for the preg-

Pelvimetry Measurements

To estimate pelvic capacity, measure the subpubic arch, intertuberous diameter, interspinous diameter, and diagonal conjugate. Ask the patient to void first. Explain that she may feel discomfort during the procedure but that you'll be very careful.

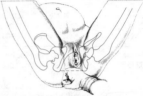

Pelvic outlet measurements: To palpate the subpubic arch—the inferior margin of the symphysis pubis—and to estimate its angle, turn your hands horizontally and place the thumbs in the arch, as shown on the left. Both thumbs should fit comfortably, forming an angle slightly more than 90°. A narrower subpubic angle may cause dystocia.

To estimate the intertuberous, or transverse, diameter, first clench your fist and measure the width of your knuckles. Then, insert the fist between the ischial tuberosities, as shown on the right. If the knuckles are a width of 8 cm or more and fit comfortably, the diameter is adequate. You may use a Thom's pelvimeter to take this measurement.

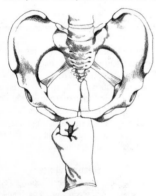

Midpelvis measurement: The interspinous diameter cannot actually be measured. But an estimate of midpelvic capacity can be made by inserting the examining finger or fingers into the vagina and palpating the ischial spines (they should be blunt), the side walls of the pelvis above and below the ischial spines (they should be straight and parallel), the sacrospinous ligament (it should be 2.5 to 3 fingerbreadths long), and the sacrum from below upward (it should be concave and hollow; you should be able to feel only the last three sacral vertebrae without indenting the perineum). Finally, gently palpate the coccyx. It should move easily.

Pelvic inlet measurement: Measurement of the diagonal conjugate may cause your patient the most discomfort. Insert two fingers into the vagina. Attempt to reach the sacral promontory by indenting the perineum with the knuckles of your third and fourth fingers and then walking your fingers up the sacrum to the promontory. If you feel the promontory, maintain contact with it while raising your hand until it touches the lower margin of the symphysis pubis. With the other hand, mark this point as shown in the illustration. Withdraw the hand from the vagina and measure the distance from the tip of your finger to the point you marked. The measurement should be 11.5 cm or more. If you cannot reach the promontory, assume that the diameter is adequate.

To obtain the obstetric conjugate, usually 10 cm, subtract 1.5 cm from the measurement of the diagonal conjugate.

Leopold's Maneuvers

Before auscultating the fetal heart rate, you'll need to determine fetal position. This is important because you will be able to hear fetal heartbeats most clearly through the fetal back. To determine fetal position, perform Leopold's maneuvers, described here. Begin by having the patient empty her bladder. Position her supine, with her abdomen exposed. To perform the first three maneuvers, stand to either side of the patient and face her. For the fourth maneuver, reverse your position and face the patient's feet.

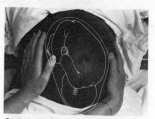

First maneuver: Place your hands on the patient's abdomen, curling your fingers around her uterine fundus. If the fetus is in a vertex position, you'll feel an irregularly shaped, soft object—the buttocks. If the fetus is in a breech position, you'll feel a hard, round, movable object—the head.

Second maneuver: Next, move your hands down the sides of the patient's abdomen, and apply firm, even inward pressure with the palms. Note whether you feel the fetal back on the patient's left side or right side and whether it's directed anteriorly, transversely, or posteriorly. If the fetus is vertex, you'll feel a smooth, hard surface on one side—the back. On the other side, you'll feel lumps and knobs—the knees, hands, feet, and elbows. If the fetus is breech, you may not be able to feel the back.

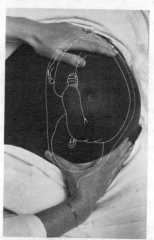

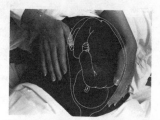

Third maneuver: Now spread apart your thumb and fingers of one hand and place them just above the patient's symphysis pubis. Bring your fingers together. If the fetus is vertex and hasn't descended, you'll feel the head; if the fetus has descended, you'll feel a less distinct mass.

Fourth maneuver: Place your hands on both sides of her lower abdomen. Apply gentle pressure with the fingers of each hand, sliding your hands down toward the symphysis pubis. If the head presents, one hand's descent will be stopped by the cephalic prominence. The other hand will descend unobstructed more deeply. If the fetus is in the vertex position, you'll feel the cephalic prominence on the same side as the small parts. In face presentation, you'll feel the cephalic prominence on the same side as the back. If the fetus is engaged, you can't feel the cephalic prominence.

Tests for Fetal Status

TEST	DESCRIPTION	USES AND INDICATIONS
Ultrasound	An ultrasonic transducer, placed on the mother's abdomen, transmits high-frequency sound waves. These pass through the abdominal wall, deflect off the fetus, and bounce back to the transducer, where they're translated into a visual image on a monitoring screen.	• Early identification of pregnancy • Biparietal diameter measurement • Placental localization • Placental anomalies • Intrauterine device detection • Identification of multiple gestation • Fetal position and presentation • Fetal anomalies • Demonstration of hydramnios and oligohydramnios • Fetal death • Detection of incomplete or missed abortion • Observation of fetal cardiac activity and breathing movements
Estriol measurement	The placenta converts fetal adrenal precursors to estriol, which enters the mother's blood and urine in measurable amounts. For correct interpretation of estriol values, serial measurements should be performed. In general, rising estriol levels are a positive indicator of fetal well-being; falling levels are a negative indicator. Chronically low estriol levels may indicate intrauterine growth retardation.	• Evaluation of placental function and fetal well-being. • Taken especially in situations involving high-risk conditions, such as maternal diabetes or hypertensive diseases, postmature pregnancy, intrauterine growth retardation syndrome, poor obstetric history, or late antepartal care
Amnio-centesis	A sample of amniotic fluid is aspirated for diagnostic tests, which are indicative of fetal well-being. After an adequate pocket of amniotic fluid is localized with sonography, a needle is inserted into the patient's abdomen, through the uterus, and into the amniotic sac to aspirate a sample of the amniotic fluid.	• Assessment of fetal maturity, especially with premature labor or when planning a cesarean section of a patient with a questionable estimated date of confinement • Biochemical monitoring of fetal well-being, especially in an Rh-isoimmunized pregnancy or if other fetal hemolytic disease is suspected • Prenatal diagnosis of genetic disorders, especially if maternal age is advanced (over 35) or a history of chromosomal abnormalities in previous pregnancies, in parents, or in close family members exists

nancy. Excessive weight gain (more than 2 lb or 0.9 kg per week) may result from excessive caloric intake or preeclampsia. An elevation from the patient's baseline blood pressure of more than 30 mm systolic/15 mm diastolic is abnormal. The presence of protein in the urine is also abnormal and may indicate preeclampsia.

Perform abdominal palpation on your patient to determine fundal height and fetal position and presentation (see *Fundal Height Measurement*, page 413, and *Leopold's Ma-*

neuvers, page 417). Also check the correlation between fetal growth and estimated gestational age. Fetal position may vary during the pregnancy, but the position of the fetus for labor is usually apparent by week 36.

Auscultate the fetal heart for rate and location. For best results, auscultate through the fetus' back.

Perform the bimanual palpation and a vaginal examination only if indicated. Repeat the hemoglobin/hematocrit test at 28 to 32 weeks' gestation and, if appropriate, the STS and GC tests at 36 weeks. If your patient is Rh negative, repeat the antibody screen test at about 28, 32, and 36 weeks' gestation.

The last four weeks

Generally, the patient will return for an examination every week during the last four weeks of pregnancy. She'll probably be especially anxious to know when she'll have her baby. Let her know that you can determine whether preparatory events are occurring, but that you can't predict when labor will begin. Be sure she knows the following signs of impending labor:
• Uterine contractions increasing in frequency, duration, and intensity
• Bloody show
• Mucous plug expulsion
• Membrane rupture.

During this stage of the pregnancy, continue to monitor fetal heart tones and movement. The fetus should continue to move during the last few weeks: If the fetus is unusually quiet, notify the doctor immediately (see *Tests for Fetal Status,* page 418).

During each visit, palpate the patient's uterus for Braxton Hicks contractions, which should now occur more frequently; they also should be more intense and last longer. For each contraction, you'll feel a tightening of the fundal region that moves downward in a wavelike motion and ends with a pulling or tugging near the cervix. The patient usually has at least one internal vaginal examination during the last four weeks of pregnancy.

The final internal examination

To perform the internal examination at this stage of pregnancy, you needn't place the patient in stirrups or use a speculum. Instead, using a sterile glove and lubricant, insert two fingers into her vagina and locate the cervix. Note its softness, the percentage of effacement, and the degree of cervical dilatation. Note that some cervical effacement and dilatation may precede labor, but often these changes do not occur until active uterine contractions have begun.

Effacement, evaluated in percentages, is the obliteration or shortening of the cervical canal from an approximate length of ⅘″ (2 cm) to a structure in which the canal is replaced by a circular opening with paper-thin edges. *Dilatation* is the progressive enlargement of the external os to 10 cm. You can judge dilatation by the number of fingertips you can rest comfortably in the external os. Record this in centimeters, not the number of fingertips.

Also determine whether the presenting part of the fetus is properly positioned, or engaged. Approximately two weeks before delivery, primigravidas generally experience *lightening,* the descent of the fetus' presenting part through the inlet of the pelvic canal. Multigravidas usually experience this during labor. You determine this engagement in relation to the level of the ischial spines—the *zero* station. Locate the ischial spines and estimate the descent of the fetus' presenting part. If the presenting part is above the ischial spines, it is not engaged (this is called *floating* and is assigned a negative station number that reflects the number of centimeters the presenting part is above the ischial spines, which are considered station zero). If the presenting part is below the ischial spines, it is engaged and a positive number is assigned to indicate how far, in centimeters, the presenting part lies below station zero. Station measurements are especially important for evaluating the progress of the patient's labor.

Finally, locate the membranes, which feel like tough, rubbery balloons. Sometimes, you can feel them bulging through the cervical os. Determine whether they've ruptured. Also find out if the pink-tinged mucous plug that has protected the developing fetus has been expelled (*bloody show*)—a reliable sign that labor is imminent.

Guide to Pregnancy Disorders

DISORDER	HISTORY AND CHIEF COMPLAINTS	
Abruptio placentae (mild, moderate, or severe)	• Most commonly occurs after 20 weeks • Higher incidence in women over age 35 • Predisposing factors include high parity, previous abruptio placentae, hypertension, inferior vena cava compression, folic acid deficiency, abdominal trauma, sudden uterine compression, short umbilical cord. • Signs and symptoms include mild to moderate abdominal pain and vaginal bleeding.	
Chronic hypertensive disease	• History of hypertension before pregnancy, and/or hypertension apparent before 20th week of gestation • No history of neoplastic trophoblastic disease or persistent hypertension after 6 weeks postpartum in previous pregnancies	
Eclampsia	• Most common in last trimester • Family history of preeclampsia or eclampsia • Signs and symptoms usually preceded by preeclampsia; in the absence of neurologic diseases, convulsions at onset • Respiratory distress	
Ectopic pregnancy	• History of endosalpingitis, adhesions in the fallopian tubes, or uterine or adnexal mass • Signs and symptoms include lower abdominal pain (may be stabbing, sharp, or dull; unilateral or bilateral; constant or intermittent), nausea, vomiting, amenorrhea in about 75% of patients; vaginal spotting or bleeding possible in tubal pregnancy	
Gestational edema	• Signs and symptoms include generalized fluid accumulation after 12 hours of bed rest.	
Gestational hypertension	• No past history of hypertension	
Gestational proteinuria	• No history of hypertension, edema, renal infection, or known renovascular disease	
Hydatidiform mole	• Highest incidence in women over age 45 • Predisposing factors include previous mole (found in only 2% of the population) and low-protein diet. • Signs and symptoms include excessive nausea and vomiting and uterine bleeding (from spotting to profuse hemorrhage).	

PHYSICAL EXAMINATION AND DIAGNOSTIC STUDIES

- In mild to moderate cases, minimal to moderate bleeding, uterine tenderness, moderate abdominal pain, uterine irritability, hypotension
- In severe cases, little or no bleeding; uterus hard, like wood; possibly maternal shock; severe, tearing abdominal pain; oliguria; anuria; absence of fetal heart sounds
- Diagnostic studies include hemoconcentration, clotting studies, and sonography.

- Systolic blood pressure: 100 mmHg or greater, or rise of 30 mmHg or greater from baseline pressure
- Diastolic blood pressure: 90 mmHg or greater, or rise of 15 mmHg or greater from baseline pressure

---

- Physical examination findings similar to those of preeclampsia, plus clonic or tonic convulsions.
- Coma or semiconscious state follows convulsions; also, hypertension, increased respiration, cyanosis, fever, pronounced proteinuria, oliguria, pronounced edema
- After delivery, urinary output increases and edema diminishes; blood pressure returns to normal within 2 weeks.
- In terminal stage of fatal eclampsia, pulmonary edema, cyanosis, and other signs of heart failure

---

- Possibly increased pulse rate or decreased blood pressure
- Inspection of the umbilicus in a slender woman or one who has an umbilical hernia may reveal Cullen's sign (a blue discoloration due to extensive intraperitoneal hemorrhage).
- Pelvic examination may reveal an abnormal pelvic mass.
- Elevated erythrocyte sedimentation rate
- WBC count: 15,000; RBC count: low, with bleeding
- Pregnancy test may be negative.
- Laparoscopy can detect ectopic pregnancy.
- Culdoscopy can detect an aborted conceptus and clotted blood.
- Laparotomy confirms the diagnosis.

- Edema (+ 1 pitting)
- Weight gain of 5 lb (2.25 kg) or more in 1 week with or without edema after bed rest

---

- May not occur until the first 24 hours postpartum and disappears within 10 days postpartum
- Blood pressure as described in chronic hypertensive disease; usually discovered on physical examination during latter half of pregnancy
- No other signs of preeclampsia or hypertensive vascular disease

---

- Urine protein level increased by 0.3 g/liter in 24-hour period, or 1 g/liter in two different specimens collected at least 6 hours apart

---

- Signs usually apparent by 18 weeks; ovaries tender to palpation; tender uterus due to stretching; uterus large for gestational date; rusty drainage; preeclampsia signs may appear before the 20th week; hypertension; fluid retention; proteinuria
- Slight drop in RBC count, hemoglobin, and hematocrit
- High or rising titers of human chorionic gonadotropin and thyroxine
- Increased WBC count
- Mole can be identified with ultrasound by 3rd month.

(continued)

Guide to Pregnancy Disorders *(continued)*

DISORDER	HISTORY AND CHIEF COMPLAINTS	
Placenta previa (total, partial, marginal, or low-lying)	● Higher incidence in women over age 35 and in multiparas; tendency for recurrence ● Bleeding may begin at any time during pregnancy, with no warning, but usually occurs after 24 weeks. ● Signs and symptoms include painless, bright red vaginal bleeding; intermittent, slight, or in gushes.	
Preeclampsia	● Occurs after 20th week of gestation. May appear earlier with an advanced hydatidiform mole or with extensive molar change; most common in primigravidas, especially older women and pregnant adolescents ● Family history of preeclampsia or eclampsia ● Signs and symptoms include visual disturbances, ranging from blurred vision to blindness in extreme cases, and headache (usually mild; uncommon). ● May be asymptomatic except for elevated blood pressure ● With severe preeclampsia, signs and symptoms include nausea, vomiting, irritability, severe frontal headache, epigastric or right upper quadrant pain (usually a sign of impending convulsion), and respiratory distress suggesting pulmonary edema.	
Spontaneous abortion (threatened, inevitable, complete, incomplete, missed, habitual)	● Usually occurs around 12th week or not later than 20th week ● Signs and symptoms include cramps, backache, vaginal bleeding; patient may complain of "not feeling pregnant anymore"; sudden gush of fluid from vagina occurs in inevitable abortion.	
Superimposed pre-eclampsia or eclampsia	● Predisposing factors include chronic hypertensive vascular disease or renal disease. ● May occur early in pregnancy and progress to eclampsia	

PHYSICAL EXAMINATION AND DIAGNOSTIC STUDIES

- Soft, nontender uterus
- May have large placenta as seen with multiple fetuses or in patient with diabetes
- Diagnostic studies include sonography and placental localization.

- Edema evidenced by puffiness of fingers and swollen eyelids; becomes generalized and is also apparent in sacral area and abdominal wall; sudden excessive weight gain; hypertension; proteinuria
- With severe preeclampsia, increased blood pressure (160/100 mmHg) that does not decrease with bed rest; proteinuria (urine protein increased 5 g in 24 hours, +3 or +4), oliguria (urinary output reduced by 500 ml or more in 24 hours); increased serum creatine, cerebral disturbances, hyperaflexia (3 to 4 + /4 + , clonus), cyanosis, severe thrombocytopenia, hepatocellular damage

---

- Weight loss; abnormally small uterus for gestational age; may find incompetent cervix if repeated abortions have occurred, especially in midpregnancy; abnormal fetal development found in high percentage of spontaneous abortions; negative or ambiguous pregnancy test

---

- Same as preeclampsia and eclampsia

20

The Neonate

Assessing the neonate in the delivery room involves swift and critical appraisal of his transition to extrauterine life—a transition accompanied by rapid physiologic changes and numerous adaptations, all necessary for survival. In a very short period (usually seconds), the neonate's external surroundings change from warm, dark, relatively quiet, and fluid-enveloped to cold, dry, noisy, and bright. Internally, he switches to totally different respiratory and circulatory systems. Hepatic and renal functions, blood oxygen saturation, and numerous metabolic processes are altered.

Probably no other 24-hour period in an individual's life is so important as the neonate's first day of adjustment to extrauterine existence. Consequently, the first *thorough* examination of the neonate takes place in the nursery, usually within 24 hours of his birth.

History data

Biographical data

Record the neonate's approximate gestational age based on obstetric tests. Then determine gestational age based on your findings during the physical examination (see *Characteristics of Gestational Age,* page 425). Compare these estimates, bearing in mind that examination techniques for establishing gestational age are more reliable than obstetric tests.

History of present illness

The most common signs and symptoms in neonates are *skin color changes, neurologic changes, respiratory distress, altered heart rate,* and *gastrointestinal abnormalities* (see *Guide to Neonatal Disorders,* pages 438 to 443).

If the neonate shows any of these signs and symptoms while he's in the nursery, record complete information about them. If signs and symptoms develop after the neonate's discharged from the nursery, ask the neonate's parents to elaborate on the problem.

• **Skin color changes.** *Cyanosis* or *pallor* may indicate an alteration in cardiovascular or respiratory function. Central cyanosis necessitates immediate attention. Because neonates have a high percentage of fetal hemoglobin, which is capable of carrying about 25% more oxygen than adult hemoglobin, central cyanosis doesn't develop until PO_2 is very low, between 30 and 44 mmHg. Pallor may occur with a decreased hemoglobin level, as in anemia. Jaundice occurring in the first 24 hours of life can indicate true hemolytic disease, such as Rh incompatibility from erythroblastosis fetalis. Jaundice occurring on the second or third day may be considered physiologic jaundice (*icterus neonatorum*), which isn't uncommon but may require further evaluation. The neonate's body may exhibit a complete division of color into a pale side and a red side (harlequin color change). This is usually temporary and of little significance to neonatal well-being.

• **Neurologic changes.** *Lethargy, irritability, hypertonia* or *hypotonia, tremors,* or *seizures* may indicate an alteration in neurologic function. Maternal drug addiction may lead to these signs and symptoms as the neonate experiences withdrawal. Hypoglycemia can also cause these signs and symptoms.

• **Respiratory distress.** *Apnea* for more than 10 seconds, as well as *dyspnea, tachypnea, grunting, nasal flaring, sternal retractions,* and

Characteristics of Gestational Age

PHYSICAL CHARACTERISTICS	LESS THAN 37 WEEKS	37 TO 38 WEEKS	MORE THAN 38 WEEKS
Sole creases	Anterior transverse crease only	Some creases in anterior two thirds	Sole covered with creases
Breast nodule diameter	2 mm	4 mm	7 mm
Scalp hair	Fine and fuzzy	Fine and fuzzy	Coarse and silky
External ear	Pliable, no cartilage	Some cartilage	Stiff, with thick cartilage
Testes and scrotum	Testes in lower canal; scrotum small with few rugae	Testes in intermediate position	Testes pendulous; scrotum full with extensive rugae

wheezing, can indicate a life-threatening problem. Examples of possible underlying conditions are infant respiratory distress syndrome and pneumonia. These conditions require immediate intervention.

• *Altered heart rate. Bradycardia* or *tachycardia* can indicate severe oxygenation problems from cardiac, respiratory, or neurologic disorders.

• *Gastrointestinal abnormalities. Abdominal distention* and *vomiting* (especially of bile-stained substances) may reflect intestinal obstruction. *Failure to pass meconium* could indicate that the enervation of the distal colon is absent (Hirschsprung's disease); another possible cause is imperforate anus. *Feeding problems* accompanied by *dyspnea* may indicate obstruction of the posterior nares (choanal atresia), tracheoesophageal fistula, or such cardiovascular disorders as congestive heart failure or atrial or ventricular septal defects.

Past history

A neonate's past history includes information about his health status before the examination. This could take only a matter of minutes, for an evaluation performed in the nursery, or may cover up to 27 days if the neonate is seen after discharge. Obtain information from family members about any known *congenital*

anomalies and other problems.

The neonate's past history, especially during the first few critical days of life, also includes the following maternal history aspects:

• *Maternal age.* The mother's age, the outcome of the pregnancy, and the neonate's health can be directly related. Mothers younger than age 20 experience more difficulties than older mothers. Some common maternal problems that affect the fetus directly are excessive weight gain, preeclampsia, and prolonged labor. Neonates born to mothers in this age-group are more likely to have a low birth weight, especially if the mother's nutritional status is poor.

The incidence of trisomy 21 (Down's syndrome) rises if the mother is over age 35. Other fetal malformations (musculoskeletal disorders, cardiovascular defects, gastrointestinal abnormalities, and central nervous system anomalies) are also more common in neonates born to mothers over age 35.

• *Drugs.* Both over-the-counter and prescription drugs taken by a woman during pregnancy may be passed to the fetus transplacentally. Neonates of drug-addicted mothers are at greater risk of being born with congenital anomalies, particularly extremity malformations. These neonates are usually premature and exhibit signs and symptoms of withdrawal, such as tremors, agitation, and seizures, shortly after delivery.

• **Alcohol.** Excessive consumption of alcohol in early pregnancy can produce congenital anomalies involving the heart, face, and extremities, and can retard fetal growth. Alcohol consumption before delivery can cause toxic symptoms in the neonate. Because alcohol is a central nervous system depressant, it can interfere with the neonate's cardiopulmonary adaptation.

• **Smoking.** Neonates born to women who smoked cigarettes during pregnancy are more likely to be underweight.

• **Infections.** Because of its inadequate immunologic system, the fetus is susceptible to many organisms. For example, rubella contracted by the mother during the first trimester can cause retarded intrauterine growth and congenital malformations in the neonate, including cardiac defects. Among infections transmitted during delivery, maternal gonorrhea can cause *ophthalmia neonatorum* and a monilial infection can cause *thrush.* Such infections usually have less severe consequences—although more serious infections, such as herpes simplex virus, can be fatal to the neonate.

• **Diseases and disorders.** Many pathologic maternal conditions, such as diabetes mellitus, chronic hypertension, cardiac disease, thyroid imbalance, preeclampsia, or eclampsia, can cause problems for the neonate. Observe the neonate of a diabetic mother for neonatal hypoglycemia, hyperbilirubinemia, hypocalcemia, and idiopathic respiratory distress syndrome. Congenital malformations, including skeletal and ventricular septal defects, are three times more likely to occur if the mother is diabetic. For neonates born to mothers with hyperthyroidism, a serum thyroxine measurement should be performed at birth, and the neonate should be observed closely during the first 2 weeks of life for signs and symptoms of hyperthyroidism. The neonate whose mother has hypothyroidism can have a congenital goiter or cretinism. These neonates also have a high incidence of congenital abnormalities. The manifestations of preeclampsia or eclampsia are mainly maternal; however, the fetus in such cases is also at risk. If maternal hypertension accompanies either of these disorders, fetal growth may be retarded. The neonate may develop hypermagnesemia

if the mother is treated with magnesium sulfate.

• **Prenatal care.** Neonates born to mothers who didn't have adequate prenatal care are more likely to have complications.

Labor and delivery history

Labor and delivery cause great stress to every neonate. Uterine contractions exert extreme pressure on the fetus at the same time that the fetus meets resistance from pelvic structures. It must also withstand brief periods of hypoxia, caused by decreased circulation during uterine contractions. This traumatic process occurs in all vaginal deliveries. For some neonates, vaginal birth may be even more dangerous, and cesarean delivery may be employed to reduce the risk.

When recording a neonate's prenatal history, consider the following complications and their effects:

• **Premature labor.** Labor that occurs before the 37th week of gestation endangers the neonate, because his major body systems, notably the respiratory system, are immature compared with the functional requirements for extrauterine survival. His ability to store and regulate body heat is also impaired.

• **Premature membrane rupture.** This can cause an infection in the neonate from amniotic fluid reaching the tracheobronchial tree. Infection transmitted through the cord vessels can also produce fetal sepsis.

• **Dysfunctional labor pattern.** In hyperactive labor, the unusually strong contractions and rapid progression can cause cerebral trauma. In hypoactive labor, the long birth process and prolonged pressure on the fetal head can result in a cephalhematoma, caput succedaneum (fetal scalp edema), or excessive molding of cranial bones.

• **Abnormal fetal presentation.** Malpresentation can injure the neonate. Brow presentation can tear the tentorium, compress the head and neck, and damage the trachea and larynx. Face presentation can cause caput succedaneum, neck swelling, and petechiae and ecchymoses of the facial skin's superficial layers. Breech presentation can result in cervical cord injury, intracranial hemorrhage, brachial plexus palsy, arm fracture, and edema of the presenting part, and kidney, liver, and spleen hemorrhage. Also, the neonate may remain in the breech posture for some time after delivery. A frank breech presentation, for example, results in extended legs and abducted, fully rotated thighs.

● *Analgesics and anesthetics.* If administered to the mother during labor and delivery, a large amount of anesthetic or such drugs as meperidine, morphine sulfate, and secobarbital cross the placental barrier and may cause respiratory depression in the neonate and decrease his responsiveness and feeding ability.

Family and psychosocial history and ADL

When recording a neonate's family history, ask the parents about congenital defects or genetically transmitted diseases, previous multiple births, infant deaths (including stillbirths and abortions), and family members' general health (ask about such diseases as diabetes or epilepsy).

Record pertinent information about the neonate's family. For example, determine what arrangements have been made at home for the neonate's care. Ask the mother if she anticipates any financial or family problems. Encourage her to discuss any emotional concerns or life-style conflicts she may have relating to the care and health of the neonate. When appropriate, determine what effects, if any, the family's religious practices may have on the care the neonate will receive at home.

If the neonate has been brought back for care after being discharged from the nursery, ask the mother about *feeding patterns* as well as the color and consistency of his feces.

Physical examination

Apgar score: The first examination

Immediately after delivery, determine the neonate's Apgar score. The purpose of the Apgar scoring system is twofold: to provide an initial assessment of the neonate's physical status and to identify indications for immediate resuscitation. Check these five objective signs quickly but carefully to compile a neonate's Apgar score: heart rate, respiratory effort, muscle tone, reflex irritability, and skin color. As you evaluate each sign, assign a score of 0,1, or 2. Repeat the Apgar scoring system again at 5

minutes (see *The Apgar Scoring System,* page 428).

Heart rate is the most important sign, so assess this first. If the umbilical cord is still pulsating, you can palpate the neonate's heart rate by placing your fingertips at the junction of the umbilical cord and the skin. You can also place two fingers or a stethoscope over the neonate's chest at the fifth intercostal space to obtain an apical pulse.

Next, check the neonate's *respiratory effort,* the second most important Apgar sign. Assess the neonate's cry, noting its volume and vigor. Then auscultate his lungs, using a pediatric stethoscope. Assess his respirations for depth and regularity.

Determine *muscle tone* by evaluating the degree of flexion in the neonate's arms and legs and their resistance to straightening. For example, try to straighten an arm or leg and note how quickly it returns to the flexed position.

Assess *reflex irritability* by evaluating the neonate's cry for presence, vigor, and pitch. He may not cry at once, but you should elicit a cry by flicking his soles. A high-pitched or shrill cry is abnormal.

Finally, observe *skin color* for cyanosis. A neonate usually has a pink body with blue extremities. This condition, called *acrocyanosis,* appears in about 85% of normal neonates 1 minute after birth. Acrocyanosis results from decreased peripheral oxygenation caused by the transition from fetal to independent circulation. When assessing a nonwhite neonate, observe for color changes in the mucous membranes of the mouth, conjunctivae, lips, palms, and soles.

The stable neonate may be weighed at this early stage. After this preliminary assessment, you'll usually take a neonate with an acceptable Apgar score to his mother, for the first few minutes of bonding.

Nursery admission assessment

After the newborn infant spends some time with his mother, you'll take him to the nursery, where pertinent data concerning labor and delivery interventions should be available. Here, the evaluation continues with assessment of the neonate's vital signs, weight, length, and general characteristics.

Take the neonate's first temperature rectally

The Apgar Scoring System

To help assess a neonate's condition, use the Apgar scoring system shown here. Make your observations within 1 minute after the neonate's delivered, then again within 5 minutes.

Notify the doctor of your findings, and document them on the neonate's chart. A neonate with a score of 10 is considered in the best possible condition. A score of 7 to 9 is considered adequate, requiring no treatment. A score of 4 to 6 requires close observation and intervention, such as suctioning. A score below 4 necessitates immediate intervention and further evaluation.

SIGN	0	1	2	Rating 1 min	5 min
Heart rate	Not detectable	Below 100	Over 100		
Respiratory effort	Absent	Slow, irregular	Good, crying		
Muscle tone	Flaccid	Some flexion of extremities	Active motion		
Reflex irritability (response to flick on sole)	No response	Grimace, slow motion	Cry		
Color	Blue, pale	Body pink, extremities blue	Completely pink		
			TOTAL		

Scoring system developed by Dr. Virginia Apgar

(normal: 96° to 99.5° F., or 35.6° to 37.5° C.), so you can also check for anal patency. Subsequent temperatures should be axillary (normal: 97.7° to 98° F., or 36.5° to 36.7° C.), to avoid perforating the bowel. When taken for at least 3 minutes, an axillary temperature provides an approximate core temperature (it may be 1° to 2° lower) and reveals any heat or cold stress. In some nurseries, a rectal temperature is taken until it reaches normal. Use a pediatric stethoscope to determine the neonate's heart rate apically. To ensure an accurate measurement, count the pulsations for 1 minute. (The normal range is from 120 to 150 beats/minute.) Then assess his respiratory rate for at least 30 seconds. (The normal rate is 30 to 60 breaths/minute.) Also note any signs of respiratory distress, such as cyanosis, tachypnea (respiratory rate greater than 60 breaths/minute), sternal retractions, grunting, nasal flaring, or periods of apnea. Rales may

be heard until fetal lung fluid is absorbed.

Measuring the neonate's length, weight, and head and chest circumference provides important baseline data and initial diagnostic information.

Even though the neonate was probably weighed in the delivery room, weigh him again on admission to the nursery. Balance the scale; then weigh the naked neonate. Most newborn infants weigh between 6 and 9 lb (2,700 and 4,000 g); the average is 7 lb 8 oz (3,400 g). Record weight in pounds and ounces as well as in grams.

Now, measure the neonate's length, from the top of the head to the heel with the leg fully extended. Normal length is 18″ to 22″ (46 to 56 cm).

Next, measure head circumference. Normal neonatal head circumference is 13″ to 14″ (33 to 35.5 cm). Remember, cranial molding or caput succedaneum from a vaginal delivery may affect this measurement, so repeat it on the second and third day and before the neonate's discharged. Measure his chest circumference at the nipple line; normal neonatal chest circumference is 12″ to 13″ (30.5 to 33 cm). Head circumference should be about 1″ (2 to 3 cm) larger than chest circumference.

Remember to observe the neonate's overall appearance, noting any obvious congenital defects or abnormalities.

Preparations for the complete examination

During the first 24 hours of life, a neonate receives a complete physical examination. This is the third and most comprehensive step in neonatal assessment, after the Apgar scoring in the delivery room and the examination on admission to the nursery. Make this head-to-toe assessment a priority in your care plan, because it serves as a baseline for future examinations and identifies normal and abnormal characteristics.

For this examination, you'll need the following items:
• Pediatric stethoscope
• Penlight or ophthalmoscope, and otoscope
• Infant tongue depressor
• Tape measure
• Bell (or appropriate substitute)
• Pacifier or water-filled nursing bottle
• Finger cot and catheter.

Perform the examination in a warm, well-lighted, draft-free area, keeping the neonate undressed for as short a time as possible. Lay him on a flat surface. Begin with nonstressful assessment techniques; defer those which may disturb the neonate until later in the examination. If possible, perform the examination in the presence of one or both parents (for example, by the side of the mother's bed). This affords an excellent opportunity for teaching parents about neonatal care and for answering any questions they may have.

Inspection and palpation of the neonate's head

Observe the general contour of the neonate's head. Be sure you inspect the head from different angles so you don't miss a prematurely closed suture or a flat occiput. In most vaginal vertex deliveries some cranial molding occurs, because the cranial bones haven't fused

and can overlap. Next, observe and palpate the sutures and fontanelles with the neonate held upright, if possible. You can feel the sutures as slightly depressed edges. (Sometimes you can palpate an osseous ridge along the suture lines.) The anterior fontanelle is approximately 2″ (5 cm) long and 1⅛″ (3 cm) wide. You can locate the posterior fontanelle, which is less than ⅜″ (1 cm) long, by tracing the sagittal suture.

Normally, the fontanelles feel soft and either flat or slightly indented. The anterior fontanelle usually bulges when a neonate cries, coughs, or vomits. Abnormally bulging fontanelles may indicate increased intracranial pressure. Possible causes include infectious or neoplastic diseases of the central nervous system or an obstruction to ventricular circulation. A sunken fontanelle may suggest dehydration.

Observe the neonate for caput succedaneum and cephalhematoma after a vaginal vertex delivery. *Caput succedaneum* is generalized edema from prolonged pressure against the cervical os. On palpation, the scalp feels soft and edematous. This condition may appear at birth or shortly thereafter and usually resolves in a few days. In *cephalhematoma*, blood collects between the cranial bone and the periosteum. Whereas caput succedaneum appears over a large area of the neonate's scalp, cephalhematoma remains within the boundaries of the cranial bones and won't cross suture lines. Cephalhematoma may not appear for several days after birth and can take several weeks to recede.

Neck assessment

Observe the general appearance of the neonate's neck: It's usually short, thick, and covered with folds of tissue. Also assess the neonate's ability to use his neck muscles. He should be able to move his head from side to side and from flexion to extension. Note if he can hold his head in the midline position; this indicates that the sternocleidomastoid muscles are equal in strength. You should also observe the neonate for torticollis or for shortening of the sternocleidomastoid muscle on one side.

Gently lift the neonate, allowing some degree of hyperextension, and note the degree of his head control. Assess range of motion by eliciting the tonic neck reflex (see *Neonatal Reflexes*, pages 431 to 432). Finally, palpate the neck for abnormal masses, such as an enlarged thyroid.

Eye inspection

Observe the neonate's eyes for symmetry of size and shape. The eyelids may be edematous for 1 or 2 days as a result of delivery and the chemical conjunctivitis caused by instillation of silver nitrate drops. Culture any purulent discharge to differentiate it from ophthalmia neonatorum caused by gonorrhea. To open a neonate's eyes for examination, gently rock him from an upright to a horizontal position, or hold him supine and gently lower his head.

The stress of delivery commonly causes subconjunctival and scleral hemorrhages. (Assure the parents that these conditions aren't pathologic.) Note the neonate's eye movements. Strabismus caused by poor neuromuscular control is normal.

Observe the color of the neonate's eyes. Light-skinned neonates usually have blue or blue-gray eyes; for darker-skinned babies, brown eyes are normal. The sclerae are usually blue-white. Redness may be caused by the instillation of silver nitrate drops. The corneas should appear clear, so note any opacity or haziness, which may be associated with congenital cataracts.

To assess a neonate's extraocular muscle movements, turn his head from side to side while observing his eye movements. A newborn infant's eyes should remain fixed (doll's eyes). An infant older than 10 days should look in the direction in which you turn. Next, gently raise the neonate to the sitting position, then quickly lower him to the supine position. If his eyes slowly drift downward, suspect cerebral dysfunction caused by kernicterus or hydrocephaly.

Next, test the red reflex of the fundus. With the diopter setting at 0, hold the ophthalmoscope 10″ (25.4 cm) from the neonate's pupils. In addition to a red reflex response, they should react to the light by constricting.

Nose and mouth

Because neonates are obligate nose breathers, nasal passage patency is essential. If the neonate has no difficulty breathing with his mouth closed, you can be fairly certain that his nasal passages are patent. If you suspect they aren't, try passing a #8 suction catheter. You can also assess nasal patency by blocking the neonate's mouth and one nasal passage, and noting air movement through the other canal. A neonate usually clears his nasal passages by sneezing. Nasal flaring indicates respiratory distress, so always note and report it. (A thin nasal discharge, an uncommon finding, may be cerebrospinal fluid and requires further evaluation.)

Examine the neonate's mouth for cleft palate by gently depressing his tongue when he cries. You can also palpate for cleft palate by running a clean finger along the soft and hard palates while testing the sucking reflex.

Rarely, you'll find teeth in the neonate's mouth, usually located in the lower incisor position. These are called *precocious teeth* (supernumerary teeth). If they're loose, you or the doctor should remove them to avoid the danger of aspiration. You may also see small, white epithelial cysts on the hard palate and gum margins (Epstein's pearls). These cysts are insignificant and usually disappear in a few weeks. Areas of a white, cheesy substance that don't rub off are usually from thrush or monilial infection.

Inspect the position of the frenulum; note if it's attached too closely to the tip of the tongue. Also, observe for *sucking blisters*—round, thickened areas on the neonate's lips, particularly in the center of the upper lip—which may disappear within a few weeks.

Ear examination

Inspect the ears for structure, shape, and position. A full-term neonate's ears should be firm, with well-formed cartilage. The tops of the auricles should be parallel to the outer canthi of the eye. Low-set ears are associated with renal anomalies and with certain chromosomal abnormalities, especially trisomy 13, 18, and 21 (Down's syndrome). Small, preauricular skin tabs may appear just in front of the ears.

In a neonate aged less than 3 days, examine the external ear canal for patency. You can't see the eardrum because vernix caseosa covers it. To see the eardrum in a neonate aged 3 days or older, gently pull the auricle downward and inspect with an otoscope. The light reflex should be diffuse, not cone-shaped as

Neonatal Reflexes

REFLEX	METHOD AND NORMAL RESPONSE	ABNORMAL RESPONSE SIGNIFICANCE
Blink or corneal	• Shine a bright light in neonate's face; he should blink.	• Absent or asymmetrical response may indicate blindness.
Pupillary	• Shine a bright light toward neonate's pupil; pupil should constrict.	• Fixed dilated pupil, asymmetrical reflex, or absent response is abnormal.
Sneezing, yawning	• Observe as spontaneous behavior.	• Absent or continuous yawning and sneezing seen in neonates with narcotic-addicted mother.
Cough	• Insert catheter into neonate's tracheobronchial tree; he should cough spontaneously from irritation.	• Absence is abnormal after 1 day.
Sucking	• Stroke around neonate's mouth with your fingertip, or insert finger into mouth; he should begin strong sucking movements; reflex should persist with stimulation for about 6 months, then disappear.	• Absence indicates central nervous system depression or immaturity.
Swallowing or gag	• Stimulate neonate's posterior pharynx with food or by inserting a suction catheter or feeding tube; he should swallow or gag.	• Absence may indicate damaged glossopharyngeal nerve.
Rooting	• Stroke both corners of neonate's mouth and the middle upper and middle lower lips; he should turn toward stimulus and open mouth; reflex should disappear by 4 months but may persist for 12 months.	• Absence indicates central nervous system depression or immaturity; persistence indicates prolonged immaturity of neuro-organization.
Asymmetrical tonic neck (fencing reflex)	• Quickly turn neonate's head to one side; he should extend arm and leg on this side and flex arm and leg on opposite side; reflex should disappear by 3 months and be replaced by symmetrical positioning.	• Absence or persistence may indicate central nervous system damage.
Head-raising	• Place neonate in prone position on a flat surface; he attempts to lift his head slightly; he should have more head control after 3 months.	• Absence may indicate neurologic or muscular disorder.
Galant (trunk incurvation)	• Stroke neonate's back next to spine; he should flex his trunk and move his hips toward stimulated side; reflex should disappear by 4 weeks.	• Absence may indicate spinal cord lesion.
Landau	• Hold neonate in prone position with your hand under his abdomen, letting his ex-	• Absence indicates loss of muscle tone requiring fur-

(continued)

Neonatal Reflexes *(continued)*

REFLEX	METHOD AND NORMAL RESPONSE	ABNORMAL RESPONSE SIGNIFICANCE
Landau *(continued)*	tremities hang; he should demonstrate some muscle tone by trying to keep spine straight.	ther neurologic examination after 3 months.
Crossed extension	• Place neonate in supine position, extend one leg, and prick sole with a pin; he should extend and adduct the opposite leg; reflex should disappear after 2 months.	• Absence indicates spinal cord or nerve damage; persistence indicates pyramidal tract lesions.
Grasp (palmar, plantar)	• Touch neonate's palm and sole near base of digits; he should tightly grasp your finger and flex his toes; palmar grasp should lessen after 3 months, being replaced by voluntary movement; plantar grasp should lessen by 8 months.	• Asymmetrical flexion may indicate paralysis.
Babinski	• Stroke neonate's outer sole upward from heel and across ball of foot; his toes should fan out, his big toe should dorsiflex; reflex should disappear after age 1.	• Persistence may indicate a pyramidal tract lesion.
Moro	• Startle the neonate (with a loud noise or by jarring crib); his extremities should extend and abduct and his index finger and thumb should form a C; then, his extremities should flex and adduct; reflex should disappear after 4 months.	• Asymmetrical response may indicate brachial plexus, clavicle, or humerus injury. Decreased or absent response indicates neurologic disorder.
Placing	• Hold neonate erect and touch dorsal surface of foot or anterior portion of the leg against a hard surface; his ipsilateral leg at knee and hip should flex, lifting his foot as though to place it on surface; reflex should disappear after 1 month.	• Absence indicates neuromuscular degeneration and spinal cord injuries.
Stepping	• Hold neonate so sole touches a hard surface; simulated walking, through reciprocal flexion and extension of the leg, should result; reflex should be replaced after 3 to 4 weeks by deliberate movement.	• Persistence or recurrence indicates spinal cord injury.
Crawling	• Place neonate on abdomen; he should make crawling movements with his arms and legs; reflex should disappear after 6 weeks.	• Asymmetrical movement may indicate neuromuscular abnormality.
Deep tendon	• Tap one of neonate's tendons with your finger; his corresponding muscle should promptly contract.	• Absence of most deep reflexes is abnormal, although triceps reflex may not appear until age 6 months.

in an infant several months old. Assess the neonate's hearing by testing for the Moro reflex (see *Neonatal Reflexes,* pages 431 to 432). Within a few hours after birth, the neonate's hearing becomes more acute, as mucus and fluid in the middle ear and eustachian tube are absorbed.

Skin and nails

Inspect the skin's general appearance, noting any birthmarks. Here are some of the most common neonatal birthmarks:

• *Mongolian spot:* a slate-blue area that appears in the gluteal and sacral regions of dark-skinned infants. It's visible at birth, then disappears in late infancy or early childhood.

• *Telangiectatic nevus* (stork bites): a small pink to red flat area that blanches easily and darkens when the patient cries. It's found on the nape of the neck, the eyelids, the upper lip, the bridge of the nose, and in the occipital area. It's visible at birth and usually disappears by age 2.

• *Nevus flammeus* (port-wine stain): a red to purple flat area that does not blanch with pressure. It's usually visible at birth and does not disappear spontaneously.

• *Nevus vascularis* (strawberry mark): a bright or dark red, raised, rough-surfaced area. It may be visible at birth but usually disappears during the 1st or 2nd month of life and usually disappears spontaneously by age 7.

Normally, the neonate's skin appears soft and puffy immediately after delivery. After a few days, it usually looks dry and flaky—especially in the postmature neonate, whose skin may crack and peel. Skin color, of course, depends on racial and genetic characteristics. A white neonate's skin should be pink to ruddy; a black neonate should appear pink-brown. Normal variations, including acrocyanosis and circumoral cyanosis, may result from poor peripheral circulation. These skin color changes may appear immediately after delivery if the neonate is exposed to cold; they should disappear in approximately 10 days.

Assess for jaundice by blanching the tip of the neonate's nose or his gum line, preferably under natural light. If jaundice is present, the blanched area appears yellow. Jaundice in the first 24 hours after birth indicates pathology, usually hemolytic disease. Although it can also occur during the second or third day—when it may not indicate pathology—jaundice may necessitate further testing to determine the cause of elevated serum bilirubin levels and to prevent serious sequelae.

A normal variation of the newborn infant's skin is erythema toxicum (newborn rash)—a pink, papular rash that appears in the first day or two after birth and spontaneously disappears after several days. You may also observe tiny white sebaceous glands (milia) on the nose and chin, which are commonly mistaken for so-called whiteheads. These disappear in a few weeks. Observe for petechiae, which may indicate a long labor, rapid delivery, intrauterine infection, or thrombocytopenia.

Immediately after birth, vernix caseosa may be found on the neonate's skin. Usually, the more premature the neonate is, the more vernix he has. Left undisturbed, vernix dries and disappears within 2 days. Lanugo—a fine, downy hair—may also be present, particularly on the arms, shoulders, back, and forehead. As with vernix, the more premature the neonate, the more abundant the lanugo.

Examine the neonate's hands and feet for normal creases (see *Characteristics of Gestational Age,* page 425). Observe for a simian crease (single horizontal palmar crease), which is associated with Down's syndrome. Then examine the neonate's nail beds, which should be pink; in acrocyanosis, they may be blue. Absent or short nails indicate prematurity; very long nails indicate postmaturity.

Chest examination

Inspect the size, shape, and symmetry of the neonate's chest. Remember that the neonate's chest is normally almost circular, or barrel-shaped, the anteroposterior diameter equaling the transverse diameter. The xiphoid process may protrude slightly. The ribs are flexible; slight retractions may occur, especially when the neonate cries. Marked retractions indicate respiratory distress and should be reported immediately. Observe the clavicles for symmetry; an abnormality may indicate a fracture.

The breast tissue of both male and female neonates may appear engorged during the first few days of life, as the result of maternal hormone influence. The breasts may even secrete a small amount of milklike fluid. This flow usually stops within 1 or 2 weeks. Don't express this fluid from the neonate's breasts or you may introduce infection. Accessory nipples may appear, usually below and medial to normal nipples. Although their size varies, they don't contain glandular tissue. The normal breast nodule has a diameter of about 6 mm, with prominent, well-formed, symmetrical nipples.

Observe the neonate's chest for the character, rate, and pattern of his respirations. The neonate's respirations are abdominal and diaphragmatic and tend to be irregular in rate and rhythm. Apnea is a sign of respiratory distress: You should report it immediately. It may indicate a metabolic, neurologic, or infectious disorder. Differentiate between true apnea (no respirations for longer than 10 seconds) and periodic breathing (periods of apnea followed by periods of rapid respiratory rate). Other signs of respiratory distress are tachycardia (an early indication), grunting, nasal flaring, tachypnea, retractions, and cyanosis.

Auscultate the neonate's lungs with the bell of your stethoscope or a small-diaphragm stethoscope. (Remember, if the neonate's head is turned to one side, breath sounds may diminish on the other side. Also, crying produces deep breathing and enhances auscultation.) Normal breath sounds are bronchovesicular. Fine crepitant rales at the end of deep inspiration may be normal initially, until fluid is absorbed by the lungs; however, rales can indicate pneumonia or infant respiratory distress syndrome.

Next, auscultate the neonate's apical heartbeat, again using the bell or a small-diaphragm stethoscope. The apical beat is heard at the fourth or fifth intercostal space (ICS), left of the midclavicular line. If you can auscultate the apical beat on the opposite side of the neonate's chest, this may indicate a mediastinal shift. The heart rate should be 120 to 150 beats/minute; sinus arrhythmias and premature ventricular contractions are common.

Auscultate heart sounds. The first and second sounds should be clear and sharp, with the second slightly higher pitched. Remember that heart sounds in neonates are normally louder than in adults. Because of the incomplete closure of the fetal shunts, murmurs are common, especially over the heart base or at the left sternal border, near the third and fourth ICS. You should report them.

Palpate the neonate's peripheral pulses, particularly the femoral, brachial, and radial pulses. A neonate's diminished or absent femoral pulse may be the only indication of coarctation of the aorta.

Abdominal assessment

Inspect the size and shape of the neonate's abdomen. It should be cylindrical; if it looks distended or scaphoid (sunken), report this finding immediately. A scaphoid abdomen may indicate a diaphragmatic hernia. Observe the umbilical cord; it should appear moist and blue-white immediately after birth. (It begins to dry and turn yellow-brown after a few hours.) You should see a definite demarcation between the cord and the skin. Normally, as the cord ages, the area around it becomes dry, without redness. Inspect for umbilical hernia, which is common in black neonates.

Check the number of vessels in the cord. Normally, it contains two arteries and one vein. A single artery usually indicates a congenital anomaly. Check for umbilical fistulas. Urine drainage from the umbilicus indicates a fistula between the umbilicus and the bladder (patent urachus).

Auscultate the neonate's abdomen for bowel sounds, which usually begin within a few hours after birth. Note any increase in pitch or diminishing sounds.

Palpate the abdominal quadrants for tenderness and masses. You should be able to feel the neonate's liver ⅜" to ¾" (1 to 2 cm) below the right costal margin. Before palpating the liver, relax the neonate's muscles by using one hand to support him in the semi-Fowler's position. (Flexing his knees toward his abdomen also relaxes the abdominal muscles.) You may be able to palpate the lower half of the right kidney and the tip of the left one ⅜" to ¾" (1 to 2 cm) above the umbilicus in the posterior flank region. (Remember, you should palpate the kidneys 4 to 6 hours after birth.) Palpate the spleen tip in the left upper quadrant's lateral aspect.

Observe for excessive drooling, coughing, gagging, or cyanosis during feeding. These symptoms may indicate an alteration in gastrointestinal patency (for example, esophageal atresia or tracheoesophageal fistula).

The spine and anal canal

With the neonate in the prone position, examine his spine for S-shaped curves and for masses and abnormal openings. A small pilonidal sinus, which may communicate with the spine, sometimes appears at the spine's base.

Inspect the neonate's back for any malformations of spinal canal closure. Such defects (*spina bifida*) may range from a small split in the vertebrae to the absence of several spinous processes. These malformations result from the neural tube's failure to close during the fourth month of gestation.

Unless it's already been done, check the neonate's anal opening for patency, using a rectal thermometer. Observe for fistula openings on the perineum that may be mistaken for the anus. Remember, meconium may pass through a fistula. The neonate should pass meconium in the first 24 to 48 hours. If he doesn't, he may have imperforate anus or congenital megacolon.

Genitalia assessment

Inspect the neonate's genitalia thoroughly. For a male neonate, inspect the penis for location of the urethral meatus. (Remember, the foreskin may be difficult to retract and shouldn't be forced.) Normally, the opening appears at the tip of the glans penis. Note abnormalities, such as hypospadias (meatus on the ventral surface) or epispadias (meatus on the dorsal surface). (See *Penis Abnormalities*, page 266.) Then inspect the scrotum, which may appear edematous and proportionately large. The scrotal skin should be darkly pigmented and have distinct rugae. Palpate the scrotal sac for the testes. Hydroceles are common in males and usually disappear in a few months.

In a female neonate, the labia majora may appear edematous and cover the clitoris and the labia minora. (The genitalia are particularly edematous or bruised after a breech delivery.) A hymenal tag, which usually disappears after a few weeks, may appear at the vagina's posterior opening. You may also see a white, mucous, vaginal discharge, possibly tinged with blood (pseudomenstruation). This discharge results from the sudden withdrawal of maternal hormones. Normally, it disappears by age 2 to 4 weeks. Examine and note any evidence of ambiguous sexual characteristics, such as enlargement of the clitoris. This is caused by excessive fetal exposure to androgenic hormones (adrenogenital syndrome).

Neuromuscular examination

The neuromuscular examination is one of the most important aspects of neonatal assessment. First, assess muscle tone by observing the neonate's spontaneous or involuntary movements for symmetry, spasticity (hypertonia), flaccidity (hypotonia), or rigidity. Scissoring of the legs is a sign of spasticity. Observe for a frog-legged position in which the hips are held in abduction and external rotation at the same time, with the legs almost flat and the knees angled out. In a breech-presentation neonate, this position is normal for a few days after birth.

To test the neonate's control of his head, trunk, arms, and legs, hold him stomach down (supporting him with your hand under his chest). A normal, full-term neonate should hold his head at about a 45° angle and keep his back straight or slightly flexed, his arms partially extended and bent at the elbows, and his knees partially bent. A hypotonic neonate shows abnormal head lag; a limp, floppy trunk; and dangling arms and legs (floppy infant syndrome). If the neonate rapidly extends his head backward or cannot flex it on his chest, his neck muscles may be hypertonic. Next, gently straighten his arm or leg. Release it and observe whether it returns to its original position. If his extremity remains limp and in the extended position, the neonate may be hypotonic. If his extremity is difficult to straighten and rapidly flexes when released, he may be hypertonic. Observe for other signs of hypertonia, such as severely arched back, coarse tremor, or jittery extremities. Remember, some infants are normally jittery. Hypotonia may indicate hypoxia, Down's syndrome, or neurologic disorders. Hypertonia with tremors may indicate neonatal drug withdrawal. Opisthotonos, a posture in which the back is arched and the neck extended, can be normal in neonates born by face presentation, but it can also indicate serious neurologic disorders, such as meningitis. Asymmetrical muscle tone may result from paralysis or trauma. Observe for seizure activity in the neonate; it may be caused by increased intracranial pres-

Congenital Hip Dislocation

Suspect hip dislocation in the neonate if you detect any of the following: asymmetrical gluteal and thigh skin folds, as shown on the left; a palpable and audible click when his affected leg is abducted (Ortolani's sign), as tested for in the top right illustration; or unequal leg lengths (Allis' sign), as shown in the bottom right illustration.

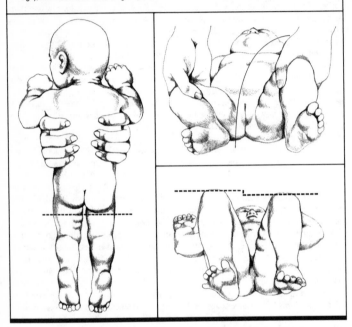

sure, meningitis, high temperature, or kernicterus.

Inspect the neonate's arms and legs for evidence of fracture or trauma. Usually the clavicle, humerus, and femur are affected. Malposition, asymmetric motion, or limited range of motion may indicate injury. Examine the hips for congenital dislocation. First, inspect the neonate for gross asymmetrical skin folds of the buttocks and thighs. With the neonate in the supine position, the knees should be flexed and able to be abducted to almost 180°. Inability to move the knee joints in this manner, an audible click during abduction (Ortolani's sign), unequal leg length (Allis' sign), or unequal gluteal or leg folds may indicate congenital dislocation (see *Congenital Hip Dislocation*).

Examine the neonate's foot position. Turned-in feet are commonly caused by intrauterine malposition. Be sure to distinguish a congenital deformity from a positional deformity by stroking the foot. This causes the positionally deformed foot to return to its normal position. Check to see if the foot and ankle align. Also, inspect the neonate's fingers and toes for polydactyly (extra toes) and syndactyly (webbing).

Test specific reflexes in the neonate, such as blinking, crying, gagging, and sneezing, as well as those involved in feeding, sucking, swallowing, and rooting. Then elicit responses, including the Moro, the tonic neck, and the grasping reflexes.

Daily assessment in the nursery

Check the neonate's vital signs and weight each day he's in the nursery. Report any weight loss greater than 7% immediately.

Continue assessing behavior and feeding patterns, because even subtle symptoms may indicate complications. For instance, the first sign of infection in a neonate may be poor feeding or lethargy, not an elevated temperature.

Normally, neonates are breast- or bottle-fed on a 3- or 4-hour schedule. Evaluate such behavior as sucking, swallowing, rooting, and alertness as well as elimination patterns. The neonate passes meconium in the first 48 hours, commonly within the first 10 hours. Transitional stools range from green-brown to green-yellow and last from a few days to 2 weeks. At first, the neonate may pass stool with each feeding, six to eight times a day. Stools eventually become yellow. The breast-fed neonate usually has soft (or even liquid), "seedy," odorless, yellow stools. The formula-fed neonate has pasty, yellow stools. Bloody or green and watery stools are abnormal.

Guide to Neonatal Disorders

DISORDER	CHIEF COMPLAINT	
Choanal atresia (upper airway obstruction)	• *Skin color changes:* cyanosis • *Respiratory distress:* lack of air exchange with absence of mouth breathing • *Neurologic changes:* irritability, agitation caused by inability to breathe	
Congenital rubella	• *Skin color changes:* cyanosis; jaundice possible with hepatitis; petechiae, purpura, pallor, and mottling with cardiac and respiratory disorders • *Neurologic changes:* lethargy, irritability • *Respiratory distress:* dyspnea; tachypnea with pneumonia • *Gastrointestinal abnormalities:* enlarged liver and spleen	
Diaphragmatic hernia	• *Skin color changes:* cyanosis caused by herniation of abdominal organs into chest, displacing space for lung expansion • *Neurologic changes:* agitation followed by lethargy, caused by respiratory failure • *Respiratory distress:* dyspnea caused by herniation of abdominal organs into chest, displacing space for lung expansion • *Gastrointestinal abnormalities:* vomiting possible if stomach is distended with swallowed air	
Duodenal atresia and stenosis	• *Neurologic changes:* lethargy caused by fluid and electrolyte loss • *Gastrointestinal abnormalities:* bile-stained vomitus	
Erythroblastosis fetalis (Rh/ABO incompatibility)	• *Skin color changes:* pallor caused by anemia; jaundice possible • *Neurologic changes:* lethargy • *Respiratory distress:* dyspnea • *Altered heart rate:* tachycardia • *Gastrointestinal abnormalities:* enlarged liver and spleen	
Galactosemia	• *Skin color changes:* jaundice • *Neurologic changes:* lethargy, irritability, seizures • *Gastrointestinal abnormalities:* vomiting and diarrhea	
Hirschsprung's disease (congenital megacolon)	• *Skin color changes:* pallor caused by dehydration • *Neurologic changes:* irritability • *Respiratory distress:* tachypnea and grunting caused by abdominal distention • *Gastrointestinal abnormalities:* stained or fecal vomiting with severe obstruction; constipation progressing to severe diarrhea if untreated; abdominal distention	

HISTORY	PHYSICAL EXAMINATION AND DIAGNOSTIC STUDIES
• Early detection less likely with only one-sided nasal obstruction	• Attempts to mouth breathe; inability to feed caused by extreme respiratory distress when swallowing; possible sternal retractions with severe respiratory distress
• Predisposing factors include maternal rubella infection, especially during first and second trimesters. • Signs and symptoms include low birth weight.	• Sternal retractions with pneumonia; decreased muscle tone in extremities; cataracts and black pigment deposits in retina may occur later.
• May be associated with congenital anomalies of heart, lungs, intestines.	• Mottled skin; fever with aspiration; flared nostrils; sternal retractions; no breath sounds on affected side; scaphoid abdomen
• Predisposing factors include Down's syndrome, maternal hydramnios, vascular insufficiency. • May occur shortly following birth, or a few weeks later if obstruction is incomplete (stenosis)	• Loss of turgor and wrinkles from fluid and electrolyte loss; distended epigastrium • Diagnostic studies include abdominal roentgenography.
• Predisposing factors include Rh/ABO incompatibility. • Most common in whites	• Flared nostrils; edema of extremities • Diagnostic studies include antibody screening tests (indirect Coombs', indirect antiglobulin test).
• Congenital (recessive gene)	• Poor feeding habits; failure to gain weight; subcutaneous bleeding; dehydration (loss of skin turgor, elevated temperature, dry mucous membranes, oliguria/anuria) • Diagnostic studies include specific enzymatic screening test and urine tests, which reveal no glucose in urine.
• Predisposing factors include family history. • May be associated with other congenital defects • Most common in white males	• Loss of turgor, wrinkled skin, sunken eyes from dehydration; poor sucking and refusal to feed; possible sternal retractions with severe abdominal distention; failure to pass meconium during first 24 to 48 hours; rectal examination results in explosive release of foul-smelling gas and liquid stool. • Diagnostic studies include rectal biopsy showing absent ganglion cells.

(continued)

Guide to Neonatal Disorders *(continued)*

DISORDER	CHIEF COMPLAINT	
Hyperglycemia	• *Neurologic changes:* lethargy, drowsiness, CNS depression • *Respiratory distress:* rapid respirations with hyperthermia; Kussmaul's respirations • *Altered heart rate:* tachycardia caused by dehydration	
Hypocalcemia	• *Skin color changes:* cyanosis • *Neurologic changes:* irritability, tetany, seizures • *Gastrointestinal abnormalities:* vomiting, diarrhea	
Hypoglycemia	• *Skin color changes:* cyanosis, pallor • *Neurologic changes:* irritability progressing to seizures and coma • *Respiratory distress:* dyspnea	
Hypomagnesemia	• *Skin color changes:* cyanosis • *Neurologic changes:* irritability, tetany, seizures • *Gastrointestinal abnormalities:* vomiting	
Idiopathic respiratory distress syndrome (hyaline membrane disease)	• *Skin color changes:* cyanosis, pallor • *Neurologic changes:* agitation progressing to lethargy • *Respiratory distress:* decreased air entry into lungs; tachypnea; apneic periods • *Altered heart rate:* tachycardia	
Imperforate anus	• *Gastrointestinal abnormalities:* no meconium or stool passed through rectum (may be passed through vagina if fistula is present); abdominal distention possible	
Intracranial hemorrhage	• *Skin color changes:* cyanosis with progressive cerebral anoxia; pallor • *Neurologic changes:* lethargy, irritability, seizures; may progress rapidly to coma as intracranial pressure increases • *Respiratory distress:* periods of apnea, irregular respirations	
Kernicterus (hyperbilirubinemia with deposits of bilirubin in brain)	• *Skin color changes:* jaundice; yellow to orange within 1st week • *Neurologic changes:* lethargy; seizures progressing to coma • *Altered heart rate:* tachycardia with dehydration	
Narcotic/barbiturate withdrawal	• *Neurologic changes:* irritability, agitation, seizures • *Respiratory distress:* rapid respirations	

HISTORY	PHYSICAL EXAMINATION AND DIAGNOSTIC STUDIES
• Predisposing factors include premature birth, I.V. glucose infusion.	• Wrinkled skin and loss of turgor from dehydration or possibly hyperthermia; sunken eyes from dehydration; increased urinary output from osmotic diuresis • Diagnostic studies reveal high blood glucose level, serum ketones, and glycosuria
• Predisposing factors include severe maternal calcium and vitamin D deficiency, maternal diabetes, premature birth, immature parathyroid, low birth weight, traumatic birth, exchange transfusion.	• Increased alertness; high-pitched cry; feeding intolerance; increased muscle tone, twitching; hyperactive reflexes • Diagnostic studies reveal low serum calcium level
• Predisposing factors include maternal diabetes, prematurity, low birth weight caused by intrauterine malnutrition. • Most common in males	• Hypothermia; abnormal eye movements; refusal to suck; shrill, high-pitched cry; hypotonia • Diagnostic studies reveal low blood glucose level.
• Predisposing factors include maternal malnutrition or diabetes, fetal malnutrition, multiple births.	• Increased alertness; high-pitched cry; feeding intolerance; increased muscle tone, twitching; hyperactive reflexes • Diagnostic studies reveal low serum magnesium level
• Predisposing factors include premature delivery, perinatal aspiration, delivery following antepartum hemorrhage, maternal diabetes.	• Possibly low body temperature; flared nostrils; frothy sputum; expiratory grunting, retractions; oliguria; peripheral edema; decreased breath sounds • Diagnostic studies reveal low PO_2 (less than 40 mmHg), high PCO_2 (greater than 40 mmHg), and acidotic pH (less than 7.36).
• Congenital	• Not possible to insert rectal thermometer • Observe for small fistula openings on perineum
• Predisposing factors include traumatic birth.	• Bulging fontanelle; retinal hemorrhage, unequal pupils not reactive to light; failure to suck effectively; poor muscle tone, possible paralysis, decreased or absent Moro reflex; nuchal rigidity with subarachnoid hemorrhage
• Predisposing factors include erythroblastosis fetalis, anoxia, infection, hypothyroidism, increased vitamin K administration.	• Loss of skin turgor with dehydration; poor feeding habits; shrill, high-pitched cry; opisthotonos position; muscle twitching, rigidity, or hypotonia; absent Moro reflex, diminished deep tendon reflexes • Diagnostic studies include serum tests for direct and indirect bilirubin and urine urobilinogen
• Predisposing factors include maternal addiction.	• Profuse perspiration; high-pitched cry; possibly chest retractions; coarse tremors; rigid, hyperreflexic *(continued)*

Guide to Neonatal Disorders *(continued)*

DISORDER	CHIEF COMPLAINT	
Narcotic/barbiturate withdrawal *(continued)*	• *Altered heart rate:* tachycardia • *Gastrointestinal abnormalities:* vomiting and diarrhea	
Phenylketonuria (PKU)	• *Neurologic changes:* microcephaly; mental deficiency in later stages	
Pyloric stenosis	• *Skin color changes:* cyanosis with aspiration or hypoxia • *Neurologic changes:* lethargy caused by fluid and electrolyte loss • *Respiratory distress:* dyspnea with aspiration; tachypnea with hypoxia • *Altered heart rate:* rapid heart rate with hypoxia • *Gastrointestinal abnormalities:* vomiting, eventually projectile	
Ruptured liver or spleen	• *Skin color changes:* pallor, jaundice • *Respiratory distress:* tachypnea • *Neurologic changes:* lethargy • *Altered heart rate:* tachycardia	
Sepsis	• *Skin color changes:* flushed, with elevated temperature or pale, cool skin; jaundice possible • *Neurologic changes:* lethargy; seizures possible with elevated temperature • *Respiratory distress:* dyspnea or tachypnea possible • *Altered heart rate:* tachycardia • *Gastrointestinal abnormalities:* distended abdomen, hepatomegaly	
Tracheoesophageal fistula	• *Skin color changes:* cyanosis • *Neurologic changes:* agitation caused by hypoxia • *Respiratory distress:* dyspnea with aspiration of amniotic fluid, feeding, excessive saliva, or gastric secretions; or with abdominal distention; tachypnea with aspiration and hypoxia • *Altered heart rate:* tachycardia caused by hypoxia • *Gastrointestinal abnormalities:* immediate vomiting of any orally ingested fluid; abdominal distention caused by air entering stomach with each breath through fistula	

HISTORY	PHYSICAL EXAMINATION AND DIAGNOSTIC STUDIES
	extremities; incomplete Moro reflex; failure to gain weight
• Signs and symptoms not seen until disease begins to cause mental retardation; early detection is imperative to prevent brain damage. • Congenital (recessive gene)	• Diagnostic studies include blood screening (Guthrie test), performed usually during neonate's 3rd to 6th day with milk or formula feeding. Urine testing may also be performed.
• May not be discovered until a few weeks after birth • Most common in firstborn males	• Dry mucous membranes and loss of turgor from fluid loss caused by vomiting; poor feeding habits; palpable, olive-shaped lump below epigastrium (best felt after vomiting); visible peristalsis from left to right upper quadrant • Diagnostic studies reveal metabolic alkalosis caused by loss of chloride from vomiting.
• Predisposing factors include breech presentations, large size at birth. • Signs and symptoms usually evident after 2 or 3 days.	• Dehydration; poor feeding habits; palpable abdominal mass in right upper quadrant
• Predisposing factors include premature birth, premature rupture of placental membranes. • Most common in males	• Warm skin with hyperthermia; cool skin with hypothermia; wrinkled skin with dehydration; rales or rhonchi heard with respiratory tract infection (pneumonia); poor feeding habits, anorexia; bulging fontanelle and stiff neck with meningitis; purulent discharge from eyes with gonorrhea; chest retractions with respiratory distress • Diagnostic studies reveal organisms in throat, blood, and cerebrospinal fluid cultures.
• Predisposing factors include maternal hydramnios, low birth weight.	• Fever with aspiration; choking, coughing; inability to pass a feeding tube

Selected References

Alexander, Mary M., and Brown, Marie S. *Pediatric History Taking and Physical Diagnosis for Nurses*, 2nd ed. New York: McGraw-Hill Book Co., 1979.

Andreoli, Kathleen, et al. *Comprehensive Cardiac Care: A Text for Nurses, Physicians and Other Health Practitioners*, 4th ed. St. Louis: C.V. Mosby Co., 1979.

Bates, Barbara. *A Guide to Physical Examination*, 3rd ed. Philadelphia: J.B. Lippincott Co., 1983.

Benson, Ralph C., ed. *Current Obstetric and Gynecologic Diagnosis and Treatment*, 4th ed. Los Altos, Calif.: Lange Medical Publications, 1982.

Brenner, Barry M., and Rector, Floyd C., eds. *The Kidney*, 2 vols. Philadelphia: W.B. Saunders Co., 1981.

Burns, Kenneth R., and Johnson, Patricia J. *Health Assessment in Clinical Practice*. Englewood Cliffs, N.J.: Prentice-Hall, Inc., 1980.

Carotenuto, Rosine, and Bullock, John. *Physical Assessment of the Gerontologic Client*. Philadelphia: F.A. Davis Co., 1981.

Christakis, George, ed. *Nutritional Assessment in Health Programs*. Washington, D.C.: American Public Health Assn., 1973.

Conn, Howard F., and Conn, Rex B., Jr. *Current Diagnosis Six*. Philadelphia: W.B. Saunders Co., 1980.

Conover, Mary B. *Understanding Electrocardiography: Physiological and Interpretive Concepts*, 3rd ed. St. Louis: C.V. Mosby Co., 1980.

Conway-Ruthkowski, Barbara L. *Carini and Owens' Neurological and Neurosurgical Nursing*, 8th ed. St. Louis: C.V. Mosby Co., 1982.

DeGowin, Elmer L., and DeGowin, Richard L. *Bedside Diagnostic Examination*, 4th ed. New York: Macmillan Publishing Co., 1981.

DeGroot, Leslie, Jr., ed. *Endocrinology*, 3 vols. New York: Grune and Stratton, Inc., 1979.

DeJong, Russell N. *The Neurologic Examination*, 4th ed. Philadelphia: J.B. Lippincott Co., 1979.

Fowler, Noble O., ed. *Cardiac Diagnosis and Treatment*, 3rd ed. Philadelphia: J.B. Lippincott Co., 1980.

Gillies, Dee A., and Alyn, Irene B. *Patient Assessment and Management by the Nurse Practitioner*. Philadelphia: W.B. Saunders Co., 1976.

Ginsburg, A. David. *Clinical Reasoning in Patient Care*. Philadelphia: J.B. Lippincott Co., 1980.

Guyton, Arthur C. *Textbook of Medical Physiology*, 6th ed. Philadelphia: W.B. Saunders Co., 1981.

Harrison, J. Hartwell, et al. eds. *Campbell's Urology*, Vol. 1-3, 4th ed. Philadelphia: W.B. Saunders Co., 1979.

Harvey, A.M., et al. *The Principles and Practice of Medicine*, 20th ed. East Norwalk, Conn.: Appleton-Century-Crofts, 1980.

Hillman, Robert S., et al. *Clinical Skills: Interviewing, History Taking, and Physical Diagnosis*. New York: McGraw-Hill Book Co., 1981.

Hilt, Nancy E., and Cogburn, Shirley B. *Manual of Orthopedic Nursing*. St. Louis: C.V. Mosby Co., 1975.

Hudak, Carolyn, et al. *Clinical Protocols: A Guide for Nurses and Physicians*. Philadelphia: J.B. Lippincott Co., 1976.

Hurst, J.W., ed. *The Heart*, 4th ed. New York: McGraw-Hill Book Co., 1978.

Isselbacher, Kurt J., et al. eds. *Harrison's Principles of Internal Medicine*, 9th ed. New York: McGraw-Hill Book Co., 1980.

Judge, Richard D., and Zuidema, George. *Clinical Diagnosis: A Physiologic Approach*, 4th ed. Boston: Little, Brown & Co., 1982.

Kraytman, Maurice. *The Complete Patient History*. New York: McGraw-Hill Book Co., 1979.

Krupp, Marcus A., and Chatlon, Milton J., eds. *Current Medical Diagnosis and Treatment*, rev ed. Los Altos, Calif.: Lange Medical Publications., 1983.

Malasanos, Lois, et al. *Health Assessment*, 2nd ed. St. Louis: C.V. Mosby Co., 1981.

Maslow, William C., et al. *Practical Diagnosis: Hematologic Disease*. New York: John Wiley & Sons, 1980.

Moschella, Samuel L., et al. *Dermatology*, 2 vols. Philadelphia: W.B. Saunders Co., 1975.

Murray, Ruth B., and Zentner, Judith P. *Nursing Assessment and Health Promotion through the Life Span*, 2nd ed. Englewood Cliffs, N.J.: Prentice-Hall, Inc., 1979.

Neeson, Jean D., and Stockdale, Connie R. *The Practitioner's Handbook of Ambulatory OB-GYN*. New York: John Wiley & Sons, 1981.

Paparella, Michael M., and Shumrick, Donald A., eds. *Otolaryngology*, Vol. 2, 2nd ed. Philadelphia: W.B. Saunders Co., 1980.

Pearson, Linda J., and Kotthoff, M. Ernestine. *Geriatric Clinical Protocols: A Guide for Nurses and Physicians*. Philadelphia: J.B. Lippincott Co., 1979.

Price, Sylvia, and Wilson, Lorraine. *Pathophysiology*. New York: McGraw-Hill Book Co., 1982.

Pringle, Sheila M., and Ramsey, Brenda. *Promoting the Health of Children: A Guide for Caretakers and Health Professionals*. St. Louis: C.V. Mosby Co., 1982.

Pritchard, Jack A., and MacDonald, Paul C. *Williams Obstetrics*, 16th ed. East Norwalk, Conn.: Appleton-Century-Crofts, 1980.

Ritota, Michael C. *Diagnostic Electrocardiography*, 2nd ed. Philadelphia: J.B. Lippincott Co., 1977.

Romney, Seymour, et al. eds. *Gynecology and Obstetrics: The Health Care of Women*, 2nd ed. New York: McGraw-Hill Book Co., 1980.

Rook, A., et al. *Textbook of Dermatology*, 2 vols., 3rd ed. St. Louis: C.V. Mosby Co., 1979.

Rossman, Isadore, ed. *Clinical Geriatrics*, 2nd ed. New York: J.B. Lippincott Co., 1979.

Sana, Josephine M., and Judge, Richard P. *Physical Assessment Skills for Nursing Practice*, 2nd ed. Boston: Little, Brown & Co., 1982.

Scheie, Harold G., and Alert, Daniel M. *Textbook of Opthamology*, 9th ed. Philadelphia: W.B. Saunders Co., 1977.

Sherman, Jacques L., Jr., and Fields, Sylvia K., eds. *Guide to Patient Evaluation*, 4th ed. New Hyde Park, N.Y.: Medical Examination Publishing Co., 1982.

Simpson, John F., and Magee, Kenneth R. *Clinical Evaluation of the Nervous System*. Boston: Little, Brown & Co., 1973.

Thompson, June M., and Bowers, Arden C. *Clinical Manual of Health Assessment*. St. Louis: C.V. Mosby Co., 1980.

Tilikian, Ara G., and Conover, Mary B. *Understanding Heart Sounds and Murmurs*. Philadelphia: W.B. Saunders Co., 1979.

Vaughan, Victor C., III, et al. *Nelson Textbook of Pediatrics*, 12th ed. Philadelphia: W.B. Saunders Co., 1983.

Walker, H. Kenneth, ed. *Clinical Methods: The History, Physical and Laboratory Examinations*. Woburn, Mass.: Butterworth Pubs., 1980.

Warwick, Roger, and Williams, Peter L., eds. *Gray's Anatomy*, 36th ed. Philadelphia: W.B. Saunders Co., 1980.

Watts, Nelson B., and Keffer, Joseph H. *Practical Endocrine Diagnosis*, 3rd ed. Philadelphia: Lea & Febiger, 1982.

Williams, Robert H. *Textbook of Endocrinology*, 6th ed. Philadelphia: W.B. Saunders, 1981.

Williams, William J., et al. *Hematology*, 2nd ed. New York: McGraw-Hill Book Co., 1977.

Wood, Raymond, and Northern, Jerry. *Manual of Otolaryngology: A Symptom-Oriented Text*. Baltimore: Williams & Wilkins Co., 1979.

Index

A

Abdomen: arterial pulsations in, 229; endocrine assessment of, 391; landmarks, 225, *226*; physical examination of, 223-230
Abdominal distention, measurement of, 230
Abdominal masses, assessment of, 229-230
Abdominal pain, 225; in child, 231; in gastrointestinal disorders, 220-221; in pregnancy, *411*
Abdominal reflexes, test of, 317
Abortion, spontaneous, *422-423*
Abruptio placentae, *420-421*; maternal hypertension and, 409
Achalasia, *236-237*
Achilles reflex, test of, 317
Acquired immune deficiency syndrome (AIDS), *376-377*
Acromegaly, *398-399*
Addison's disease, 389, 390, *398-399*
Adrenal virilizing syndrome, *398-399*
Airway obstruction, *161*
Alcohol abuse, 81; in female reproductive disorders, 283; in gastrointestinal disorders, 223; in male reproductive disorders, 264; in pregnancy, 426
Aldosteronism, *402-403*
Allen cards, in visual acuity testing, 123
Alzheimer's disease, 321, *322-323*
Amblyopia, 124
Amenorrhea, 280; in pregnancy, 407
Amnesia, *72-73*
Amniocentesis, *418*
Amyotrophic lateral sclerosis, *322-323*
Aneurysm: aortic, *208-211*; cerebral, *324-325*
Angina pectoris, *208-209*
Ankle: assessment, 348; range of motion of, *352*
Ankylosing spondylitis, 338, 340, *354-355*
Anterior chest: physical examination of, 169-171
Antisocial personality, *72-73*
Anxiety, 62; in child, 68-69; disorder, *72-73*; in elderly, 71; signs, 65
Aortic regurgitation, *208-211*
Aortic stenosis, *210-211*
Apgar score, calculation of, 427, *428*
Apical impulse, 193-194, 195; in elderly, 207
Aplastic anemia, *376-377*
Apnea, *160*
Apneustic respiration, *160*
Appendicitis, *236-237*
Arm measurements, 83-85
Arteriovenous malformation, *322-323*
Arthritis, rheumatoid, *380-381*; juvenile, 374, *378-379*
Ascites: assessment of, 230; in neonate, 233
Asthenia, nutritional deficiencies and, 78
Asthma, 172, *174-175*, 374, *376-377*; attacks, stress and, 65; history of, 365

B

Babinski's reflex, 317
Back: lower, strain of, *358-359*; musculoskeletal assessment of, 345; pain, 338; range of motion of, *349*
Ballottement, 39, *40*
Barrel chest, 169, *170*
Bartholinitis (Bartholin adenitis), *294-295*
Beau's lines, *104*
Behavior problems, in child, 68, 69
Bender visual-motor gestalt test, *66*
Benton visual retention test, *66*
Biceps reflex, test of, 316
Biot's respiration, *160*
Bipolar affective disorders, *72-73*
Bladder: carcinoma of, *256-257*; examination 251, *252*; neck, obstruction of, *256-257*
Bleeding, abnormal, in blood-forming and immune disorders, 364
Blepharitis, *126-127*
Blepharochalasis, 124
Blindness: color, 124; leading cause of, 125; preventability of, 114
Blood: chemistry measurements, in urinary disorders, 252; clotting abnormalities, 371; tests, *366*
Blood-forming and immune systems, 364-383; of child, 373-375; disorders of, *376-383*; of elderly, 375; examination of, 367-373; history data, 364-367
Blood pressure, 34-35; age effects on, *191*; child's, 205; in elderly, 207; fluctuation, tinnitus and, 138; measurement of, 35; readings, normal and abnormal, 35-36
Body frame type: determination, 83; relation to weight, 83
Body temperature, 31-32
Bone pain, 338
Botulism, *322-323*
Bowel sounds, auscultation for, 227
Bowlegs, 348, 350
Brachial pulse, 202
Brachioradialis reflex, test of, 316
Bradycardia, 32; sinus, *198*
Bradypnea, *160*
Brain, abscess of, *322-323*

Atelectasis, *174-175*
Athlete's foot, *112-113*
Atrial contraction, premature, *198*
Atrial fibrillation, *198*
Atrial gallop, auscultation for, 195, *196-197*, 200
Attention span, test of, in child, 319
Auscultation, 43; sequence of, 43, *167*
Autoimmune diseases, 364, 365, *369*; in child, 374; rashes in, 371; relationship to other systemic conditions, 367
Axillary nodes, palpation of, *371, 372*

Breast: cancer, 278, 279, 280, 281, 293, *294-295*; cystic disease of, 201, 296-297; discharge, 279; endocrine assessment of, 391; enlargement, 386; examination, 284-285, *284*; fibroadenoma of, 296-297; lumps and masses, 279, 283; variations, normal, 285
Breath sounds, *168*
Bronchiectasis, *174-177*
Bronchitis, 172
Bronchophony, 169
Bruits, abdominal, 227
Burn patient, assessment of, *96, 97*
Bursitis, *354-355*

C

Caffeine consumption: breast lumps and, 283; gastrointestinal disorders and, 223
Calorie(s): adult intake of, recommended, *83*; counts, 82; deficiency, *92-93*
Capsulitis, adhesive, *354-355*
Caput succedaneum, 429
Carbon monoxide poisoning, *322-323*
Cardiac auscultation, 200, *203*
Cardiac catheterization, 190
Cardiac emergency, assessment of, *189*
Cardiac landmarks, 193, *193*
Cardiac output: calculating, 32
Cardiac rhythm, classification of, *198-199*
Cardiomyopathies, *210-211*
Cardiovascular system, 184-219; in child, 204-206; disorders of, *208-219*; in elderly, 206-207; examination of, 189-204; history data, 184-189
Carotid pulse: in elderly, 207; examination of, 192-193
Carpal tunnel syndrome, 338, *354-355*; testing for, 344
Cataracts, 125, *126-127*
Catatonic schizophrenia, *74-75*
Cerebellar functions, tests of, 313; in child, 319
Cerebral function, test of, 306-307; in child, 318-319
Cerebral hypoperfusion, in elderly, 206-207
Cerebral palsy, *324-325*
Cerebrovascular accident, *324-325*
Cervical disk herniation, *354-355*
Cervix: physical examination of, 286-290
Chalazion, 118, *126-127*
Chancre, syphilitic, *276-277*
Chest: deformities, *170, 176-177*; movement, 162-163; musculoskeletal assessment of, 345
Chest pain, *186-187*; in cardiovascular disorders, 184; in elderly, 206; in respiratory disorders, 157
Cheyne-Stokes respiration, 160
Chicken pox, *109, 112-113*
Child abuse: characteristics of, *70*; musculoskeletal injuries in, 350
Child's apperception test (CAT), *66*
Chlamydia, *294-295*
Choanal atresia, *438-439*
Cholecystitis, *236-237*
Cholelithiasis, in elderly, 235

Chronic obstructive pulmonary disease (COPD), *176-177*
Chvostek's sign, 393
Cirrhosis, *236-237*
Cleft lip, 232
Cleft palate, 232
Climacteric, 270, *271*
Clitoris, enlargement of, in neonate, 435
Clubbing: of fingers, 205; of nails, *104*, 371
Cluster headache, 302, 303, *324-327*
Colitis, ulcerative, *242-243*
Concentration testing, in child, 319
Conjunctivitis, *126-127*
Connective tissue disease, affecting the lungs, *176-177*
Consciousness level: altered, in endocrine disorders, 393; altered, in neurologic disorders, 304; in child, test of, 318
Constipation, 222; in elderly, 235
Contraception, history of, in pregnancy, 408
Contraceptives, and female reproductive disorders, 279
Contractures, *354-355*
Conversion disorders, *74-75*
Cooley's anemia, *382-383*
Coombs' test, direct and indirect, *366*
Coordination testing, 313
Corneal abrasion, *126-127*
Corneal reflex, test of, 119, *120*, 121
Corneal ulcer, *126-127*
Coronary artery disease, 184, 188
Cough: in cardiovascular disorders, 188; in respiratory disorders, 156
Cover-uncover test, 119, *120*; in child, 124
Cradle cap, 103
Cranial nerves: abnormal response of, *308-311*; function, testing of, 307, 309-313, 319
Craniosynostosis, 318
Craniotabes, 318
Cremasteric reflex, 268-269, *270*; test of, 317
Cretinism, 396
Crohn's disease, *236-237*
Croup, 172
Cryptorchidism, 269
Cushing's syndrome, 389, 390, 393, *398-399*; in child, 396-397
Cyanosis: in blood-forming and immune disorders, 369; in cardiovascular disorders, 204; in respiratory disorders, 161-162
Cyst, ovarian, *296-297*
Cystitis, *258-259*
Cystocele, *296-297*

D

Dacryocystitis, *128-129*
Deep tendon reflexes: in elderly, 321; in endocrine disorders, 393; test of, 316-317
Defense mechanisms, common, *63*
Deformity, in musculoskeletal disorders, 339
Dehydration: in infant, testing for, 232; in urinary disorders, 249
Depression, 62; in elderly, 70-71; precipitating factors, 63; types, 62

Depressive disorder, 74-75
de Quervain's disease, 345
Dermatitis: allergic contact, 105; atopic, 103, 105; pattern of rash, 106; seborrheic, 103
Dermatomes, 315
Dermatomyositis, 380-381
Diabetes insipidus, 398-399
Diabetes mellitus, 389, 390, 398-399; in cardiovascular disorders, 185; in female reproductive disorders, 281; in male reproductive disorders, 264; in musculoskeletal disorders, 339, 348; nutritional status and, 81
Diabetic complications, 388-389
Diabetic ketoacidosis, 388-389; Kussmaul's respiration in, 389
Diabetic retinopathy, 128-129
Diaphragmatic excursion, 164
Diaphragmatic hernia, 438-439
Diarrhea, 222; in child, 231
Dietary allowances, recommended, 79, 80, 88, 89
Diethylstilbestrol, family history of use of, 281
Diplopia, 124
Discharge: breast, 279; from ear, 136-137; penile, 262-263; vaginal, 279
Discrimination testing, neurologic, 314, 316; in child, 320
Diverticulitis, 235, 238-239
Diverticulosis, 235
Dizziness: in cardiovascular disorders, 189; drug-induced, 138; in endocrine dysfunction, 138; history of, 137; in pregnancy, 411, 411
Down's syndrome, 320-321, 326-327; ear deformities in, 147; maternal age and, 425
Draw-a-Family (DAF)-House-Tree-Person test, 66
Draw-a-Person (DAP) test, 66
Drug abuse, 74-75; maternal, effect of, on neonate, 425
Drug reactions, in elderly, 71, 125, 206
Duchenne's muscular dystrophy, 352
Dysmenorrhea, 279; in adolescent, 292
Dyspareunia, 279; in geriatric patient, 293; in pregnancy, 412
Dyspepsia, 221
Dysphagia, 221
Dyspnea: in blood-forming disorders, 367; in cardiovascular disorders, 184, 204; paroxysmal nocturnal, 184; in pregnancy, 411; in respiratory disorders, 156-157; in thyroid gland enlargement, 388
Dysuria, 279, 386

E

Ears and hearing, 136-155; of child, 144-145, 147-148; disorders of, 150-155; of elderly, 148-149; examination, 139-144, 147-148; history data, 136-139, 144-145, 148-149
E chart, in visual acuity testing, 123
Echocardiography, 190
Eclampsia, 420-421
Ectopic pregnancy, 420-422
Edema: in endocrine disorders, 390; gesta-

(Edema cont'd)
tional, 408, 411, 420-421; in musculoskeletal disorders, 390; peripheral, testing for, 250; pitting, scale of, 250; pulmonary, 180-181
Effacement, cervical, 419
Egophony, 169
Elbow: examination, 342
Electrocardiography, 190
Elimination patterns, changes in, 221
Embolism, pulmonary, 180-181; chest pain of, 186-187
Emotional status, evaluation of, 65, 67-68
Encephalitis, 326-327
Endocarditis, 216-217
Endocrine system, 384-405; in child, 393-397; disorders of, 398-405; in elderly, 397; examination of, 388-393; function, tests for, 393, 394-395; history data, 384-388
Endometriosis, 279, 296-297
Endometrium, cancer of, 278, 293, 296-297
Enophthalmos, 118
Epididymitis, 272-273
Epigastric pulsations, 200, 202
Epiglottitis, 172
Epilepsy, 302; senile, 321
Epispadias, 266
Epitrochlear lymph nodes, palpation of, 372
Equilibrium, 144
Erythema, 102
Erythroblastosis fetalis, 438-439
Erythrocyte sedimentation rate, 366
Esophageal disturbance, in elderly, 235
Esophageal pain, 186-187
Esotropic deviation, of eye, 119
Estriol measurement, to assess fetus, 418
Eupnea, 160
Eustachian tube: blocked, 137, 144-145, 148, 150, 151; in pregnancy, 411
Exanthema subitum, 110-111
Exophthalmos, 115, 118; in thyroid disorders, 387, 390
Exotropic deviation, of eye, 119
Extinction phenomenon, 314, 316; in child, 320
Extraocular motor nerve palsies, 128-129
Extraocular muscles, assessment of, 119, 120
Extremities, pain in, 185
Eyes and vision, 114-135; of child, 123-124; disorders of, 126-135; of elderly, 124-125; examination of, 117-123

F

Facial pulse, 202
Falling test, of equilibrium, 144
Fat, body, distribution of, 389
Fatigue: in blood-forming and immune disorders, 367; in cardiovascular disorders, 184-185; in endocrine disorders, 384; in pregnancy, 411
Feet, assessment of, 348, 352
Female reproductive system, 278-301; of child, 290-292; disorders of, 294-301; of elderly, 292-293; examination of, 283-291; history data, 278-283

Femoral epiphysis, slipped, 353, *362-363*
Femoral pulse, 202
Fetal movement, cessation of, *411*
Fetal status, tests for, *418*
Fever, in blood-forming and immune disorders, 365
Fibrinogen, *366*
Fibrosis, pulmonary, *180-183*
Fingers: range of motion of, 345, *347*
Finkelstein's test, 345
Fissures, of skin, *100*
Floaters, 114-115, 125
Fluid status, assessment of, *248*
Folic acid deficiency, *92-93*
Fornix: bimanual examination of, 289, *290*; palpation of, *287*
Fractures, 356-357; greenstick (infraperiosteal), 350
Fremitus, palpation for, 163, 169
Friction rub: abdominal, 227; pericardial, 200; pleural, *168*
Fugue states, *72-73*
Fundal height measurement, *413*
Funnel chest, *170*
Furunculosis, *152-153*

G

Gag reflex, 313; in child, 172, 231
Gait: abnormalities, 345; disturbances, drug-induced, 138; observation of, in musculoskeletal assessment, 345, 350
Galactorrhea, 391
Galactosemia, *438-439*
Gammopathy, *369*
Ganglion, *356-357*
Gastritis, *238-239*; atrophic, 235
Gastrointestinal system, 220-245; in child, 230-234; disorders of, *236-245*; in elderly, 234-235; examination of, 223-230; history data, 220-223
Gaze, six cardinal fields of, testing, 119, *120*
Genital injuries, in pediatric patient, 292
Genital tumors, in child, 292
German measles, *110-111*; pattern of rash, *109*
Gesell developmental schedules, *66*
Gestational age, characteristics of, *425*
Gingivitis, *238-239*; in child, 232
Gingivostomatitis, *240-241*
Glaucoma, 115, 125, *128-131*
Glomerular filtration rate, 252; in elderly, 254; in infant, 252
Glomerulonephritis, *256-257*
Glossitis, *238-239*
Gluteal reflex, test of, 317
Glycosuria, 251
Goiter, multinodal, *402-403*
Gonorrhea, 262; in female, 287, 290, *298-299*; in male, *274-275*; penile discharge in, 263
Goodell's sign, 413
Gout, 340, *356-357*
Graphesthesia testing, 314; in child, 320
Graves' disease, 397
Groin, pain in, 279

Growth grids, 87
Growth hormone abnormalities, 396
Guillain-Barré syndrome, *330-331*

H

Hair and scalp, examination of, 102-103; in elderly, 109
Hallpike maneuvers, 144
Hands, examination of, 344, 345
Hay fever, *376-377*
Head: examination of, in musculoskeletal assessment, 341-342; examination of, in nervous system assessment, 306, 318; injury, 304, *328-329*; range of motion testing of, 342; trauma, effect of, on ears and hearing, 138
Headache, 302-303; in pregnancy, 411, *411*
Head-to-toe physical examination, *44-45*
Health history, 4-27; communication problems in, 15, 17-19; geriatric, 23-27; interviewing skills of, 4-8; pediatric, 19-23; record of, 9-15
Hearing, 136-155
Heartbeat: fetal, 412; irregular, 185
Heart block, first and second degree, *199*
Heartburn: as complication of stress, 65; in gastrointestinal disorders, 220-221; in pregnancy, 412
Heart murmurs, *201*; auscultation for, 195, 200; in blood-forming and immune disorders, 372; in child, 205; in elderly, 207
Heart rate: altered, in neonate, 425; classification, *198-199*; in elderly, 207; in thyroid disease, 389
Heart sounds: auscultation for, 195, *196-197*, 200; in child, 205; classification, *198-199*; in elderly, 207
Hegar's sign, 413
Hematomas, epidural and subdural, 326-327
Hemolytic anemias, *376-377*
Hemophilia, 375, *376-377*
Hemophilus vaginalis infection, *298-299*
Hemorrhage: intracerebral, *324-325*; intracranial, *440-441*; subarachnoid, *324-325*
Hemorrhoids, *238-241*
Hepatitis, viral, *242-245*
Hernia: hiatal, 234-235, *240-241*; inguinal, 263, 269; scrotal, *274-275*; umbilical, 234
Herpes, genital: in female, *298-299*; in male, *274-275*; in pregnancy, 410
Herpes simplex, 96-97, *110-111*; *240-241*
Herpes zoster, *112-113*; pattern of rash, *106*
Hip: dislocation, in child, 350; dislocation, congenital; musculoskeletal assessment of, 347-348; range of motion of, *351*
Hirschberg's test, 124
Hirschsprung's disease, *438-439*
Hodgkin's disease, 365, *376-379*
Hordeolum, 115, 118, *130-131*
Hyaline membrane disease, *440-441*
Hydatidiform mole, *420-421*
Hydrocele, 268, 274-275
Hydrocephalus, 320, *328-329*
Hyperglycemia, *440-441*

Hyperglycemic hyperosmolar nonketotic (HHNK) coma, *388-389*
Hypernephroma, *258-259*
Hyperparathyroidism, *400-401*; osteoporosis, as complication of, 353
Hyperpnea, *160*
Hyperproteinemia, 185
Hypersensitivity, *369*
Hypertension, 184; in cardiovascular disorders, 185; gestational, *420-421*; tinnitus in, 138; in urinary disorders, 248, 249
Hypertensive retinopathy, 130-131
Hyperthyroidism, 389, 390, 393, *400-401*; in child, 396; in elderly, 397
Hypertropic deviation, of eye, 119
Hypocalcemia, *440-441*
Hypocalcemic tetany, 393
Hypochondriasis, *76-77*
Hypoglycemia, *388-389*; fasting, *400-401*; neonatal, *440-441*
Hypomagnesemia, *440-441*
Hypoparathyroidism, *400-401*
Hypopituitarism, *400-401*
Hypospadias, *266*
Hypotension, in urinary disorders, 248
Hypothyroidism, 389, 393, *400-401*; in child, 396; hearing loss and, 138; in neonate, 396

Ichthyosis, 102
Iliac crest, in musculoskeletal assessment, 345
Immobility, in musculoskeletal disorders, 339
Immune disorders, *369*
Immunity, *368*
Immunosuppressive therapy, 97
Imperforate anus, *440-441*
Impetigo, *110-111*
Impotence, sexual, 263-264
Incontinence, fecal, 235; urinary, 254
Indentation tonometry, 120
Infantile spasm, *328-329*
Infection: in blood-forming and immune disorders, 367, 374; ear, 136, 137, 138; 148; intraocular, 115; kidney, in elderly, 255; in male reproductive disorders, 263, 264; monilial, 293; in neurologic disorders, 304; thought disturbance, as complication of, 63; in urinary disorders, 247, 253
Infertility, male, 264
Inflammation, in musculoskeletal disorders, 339
Inguinal lymph nodes, palpation of, 267, 372
Inguinal mass, 263
Inspection, 36-37
Insulin disorders, pediatric, 396
Insulin shock, *388-389*
Intellectual status, evaluation of, 65, 67-68
Intestinal disorders, 235
Intraocular pressure, measurement of, 120
Iodine deficiency, *92-93*
Iron deficiency, *92-93*
Iron deficiency anemia, *378-379*; in child, 89-90, 375; in elderly, 375; laboratory test results in, 90

Ischemic attack, transient, *336-337*
Itching, in skin disorders, 96

J

Jaundice, in blood-forming and immune disorders, 369, 371
Jock itch, *112-113*
Joint: disease, degenerative, 338, 339; pain, 338, 365; stiffness, 339; temporomandibular, 136, 342, *362-363*

K

Keloids, 96
Keratitis, *130-131*
Keratoconjunctivitis, *130-131*
Keratoconus, *132-133*
Kernicterus, *440-441*
Kilocalorie, *82*
Klinefelter's syndrome, 264
Knee: assessment, 348; range of motion of, *351*
Knock-knees, 348, 350
Kocher's test, 391
Koilonychia, 371
Kussmaul's respiration, 160, 248, 389
Kyphosis, 345, *356-357*; in child, 350

L

Labia: examination of, 286; pain in, 279
Labyrinthine disorders, 137, 139, *152-153*
Landouzy-Déjerine muscular dystrophy, 352
Landry's syndrome, *330-331*
Laxative use, chronic, 222
Lead poisoning, *330-331*
Leg: assessment, in child, 350; pain, 338
Leopold's maneuvers, *417*
Lesions, skin, 96-97, *100-101*
Leukemia, *378-379*
Lice: head, 103; pubic, *300-301*
Lichen planus, distribution patterns of, *106*
Ligamental tear, *356-359*
Lightening, 419
Light perception, testing of, 117-118
Light reflection, testing of, 124
Limb-girdle muscular dystrophy, *358-359*
Lips: in child, 232; examination of, 224
Liver: palpation, in child, 374; percussion, 229, 374; size, 229, *229*
Lockjaw, *336-337*
Lordosis: in child, 350; inspection for, 345
Lumbosacral disk, herniated, 338, *356-357*
Lung: abscess, *178-179*; tumor, *178-179*
Lung disease: in elderly, 206; smoking and, 158
Lupus erythematosus, systemic, *382-383*; cardiovascular assessment for, 372; in child, 374; complications, 367; mouth assessment for, 372; neuromuscular assessment for, 373; respiratory assessment for, 372
Lymphadenopathy, 364-365, 372
Lymph nodes, inspection and palpation of, *370*, *371*, 371-372; in child, 374
Lymphoma, 365

M

Macewen's sign, 318
Macule, *100*
Major body systems physical examination, 56-58
Male reproductive system, 262-277; in child, 268-270; disorders of, *272-277*; in elderly, 270-271; examination of, 265, 268, *269*; history data, 262-265
Manic-depressive disorder, *72-73*
Marasmus, *92-93*
Mastitis, *298-299*
Mastoiditis, *152-153*
Measles, distribution pattern of, *109*
Mees' lines, *104*
Megacolon, congenital, *438-439*
Memory testing, in child, 319
Menarche, 278
Meniere's disease, 139, *152-153*
Meningitis, *330-331*
Meniscal tear, *358-359*
Menopause, 278, 397
Menstrual cycle: abnormal, 280; missed, 280
Menstruation: adolescent problems of, 292; pregnancy changes of, 408
Mental status examination, 65, 67-68
Metabolic requirements, 80
Methyl alcohol ingestion, *330-331*
Microtia, 147
Midarm circumference, 85, *85*
Migraine headache, 302, 303, *330-333*
Minerals, recommended dietary allowances of, *79, 80 88, 89*
Minnesota multiphasic personality inventory (MMPI), *66*
Mitral regurgitation, *212-213*
Mitral stenosis, *212-213*
Mittelschmerz, 279
Monilial infection, *298-299*; in geriatric patient, 293; in pregnancy, 409, 412
Morton's neuroma, *358-359*
Motor disturbances, 303
Motor function, test of, 313; in child, 319; in endocrine disorders, 393
Mouth assessment, 224-225; in child, 231-232
Multiple personality, *72-73*
Multiple sclerosis, 302, 303, *332-333*
Muscle: cramp, *358-359*; pain, 338; strength, test of, 341, 342, 345, 348; strength, test of, in child, 350
Muscular dystrophy, 302, 340; Duchenne's, 352; Landouzy-Déjerine, 352
Musculoskeletal deformities, nutrition and, 79
Musculoskeletal system, 338-363; of child, 348-350, 352-353; disorders of, *354-363*; of elderly, 353; endocrine assessment of, 392-393; examination of, 340-348; history data, 338-340
Myasthenia gravis, *332-333*
Myeloma, multiple, *378-379*
Myocardial infarction, *208-209*; chest pain of, *186-187*
Myocardial ischemia, chest pain of, *186-187*
Myringitis, *150-151*

Myringotomy, middle ear infection and, 148
Myxedema, *402-403*

N

Nägele's rule, 408
Nail(s): abnormalities, *104-105*; clubbing of, *104*, 371; in elderly, 109; inspection, 103
Nausea and vomiting: in cardiovascular disorders, 188-189; in child, 231; in gastrointestinal disorders, 221-222; in neurologic disorders, 303; in pregnancy, 408, *411*, 412
Neck: examination in musculoskeletal assessment, 342; examination in nervous system assessment, 306, 318; nodes, palpation of, *370*, 372; range of motion testing of, 342, *343*
Neonate, 424-443; Apgar score of, 427; disorders of, *420-423*; examination of, 427-437; gestational age of, *425*; history data, 424-427
Nephritis, chronic interstitial, *256-259*
Nephrolithiasis, *258-259*
Nervous system, 302-337; of child, 317-321; disorders of, *322-337*; of elderly, 321; examination of, 305-317; history data, 302-305
Neurofibromatosis, *322-333*
Niacin deficiency, *92-93*
Nocturia: in cardiovascular disorders, 189; in male reproductive disorders, 262
Nodal rhythm, *198*
Nutrients, malabsorption of, 81
Nutrition, 78-95; of child, 85-90; in elderly, 90-91; examination to assess status of, 82-85, 91; history data of, 78-82, 90-91; immune system, effects of, 367; in pregnancy, 410
Nystagmus, 119

O

Obesity, 81, *92-93*; in child, 87-88; triceps skinfold thickness measurement for, 83, *86*
Obsessive-compulsive disorder, *76-77*
Obstetric history, 409, *409*
Onycholysis, 103, *104*, 371
Ophthalmoscope, *121-123*
Opisthotonos, 435
Optic atrophy, *132-133*
Optic disk, *121*; examination of, 123
Orbital cellulitis, *132-133*
Orchitis, *274-275*
Organic brain syndrome, 62, 70, 321
Orthopnea, 184, 204, 367
Ortolani's sign, 350
Osteoarthritis, 338, *358-359*
Osteomyelitis, *360-361*
Osteoporosis, 338, 349, 353, *360-361*
Osteosarcoma, 338, 353, *358-359*
Otitis externa, *150-151*
Otitis media, 145, 148, *152-155*
Otomycosis, *150-151*
Otosclerosis, 136, *150-151*
Otoscope, *141*; in examination of ear canal and eardrum, 139, 147-148, 149
Ototoxicity, *152-153*
Ovary(ies): cancer of, 293, *300-301*; cysts of, *296-297*; tumor of, 279, 281, 289

P

Paget's disease, *360-361*
Pain: organ, referred, *221;* test of, 314
Palates: in child, 232; examination of, 224-225
Palpation, 37-39; ballottement technique of, 39, *40;* deep, 38-39, *38;* light, 37-38, *38;* sequence of, *171;* techniques, 37
Pancreatitis, *240-241*
Pap smear, obtaining, 287-288, *289*
Paranoia, in elderly, 71
Paranoid schizophrenia, *76-77*
Paraphimosis, *266*
Parathyroid glands, function of, *385*
Parent-child relationship, 64, 69, 70, *70*
Parkinsonism, 321
Parkinson's disease, *332-333*
Paronychia, 103, *104*
Past-pointing test, of equilibrium, 144
Patellar reflex, test of, 317
Peau d'orange, 284
Pedal pulses, 202-203
Pediculosis, 103; inspection of scalp for, 103; pubis, *300-301*
Pelvic examination: bimanual, 288-290, *290;* external, 286; of geriatric patient, 293; internal, 286-287, *287;* of pediatric patient, 290-291; preparation, 285-286; with speculum, 286-287, *288*
Pelvic inflammatory disease, 281, *294-295*
Pelvimetry measurements, 413, 415, *416*
Penis: abnormalities, *266;* cancer of, *272-273;* discharge from, 263; inspection and palpation of, 265, 268
Percussion, 39-43; fist, 227-228; methods, 41, *42;* sounds, 42-43, *166;* sequence, 41-42, *167*
Perfusion status, assessment of, 203-204
Pericardial chest pain, *186-187*
Pericarditis, *214-215*
Perilymph fistula, *152-153*
Perineum: lump of, 279-280; pruritus of, 280
Periodontitis, *242-243*
Peripheral circulation, 372
Peripheral pulses: palpation of, 202-203; rate, 202; symmetry of, 202; volume of, 202
Peritonitis, *242-243*
Pernicious anemia, 353, 367, *380-381*
Perthes disease, 350, 352
Phalen's sign, 344
Pharynx, examination of, 162, 225
Phenylketonuria (PKU), *442-443*
Pheochromocytoma, 387, 390, *402-403*
Phimosis, 265, *266*
Phobias, *76-77*
Physical examination, 28-61; chief complaint and, 59; draping for, *30;* equipment for, *29;* head-to-toe method, *44-45;* major body systems method, *56-58;* position for, *30;* recording results of, 59-60; of vital signs, 31
Pickwickian syndrome, *178-179*
Pigeon chest, *170*

Pigmentation, in endocrine disorders, 389-390
Pigment band, on nails, *104*
Pituitary gland: function of, *385;* tumor, 402-403
Pityriasis rosea, 105, *106*
Placenta previa, *422-423*
Plantar reflex, test of, 317
Plaque, on skin, *101*
Platyonychia, 371
Pleural effusion, *178-182;* in blood-forming and immune disorders, 372
Pleurisy, chest pain of, *186-187*
Pneumonectomy, *180-181*
Pneumonia: bacterial, 174-175; in child, 172; mycoplasmal, *178-179*
Pneumothorax, *180-181;* spontaneous, chest pain of, *186-187;* tension, *182-183*
Poliomyelitis, *360-361*
Polycystic kidney disease, 246, *258-259*
Polycythemia, 369, *380-381*
Polydipsia, 386-387
Polymyositis, *380-381*
Polyneuritis, *330-331, 334-335*
Polyuria, 386
Popliteal pulse, 202
Position sense, test of, 314; in child, 319-320; in elderly, 321
Posterior chest: auscultation of, 166, 169; inspection of, 162-163; palpation of, 163; percussion of, 163-164
Posture, 340, 345.
Precordium: examination of, 193-195
Preeclampsia, 410, *422-423*
Pregnancy, 406-423; antepartal care in, 412; assessment guide, *414-415;* disorders of, *420-423;* examination in, 412-419; history data, 406-412
Presbycusis, 136, 148, 149
Presbyopia, 125
Prostate gland: cancer of, 262, *272-273;* hypertrophy of, 255, 262, 270-271, *272-273;* palpation of, 267-268, *269*
Prostatitis, *274-275*
Protein, recommended dietary allowances of, *79, 80, 88, 89*
Protein-calorie malnutrition, 91
Proteinuria, 251; gestational, *420-421*
Prothrombin time, *366*
Pruritus, in pregnancy, 411
Psoriasis, 96; distribution pattern of, *106*
Psoriatic arthritis, 340
Psychological assessment, 62; of child, 68-70; disorders in, 72-77; of elderly, 70-71; history data for, 62-65; mental status examination, as part of, 65, 67-68
Psychological tests, *66*
Pterygium, *104,* 125
Ptosis, 118
Puberty: delayed, 387; precocious and pseudoprecocious, in female, 292; precocious and pseudoprecocious, in male, 270
Pulmonary artery, catheterization of, *190*
Pulmonary function tests, 159
Pulmonic regurgitation, *214-215*

Pulmonic stenosis, *214-215*
Pulse, 32-33; peripheral sites of, *33*
Pulse rate, age effects on, *191*
Pupil(s): dilation, in child, 124; in elderly, 125; inspection of, 121
Pupillary response, consensual, 121
Pyelonephritis, *256-257*
Pyloric stenosis, *442-443*; in infant, 234
Pyuria, 252

━━━━━ Q ━━━━━

Quick's test, *366*

━━━━━ R ━━━━━

Radial pulse, 202
Radiation exposure, female reproductive disorders and, 281
Radiation therapy: blood-forming and immune disorders and, 365; effect of, on nutrition, 81
Radius, subluxation of, in child, 350
Rales, *169*
Range of motion: in child, 350; test of, 341, 342, *343*
Rape victim, emergency assessment of, *282*
Rash: in autoimmune disorders, 371; in skin disorders, 96, 105
Raynaud's disease, *214-217*
Raynaud's phenomenon, *214-217*; in autoimmune disorders, 372
Recommended dietary allowances: for children and adolescents, *88, 89*; for men, *79*; for women, *80*
Rectal examination, 230
Rectocele, *300-301*
Reflexes: grades, *316*; neonatal, *431-432*; test of, 316-317, 320
Reiter's syndrome, 338, *360-361*
Renal artery: occlusion of, *256-257*; stenosis, chronic, *258-259*
Renal failure, signs of, 248-249
Renal function, age changes of, 254
Renal vein, thrombosis of, *258-259*
Resonance: in chest, 163, 164, *166*, 169, 170; vocal, 169
Respiration, 33-34; normal, *162*
Respiratory arrest, assessment and intervention, *161*
Respiratory distress: in adult, *174-175*; in child, 172; in immune disorders, 372; in neonate, *424-425*
Respiratory excursion, palpation for, 163
Respiratory expansion, symmetrical, assessing for, 169
Respiratory patterns, *160*
Respiratory rate, in adult, 162
Respiratory system, 156-183; in child, 171-172; disorders of, *174-183*; in elderly, 172-173; examination of, 158-171; history data, 156-158
Reticulocyte count, *366*
Retina, *121*; ophthalmoscopic examination of, 123
Retinal artery occlusion, *132-133*
Retinal detachment, 125, *132-133*

Retinitis pigmentosa, *134-135*
Reye's syndrome, *334-335*
Rheumatic fever, *216-217*; in cardiovascular disorders, 185, 188
Rhinitis, allergic, *376-377*
Rhonchi, *168*
Riboflavin deficiency, *94-95*
Ringworm, *112-113*; Wood's light examination of, 103
Rinne test, 143, *146, 147*; in presbycusis, 149
Romberg test, 345-346
Rorschach test, *66*
Rosacea, 96
Roseola infantum, *110-111*
Rubella, *110-111*; congenital, *438-439*; distribution pattern of, *109*; in pregnancy, 410
Rule of Nines, *99*

━━━━━ S ━━━━━

Sarcoma, osteogenic, 338, 353, *358-359*
Scabies, 96, *110-111*
Scarlet fever, *112-113*
Schilling test, *366*
Schizophrenia, disorganized, *74-75*
Schönlein-Henoch purpura, 374, *380-381*
Schwabach test, 143-144, *146, 147*
Sclera, 118-119, *119, 121*
Scleroderma, *382-383*
Scoliosis, *360-361*; in child, 350, 353; inspection for, 345, 350; postural (functional), 350, 353; structural, 350, 353
Scotoma, 114
Scratch test, to locate liver, 229
Scrotal hernia, *274-275*
Scrotal mass, 263; transillumination of, *267*
Scrotum: inspection and palpation of, 265, 267, *267*, 268; pain in, 263
Seizures: grand mal, *326-329*; jacksonian, *330-331*; in neurologic disorders, 303-304; petit mal, *334-335*; psychomotor, *334-335*
Sensory changes: in endocrine disorders, 393; in musculoskeletal disorders, 339; in neurologic disorders, 304
Sensory function, test of, 313-314; in child, 319-320
Sepsis, *442-443*
Sexual function abnormalities, in endocrine disorders, 386
Sexual impotence, 263-264; causes, 264; as symptom of other conditions, 264
Sexually transmitted diseases, 262; female reproductive disorders and, 278, 279, 281-282; in urinary disorders, 247
Sexual maturation disturbance, in child, 397
Shingles, *106, 112-113*
Shoulder: dislocation of, *354-357*; examination of, 342; range of motion testing of, 342, *343*; subluxation of, in child, 350
Sickle cell anemia, 364, *382-383*
Sideroblast test, *366*
Sinus: bradycardia, *198*; rhythm, normal, *198*; tachycardia, *198*
Skin, 96-113; of child, 103, 105, 109; disorders

(Skin cont'd)
of, *110-113;* of elderly, 109; examination of,
97-103; history data, 96-97
Skull, transillumination of, in pediatric neuro-
logic examination, 318
Sleep disturbance, in renal failure, 247
Smallpox, distribution pattern of, *109*
Smoking: cardiovascular disorders and, 188;
gastrointestinal disorders and, 223; in preg-
nancy, 410, 426; respiratory disorders and,
158
Snellen chart, *117*
Somnambulism, *72-73*
Speech assessment, in neurologic examination,
307; in child, 319
Spina bifida, *334-335*
Spinal accessory nerve: abnormal response of,
310-311; test of, 313
Spinal cord injury, *334-337*
Spleen: enlargement, 373; palpation and per-
cussion, 372-373, *373, 374*
Splinter hemorrhage, of nail, *105*
Spondylitis, ankylosing, 338, 340, *354-355*
Sprain, *362-363*
Sputum: characteristics of, 156; production,
156
Stanford-Binet test, *66*
Stereognosis testing, 314; in child, 320
Stomach disturbances, in elderly, 235
Stomatitis, aphthous, *236-237*
Strabismus, 114, 124, *134-135*
Straight-leg raising test, *347-348*
Stress: of aging, 70; asthma attacks and, 65;
autoimmune disorders and, 365, 367; female
reproductive disorders and, 281; male repro-
ductive disorders and, 264; neurologic disor-
ders and, 303, 305; patient coping with, 64;
respiratory disorders and, 158; response, di-
minished, in elderly, 397; skin disorders and,
65
Striae, 97
Striated nails, *105*
Stridor, 157; in thyroid disorder, 388
Stye, 115, 118, *130-131*
Subluxation: of radius, 350; of shoulder, 350
Subscapular skinfold thickness, 84-85
Subungual hematoma, *105*
Sugar-water test, *366*
Suicide potential, *67*
Summation gallop, 200
Superficial reflexes, test of, 317
Swallowing difficulty: in endocrine disorders,
388; in nutritional status, 80-81
Sydenham's chorea, *336-337*
Syphilis, primary, *300-301*
Syringomyelia, *336-337*
Systolic click, auscultation for, 200

T

Tachycardia, 32; in blood-forming system, 367;
paroxysmal atrial, *198;* sinus, *198;* ventricular,
199
Tachypnea, *160*

Teeth: in child, 231-232; inspection of, 224; pre-
cocious, 430
Telangiectasias, 102
Temporal pulse, 202
Tenosynovitis, chronic stenosing, *362-363;* test-
ing for, 345
Tension headache, 302, 303
Testes: cancer of, 262, 263, *272-273;* cremas-
teric reflex of, 268-269, *270;* torsion of, 263,
269-270; transillumination of, 267; undes-
cended, 269
Tetanus, *336-337*
Thalassemia, *382-383*
Thematic apperception test (TAT), *66*
Thiamine deficiency, *94-95*
Thighs, musculoskeletal assessment of, 348
Thomas test, 347
Thoracic landmarks, *164*
Thought disturbances, 63; precipitating factors,
63
Thrombin time, *366*
Thrombophlebitis, *218-219*
Thromboplastin time, partial, *366*
Thrush, 232
Thumb, range of motion of, *346*
Thyroid gland: auscultation of, 391; dysfunction,
signs of, 396; function of, *385;* palpation of,
391, *392;* tumor, *404-405*
Thyroiditis, *402-403*
Tibial torsion, testing for, 350
Tinea: capitis, *112-113;* corporis, *112-113;*
pedis, *112-113;* versicolor, *112-113*
Tinel's sign, 344
Tinnitus, 137; in hypertension, 138
Toddler, nutritional assessment of, 86
Toes, range of motion of, *352*
Tongue: in child, 232; inspection and palpation
of, 224
Torticollis, spasmodic, *362-363*
Touch sensation, test of, 314
Toxic shock syndrome, 281, *300-301*
Trachea, inspection of, 162
Tracheoesophageal fistula, of neonate, *442-443*
Trachoma, *134-135*
Trauma: birth, 304; cognitive dysfunction, as
complication of, 63; in endocrine disorders,
387; in female reproductive disorders, 281;
ocular, 114, *115, 128-129*
Tremors: in neurologic disorders, 303; senile,
321; in thyroid gland enlargement, 388
Trench mouth, *240-241*
Trendelenburg gait, 345
Triceps reflex, test of, 316
Triceps skinfold thickness, 83-84, *84,* 87; normal
values for, *85;* as obesity measurement, *86*
Trichomoniasis, *300-301*
Tricuspid regurgitation, *218-219*
Tricuspid stenosis, *218-219*
Trigeminal nerve: abnormal response of, *308-
309;* test of, *311-312,* 319
Trochlear nerve: abnormal response of, *308-
309;* test of, 310-311
Trousseau's sign, 393

Tuberculosis, of lung, *178-179*
Tubular necrosis, *256-257*
Tumor(s): bronchial, *182-183;* cognitive dys-function, as complication of, 63; extramedul-lary spinal, *325-327;* genital, in child, 292; intracranial, *328-329;* intramedullary spinal, *328-329;* lung, *178-179;* ovarian, 279, 281, 289; pituitary, *402-403;* thyroid, *404-405;* uterine, benign, 278, 281
Tuning fork, for hearing tests, 143, *146*
Twenty-four-hour recall of intake, 81-82
Two-point stimulation, 314; in child, 320
Tympany: in abdomen, 227; in chest, 164, *166, 170*

U

Ulcer: peptic, 235, *242-243;* on skin, *101*
Ulnar pulse, 202
Ultrasonography, to assess fetus, *418*
Umbilicus, in pregnancy, 412
Undernutrition, in child, 87
Undifferentiated schizophrenia, *76-77*
Uremia, in elderly, 255
Urethra, female, 286, *287*
Urethral meatus, inspection of, in child, 254
Urethral obstruction, *258-261*
Urethritis, *260-261;* penile discharge in, 263
Urinalysis, 251
Urinary system, 246-261; in child, 252-254; dis-orders of, *256-261;* in elderly, 254-255; examin-ation of, 248-252; history data, 246-248
Urination, painful, 246-247; in male reproductive disorders, 263
Urine: color, changes in, 246; *253;* output, changes in, 246
Uterine souffle, 412
Uterus: bimanual examination of, 289, *290;* can-cer of, 293; disorders of, 293; leiomyoma of, *300-301;* prolapsed, *300-301*
Uveitis, *134-135*

V

Vagina: bimanual examination of, 288-290, *290;* discharge from, 279; disorders of, 293; fluid escape, in pregnancy, *411;* palpation of, 286, *287;* pediatric examination of, 291; pruritus of, 280; speculum examination of, 286-287, *288*
Vaginal bleeding, in pregnancy, 407-408, *411*
Vaginal discharge, 279; in pregnancy, 412
Vaginitis: of adolescent, 291-292; atrophic, 293, *294-295;* foreign-body, *296-297;* in preg-nancy, 412; senile, 293
Vagus nerve, abnormal response of *310-311;* test of, 312-313
Varicella, *112-113;* distribution pattern of, *109*
Varicose veins, *218-219*
Variocele, 267, *276-277*
Venereal warts, *294-297*
Venous hum, abdominal, 227
Venous pressure, measurement of, 191-192
Venous pulse, 190-191
Ventricular contraction, premature, *199*

Ventricular failure, *212-213, 216-217*
Ventricular fibrillation, *199*
Ventricular gallop, auscultation for, 195, *196-197*
Ventricular hypertrophy, left and right, 194
Verrucae, *112-113*
Vertigo, 137, *150-151;* Hallpike maneuvers and, 144; from head trauma, 138
Vesicle, *101*
Vibration, sensation of, test of, 314; in elderly, 321
Vineland social maturity scale, *66*
Vision: blurred, 114; care, past history of, 115-116; changes, in pregnancy, *411;* color, test-ing of, 118, 124; decreased or absent, 114; distance, testing of, 117, *117;* distorted, 114; double, 114; near, testing of, 118; peripheral, testing of, 119-120; sooty, 114-115
Visual acuity testing, 117; in child, 123
Visual field testing, 119-120; in child, 124
Vital signs, 31
Vitamin(s): deficiencies of, *94-95;* recom-mended dietary allowances of, *79, 80, 88, 89*
Vitreous hemorrhage, *134-135*
Voiding pattern changes: in male reproductive disorders, 262; in urinary disorders, 246
von Recklinghausen's disease, *332-333*
von Willebrand's disease, 375
Vulva: disorders of, 293; lump of, 279-280; pain in, 279; pruritus of, 280, 293
Vulvovaginitis, nonspecific, premenarchal, 291

W

Waardenburg's syndrome, 138
Warts, *112-113*
Watch-tick test, of hearing loss, 140, 142
Weakness: in blood-forming and immune disor-ders, 365; in cardiovascular disorders, 184-185; in endocrine disorders, 384
Weber test, 143, *146, 147;* in elderly, 149
Wechsler adult intelligence scale (WAIS), *66*
Wechsler intelligence scale for children (WISC), *66*
Weight changes: in blood-forming and immune disorders, 368; in cardiovascular disorders, 185; in endocrine disorders, 384, 386; nutri-tional status and, 78; in pregnancy, 411; in urinary disorders, 248
Wernicke's encephalopathy, *336-337*
Wheezing, 157, *168;* in cardiovascular disor-ders, 188; in immune disorders, 367, 372
Whispered pectoriloquy, 169
Whispering test, of hearing loss, 140, 142-143
White blood cell count, *366*
Winter itch, 97
Wood's light, 103
Wrist(s): examination of, 342, 345; range of mo-tion testing of, 344, *344*

X

Xanthelasma, 118

Z

Zenker's diverticulum, *244-245*